CARNEGIE LEARNING
LONG + LIVE + MATH

Middle School Math Solution
Course 2

Student Edition

Sandy Bartle Finocchi and Amy Jones Lewis
with Kelly Edenfield and Josh Fisher

CARNEGIE LEARNING

501 Grant St., Suite 1075
Pittsburgh, PA 15219
Phone 888.851.7094
Customer Service Phone 412.690.2444
Fax 412.690.2444

www.carnegielearning.com

Cover Design by Anne Milliron

ISBN: 978-1-60972-890-8
Student Edition

Printed in the United States of America
1 2 3 4 5 6 7 8 9 B&B 21 20 19

LONG + LIVE + MATH

Acknowledgments

Middle School Math Solution Authors

- Sandy Bartle Finocchi, Senior Academic Officer
- Amy Jones Lewis, Director of Instructional Design
- Kelly Edenfield, Instructional Designer
- Josh Fisher, Instructional Designer

Foundation Authors (2010)

- William S. Hadley, Algebra and Proportional Reasoning
- Mary Lou Metz, Data Analysis and Probability
- Mary Lynn Raith, Number and Operations
- Janet Sinopoli, Algebra
- Jaclyn Snyder, Geometry and Measurement

Vendors

- Lumina Datamatics, Ltd.
- Cenveo Publisher Services, Inc.

Images

- www.pixabay.com

Special Thanks

- Alison Huettner for project management and editorial review.
- Jacyln Snyder and Janet Sinopoli for their contributions to the Teacher's Implementation Guide facilitation notes.
- Victoria Fisher for her review of content and contributions to all the ancillary materials.
- Valerie Muller for her contributions and review of content.
- The members of Carnegie Learning's Cognitive Scientist Team—Brendon Towle, John Connelly, Bob Hausmann, Chas Murray, and Martina Pavelko—for their insight in learning science and review of content.
- Bob Hausmann for his contributions to the Family Guide.
- John Jorgenson, Chief Marketing Officer, for all his insight and messaging.
- Carnegie Learning's Education Services Team for content review and providing customer feedback.
- In Memory of David Dengler, Director of Curriculum Development (Deceased), who made substantial contributions to conceptualizing Carnegie Learning's middle school software.

"Mathematics is so much more than memorizing rules. It is learning to reason, to make connections, and to make sense of the world. We believe in Learning by Doing(TM)—you need to actively engage with the content if you are to benefit from it. The lessons were designed to take you from your intuitive understanding of the world and build on your prior experiences to then learn new concepts. My hope is that these instructional materials help you build a deep understanding of math."

Sandy Bartle Finocchi, Senior Academic Officer

"My hope is that as you work through this course, you feel capable—capable of exploring new ideas that build upon what you already know, capable of struggling through challenging problems, capable of thinking creatively about how to fix mistakes, and capable of thinking like a mathematician."

Amy Jones Lewis, Director of Instructional Design

"At Carnegie Learning we have created an organization whose mission and culture is defined by your success. Our passion is creating products that make sense of the world of mathematics and ignite a passion in you. Our hope is that you will enjoy our resources as much as we enjoyed creating them."

Barry Malkin, CEO

Table of Contents

Module 1: Thinking Proportionally

Module 2: Operating with Signed Numbers

Topic 1: Adding and Subtracting Rational Numbers

Topic 2: Multiplying and Dividing Rational Numbers

Module 3: Reasoning Algebraically

Topic 1: Algebraic Expressions

Topic 2: Two-Step Equations and Inequalities

Topic 3: Multiple Representations of Equations

Module 4: Analyzing Populations and Probabilities

Topic 1: Introduction to Probability

Topic 2: Compound Probability

Topic 3: Drawing Inferences

Module 5: Constructing and Measuring

Topic 1: Angles and Triangles

Topic 2: Three-Dimensional Figures

1. Learning Goals
Learning goals are stated for each lesson to help you take ownership of the learning objectives.

2. Connection
Each lesson begins with a statement connecting what you have learned with a question to ponder.

Return to this question at the end of this lesson to gauge your understanding.

Stretches, Stacks, and Structure

2

Structure of Linear Equations

WARM UP
Use properties to rewrite.

1. $3(x - 1)$

2. $-9(-2 + x)$

3. $\frac{1}{2}(x - 6)$

4. $6 + 3(x + 4)$

LEARNING GOALS (1)

- Write and solve two-step equations.
- Compare two linear problem situations.
- Rewrite expressions in different forms in problem contexts in order to interpret how quantities are related.
- Compare graphs of linear problem situations.
- Compare and interpret forms of linear equations.

(2) All of the linear equations you have written for problem situations have been in the form $y = ax + b$. Are there other common forms of equations used to express linear problem situations?

LESSON 2: Stretches, Stacks, and Structure • M3-139

3 Getting Started

Learning the Limo Business

Katie is starting her own limousine rental company. She wisely decides to check her competitors' pricing plans before setting her own plan. The table shows the fees from two rival limousine rental companies.

Examine the fee schedule for the two limousine companies provided in the table.

Number of Hours Rented	Limousines by Lilly Fees (in dollars)	Transportation with Class Fees (in dollars)
1	99.99	89.99
2	123.74	126.54
3	147.49	163.09
4	171.24	199.64
5	194.99	236.19

1. **Which company would you choose if you were renting a limousine? Support your answer with information from the table.**

M3-140 • TOPIC 3: Multiple Representations of Equations

3. Getting Started

Each lesson begins with a Getting Started. When working on the Getting Started, use what you know about the world, what you have learned previously, or your intuition. The goal is just to get you thinking and ready for what's to come.

4. Activities

You are going to build a deep understanding of mathematics through a variety of activities in an environment where collaboration and conversations are important and expected.

You will learn how to solve new problems, but you will also learn why those strategies work and how they are connected to other strategies you already know.

Remember:

- It's not just about answer-getting. The process is important.
- Making mistakes is a critical part of learning, so take risks.
- There is often more than one way to solve a problem.

Activities may include real-world problems, sorting activities, worked examples, or analyzing sample student work.

Be prepared to share your solutions and methods with your classmates.

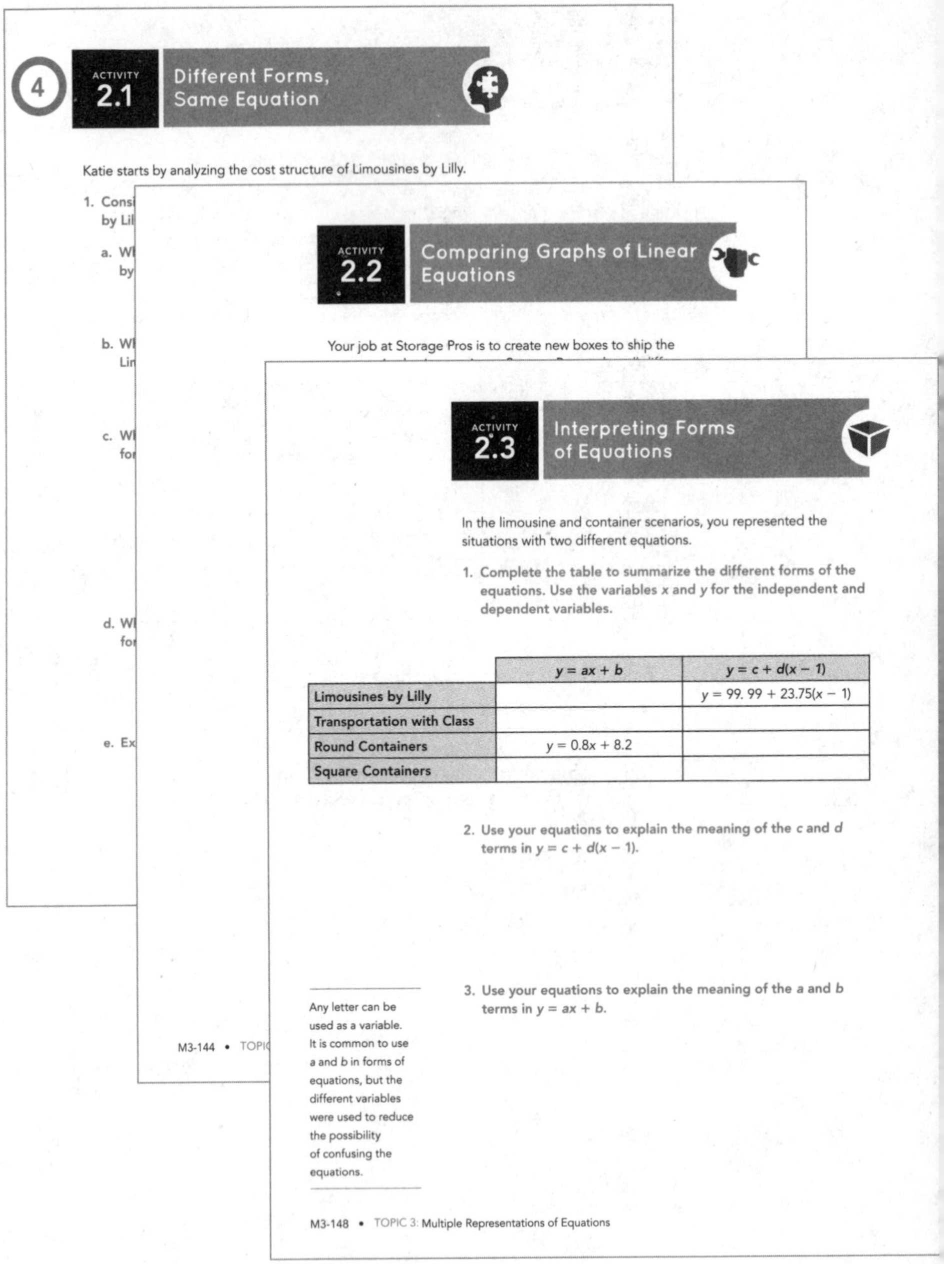

4

ACTIVITY 2.1 Different Forms, Same Equation

Katie starts by analyzing the cost structure of Limousines by Lilly.

1. Consi… by Lil…

a. Wl… by…

b. Wl… Lir…

c. Wl… fo…

d. Wl… fo…

e. Ex…

ACTIVITY 2.2 Comparing Graphs of Linear Equations

Your job at Storage Pros is to create new boxes to ship the

M3-144 • TOPIC

ACTIVITY 2.3 Interpreting Forms of Equations

In the limousine and container scenarios, you represented the situations with two different equations.

1. Complete the table to summarize the different forms of the equations. Use the variables x and y for the independent and dependent variables.

	$y = ax + b$	$y = c + d(x - 1)$
Limousines by Lilly		$y = 99.99 + 23.75(x - 1)$
Transportation with Class		
Round Containers	$y = 0.8x + 8.2$	
Square Containers		

2. Use your equations to explain the meaning of the c and d terms in $y = c + d(x - 1)$.

3. Use your equations to explain the meaning of the a and b terms in $y = ax + b$.

Any letter can be used as a variable. It is common to use a and b in forms of equations, but the different variables were used to reduce the possibility of confusing the equations.

M3-148 • TOPIC 3: Multiple Representations of Equations

NOTES

5 TALK the TALK

Back to the Limos!

At the beginning of the lesson, you wrote equations for the fee schedule of Limousines by Lilly and Transportation with Class.

1. **Determine which graph represents each equation. Use your equations to explain your reasoning.**

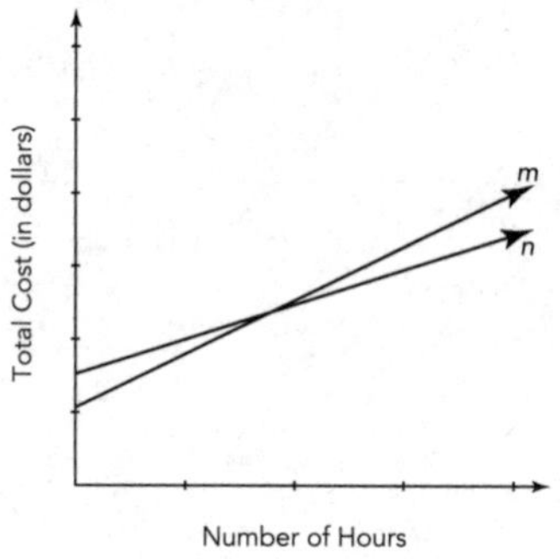

2. **Suppose Katie decides to charge $124.99 for the first *three* hours and then $49.99 for each additional hour. Write an equation to represent Katie's fee schedule.**

M3-150 • TOPIC 3: Multiple Representations of Equations

5. Talk the Talk

Talk the Talk gives you an opportunity to reflect on the main ideas of the lesson.

- Be honest with yourself.
- Ask questions to clarify anything you don't understand.
- Show what you know!

Don't forget to revisit the question posed on the lesson opening page to gauge your understanding.

Assignment

6. Write
Reflect on your work and clarify your thinking.

7. Remember
Take note of the key concepts from the lesson.

8. Practice
Use the concepts learned in the lesson to solve problems.

9. Stretch
Ready for a challenge?

10. Review
Remember what you've learned by practicing concepts from previous lessons and topics.

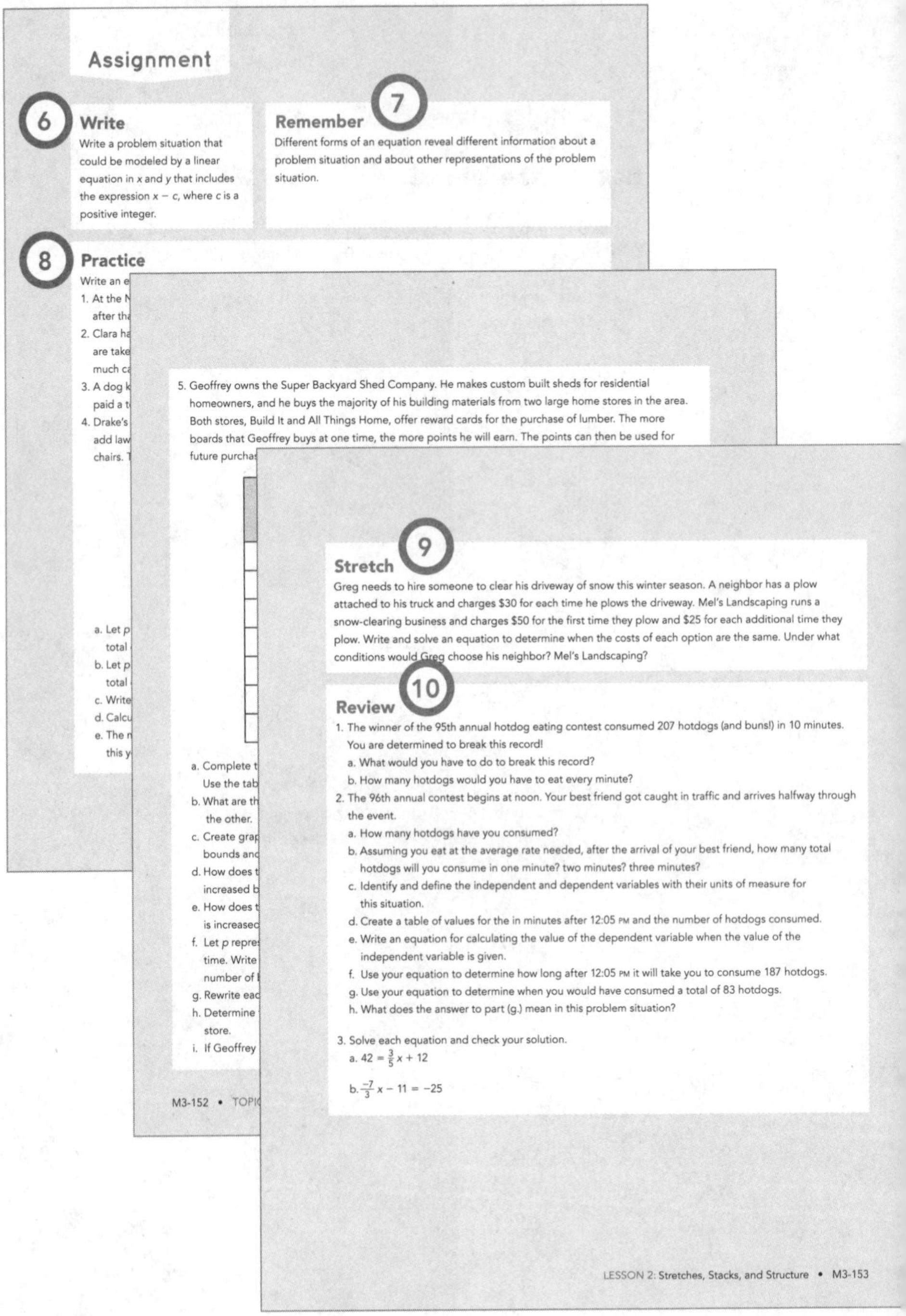

Assignment

6 **Write**
Write a problem situation that could be modeled by a linear equation in x and y that includes the expression $x - c$, where c is a positive integer.

7 **Remember**
Different forms of an equation reveal different information about a problem situation and about other representations of the problem situation.

8 **Practice**
Write an e...
1. At the N... after th...
2. Clara ha... are take... much ca...
3. A dog k... paid a t...
4. Drake's... add law... chairs. ...

5. Geoffrey owns the Super Backyard Shed Company. He makes custom built sheds for residential homeowners, and he buys the majority of his building materials from two large home stores in the area. Both stores, Build It and All Things Home, offer reward cards for the purchase of lumber. The more boards that Geoffrey buys at one time, the more points he will earn. The points can then be used for future purcha...

a. Let p... total ...
b. Let p... total ...
c. Write ...
d. Calcu...
e. The ... this y...

a. Complete t... Use the tab...
b. What are th... the other.
c. Create grap... bounds and...
d. How does t... increased b...
e. How does t... is increased...
f. Let p repres... time. Write ... number of ...
g. Rewrite eac...
h. Determine ... store.
i. If Geoffrey...

9 **Stretch**
Greg needs to hire someone to clear his driveway of snow this winter season. A neighbor has a plow attached to his truck and charges $30 for each time he plows the driveway. Mel's Landscaping runs a snow-clearing business and charges $50 for the first time they plow and $25 for each additional time they plow. Write and solve an equation to determine when the costs of each option are the same. Under what conditions would Greg choose his neighbor? Mel's Landscaping?

10 **Review**
1. The winner of the 95th annual hotdog eating contest consumed 207 hotdogs (and buns!) in 10 minutes. You are determined to break this record!
   a. What would you have to do to break this record?
   b. How many hotdogs would you have to eat every minute?
2. The 96th annual contest begins at noon. Your best friend got caught in traffic and arrives halfway through the event.
   a. How many hotdogs have you consumed?
   b. Assuming you eat at the average rate needed, after the arrival of your best friend, how many total hotdogs will you consume in one minute? two minutes? three minutes?
   c. Identify and define the independent and dependent variables with their units of measure for this situation.
   d. Create a table of values for the in minutes after 12:05 PM and the number of hotdogs consumed.
   e. Write an equation for calculating the value of the dependent variable when the value of the independent variable is given.
   f. Use your equation to determine how long after 12:05 PM it will take you to consume 187 hotdogs.
   g. Use your equation to determine when you would have consumed a total of 83 hotdogs.
   h. What does the answer to part (g.) mean in this problem situation?
3. Solve each equation and check your solution.
   a. $42 = \frac{3}{5}x + 12$
   b. $\frac{-7}{3}x - 11 = -25$

LESSON 2: Stretches, Stacks, and Structure • M3-153

Problem Types You Will See

WORKED EXAMPLE

	$\frac{11}{3}x + 5 = \frac{17}{3}$	$\frac{1}{2}x + \frac{3}{4} = 2$
Step 1:	$3\left(\frac{11}{3}x + 5\right) = 3\left(\frac{17}{3}\right)$	$4\left(\frac{1}{2}x + \frac{3}{4}\right) = 4(2)$
Step 2:	$11x + 15 = 17$	$2x + 3 = 8$
Step 3:	$x = \frac{17 - 15}{11}$	$x = \frac{8 - 3}{2}$
	$= \frac{2}{11}$	$= \frac{5}{2}$

Worked Example

When you see a Worked Example:

- Take your time to read through it.
- Question your own understanding.
- Think about the connections between steps.

Ask Yourself:

- What is the main idea?
- How would this work if I changed the numbers?
- Have I used these strategies before?

Thumbs Up

When you see a Thumbs Up icon:

- Take your time to read through the correct solution.
- Think about the connections between steps.

Ask Yourself:

- Why is this method correct?
- Have I used this method before?

Thumbs Down

When you see a Thumbs Down icon:

- Take your time to read through the incorrect solution.
- Think about what error was made.

Ask Yourself:

- Where is the error?
- Why is it an error?
- How can I correct it?

Analyze the solution strategy and solution for each inequality.

Ella

$$-\frac{1}{2}x + \frac{3}{4} < 2$$
$$-4\left(-\frac{1}{2}x + \frac{3}{4} < 2\right)$$
$$2x - 3 > -8$$
$$2x > -5$$
$$x > \frac{-5}{2}$$
$$x > -2.5$$

Describe the strategy that Ella used correctly.

Jeff

$$-12x + 20 < 32$$
$$\frac{-12x + 20}{-4} < \frac{32}{-4}$$
$$3x - 5 < -8$$
$$3x < -3$$
$$x < -1$$

Identify the error in Jeff's strategy and determine the correct solution.

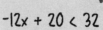

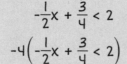

Who's Correct

When you see a Who's Correct icon:

- Take your time to read through the situation.
- Question the strategy or reason given.
- Determine correct or not correct.

Ask Yourself:

- Does the reasoning make sense?
- If the reasoning makes sense, what is the justification?
- If the reasoning does not make sense, what error was made?

Vanessa was given a math problem to determine how many different rectangles can be constructed with an area of 12 square inches.

Vanessa thinks that there are only two: one with a width of 2 inches and a length of 6 inches, and another with a width of 3 inches and a length of 4 inches.
Is she correct? Explain your reasoning.

The Crew

The Crew is here to help you on your journey. Sometimes they will remind you about things you already learned. Sometimes they will ask you questions to help you think about different strategies. Sometimes they will share fun facts. They are members of your group—someone you can rely on!

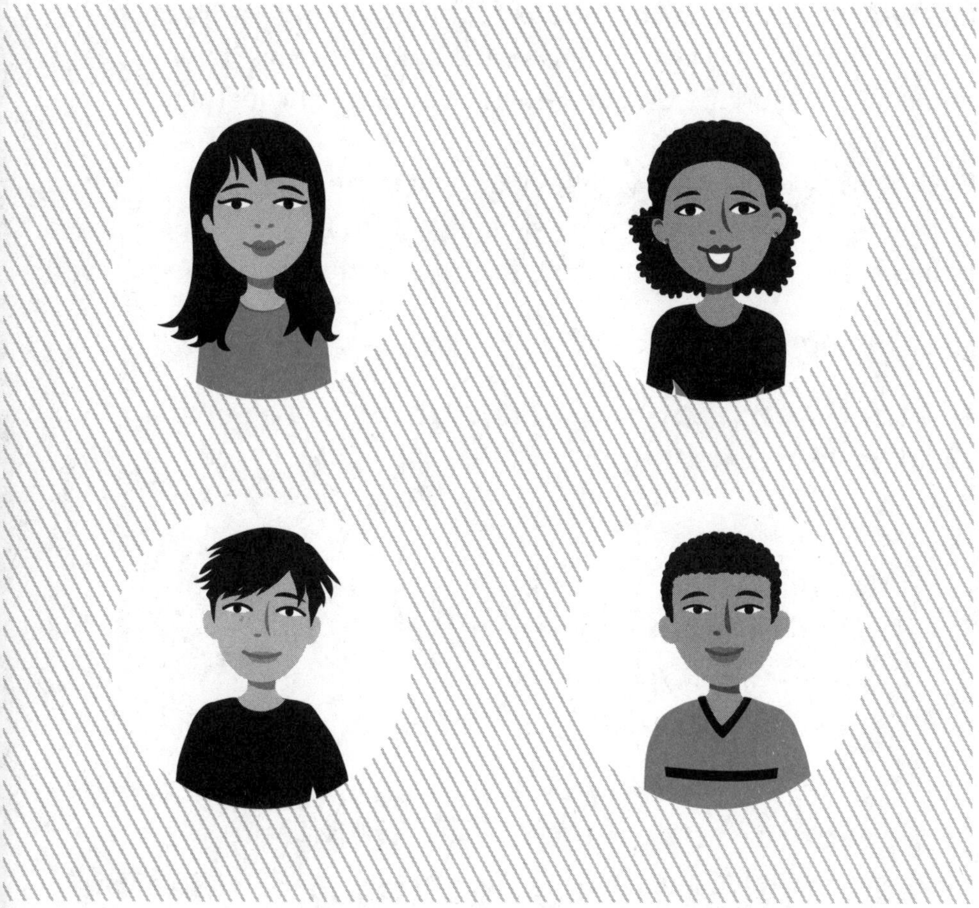

Teacher aides will guide you along your journey. They will help you make connections and remind you to think about the details.

Habits of Mind

Mathematical Practices

The types of activities within this book require you to make sense of mathematics and to demonstrate your reasoning through problem solving, writing, discussing, and presenting. Effective communication and collaboration are essential skills of a successful learner.

With practice, you can develop the habits of mind of a productive mathematical thinker.

Each activity is denoted with an icon that represents a practice or pair of practices intentionally being developed. To help develop these habits of mind ask yourself the types of questions listed as you work.

▶ Make sense of problems and persevere in solving them.

This practice is evident every day in every lesson. No icon used.

Questions to ask:

- What is this problem asking and what is my plan for answering it?
- What tools do I need to solve this problem?
- Does my answer make sense?

▶ Reason abstractly and quantitatively.
▶ Construct viable arguments and critique the reasoning of others.

Questions to ask:

- What representation can I use to solve this problem?
- How can this problem be represented with symbols and numbers?
- How can I explain my thinking?
- How does my strategy compare to my partner's?

"I hope that every once in a while you will see something that you weren't quite expecting. These are my favorite parts! Because I <3 being confused at first, and then figuring it out."

Josh Fisher, Instructional Designer

- ▶ **Model with mathematics.**
- ▶ **Use appropriate tools strategically.**

Questions to ask:

- What expression or equation could represent this situation?
- What tools would help me solve this problem?
- What representations best show my thinking?
- How does this answer make sense in the context of the original problem?

- ▶ **Attend to precision.**

Questions to ask:

- Is my answer accurate?
- Did I use the correct units or labels?
- Is there a more efficient way to solve this problem?
- Is there more sophisticated vocabulary that I could use in my explanation?

- ▶ **Look for and make use of structure.**
- ▶ **Look for and express regularity in repeated reasoning.**

Questions to ask:

- What characteristics of this expression or equation are made clear through this representation?
- How can I use what I know to explain why this works?
- Can I develop a more efficient method?
- How could this problem help me to solve another problem?

> “This book is your place to record your thoughts, your conjectures, your mistakes, your strategies, and your 'ah-has' about the mathematics you need to learn this year. Don't erase when you make mistakes; cross it out so that you can still see your original thinking. Learn from your mistakes and grow your brain.”

Kelly Edenfield, Instructional Designer

Academic Glossary

There are important terms you will encounter throughout this book. It is important that you have an understanding of these words as you get started on your journey through the mathematical concepts. Knowing what is meant by these terms and using these terms will help you think, reason, and communicate your ideas.

ANALYZE

Related Phrases

- Examine
- Evaluate
- Determine
- Observe
- Consider
- Investigate
- What do you notice?
- What do you think?
- Sort and match

Definition

To study or look closely for patterns. Analyzing can involve examining or breaking a concept down into smaller parts to gain a better understanding of it.

Ask Yourself

- Do I see any patterns?
- Have I seen something like this before?
- What happens if the shape, representation, or numbers change?

EXPLAIN YOUR REASONING

Related Phrases

- Show your work
- Explain your calculation
- Justify
- Why or why not?

Definition

To give details or describe how to determine an answer or solution. Explaining your reasoning helps justify conclusions.

Ask Yourself

- How should I organize my thoughts?
- Is my explanation logical?
- Does my reasoning make sense?
- How can I justify my answer to others?

REPRESENT

Definition

To display information in various ways. Representing mathematics can be done using words, tables, graphs, or symbols.

Ask Yourself

- How should I organize my thoughts?
- How do I use this model to show a concept or idea?
- What does this representation tell me?
- Is my representation accurate?

Related Phrases

- Show
- Sketch
- Draw
- Create
- Plot
- Graph
- Write an equation
- Complete the table

ESTIMATE

Definition

To make an educated guess based on the analysis of given data. Estimating first helps inform reasoning.

Ask Yourself

- Does my reasoning make sense?
- Is my solution close to my estimation?

Related Phrases

- Predict
- Approximate
- Expect
- About how much?

DESCRIBE

Definition

To represent or give an account of in words. Describing communicates mathematical ideas to others.

Ask Yourself

- How should I organize my thoughts?
- Is my explanation logical?
- Did I consider the context of the situation?
- Does my reasoning make sense?

Related Phrases

- Demonstrate
- Label
- Display
- Compare
- Determine
- Define
- What are the advantages?
- What are the disadvantages?
- What is similar?
- What is different?

MODULE 1

THINKING PROPORTIONALLY

The lessons in this module build on your experiences with ratios and proportional relationships from grade 6. You will investigate special ratios to develop and connect formulas for the circumference and area of circles. You will identify and describe proportional and non-proportional mathematical and real-world situations to understand the characteristics of proportional relationships. You will then use formal strategies to solve proportion and percent problems.

TOPIC 1

Circles and Ratio

Dropping something into water causes a series of ripples to expand from the point of impact, forming concentric circles.

Lesson 1

Lesson 2

Lesson 3

Module 1: Thinking Proportionally

TOPIC 1: CIRCLES AND RATIO

In this topic, students learn formulas for the circumference and area of circles and use those formulas to solve mathematical and real-world problems. To fully understand the formulas, students develop an understanding of the irrational number pi (π) as the ratio of a circle's circumference to its diameter. Throughout the topic, students practice applying the formulas for the circumference and area of a circle, often selecting the appropriate formula. Finally, students practice applying the formulas by using them to solve a variety of problems, including calculating the area of composite figures.

Where have we been?

Throughout elementary school, students used and labeled circles and determined the perimeters of shapes formed with straight lines. In grade 6, students worked extensively with ratios and ratio reasoning. To begin this topic, students draw on these experiences as they use physical tools to investigate a constant ratio, pi.

Where are we going?

This early review of and experience with ratios prepares students for future lessons where they will move from concrete representations and reasoning about ratios and proportions to more abstract and symbolic work with solving proportions and representing proportional relationships. In future grades, students will use the circumference and area formulas of a circle to calculate surface areas and volumes of cylinders and composite three-dimensional shapes that include circles.

Modeling the Area of a Circle Using Wedges

Divide a circle into a large number of equal-sized wedges. Laying these wedges as shown, you can see that they approximate a rectangle with a length of πr and a height of r. The more wedges are added, the closer the figure will be to an exact rectangle. So, the rectangle of wedges, and thus, the circle, each has an area of πr^2.

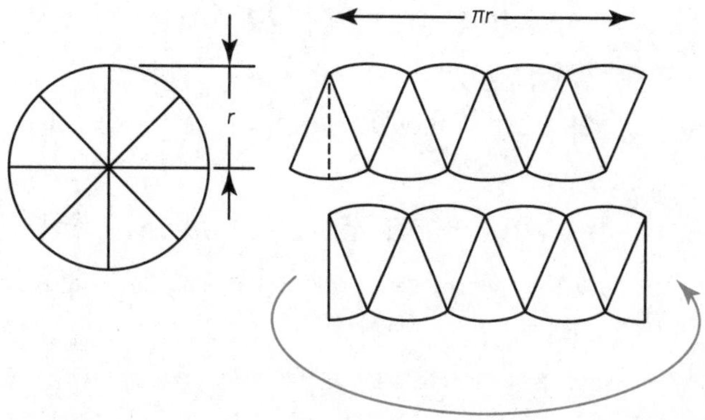

Myth: "I don't have the math gene."

Let's be clear about something. There isn't ***a*** gene that controls the development of mathematical thinking. Instead, there are probably ***hundreds*** of genes that contribute to our ability to reason mathematically. Moreover, a recent study suggests that mathematical thinking arises from the ability to learn a language. Given the right input from the environment, children learn to speak without any formal instruction. They can learn number sense and pattern recognition the same way.

To further nurture your child's mathematical growth, attend to the learning environment. You can think of it as providing a nutritious mathematical diet that includes discussing math in the real world, offering the right kind of encouragement, being available to answer questions, allowing your student to struggle with difficult concepts, and giving them space for plenty of practice.

#mathmythbusted

Talking Points

You can further support your student's learning by asking questions about the work they do in class or at home. Your student is learning to think flexibly about mathematical relationships involving multiplication, area, and number properties.

Questions to Ask

- How does this problem look like something you did in class?
- Can you show me the strategy you used to solve this problem? Do you know another way to solve it?
- Does your answer make sense? How do you know?
- Is there anything you don't understand? How can you use today's lesson to help?

Key Terms

radius

The radius of a circle is a line segment formed by connecting a point on the circle and the center of the circle.

diameter

The diameter of a circle is a line segment formed by connecting two points on the circle such that the line segment passes through the center point.

circumference

The circumference of a circle is the distance around the circle. The circumference is calculated using the formula $C = \pi d$.

pi

The number pi (π) is the ratio of the circumference of a circle to its diameter.

Pi: The Ultimate Ratio

1

Exploring the Ratio of Circle Circumference to Diameter

WARM UP

Scale up or down to determine an equivalent ratio.

1. $\frac{18 \text{ miles}}{3 \text{ hours}} = \frac{?}{1 \text{ hour}}$

2. $\frac{\$750}{4 \text{ days}} = \frac{?}{1 \text{ day}}$

3. $\frac{12 \text{ in.}}{1 \text{ ft}} = \frac{?}{5 \text{ ft}}$

4. $\frac{48 \text{ oz}}{3 \text{ lb}} = \frac{?}{1 \text{ lb}}$

LEARNING GOALS

- Identify pi (π) as the ratio of the circumference of a circle to its diameter.
- Construct circles using a compass and identify various parts of circles.
- Know and write the formula for the circumference of a circle, and use the formula to solve problems.

KEY TERMS

- congruent
- circle
- radius
- diameter
- circumference
- pi

You have learned about ratios. How can you use ratios to analyze the properties of geometric figures such as circles?

Getting Started

Across and Around

A circle is shown with a point drawn at the center of the circle. The name of the point is O, so let's call this Circle O.

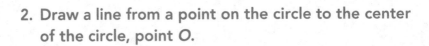

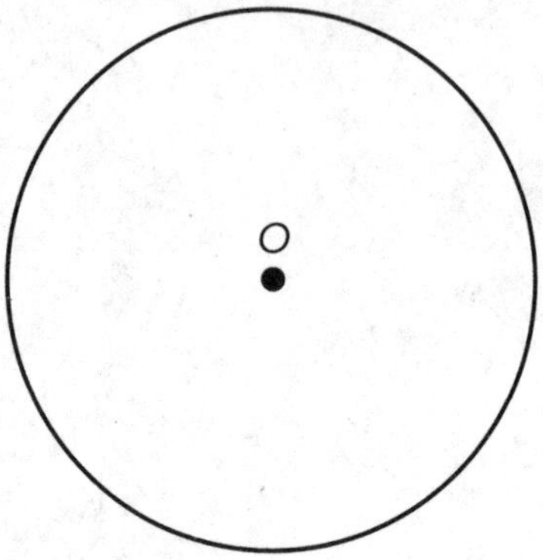

Be sure to include units when you record your measurements.

1. **Analyze the distance around the circle.**

   a. **Use a string and a centimeter ruler to determine the distance around the circle.**

   b. **How does your measurement compare to your classmates' measurements? Summarize the similarities and differences.**

2. **Draw a line from a point on the circle to the center of the circle, point O.**

   a. **Measure your line using your centimeter ruler.**

   b. **How does your measurement compare to your classmates' measurements? Summarize the similarities and differences.**

ACTIVITY 1.1

Analyzing the Parts of a Circle

Everyone can identify a circle when they see it, but defining a circle is a bit harder. Can you define a circle without using the word *round*? Investigating how a circle is formed will help you mathematically define a circle.

1. Follow the given steps to investigate how a circle is formed.

Step 1: In the space provided, draw a point and label the point *A*.

Step 2: Use a centimeter ruler to locate and draw a second point that is exactly 5 cm from point *A*. Label this point *B*.

Step 3: Locate a third point that is exactly 5 cm from point *A*. Label this point *C*.

Step 4: Repeat this process until you have drawn at least ten distinct points that are each exactly 5 cm from point *A*.

2. How many other points could be located exactly 5 cm from point *A*? How would you describe this collection of points in relation to point *A*?

3. Define the term *circle* without using the word *round*.

A **circle** is a collection of points on the same plane equidistant from the same point. The center of a circle is the point from which all points on the circle are equidistant. Circles are named by their center point.

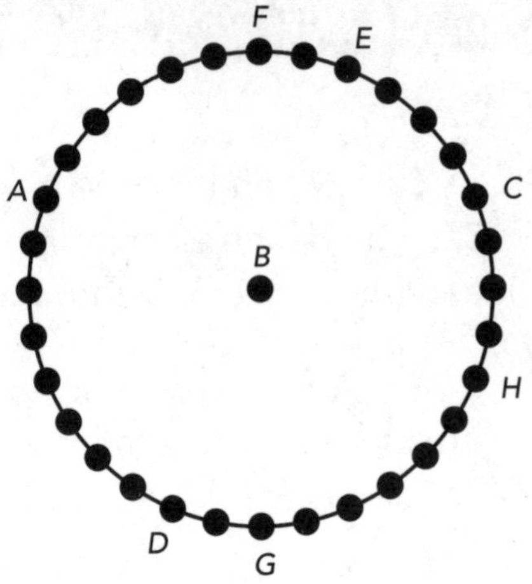

4. Use the circle shown to answer each question.

a. Name the circle.

The **radius** of a circle is a line segment formed by connecting a point on the circle and the center of the circle. The distance across a circle through the center is the diameter of the circle. The **diameter** of a circle is a line segment formed by connecting two points on the circle such that the line segment passes through the center point. The distance around a circle is called the **circumference** of the circle.

b. Identify a radius of the circle.

The plural of *radius* is *radii.*

c. Identify a diameter of the circle.

d. Are all radii of this circle the same length? Explain your reasoning.

5. What is the relationship between the length of a radius and the length of a diameter?

ACTIVITY
1.2

Measuring the Distance Around a Circle

Let's explore circles. Use circles *A, B, D, E,* and *O* provided at the end of the lesson. Circle *O* is the same as the circle from the activity *Across and Around.*

1. **Use a string and a centimeter ruler to measure the distance from a point on the circle to the center and the distance around each circle. Record your measurements in the table. In the last column, write the ratio of *Circumference : Diameter* in fractional form.**

Circle	Circumference	Radius	Diameter	$\frac{\text{Circumference}}{\text{Diameter}}$
Circle *A*				
Circle *B*				
Circle *O*				
Circle *D*				
Circle *E*				

2. **Average the ratios recorded for $\frac{\text{Circumference}}{\text{Diameter}}$. What is the approximate ratio for the circumference to the diameter for the set of circles? Write the approximate ratio as a fraction and as a decimal.**

3. **How does your answer to Question 2 compare to your classmates' answers?**

4. **Average all of your classmates' answers to Question 3. Write the approximate ratio of circumference to the diameter as a fraction and as a decimal.**

NOTES

ACTIVITY 1.3

The Circumference Formula

The number **pi** (π) is the ratio of the circumference of a circle to its diameter. That is pi $= \frac{\text{circumference of a circle}}{\text{diameter of a circle}}$, or $\pi = \frac{C}{d}$, where C is the circumference of the circle, and d is the diameter of the circle. The number π has an infinite number of decimal digits that never repeat. Some approximations used for the value π are 3.14 and $\frac{22}{7}$.

1. Use this information to write a formula for the circumference of a circle, where *d* represents the diameter of a circle and *C* represents the circumference of a circle.

2. Rewrite the formula for the circumference of a circle, where *r* represents the radius of a circle and *C* represents the circumference of a circle.

3. Use different representations for π to calculate the circumference of a circle.

a. Calculate the circumference of a circle with a diameter of 4.5 centimeters and a circle with a radius of 6 inches. Round your answer to the nearest ten-thousandths, if necessary.

Value for π	$d = 4.5$ centimeters	$r = 6$ inches
π		
Use the π Key on a Calculator		
Use 3.14 for π		
Use $\frac{22}{7}$ for π		

b. Compare your circumference calculations. How do the different values of π affect your calculations?

When you use 3.14 for pi, your answers are approximations. But an answer like 12π is exact.

4. Use the circumference of a circle formula to determine each unknown. Use 3.14 for π.

   a. Compute the diameter of the circle with a circumference of 65.94 feet.

   b. Compute the radius of the circle with a circumference of 109.9 millimeters.

5. What is the minimum amount of information needed to compute the circumference of a circle?

NOTES

TALK the TALK

Twice

Use what you have learned to compare circles by their characteristics.

1. **Draw each circle.**

   a. **radius length of 3 centimeters**

   b. **diameter length of 3 centimeters**

2. **Describe the similarities and differences between your two circles.**

3. **Describe the relationship between the circumferences of the two circles.**

4. **Describe the circumference-to-diameter ratio of all circles.**

Measuring the Distance Around a Circle

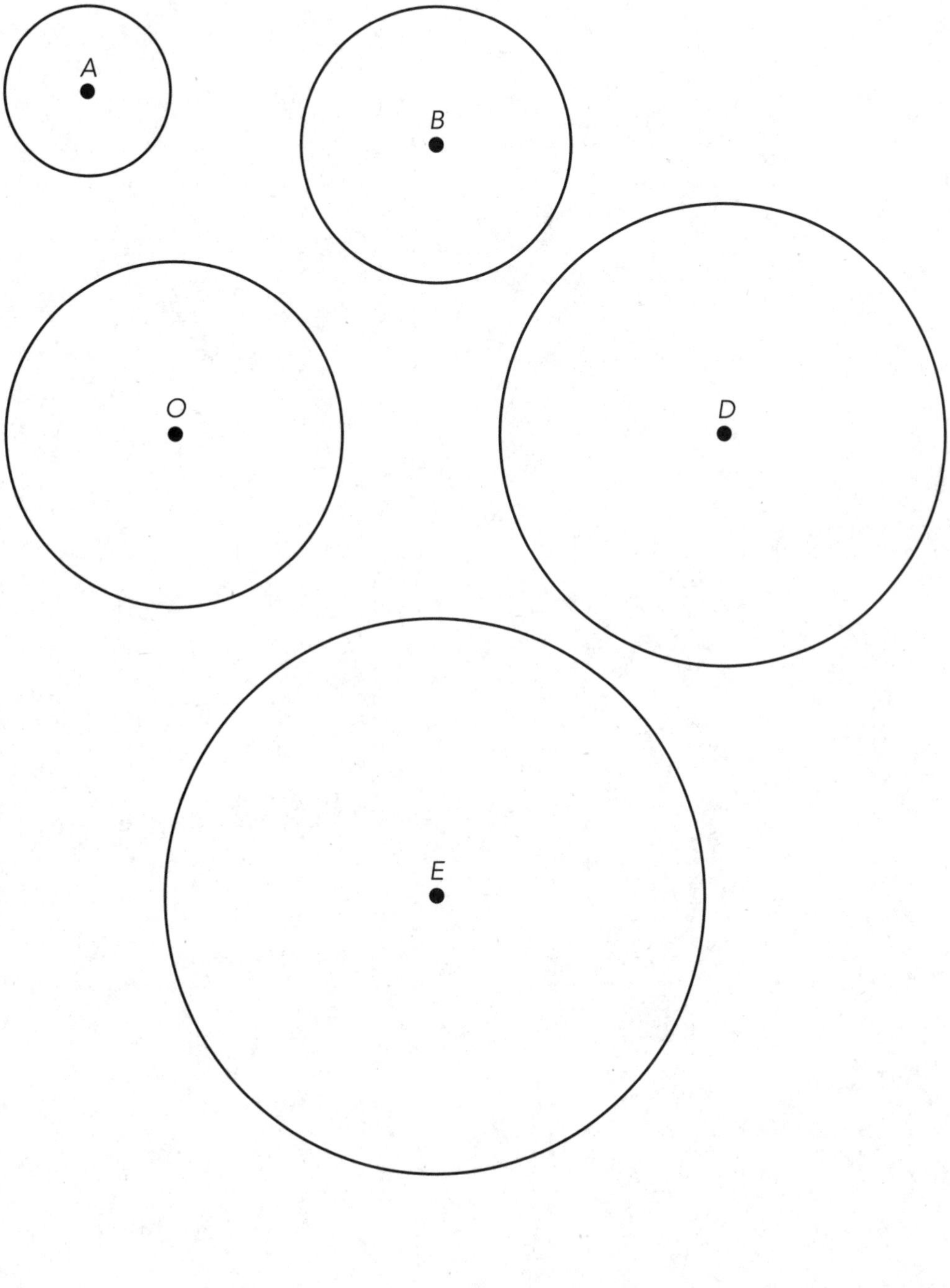

Assignment

Write

Define each term in your own words.

1. circle
2. radius
3. diameter
4. pi

Remember

The circumference of a circle is the distance around the circle. The formulas to determine the circumference of a circle are $C = \pi d$ or $C = 2\pi r$, where d represents the diameter, r represents the radius, and π is a constant value equal to approximately 3.14 or $\frac{22}{7}$.

The constant pi (π) represents the ratio of the circumference of a circle to its diameter.

Practice

Answer each question. Use 3.14 for π. Round your answer to the nearest hundredth, if necessary.

1. Although she's only in middle school, Tameka loves to drive go-carts! Her favorite place to drive go-carts, Driver's Delight, has 3 circular tracks. Track 1 has a radius of 60 feet. Track 2 has a radius of 85 feet. Track 3 has a radius of 110 feet.
   a. Compute the circumference of Track 1.
   b. Compute the circumference of Track 2.
   c. Compute the circumference of Track 3.
   d. Driver's Delight is considering building a new track. They have a circular space with a diameter of 150 feet. Compute the circumference of the circular space.
2. Tameka wants to build a circular go-cart track in her backyard.
   a. If she wants the track to have a circumference of 150 feet, what does the radius of the track need to be?
   b. If she wants the track to have a circumference of 200 feet, what does the radius of the track need to be?
   c. If she wants the track to have a circumference of 400 feet, what does the diameter of the track need to be?

Stretch

A rope is arranged using three semi-circles to form the pattern shown. Determine the length of the rope.

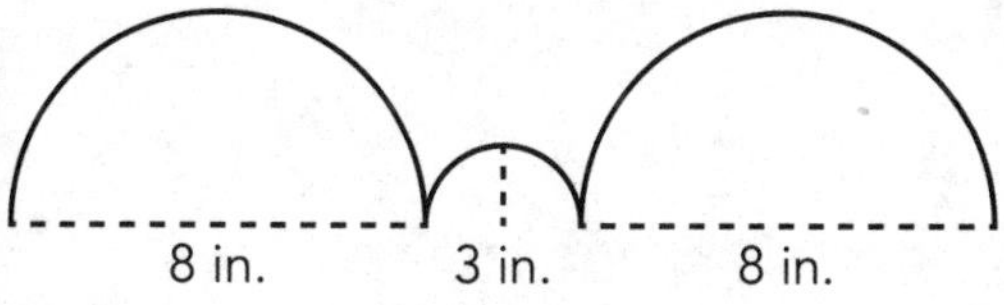

Review

1. Ethan and Corinne are training for a marathon.
   a. Corinne runs 13.5 miles in 2 hours. What is her rate?
   b. Ethan wants to run the 26.2 miles of the marathon in 4.5 hours. At about what rate will he have to run to reach this goal? Round to the nearest tenth.
2. Fifteen seventh graders were randomly selected to see how many pushups in a row they could do. Their data are shown.

   45, 40, 36, 38, 42, 48, 40, 40, 70, 45, 42, 43, 48, 36

   a. Determine the mean of this data set.
   b. Determine the median of this data set.
3. Convert each measurement.
   a. $4\frac{1}{2}$ pounds = ____ oz
   b. 22.86 cm = ____ in.

That's a Spicy Pizza!

Area of Circles

2

WARM UP

Determine a unit rate for each situation.

1. $38.40 for 16 gallons of gas
2. 15 miles jogged in 3.75 hours
3. $26.99 for 15 pounds

LEARNING GOALS

- Give an informal derivation of the relationship between the circumference and area of a circle and use the area formula to solve problems.
- Decide whether circumference or area is an appropriate measure for a problem situation.
- Calculate unit rates associated with circle areas.

KEY TERM

- unit rate

You have learned about the different parts and measures of a circle, including radius, diameter, and circumference. How can you use the parts of a circle to determine the area of a circle?

Getting Started

What Changed? What Stayed the Same?

The length of the base and height are the same in the parallelogram and rectangle shown.

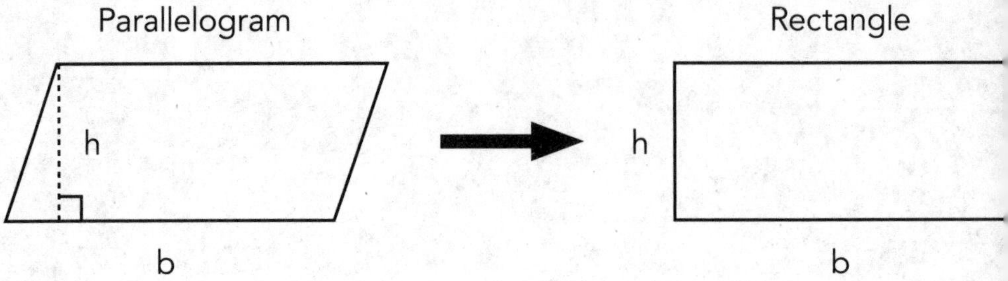

1. **How could you rearrange the parallelogram to create the rectangle?**

2. **What is the area of each figure?**

ACTIVITY
2.1

Deriving the Area Formula

In the last lesson you derived formulas for the distance around a circle. In this lesson you will investigate the space within a circle. Use the circle at the end of the lesson that is divided into 4, 8, and 16 equal parts.

1. **Follow the steps to decompose the circle and compose it into a new figure.**

   a. **First, cut the circle into fourths and arrange the parts side by side so that they form a shape that looks like a parallelogram.**

   b. **Then cut the circle into eighths and then sixteenths. Each time, arrange the parts to form a parallelogram.**

2. **Analyze the parallelogram you made each time.**

   a. **How did the parallelogram change as you arranged it with the smaller equal parts of the same circle?**

   b. **What would be the result if you built the parallelogram out of 40 equal circle sections? What about 100 equal circle sections?**

   c. **Represent the approximate base length and height of the parallelogram in terms of the radius and circumference of the circle.**

NOTES

d. Use your answers to part (c) to determine the formula for the area of the parallelogram.

e. How does the area of the parallelogram compare to the area of the circle?

f. Write a formula for the area of a circle.

3. Use different representations for π to calculate the area of a circle.

a. Calculate the area of each circle with the given radius. Round your answers to the nearest ten-thousandths, if necessary.

Value for π	$r = 6$ units	$r = 1.5$ units	$r = \frac{1}{2}$ units
π			
Use the π Key on a Calculator			
Use 3.14 for π			
Use $\frac{22}{7}$ for π			

b. Compare your area calculations for each circle. How do the different values of π affect your calculations?

4. Suppose the ratio of radius lengths of two circles is 1 unit to 2 units.

   a. What is the ratio of areas of the circles? Experiment with various radius lengths to make a conclusion.

   b. If the length of the radius of a circle is doubled, what effect will this have on the area?

ACTIVITY
2.2 Circumference or Area

Circle Formulas
$C = \pi d$, or $2\pi r$
$A = \pi r^2$

The circumference of a circle is the distance around the circle, while the area of a circle is the amount of space contained inside the circle. When solving problems involving circles, it is important to think about what you are trying to determine.

1. A city park has a large circular garden with a path around it. The diameter of the garden is 60 feet.

a. Gina likes to walk along the circular path during her lunch breaks. How far does Gina walk if she completes one rotation around the path?

b. Jason works for the City Park Department. He needs to spread plant food all over the garden. What is the area of the park he will cover with plant food?

2. Samantha is making a vegetable pizza. First, she presses the dough so that it fills a circular pan with a 16-inch diameter and covers it with sauce. What is the area of the pizza Samantha will cover with sauce?

3. Members of a community center have decided to paint a large circular mural in the middle of the parking lot. The radius of the mural is to be 11 yards. Before they begin painting the mural, they use rope to form the outline. How much rope will they need?

ACTIVITY
2.3

Unit Rates and Circle Area

Talarico's Pizza has a large variety of pizza sizes.

	Small	Medium	Large	X-Large	Enorme	Ginorme	Colossale
Diameter	10 in.	13 in.	16 in.	18 in.	24 in.	28 in.	36 in.
Slices	6	8	10	12	20	30	40
Cost	$6.99	$9.99	$12.99	$14.99	$22.99	$28.99	$54.99

Recall that a **unit rate** is a ratio of two different measures in which either the numerator or denominator is 1.

Lina and Michael are trying to decide whether to get two pizzas or one Ginorme pizza. They ask themselves, "Which choice is the better buy?"

They each calculated a unit rate for the Ginorme pizza.

Lina

1 Ginorme: $\frac{\pi(14)^2}{28.99} = \frac{196\pi}{28.99} \approx 21.24$ square inches per dollar

The Ginorme gives you approximately 21.24 square inches of pizza per dollar.

Michael

1 Ginorme: $\frac{28.99}{14^2\pi} = \frac{28.99}{196\pi} \approx \$0.05$ per square inch

The Ginorme costs approximately \$0.05 for each square inch of pizza.

. Consider Lina's and Michael's work.

a. Explain why Lina's and Michael's unit rates are different but still both correct.

b. How would you decide which pizza was the better buy if you calculated the unit rate for each pizza using Lina's method versus Michael's method.

. Which of the seven sizes of pizza from Talarico's Pizza is the best buy? Explain your answer.

NOTES

TALK the TALK

Go With the Flow

1. Which pipe configuration can deliver more water to residents, one 8-cm pipe or two 4-cm pipes? Show your work and explain your reasoning.

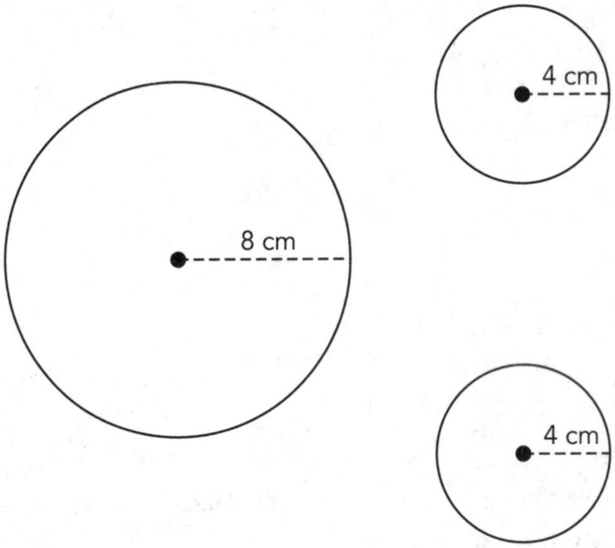

Circle Area Cutouts

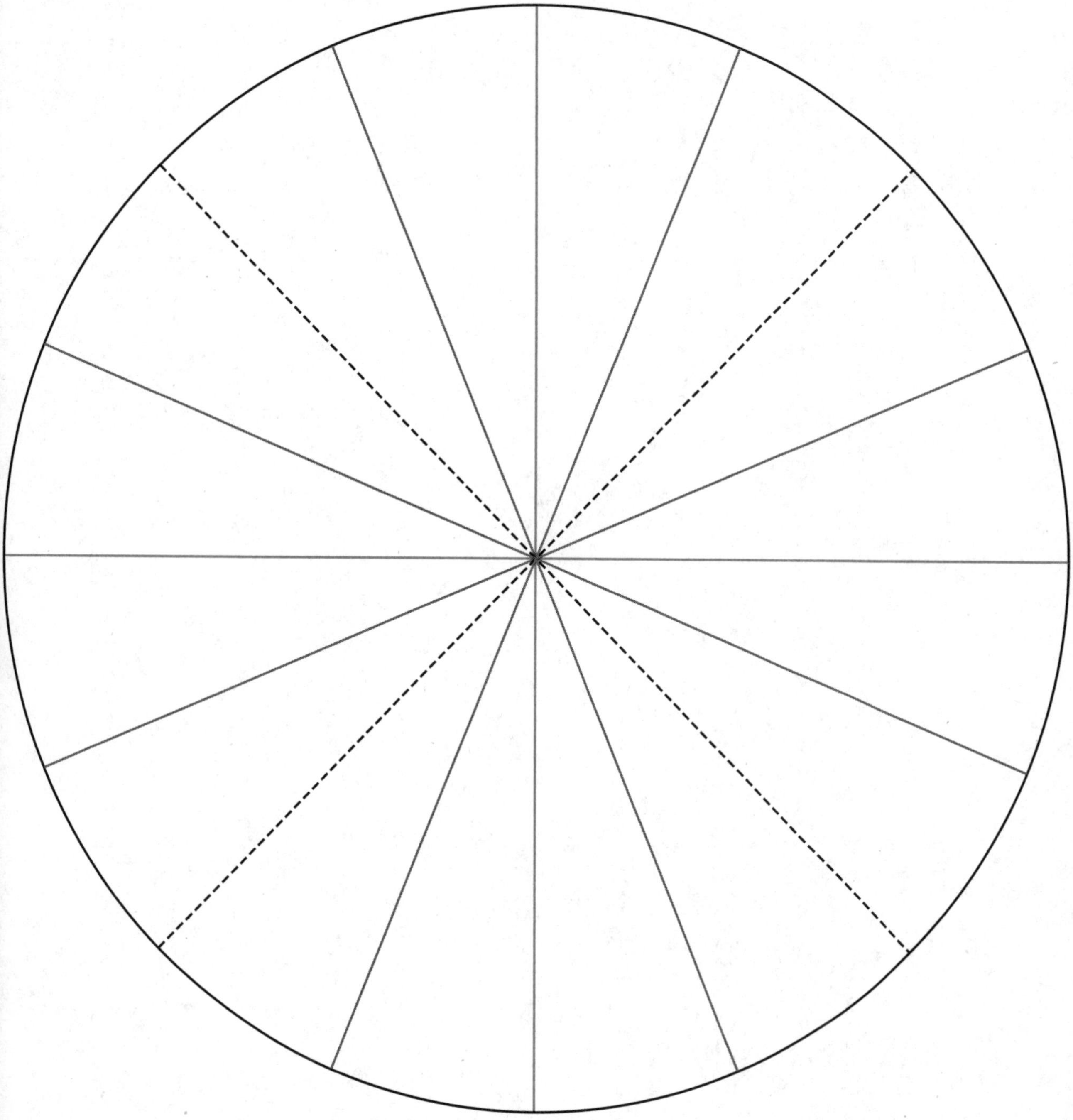

Assignment

Write

Explain in your own words how to derive the formula for the area of a circle.

Remember

A formula for the area of a circle is $A = \pi r^2$.

Practice

Determine the area of the circle, given each measurement. Use 3.14 for π and round to the nearest hundredth.

1. Diameter: 8 in.
2. Radius: 10 in.
3. Radius: 1.5 ft
4. Diameter: 8.8 yd
5. Diameter: $1\frac{3}{4}$ in.
6. Radius: $2\frac{1}{2}$ cm

Determine which pizza is the better buy in each situation.

7. The 10-inch diameter pizza for $8.99 or the 6-inch diameter pizza for $5.
8. The large 16-inch diameter pizza for $12.99 or the $26 X-large with a radius of 16 in.
9. The 12-inch diameter pizza for $12.50 or the 20-inch diameter pizza for $17.50.
10. The 4-inch radius pizza for $3 or the 8-inch radius pizza for $14.
11. Two 12-inch diameter pizzas for $12.98 or one large 14-inch diameter pizza for $7.99.
12. The 1-inch diameter pizza bite for $1 or the 10-inch diameter pizza for $10.

Stretch

The radius of the small circle is 0.5 millimeter. The area of the large circle is 28.26 square millimeters. Calculate the area of the shaded region.

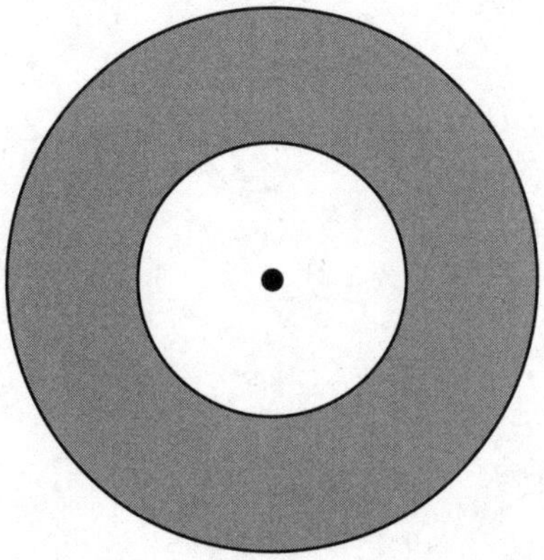

Review

Determine the circumference of each circle, given its radius or diameter. Use 3.14 for π and round to the nearest tenth.

1. Radius: 4.5 cm
2. Diameter: 12 ft

Determine each unit rate.

3. 75 square feet of tile for $126
4. 420 miles in 6.5 hours

Compare the fractions in each pair using the symbol >, <, or =.

5. $\frac{3}{5}, \frac{2}{3}$
6. $\frac{6}{7}, \frac{8}{9}$

Circular Reasoning

3

Solving Area and Circumference Problems

WARM UP

Determine the area of each circle. Use 3.14 for π.

1.

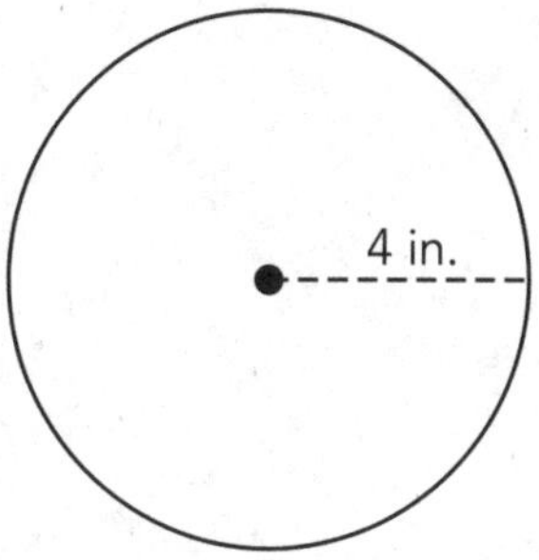

2.

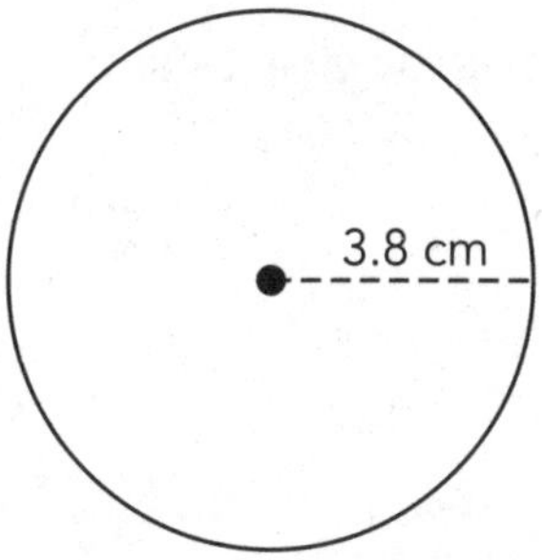

3.

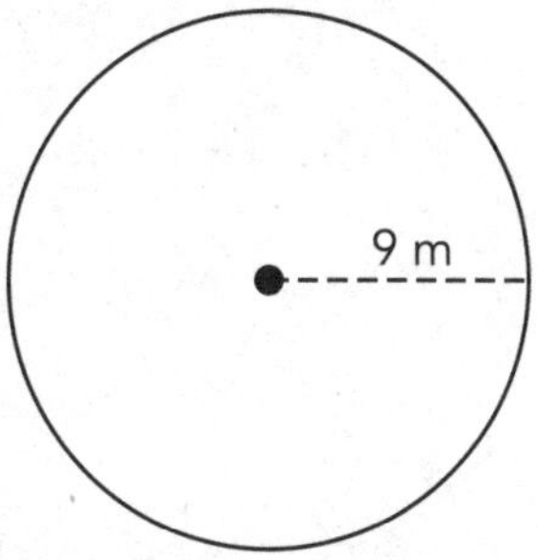

4.

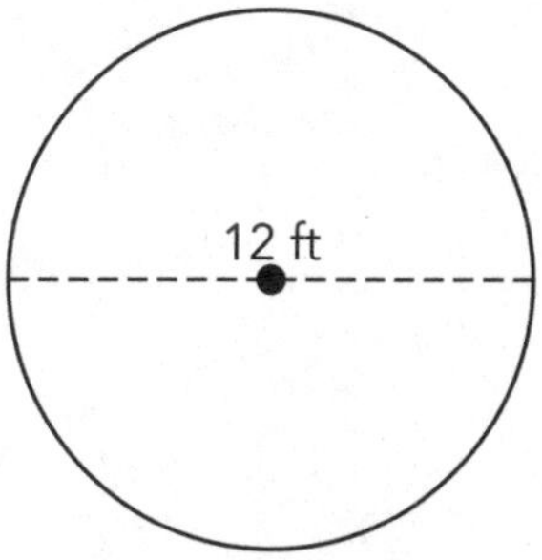

LEARNING GOALS

- Use the area and circumference formulas for a circle to solve problems.
- Calculate the areas of composite figures.

You encounter circles regularly in life. Now that you know how to calculate the circumference and area of circles, what kind of problems can you solve?

Getting Started

A Winning Formula

Suppose that the circumference of a circle is approximately 157 centimeters.

1. **Describe a strategy you can use to solve for the area of the circle.**

When in doubt, use 3.14 for pi throughout this lesson.

2. **Solve for the area of the circle. Use 3.14 for π.**

ACTIVITY 3.1

A Maximum Area Problem

A friend gave you 120 feet of fencing. You decide to fence in a portion of the backyard for your dog. You want to maximize the amount of fenced land.

1. **Draw a diagram, label the dimensions, and compute the maximum fenced area. Assume the fence is free-standing and you are not using any existing structure.**

ACTIVITY
3.2 Composite Figure Problems

In previous grades you worked with composite figures made up of triangles and various quadrilaterals. Now that you know the area of a circle, you can calculate the area of more interesting composite figures.

1. A figure is composed of a rectangle and two semicircles. Determine the area of the figure.

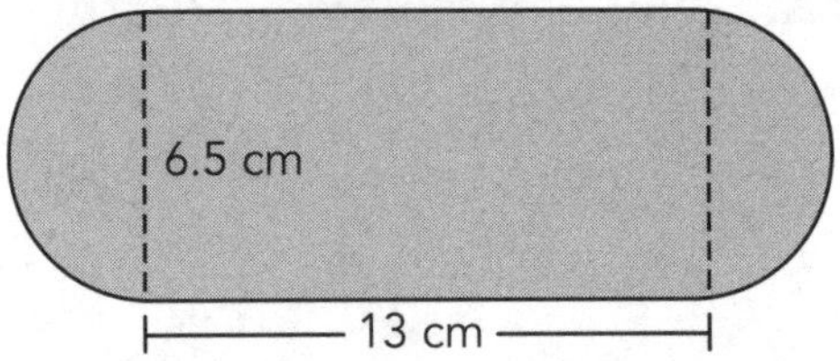

2. A figure is composed of a trapezoid and a semicircle. Determine the area of the figure.

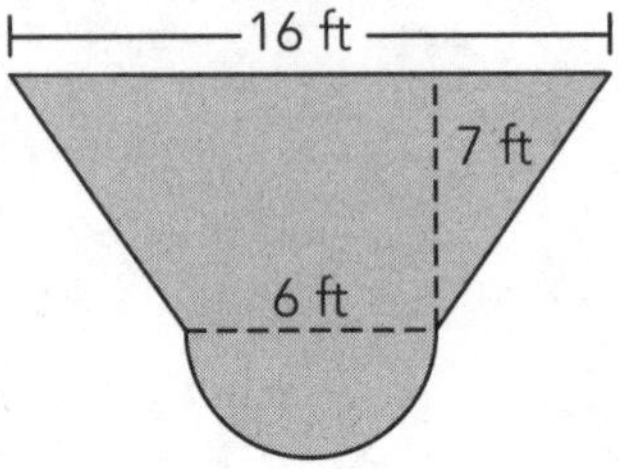

3. A figure is composed of a triangle and three semicircles. Determine the area of the figure.

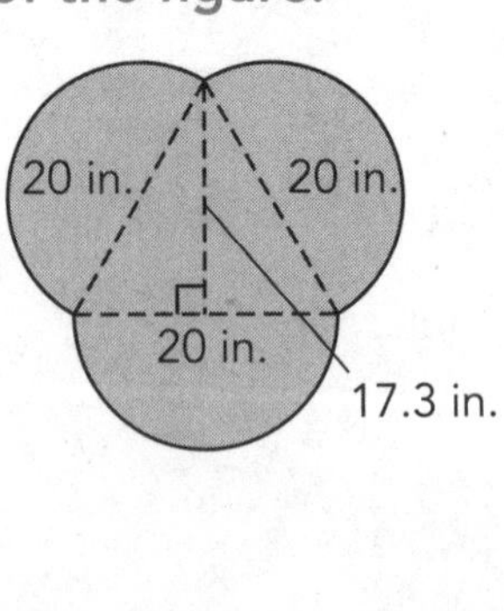

ACTIVITY 3.3

Shaded Region Problems

'ou have worked with composite figures by adding on areas. Now let's hink about subtracting areas.

1. In the concentric circles shown, *R* represents the radius of the larger circle and *r* represents the radius of the smaller circle. Suppose that $R = 8$ centimeters and $r = 3$ centimeters. Calculate the area of the shaded region.

Concentric circles are circles with a common center. The region bounded by two concentric circles is called the annulus.

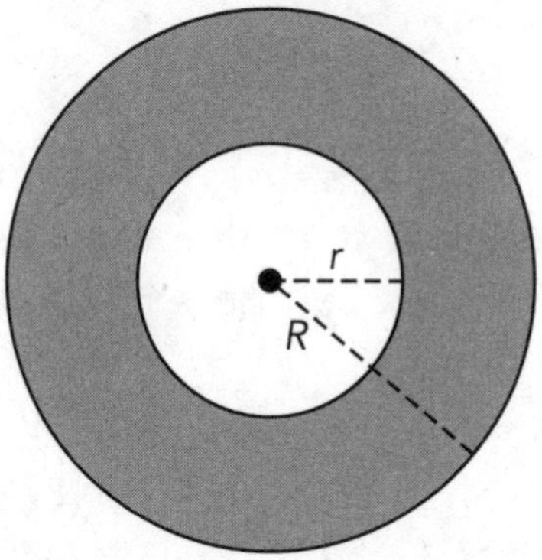

2. A circle is inscribed in a square. Determine the area of the shaded region.

When a circle is inscribed in a square, the diameter of the circle is equal to the side length of the square.

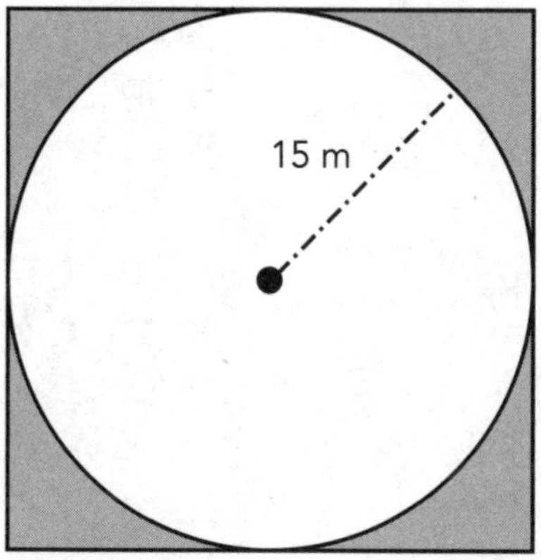

NOTES

3. Two small circles are drawn that touch each other, and both circles touch the large circle. Determine the area of the shaded region.

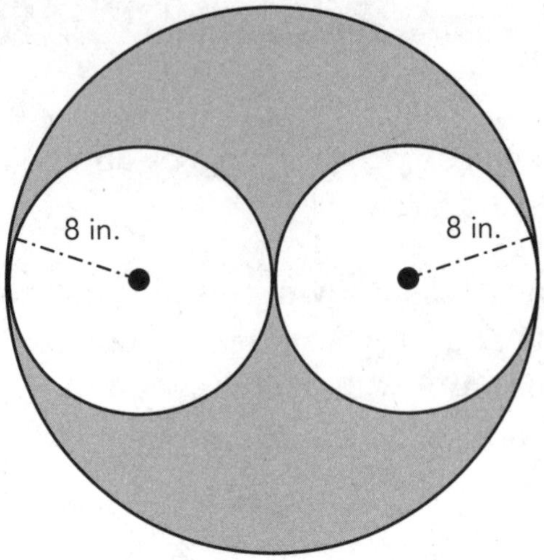

4. Jimmy and Matthew each said the area of the shaded region is about 402 square inches. Compare their strategies.

Jimmy

Area of 1 small circle
$A \approx 3.14(8)^2$
$A \approx 3.14(64)$
$A \approx 200.96$

Area of 2 small circles
$A \approx 2(200.96)$
$A \approx 401.92$

Area of large circle
$A \approx (3.14)(16)^2$
$A \approx (3.14)(256)$
$A \approx 803.84$

Area of shaded region
$803.84 - 401.92 \approx 401.92$

The area of the shaded region is about 402 sq in.

Matthew

Area of 1 small circle
$A = \pi(8)^2$
$A = 64\pi$

Area of 2 small circles
$A = 2(64\pi)$
$A = 128\pi$

Area of large circle
$A = \pi(16)^2$
$A = 256\pi$

Area of shaded region
$256\pi - 128\pi = 128\pi$
$A = 128\pi$
$A \approx 402.12$

This means the area of the shaded region is about 402 sq in.

a. What did Jimmy and Matthew do the same?

b. What was different about their strategies?

c. Which strategy do you prefer?

5. Determine the area of each shaded region.

a. One medium circle and one small circle touch each other, and each circle touches the large circle.

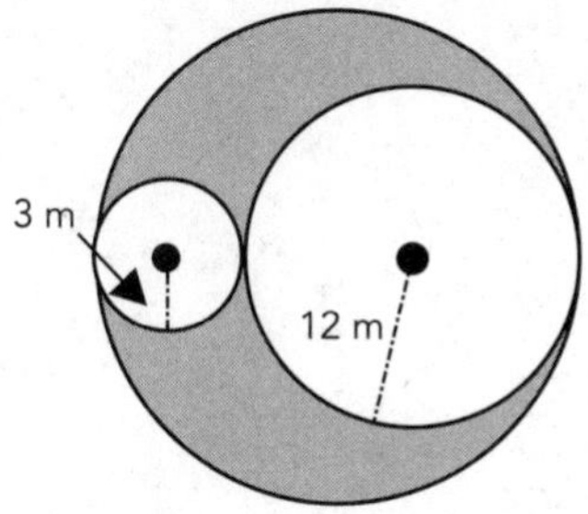

b. A rectangle is inscribed in a circle.

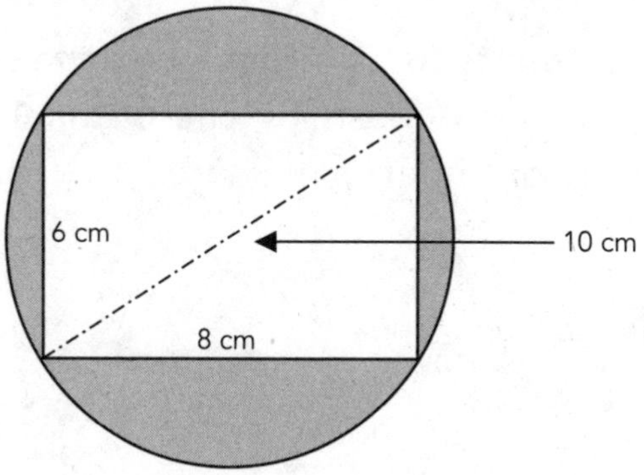

A rectangle is inscribed in a circle when all the vertices of the rectangle touch the circumference of the circle.

c. A circle is inside a regular hexagon.

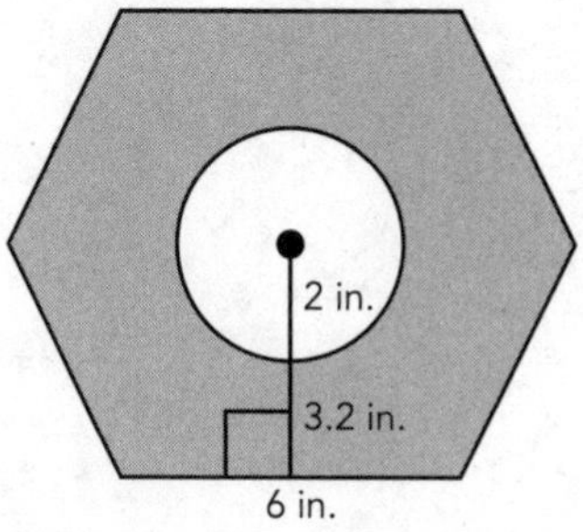

NOTES

TALK the TALK

Rupert's Leash

Jamal loves his dog, Rupert. On sunny days, Jamal keeps Rupert on a 12-foot leash in the backyard. The leash is secured to a stake in the ground.

1. **Determine the diameter, circumference, and area of Rupert's play area. Use 3.14 for π.**

2. **Suppose Jamal wants to give Rupert a little more room to play. He uses a 15-foot leash instead of the 12-foot leash. What is the area of Rupert's play area now? Use 3.14 for π.**

Assignment

Write

Write the area and circumference formulas for circles.

Describe pi in terms of the area and radius of a circle. Describe pi in terms of the circumference and radius of a circle.

Remember

Given a specific length to form a perimeter or circumference, arranging that length into the shape of a circle provides the maximum area.

Practice

Calculate the area of the shaded region in each figure. Use 3.14 for π and round to the nearest tenth, if necessary.

1.

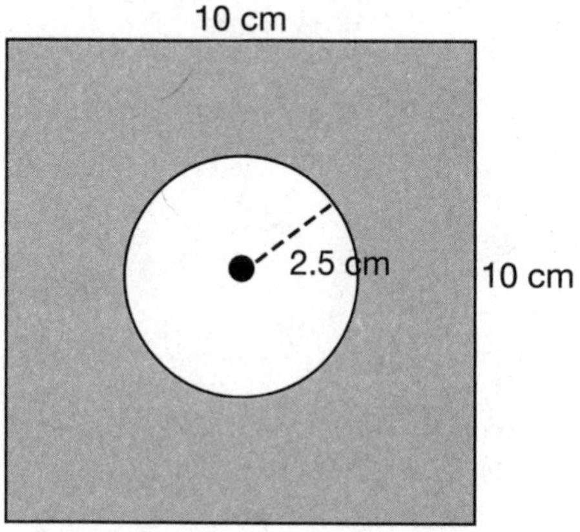

2.

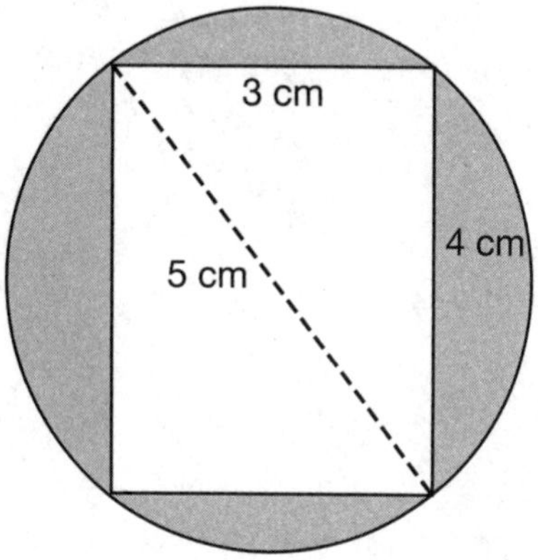

3.

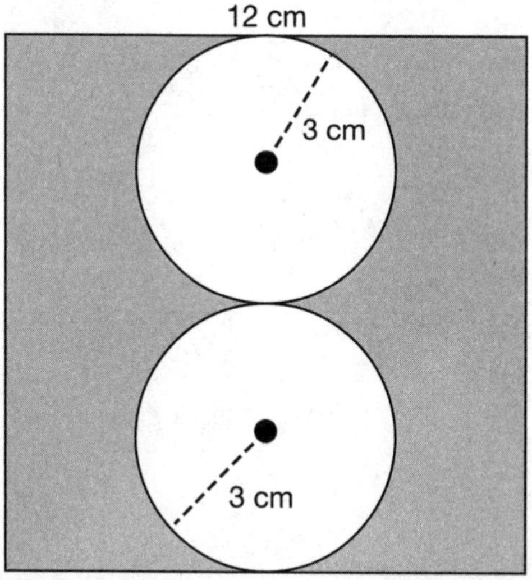

4.

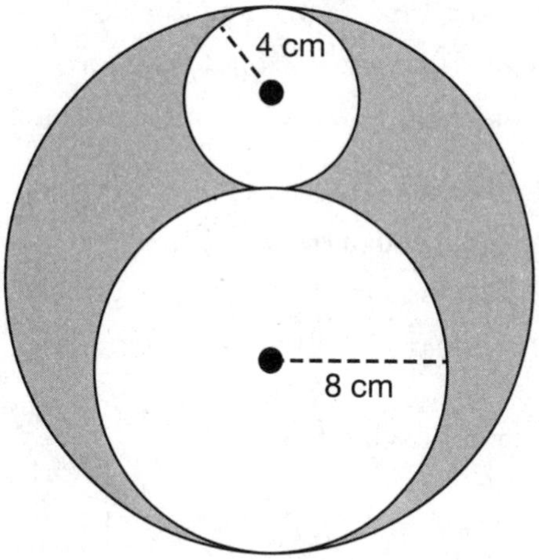

Stretch

1. Determine the area of the shaded region. All circles have the same radius of 10 inches.

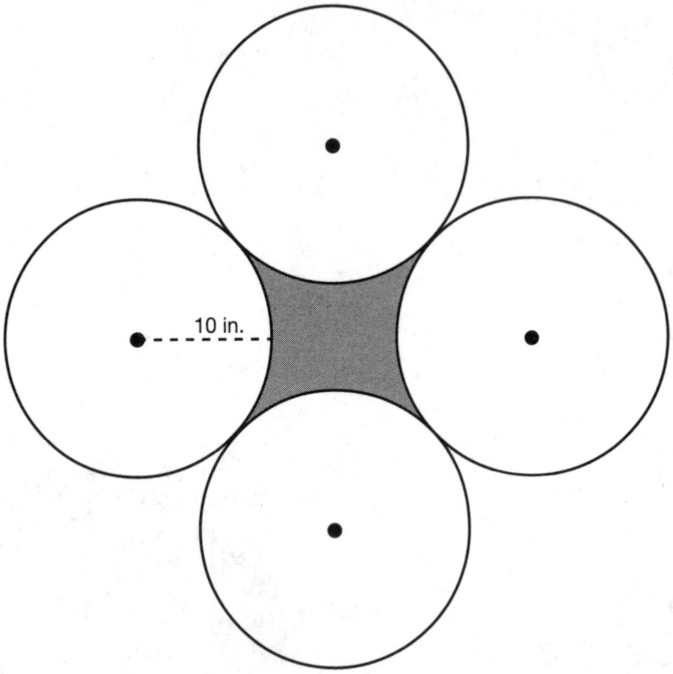

Review

Solve each problem.

1. Jose is adding mulch to an existing round flower bed. The length of the rubber edging around the flower bed is 25.12 feet. What is the area that Jose needs to cover with mulch?
2. Nami is adding a mosaic pattern to the top of a small round table. The distance around the edge of the table top is 4.7 feet. What is the area that Nami needs to cover with the mosaic pattern?

Determine each area.

3. Area of a triangle with a base length of 4 in. and a height of 9 in.
4. Area of a parallelogram with a base length of 2.9 ft and a height of 5.5 ft.
5. Area of a trapezoid with a top base length of 6 cm, a bottom base length of 12 cm, and a height of 5 cm.

Write a unit rate for each ratio.

6. $\frac{\text{28 cm}}{\text{4 square feet}}$

7. $\frac{\text{5.15 yd}}{\text{5 square feet}}$

Circles and Ratio Summary

KEY TERMS

- congruent
- circle
- radius
- diameter
- circumference
- pi
- unit rate

LESSON 1 Pi: The Ultimate Ratio

A **circle** is a collection of points on the same plane equidistant from the same point. The center of a circle is the point from which all points on the circle are equidistant.

A **radius** of a circle is a line segment formed by connecting a point on the circle and the center of the circle. The distance across a circle through the center is a **diameter** of the circle. A diameter of a circle is a line segment formed by connecting two points on the circle such that the line segment passes through the center point.

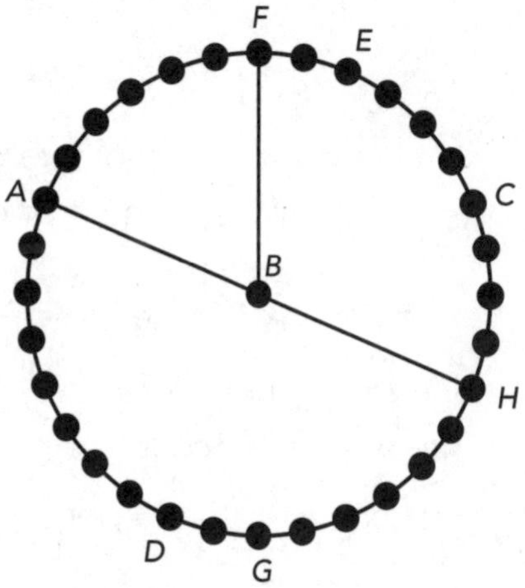

Circles are named by their center point. For example, the circle shown is Circle *B*. A radius of Circle *B* is line segment *FB*. A diameter of Circle *B* is line segment *AH*.

The distance around a circle is called the **circumference** of the circle. The number **pi** (π) is the ratio of the circumference of a circle to its diameter. That is, pi $= \frac{\text{circumference of a circle}}{\text{diameter of a circle}}$, or $\pi = \frac{C}{d}$, where *C* is the circumference of the circle, and *d* is the diameter of the circle. The number π has an infinite number of decimal digits that never repeat. Some approximations used for the value π are 3.14 and $\frac{22}{7}$. You can use the ratio to write a formula for the circumference of a circle: $C = \pi d$.

Congruent means that it has the same shape and size. For example, Circle X is congruent to Circle B. If line segment AH on Circle B has a length of 10 centimeters, then the circumference of Circle X is $C = \pi(10)$ centimeters, or approximately 31.4 centimeters.

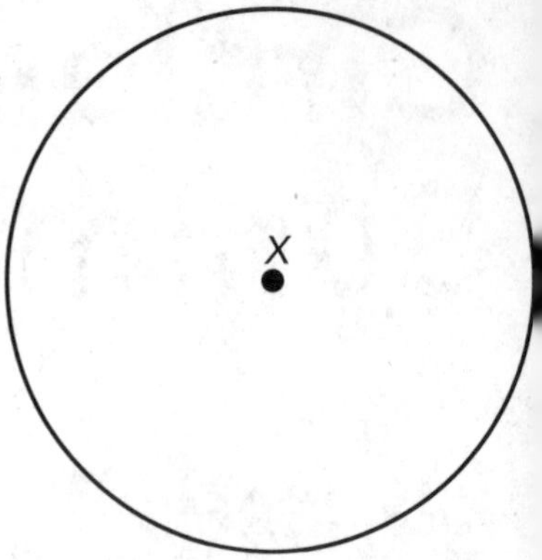

LESSON 2

That's a Spicy Pizza!

The circumference of a circle is the distance around the circle, while the area of a circle is the amount of space contained inside the circle. The formula for the area of a circle is $A = \pi r^2$.

The area formula for a circle can be derived by dividing a circle into a large number of equal-sized wedges. Laying these wedges as shown, you can see that they will form an approximate rectangle with a length of πr and a height of r.

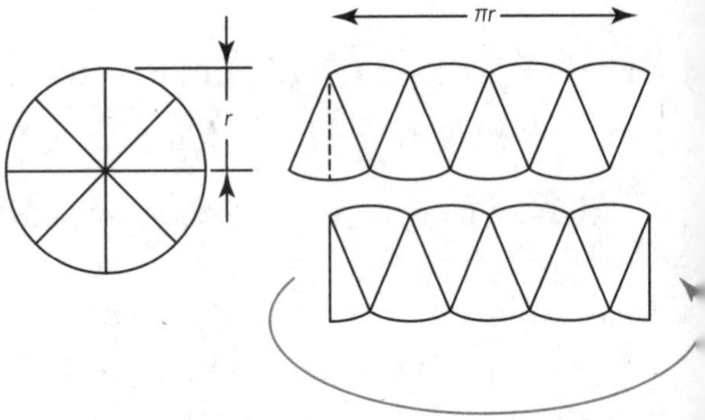

A **unit rate** is a ratio of two different measures in which either the numerator or denominator is 1.

For example, a large pizza with a diameter of 18 inches costs $14.99. The rate of area to cost is $\frac{\pi \cdot 9^2}{14.99} = \frac{81\pi}{14.99}$. Using 3.14 for π, the unit rate is approximately 16.97 square inches per dollar. The unit rate of cost to area is $\frac{1}{16.97}$, or approximately $0.06 per square inch.

LESSON 3

Circular Reasoning

Given a specific length to form a perimeter or circumference, arranging that length into the shape of a circle provides the maximum area.

For example, suppose you have 176 feet of fencing to use to fence off a portion of your backyard for planting vegetables. You want to maximize the amount of fenced land. Calculate the maximum fenced area you will have.

The length of fencing you have will form the circumference of a circle. Use the formula for the circumference of a circle to determine the diameter of the fenced area.

$$C = \pi d$$
$$176 = \pi d$$
$$56 \approx d$$

If the diameter of the fenced area is about 56 feet, the radius is 28 feet. Use this information to calculate the area of the fenced land.

$$A = \pi r^2$$
$$A = \pi \cdot 28^2$$

The maximum fenced area you will have is about 2461.76 square feet.

$$A = 784\pi \approx 2461.76$$

Many geometric figures are composed of two or more geometric shapes. These figures are known as composite figures. When solving problems involving composite figures, it is often necessary to calculate the area of each figure and then add these areas together.

For example, a figure is composed of a rectangle and two semi-circles. Determine the area of the figure.

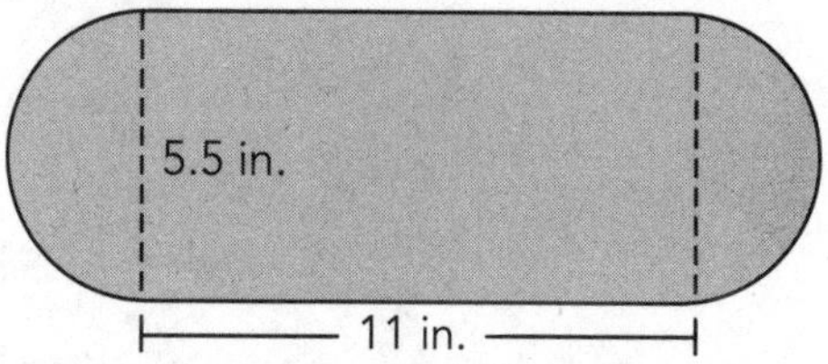

Calculate the area of the rectangle.

$A = l \times w$

$A = (11)(5.5)$

$A = 60.5$ square inches

The two semi-circles together make one circle. Calculate the area of the circle.

$A = \pi r^2$

$A = \pi(2.75)^2$

$A = 7.5625\pi \approx 23.75$ square inches

The area of the composite figure is approximately 60.5 square inches plus 23.75 square inches, or 84.55 square inches.

When determining the area of a shaded region of a figure, it is often necessary to calculate the area of a figure and subtract it from the area of a second figure.

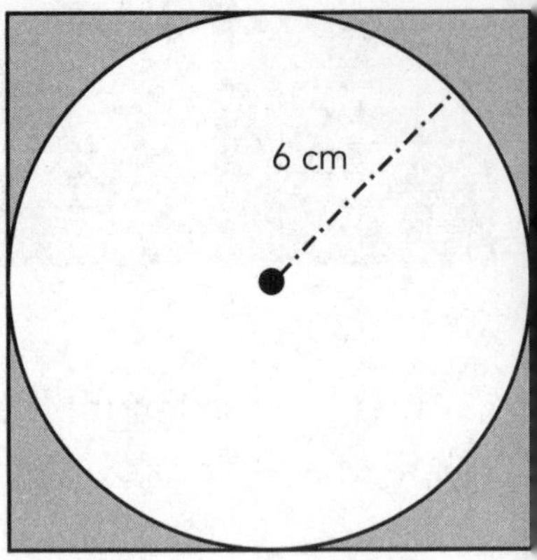

For example, this figure shows a circle inscribed in a square. Determine the area of the shaded region.

When a circle is inscribed in a square, the diameter of the circle is equal to the side length of the square.

Calculate the area of the square.

$A = s^2$

$A = 12^2$

$A = 144$ square centimeters

Calculate the area of the circle.

$A = \pi r^2$

$A = \pi(6)^2$

$A = 36\pi \approx 113.04$ square inches

The area of the shaded region is approximately 144 square centimeters minus 113.04 square centimeters, or 30.96 square centimeters.

TOPIC 2

Fractional Rates

The brain-to-body mass ratio for an elephant is 1:560. For a human it's 1:50.

Module 1: Thinking Proportionally

TOPIC 2: FRACTIONAL RATES

In this topic, students extend their work with rates to include rates with fractional values. To begin the topic, students write, analyze, and use unit rates with whole numbers and fractions to solve problems. Next, students calculate and use unit rates from ratios of fractions. Finally, students review strategies for solving problems involving equivalent ratios and proportions.

Where have we been?

In grade 6, students learned about ratios, rates, unit rates, and proportions, and they represented ratios and unit rates with tables and graphs. Students used a variety of informal strategies to compare ratios and to determine equivalent ratios and solve simple proportions (e.g., double number lines, scaling up and down, conversion factors).

Where are we going?

This topic broadens students' range of numbers and strategies for solving ratio and proportion problems, preparing them to dig deeper into representations of proportional relationships in the next topic and solving multistep ratio and percent problems in future lessons.

Using Means and Extremes to Solve Proportions

In the proportion $\frac{a}{b} = \frac{c}{d}$, the terms *b* and *c* are called the means, and the terms *a* and *d* are called the extremes.

extremes

3 : 4 = 9 : 12

means

(4)(9) = (3)(12)

or

$\frac{3}{4} = \frac{9}{12}$

means extremes

(4)(9) = (3)(12)

Myth: "If I can get the right answer, then I should not have to explain why."

Sometimes you get the right answer for the wrong reasons. Suppose a student is asked, "What is 4 divided by 2?" and she confidently answers "2!" If she does not explain any further, then it might be assumed that she understands how to divide whole numbers. But, what if she used the following rule to solve that problem? "Subtract 2 from 4 one time." Even though she gave the right answer, she has an incomplete understanding of division.

However, if she is asked to explain her reasoning, either by drawing a picture, creating a model, or giving a different example, the teacher has a chance to remediate her flawed understanding. If teachers aren't exposed to their students' reasoning for both right and wrong answers, then they won't know about or be able to address misconceptions. This is important because mathematics is cumulative in the sense that new lessons build upon previous understandings.

You should ask your student to explain his or her thinking, when possible, even if you don't know whether the explanation is correct. When children (and adults!) explain something to someone else, it helps them learn. Just the process of trying to explain is helpful.

#mathmythbusted

Talking Points

You can further support your student's learning by asking questions about the work they do in class or at home. Your student is learning to reason using fractional rates.

Questions to Ask

- How does this problem look like something you did in class?
- Can you show me the strategy you used to solve this problem? Do you know another way to solve it?
- Does your answer make sense? How do you know?

Key Terms

complex ratio

A complex ratio is a ratio in which the numerator, denominator, or both are fractions.

isolate the variable

When you isolate the variable in an equation, you perform an operation, or operations, to get the variable by itself on one side of the equals sign.

inverse operations

Inverse operations are operations that "undo" each other. Multiplication and division are inverse operations.

Making Punch

1

Unit Rate Representations

WARM UP

Determine a unit rate in terms of each quantity for the given ratio.

1. 24 bracelets : 6 hours
2. 153 miles : 9 gallons
3. $48 : 3 pounds
4. 45 students : 3 teachers

LEARNING GOALS

- Compute unit rates associated with ratios of whole numbers and fractions.
- Represent unit rates using tables and graphs.
- Use unit rates to solve problems.

You have learned about ratios, rates, and unit rates. How can you use tables and graphs to represent unit rates and solve problems?

Getting Started

The Pumpkin-iest!

Paige loves everything pumpkin: pumpkin waffles, pumpkin hand soap, pumpkin chili . . . Now she's trying to make the perfect pumpkin smoothie. She is using this recipe:

Pumpkin Smoothie Recipe	
• 1 banana ($\frac{3}{4}$ cup)	• $\frac{1}{4}$ teaspoon pumpkin pie spice
• $\frac{1}{4}$ teaspoon cinnamon	• 1 cup ice
• 2 tablespoons maple syrup	• $\frac{2}{3}$ cup pumpkin puree
• $\frac{1}{2}$ cup milk	• $\frac{1}{2}$ cup vanilla yogurt

Paige wants to experiment with the given recipe.

1. **What ingredients can Paige increase to make the smoothie more pumpkin-y? Less pumpkin-y?**

2. **What ingredients can Paige decrease to make the smoothie more pumpkin-y? Less pumpkin-y?**

ACTIVITY
1.1

Determining Unit Rates

Four students share their recipes for lemon-lime punch. The class decides to analyze the recipes to determine which one will make the fruitiest tasting punch.

Mason's Recipe	Tyler's Recipe
4 cups lemon-lime concentrate 8 cups club soda	3 cups lemon-lime concentrate 5 cups club soda
Carlos's Recipe	**Zeb's Recipe**
2 cups lemon-lime concentrate 3 cups club soda	1 cup lemon-lime concentrate 4 cups club soda

1. **Which recipe has the strongest taste of lemon-lime? Show your work and explain your reasoning.**

2. **Which has the weakest taste of lemon-lime? Show your work and explain your reasoning.**

Emily and Julio each used unit rates to compare Mason's and Tyler's recipes.

Emily

Mason's recipe
4 cups lemon-lime : 8 cups club soda
The unit rate is $\frac{1}{2}$ cup lemon-lime per 1 cup of club soda

Tyler's recipe
3 cups lemon-lime : 5 cups club soda
The unit rate is $\frac{3}{5}$ cup lemon-lime per 1 cup of club soda

$\frac{3}{5} > \frac{1}{2}$, so Tyler's recipe has the stronger taste of lemon-lime.

Julio

Mason's recipe
4 cups lemon-lime : 12 cups total punch
The unit rate is $\frac{1}{3}$ cup lemon-lime per cup of punch

Tyler's recipe
3 cups lemon-lime : 8 cups total punch
The unit rate is $\frac{3}{8}$ cup lemon-lime per cup of punch

$\frac{3}{8} > \frac{1}{3}$, so Tyler's recipe has the stronger taste of lemon-lime.

3. **Compare Julio's and Emily's strategies. In what ways are they different? How did they arrive at the same answer?**

4. **Complete each table and include the unit rate of lemon-lime for each cup of punch for each recipe. Then draw a graph for each recipe on the coordinate plane. Label each graph with the person's recipe and the unit rate.**

Mason's Recipe				
Lemon-Lime (c)				
Total Punch (c)	1			

Tyler's Recipe				
Lemon-Lime (c)				
Total Punch (c)	1			

Carlos's Recipe				
Lemon-Lime (c)				
Total Punch (c)	1			

Zeb's Recipe				
Lemon-Lime (c)				
Total Punch (c)	1			

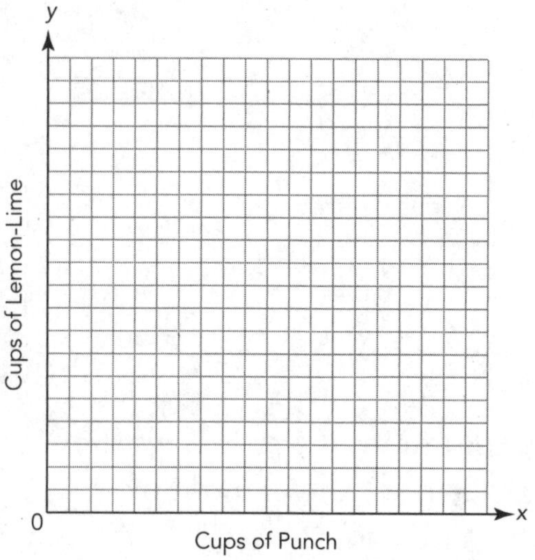

The steepness of a graphed line is called its slope.

5. **What does the steepness of each line represent?**

6. **How could you use the graphs to determine which recipe has the strongest lemon-lime taste?**

NOTES

TALK the TALK

Getting Unit Rate-ier

Look back at the activity *The Pumpkin-iest!* Use the smoothie recipe to answer each question.

1. **One teaspoon is approximately $\frac{1}{50}$ cup, and 1 tablespoon is equal to 3 teaspoons. Approximately how many cups of smoothie does Paige's recipe make?**

2. **How pumpkin-y are Paige's smoothies if she follows the recipe? Write a unit rate to represent the amount of pumpkin-y ingredients per cup of smoothie.**

Assignment

Write

How can unit rates be helpful when solving problems?

Remember

A rate is a ratio that compares quantities with different units. A unit rate is a rate in which the numerator or denominator (or both) is 1.

A unit rate is represented by the ordered pair (1, *r*) on a coordinate plane.

Practice

Complete each table and write a unit rate for the given situation.

1. General house cleaning (sweeping the floors, vacuuming, laundry, etc.) can burn 470 calories every 2 hours.

Time (hours)	1	2	3	4	5
Calories burned					

2. A full strip plus another half of a strip of staples contains 315 staples.

Number of Strips	$\frac{1}{2}$	1	$1\frac{1}{2}$	2	$2\frac{1}{2}$
Number of Staples					

3. Victoria is making punch for a school party. The recipe she is using calls for 2 cups of lemonade to make 5 cups of punch.

Cups of Lemonade					
Cups of Punch					

Complete each table and write a unit rate for the given situation. Then, graph the relationship on a coordinate plane.

4. The owner of a city parking garage uses a rate table so that he can look up the parking charges quickly.

Hours	$\frac{1}{2}$	1	$1\frac{1}{2}$	2	$2\frac{1}{2}$	3	$3\frac{1}{2}$	4
Charge	$2.25							

5. The owner of a city parking garage uses a rate table so that he can look up the parking charges quickly.

Hours	$\frac{1}{2}$	1	$1\frac{1}{2}$	2	$2\frac{1}{2}$	3	$3\frac{1}{2}$	4
Charge				$13.00				

Stretch

A line is graphed through points at (4, 5) and (8 10). What is the ordered pair of the unit rate?

Review

Use the circle shown to answer each question. Use 3.14 for π. Round to the nearest hundredth.

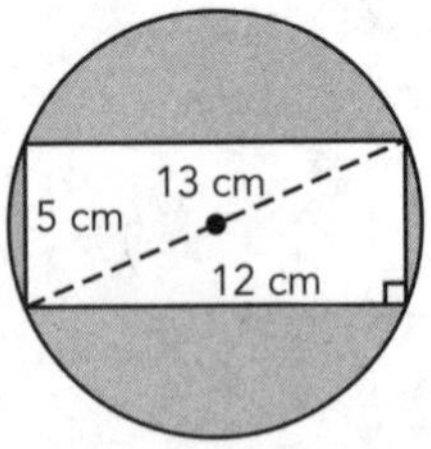

1. Calculate the exact area of the circle.
2. Calculate the circumference of the circle.
3. Determine the total area of the shaded regions.

Use 3.14 for π. Round to the nearest hundredth.

4. Ben's dog, Tripp, is on a leash that is 6 feet long. What is the approximate circular area of Tripp's play area?

Determine each number.

5. 49 is 70% of what number?
6. 99 is 36% of what number?

Eggzactly!

Solving Problems with Ratios of Fractions

2

WARM UP

Determine each product or quotient.

1. $\frac{1}{2} \times \frac{3}{5}$

2. $\frac{5}{8} \times \frac{8}{5}$

3. $\frac{2}{3} \div \frac{3}{8}$

4. $\frac{3}{4} \div 1\frac{1}{2}$

LEARNING GOALS

- Compute unit rates from ratios of fractions, including ratios of lengths and areas.
- Interpret complex rates to solve real-world problems involving lengths and areas.

KEY TERM

- complex ratio

You have learned about rates and unit rates. You have written unit rates from ratios of whole numbers. How can you write ratios of fractions as unit rates in order to solve problems?

Getting Started

A Different Form, But Still the Same

Ratios can be written using any numbers. A ratio in which one or both of the quantities being compared are written as fractions is called a **complex ratio**.

For example, traveling $\frac{1}{3}$ mile in $\frac{1}{2}$ hour represents a ratio of fractions, or a complex ratio. It is also an example of a rate, since the units being compared are different.

You can write this ratio in fractional form: $\frac{\frac{1}{3}}{\frac{1}{2}}$.

1. **Rewrite each given rate as an equivalent ratio of fractions, or complex ratio, by converting one or both units of measure.**

   a. **One half-inch of rain fell in fifteen minutes.**

   b. **Sam ran 3520 feet in 20 minutes.**

   c. **The baby gained 6 ounces every week.**

   d. **Gas costs $2.50 per gallon.**

"Think about equivalent relationships. Fifteen minutes is what fraction of an hour?"

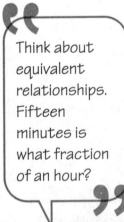

ACTIVITY 2.1

Comparing Ratios of Fractions

The table shows the weights of four different adult birds and the weights of their eggs.

	Mother's Weight (oz)	Egg Weight (oz)
Pigeon	10	$\frac{3}{4}$
Chicken	80	2
Swan	352	11
Robin	$2\frac{1}{2}$	$\frac{1}{10}$

1. **Compare the weights of the eggs. List the birds in order from the bird with the heaviest egg to the bird with the lightest egg.**

2. **Determine the ratio of egg weight to mother's weight for each bird.**

3. **Compare the ratios of egg weight to mother's weight. List the birds in order from greatest to least ratio.**

"The strategy to compare ratios is the same regardless of the types of numbers used."

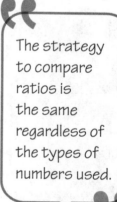

ACTIVITY 2.2

Determining Unit Rates from Ratios of Fractions

Although the ostrich is the largest living bird, it is also the fastest runner. The table shows distances that four birds ran, and the amount of time it took each bird to run that distance.

Bird	Distance Covered	Time
Ostrich	22 miles	$\frac{1}{2}$ hour
Greater Roadrunner	300 yards	$\frac{1}{2}$ minute
Quail	20 yards	$2\frac{1}{2}$ seconds
Pheasant	200 yards	$\frac{5}{6}$ minute

"Remember, a rate is a ratio that compares two quantities that are measured in different units."

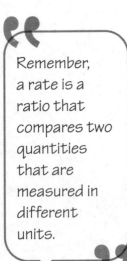

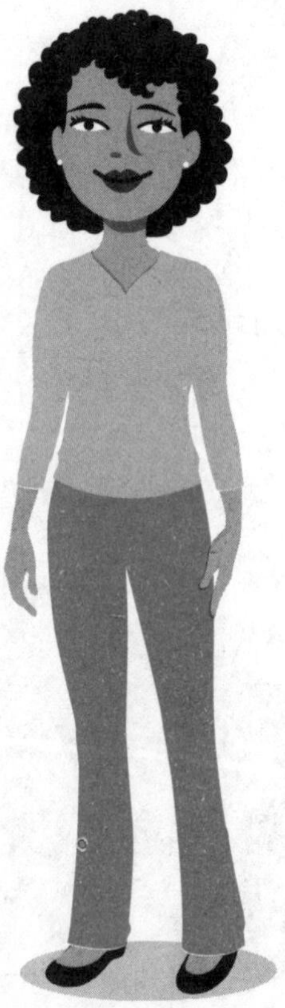

Each row in the table shows a rate. The rate for each bird in this situation is the distance covered per the amount of time.

1. Write the rate for each bird as a complex rate.

a. Ostrich

b. Greater Roadrunner

c. Quail

d. Pheasant

NOTES

The rates you wrote in Question 1 are each represented using different units of measure. In order to compare speeds let's determine the unit rate in miles per hour for each bird. Consider the numbers and units of the original rate to choose a strategy. Analyze each worked example.

You know that the ostrich ran 22 miles in $\frac{1}{2}$ hour.

WORKED EXAMPLE

The rate of the ostrich is already measured in miles and hours. You can set up a proportion and scale the original rate up to 1 hour.

$$\frac{\text{distance}}{\text{time}} \rightarrow \frac{22 \text{ mi}}{\frac{1}{2} \text{ h}} \overset{\times 2}{=} \frac{44 \text{ mi}}{1 \text{ h}}$$

$$= \frac{44 \text{ mi}}{1 \text{ h}}$$

The ostrich's speed is 44 miles per hour.

2. Why was the scale factor of 2 used in this worked example?

There are 1760 yards in 1 mile.

You know that the Greater Roadrunner ran 300 yards in $\frac{1}{2}$ minute.

WORKED EXAMPLE

The rate of the Greater Roadrunner is written in yards per minute. You can use conversion rates to rewrite the rate in miles per hour.

$$\frac{300 \text{ yd}}{\frac{1}{2} \text{ min}} \cdot \frac{60 \text{ min}}{1 \text{ hr}} \cdot \frac{1 \text{ mi}}{1760 \text{ yd}}$$

$$\frac{300 \cancel{\text{yd}}}{\frac{1}{2} \cancel{\text{min}}} \cdot \frac{60 \cancel{\text{min}}}{1 \text{ hr}} \cdot \frac{1 \text{ mi}}{1760 \cancel{\text{yd}}}$$

$$\frac{300}{\frac{1}{2}} \cdot \frac{60}{1} \cdot \frac{1}{1760} \frac{\text{mi}}{\text{hr}}$$

$$600 \cdot 60 \cdot \frac{1}{1760} \frac{\text{mi}}{\text{hr}} \approx \frac{20.5 \text{ mi}}{1 \text{ hr}}$$

3. Why is the fractional representation of each conversion rate important?

4. Determine the quail's and pheasant's speeds in miles per hour.

a. quail's speed:

b. pheasant's speed:

5. Write the birds in order from the fastest rate to the slowest rate.

ACTIVITY
2.3 Solving Problems with Fractional Rates

1. Tony needs a rate table for his tutoring jobs so that he can look up the charge quickly.

   a. Complete the rate table.

Time (Hours)	$\frac{1}{2}$	1	$1\frac{1}{2}$	2	3	$3\frac{1}{2}$	4
Charge ($)			37.50				

   b. How much would Tony charge for $7\frac{1}{2}$ hours of tutoring?

   c. Tony made $212.50 last weekend. How long did he tutor? Explain how you solved the problem.

2. At Pepe's Pizzas, a new deal gives you $1\frac{1}{2}$ orders of wings for half the price of a single order. Without the deal, a single order of wings costs $12. What is the cost of a single order of wings with the deal?

3. Abby uses $3\frac{3}{4}$ scoops of drink mix to make 10 cups of drinks.

   a. How much drink mix would she need to use to make 1 cup of drink?

   b. She only has $11\frac{1}{4}$ scoops of drink mix remaining. How many cups of drink can she make?

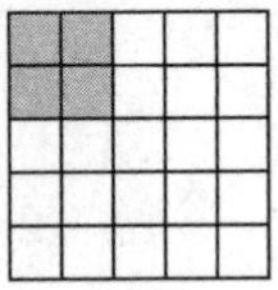

4. The square shown is composed of smaller equally-sized squares. The shaded section has an area of $\frac{9}{25}$ square inches. What is the area of the large square?

NOTES

TALK the TALK

True, False, Example

Determine whether each statement is true or false. Provide one or more examples and an explanation to justify your answer.

1. To compute a unit rate associated with a ratio of fractions, multiply both the numerator and denominator by the reciprocal of the denominator. True False

2. Any ratio can be written as a complex ratio. True False

3. You never scale down to write a complex rate as a unit rate. True False

4. A statement with the word "per" is always a unit rate. True False

5. Dividing the numerator by the denominator is one way to convert a rate to a unit rate. True False

Assignment

Write

Write a definition for *complex ratio*, provide an example, and show how your example can be converted into a unit rate.

Remember

To convert a complex rate to a unit rate, you can multiply the numerator and denominator by the reciprocal of the denominator, or you can use the definition of division.

$$\frac{\frac{1}{2}}{\frac{1}{4}} \times \frac{\frac{4}{1}}{\frac{4}{1}} = \frac{\frac{4}{2}}{1}$$

$$= 2$$

$$\frac{\frac{1}{2}}{\frac{1}{4}} = \frac{1}{2} \div \frac{1}{4}$$

$$= \frac{1}{2} \cdot 4 = 2$$

Practice

1. The table shows the gallons filled in a pool over time.

Number of Hours	$\frac{1}{4}$	$\frac{3}{4}$	$1\frac{1}{2}$	$2\frac{1}{2}$
Gallons Filled		$637\frac{1}{2}$		

   a. Complete the table.
   b. Determine a unit rate for this situation.
   c. Use a unit rate to calculate the gallons filled in 5.5 hours.
   d. Use a unit rate to determine about how many minutes it will take to fill 100 gallons in the pool.

2. The rectangle shown is composed of smaller equally-sized squares. The shaded section has an area of $\frac{3}{16}$ square inches. Use a unit rate to determine the area of the larger rectangle.

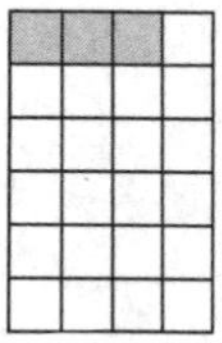

Stretch

An HOn2-scale train is a model train that is constructed at the ratio 1 : 87.1. If an HOn2 model of a locomotive is 10.4712 inches long, how long is the actual locomotive in feet?

Review

Determine each unit rate and graph each rate on the coordinate plane.

1. $\frac{3}{4}$ cup of punch to $\frac{1}{8}$ cup of lemon-lime

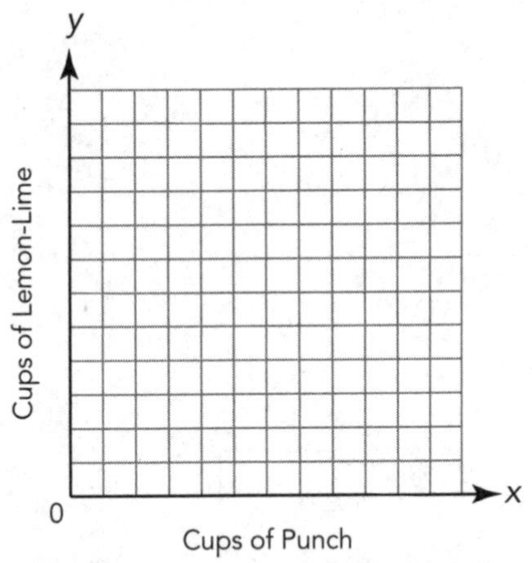

2. 1 cup of lemon-lime : $1\frac{1}{2}$ cups of punch

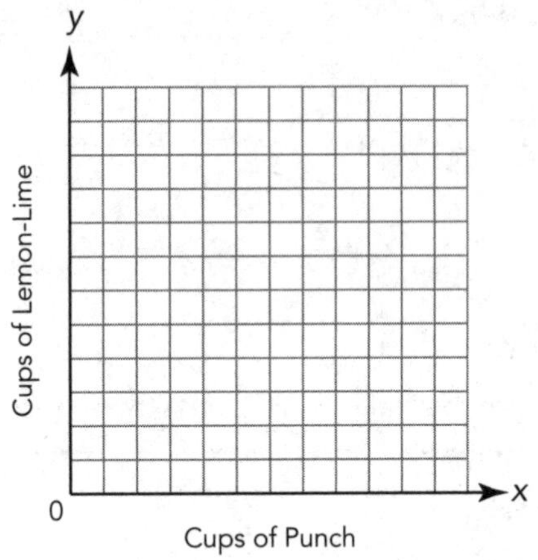

Answer each question. Use 3.14 for π. Round to the nearest hundredth.

3. The diameter of a circle is 4 cm. Determine the area of the circle.
4. The radius of a circle is 5.24 ft. Determine the circumference of the circle.

Determine each sum or product.

5. $71.05 + 0.54$
6. 89.2×5.3

Tagging Sharks

3

Solving Proportions Using Means and Extremes

WARM UP

Solve each equation.

1. $w - 5 = 25$
2. $9x = 990$
3. $\frac{c}{12} = 48$
4. $1.15 + m = 10$

LEARNING GOALS

- Rewrite proportions to maintain equality.
- Represent proportional relationships by equations.
- Develop strategies to solve proportions.
- Use proportional relationships to solve multistep problems.

KEY TERMS

- proportion
- variable
- means
- extremes
- solve a proportion
- isolate the variable
- inverse operations

You have learned how to write proportions and calculate unknown values through scaling up and scaling down. Is there a more efficient strategy that works for any unknown in any proportion?

Getting Started

Mix-N-Match

Recall that a **proportion** is an equation that states that two ratios are equal.

A proportion can be written several ways. Each example shows three proportions using the same four quantities.

	Example 1	Example 2
Proportion 1	$\frac{2}{3} = \frac{4}{6}$	$\frac{5}{7} = \frac{15}{21}$
Proportion 2	$\frac{6}{3} = \frac{4}{2}$	$\frac{21}{7} = \frac{15}{5}$
Proportion 3	$\frac{2}{4} = \frac{3}{6}$	$\frac{5}{15} = \frac{7}{21}$

1. In each example, use arrows to show how the numbers were rearranged from the:

a. first proportion to the second proportion.

b. first proportion to the third proportion.

ACTIVITY 3.1

Maintaining Equality with Proportions

Because it is impossible to count each individual animal, marine biologists use a method called the capture-recapture method to estimate the population of certain sea creatures. In certain areas of the world, biologists randomly catch and tag a given number of sharks. After a period of time, such as a month, they recapture a second sample of sharks and count the total number of sharks as well as the number of recaptured tagged sharks. Then, the biologists use proportions to estimate the population of sharks living in a certain area.

Biologists can set up a proportion to estimate the total number of sharks in an area.

$$\frac{\text{Original number of tagged sharks}}{\text{Total number of sharks in an area}} = \frac{\text{Number of recaptured tagged sharks}}{\text{Number of sharks caught in the second sample}}$$

Although capturing the sharks once is necessary for tagging, it is not necessary to recapture the sharks each time. At times, the tags can be observed through binoculars from a boat or at shore.

Biologists originally caught and tagged 24 sharks off the coast of Cape Cod, Massachusetts, and then released them back into the bay. The next month, they caught 80 sharks with 8 of the sharks already tagged. To estimate the shark population off the Cape Cod coast, biologists set up the following proportion:

$$\frac{24 \text{ tagged sharks}}{p \text{ total sharks}} = \frac{8 \text{ recaptured tagged sharks}}{80 \text{ total sharks}}$$

Notice the variable p in the proportion. In this proportion, let p represent the total shark population off the coast of Cape Cod.

A **variable** is a letter or symbol used to represent a number.

1. Write three additional different proportions you could use to determine the total shark population off the coast of Cape Cod.

2. Estimate the total shark population using any of the proportions.

3. Did any of the proportions seem more efficient than the other proportions?

4. Wildlife biologists tag deer in wildlife refuges. They originally tagged 240 deer and released them back into the refuge. The next month, they observed 180 deer, of which 30 deer were tagged. Approximately how many deer are in the refuge? Write a proportion and show your work to determine your answer.

A proportion of the form $\frac{a}{b} = \frac{c}{d}$ can be written in many different ways.

Another example is $\frac{d}{b} = \frac{c}{a}$ or $\frac{c}{a} = \frac{d}{b}$.

5. **Show how the variables were rearranged from the proportion in the "if" statement to each proportion in the "then" statement to maintain equality.**

   If $\frac{a}{b} = \frac{c}{d}$, then $\frac{d}{b} = \frac{c}{a}$.

   If $\frac{d}{b} = \frac{c}{a}$, then $\frac{c}{a} = \frac{d}{b}$.

6. **Write all the different ways you can rewrite the proportion $\frac{a}{b} = \frac{c}{d}$ and maintain equality.**

ACTIVITY 3.2 Solving Proportions with Means and Extremes

A quality control department checks the product a company creates to ensure that the product is not defective.

The Ready Steady Battery Company tests batteries as they come through the assembly line and then uses a proportion to predict how many of its total production might be defective.

On Friday, the quality controller tested every tenth battery and found that of the 320 batteries tested, 8 were defective. If the company shipped a total of 3200 batteries, how many might be defective?

NOTES

Let's analyze a few methods.

John David

$$\frac{8 \text{ defective batteries}}{320 \text{ batteries}} = \frac{d \text{ defective batteries}}{3200 \text{ batteries}}$$

$$\frac{8}{320} = \frac{d}{3200} \quad (\times 10 \text{ numerator and denominator})$$

$d = 80$

So, 80 batteries might be defective.

Parker

8 defective batteries : 320 batteries

$\times 10$ $\times 10$

d defective batteries : 3200 batteries

$d = 80$

About 80 batteries will probably be defective.

1. **How are Parker's and John David's methods similar?**

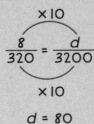

NOTES

Nora

÷8 ×80

$$\frac{\text{8 defective batteries}}{\text{320 batteries}} = \frac{\text{1 defective battery}}{\text{40 batteries}} = \frac{\text{80 defective batteries}}{\text{3200 batteries}}$$

÷8 ×80

"One out of every 40 batteries is defective. So, out of 3200 batteries, 80 batteries could be defective because 3200 ÷ 40 = 80."

2. Describe the strategy Nora used.

Natalie

When I write Nora's ratios using colons like Parker, I notice something about proportions . . .

8 : 320 = 1 : 40

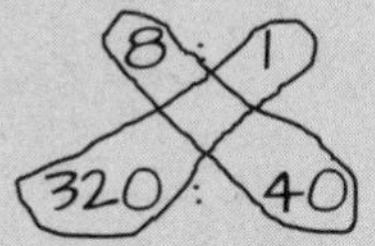

1 : 40 = 80 : 3200

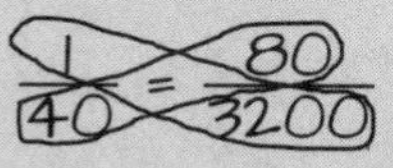

. . . the two middle numbers have the same product as the two outside numbers. So, I can solve any proportion by setting these two products equal to each other.

3. Verify that Natalie is correct.

4. **Try the various proportion-solving methods on these proportions and determine the unknown value. Explain which method you used.**

   a. $\frac{\text{3 granola bars}}{\text{420 calories}} = \frac{g\text{ granola bars}}{\text{140 calories}}$

   b. **8 correct : 15 questions = 24 correct : *q* questions**

   c. $\frac{d\text{ dollars}}{\text{5 miles}} = \frac{\$9}{\text{7.5 miles}}$

Multiplying the means and extremes is like "cross-multiplying."

The relationship that Natalie noticed is between the *means* and *extremes*. In a proportion that is written a : b = c : d, the product of the two values in the middle (the **means**) equals the product of the two values on the outside (the **extremes**).

extremes

a : b = c : d

means

$bc = ad$

or

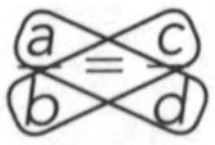

a
c
=
b
d

means extremes

$bc = ad$

when $b \neq 0$, $d \neq 0$

To solve a proportion using this method, first, identify the means and extremes. Then, set the product of the means equal to the product of the extremes and solve for the unknown quantity. To **solve a proportion** means to determine all the values of the variables that make the proportion true.

WORKED EXAMPLE

You can rewrite a proportion as the product of the means equal to the product of the extremes.

7 books : 14 days = 3 books : 6 days

means

extremes

$$(14)(3) = (7)(6)$$

$$42 = 42$$

$$\frac{7 \text{ books}}{14 \text{ days}} = \frac{3 \text{ books}}{6 \text{ days}}$$

$$(14)(3) = (7)(6)$$

$$42 = 42$$

You can rewrite the product of the means and extremes from the worked example as four different equations. Analyze each equation.

$$3 = \frac{(7)(6)}{14} \qquad 14 = \frac{(7)(6)}{3} \qquad \frac{(3)(14)}{7} = 6 \qquad \frac{(3)(14)}{6} = 7$$

a. Why are these equations all true? Explain your reasoning.

b. Compare these equations to the equation showing the product of the means equal to the product of the extremes. How was the balance of the equation maintained in each?

Why is it important to maintain balance in equations?

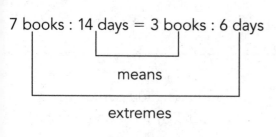

NOTES

WORKED EXAMPLE

In the proportion $\frac{a}{b} = \frac{c}{d}$, you can multiply both sides by b to *isolate the variable a.*

$$b \cdot \frac{a}{b} = b \cdot \frac{c}{d} \longrightarrow a = \frac{bc}{d}$$

When you **isolate the variable** in an equation, you perform an operation, or operations, to get the variable by itself on one side of the equals sign. Multiplication and division are *inverse operations.* **Inverse operations** are operations that "undo" each other.

WORKED EXAMPLE

Another strategy to isolate the variable a is to multiply the means and extremes and then isolate the variable by performing inverse operations.

$$\frac{a}{b} = \frac{c}{d}$$

Step 1: $ad = bc$

Step 2: $\frac{ad}{d} = \frac{bc}{d}$

Step 3: $a = \frac{bc}{d}$

7. Describe each step shown.

8. Rewrite the proportion $\frac{a}{b} = \frac{c}{d}$ to isolate each of the other variables: b, c, and d. Explain the strategies you used to isolate each variable.

ACTIVITY 3.3

Solving Problems with Proportions

Write and solve proportions to solve each problem.

1. **An astronaut who weighs 85 kilograms on Earth weighs 14.2 kilograms on the Moon. How much would a person weigh on the Moon if they weigh 95 kilograms on Earth? Round your answer to the nearest tenth.**

2. **Water goes over Niagara Falls at a rate of 180 million cubic feet every $\frac{1}{2}$ hour. How much water goes over the Falls in 1 minute?**

3. **The value of the U.S. dollar in comparison to the value of foreign currency changes daily. Complete the table shown. Round to the nearest hundredth.**

Euro	U.S. Dollar
1	1.07
	1.00
	6.00
6	
10	

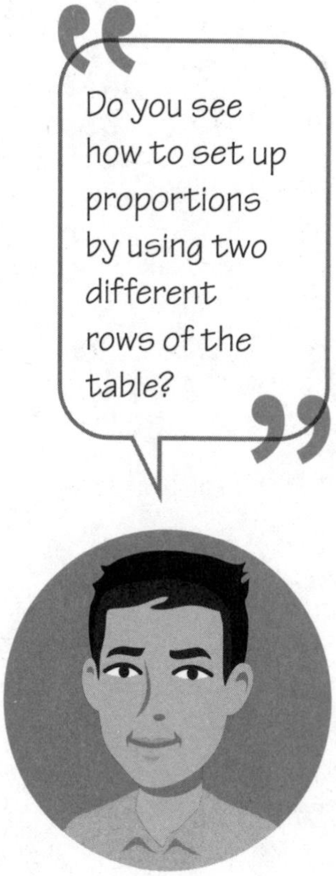

Do you see how to set up proportions by using two different rows of the table?

4. **To make 4.5 cups of fruity granola, the recipe calls for 1.5 cups of raisins, 1 cup of granola, and 2 cups of blueberries. If you want to make 18 cups of fruity granola, how much of each of the ingredients do you need?**

NOTES

TALK the TALK

Choose Your Own Proportion Adventure

Write a problem situation for each proportion. Show the solution.

1. $\frac{8}{3} = \frac{2}{n}$

2. $\frac{\frac{1}{2}}{\frac{1}{4}} = \frac{h}{1}$

Assignment

Write

Describe a situation in which you would use each.

1. variable
2. means and extremes
3. inverse operations
4. isolate the variable

Remember

To solve a proportion means to determine all the values of the variables that make the proportion true.

You can rewrite a proportion as the product of the means and extremes.

If $\frac{a}{b} = \frac{c}{d}$, then $bc = ad$.

Practice

Write and solve a proportion to answer each question.

1. Carmen is making a strawberry drink. The recipe calls for 5 parts strawberry juice to 3 parts water. Carmen would like to make 64 fluid ounces of the strawberry drink. How many fluid ounces of strawberry juice and water does Carmen need?
2. Elena is making a grape drink. The recipe calls for 2 parts grape juice concentrate to 6 parts water. Elena would like to make 80 fluid ounces of the grape drink. How many fluid ounces of grape juice concentrate and water does Elena need?
3. Jose is making a trail mix. The recipe calls for 3 parts golden raisins to 2 parts cashews. Jose would like to make 30 cups of trail mix. How many cups of golden raisins and cashews does Jose need?
4. Miguel is making a snack mix. The recipe calls for 6 parts of spicy tortilla chips to 3 parts of corn chips. Miguel would like to make 45 cups of snack mix. How many cups of spicy tortilla chips and corn chips does Miguel need?
5. Carla is making a bean salad. The recipe calls for 4 parts green beans to 3 parts yellow wax beans. Carla would like to make 56 ounces of bean salad. How many ounces of green beans and yellow wax beans does Carla need?
6. Shawna is making smoothies. The recipe calls for 2 parts yogurt to 3 parts blueberries. Shawna wants to make 10 cups of smoothie mix. How many cups of yogurt and blueberries does Shawna need?

Stretch

The word *four* has 4 letters, so the number-to-letter-count ratio for 4 is 1 : 1, or just 1. Are there any other numbers between 1 and 20 that have equal number-to-letter-count ratios? What are they?

Review

1. The table shows the gallons filled in a pool over time.

   a. Complete the table.

Number of Hours	$\frac{1}{8}$	$\frac{1}{4}$	$\frac{1}{2}$	$\frac{5}{8}$
Gallons Filled			500	

   b. Determine a unit rate for this situation.

2. Pi is the ratio of what two measures of a circle?

3. Which is a better deal—a 16-inch diameter pizza for $12.99 or an 8-inch diameter pizza for $6?

4. Evaluate each expression for $g = 10$.

   a. $9 - 4g + 1$

   b. $\frac{20}{g} \div g + (8 - 5)$

Fractional Rates Summary

KEY TERMS

- complex ratio
- proportion
- variable
- means
- extremes
- solve a proportion
- isolate the variable
- inverse operations

LESSON 1 Making Punch

A rate is a ratio that compares quantities with different units. A unit rate is a rate in which the numerator or denominator (or both) is 1. Two or more ratios or rates can be compared.

For example, two friends make lemon-lime punch using the following recipes.

Jade's Recipe	Kim's Recipe
1 cup lemon-lime concentrate 3 cups club soda	2 cups lemon-lime concentrate 5 cups club soda

Determine which recipe has the stronger taste of lemon-lime.

For Jade's recipe, the ratio of lemon-lime to club soda is 1 cup : 3 cups, so the unit rate is $\frac{1}{3}$ cup lemon-lime per 1 cup club soda. For Kim's recipe, the ratio of lemon-lime to club soda is 2 cups : 5 cups, so the unit rate is $\frac{2}{5}$ cup lemon-lime per 1 cup club soda.

$\frac{1}{3} < \frac{2}{5}$, so Kim's recipe has the stronger taste of lemon-lime.

A unit rate can be represented by the ordered pair (1, *r*) on a coordinate plane.

For example, the graph shows the ratios of lemon-lime to club soda for Jade's and Kim's recipes.

The point $(1, \frac{1}{3})$ represents the unit rate for Jade's recipe, and the point $(1, \frac{2}{5})$ represents the unit rate for Kim's recipe.

The graph of Kim's line is steeper than the graph of Jade's line, which shows that Kim's recipe has a stronger taste of lemon-lime.

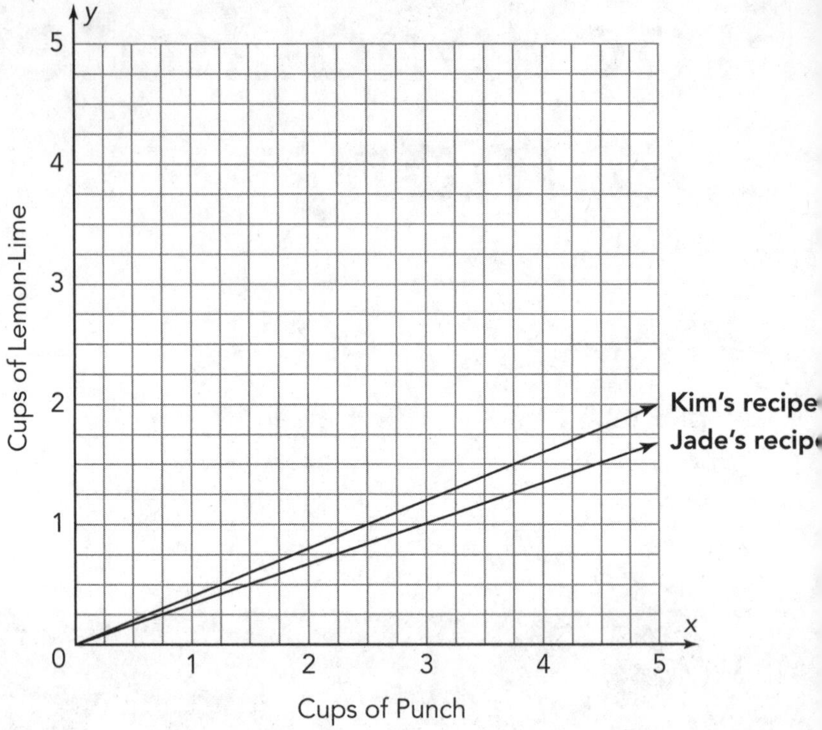

LESSON
2 Eggzactly!

A ratio in which one or both of the quantities being compared are written as fractions is called a **complex ratio**.

For example, traveling $\frac{1}{2}$ mile in $\frac{1}{4}$ hour represents a ratio of fractions, or a complex ratio. You can write this ratio, which is also a rate, in fractional form: $\frac{\frac{1}{2}}{\frac{1}{4}}$.

To convert a complex rate to a unit rate, you can multiply the numerator and denominator by the reciprocal of the denominator, or you can use the definition of division.

For example, the unit rate for traveling $\frac{1}{2}$ mile in $\frac{1}{4}$ hour is 2 miles per hour.

$$\frac{\frac{1}{2}}{\frac{1}{4}} \times \frac{\frac{4}{1}}{\frac{4}{1}} = \frac{\frac{4}{2}}{1} = 2$$

$$\frac{\frac{1}{2}}{\frac{1}{4}} = \frac{1}{2} \div \frac{1}{4} = \frac{1}{2} \cdot 4 = 2$$

To compare unit rates that are given in different units, you can use proportions and conversion rates.

For example, an ostrich can run 22 miles in $\frac{1}{2}$ hour. The Greater Roadrunner can run 300 yards in $\frac{1}{2}$ minute. Which bird runs faster?

distance → 22 mi; time → $\frac{1}{2}$ h

$$\frac{22 \text{ mi}}{\frac{1}{2} \text{ h}} \overset{\times 2}{=} \frac{44 \text{ mi}}{1 \text{ h}}$$

$$= \frac{44 \text{ mi}}{1 \text{ h}}$$

The rate of the ostrich is already measured in miles and hours. You can set up a proportion and scale the original rate up to 1 hour.

The ostrich's speed is 44 miles per hour.

The rate of the Greater Roadrunner is written in yards per minute. You can use conversion rates to rewrite the rate in miles per hour.

$$\frac{300 \text{ yd}}{\frac{1}{2} \text{ min}} \cdot \frac{60 \text{ min}}{1 \text{ hr}} = \frac{1 \text{ mi}}{1760 \text{ yd}}$$

$$\frac{300 \cancel{\text{yd}}}{\frac{1}{2} \cancel{\text{min}}} \cdot \frac{60 \cancel{\text{min}}}{1 \text{ hr}} = \frac{1 \text{ mi}}{1760 \cancel{\text{yd}}}$$

$$\frac{300}{\frac{1}{2}} \cdot \frac{60}{1} = \frac{1 \text{ mi}}{1760 \text{ hr}}$$

$$600 \cdot \frac{60}{1} \cdot \frac{1 \text{ mi}}{1760 \text{ hr}} \approx \frac{20.5 \text{ mi}}{1 \text{ hr}}$$

The Greater Roadrunner's speed is about 20.5 miles per hour.

The ostrich runs faster.

LESSON 3

Tagging Sharks

A **proportion** is an equation that states that two ratios are equal. A **variable** is a letter or symbol used to represent a number. A proportion of the form $\frac{a}{b} = \frac{c}{d}$ can be written in many different ways. Another example is $\frac{d}{b} = \frac{c}{a}$ or $\frac{c}{a} = \frac{d}{b}$.

In a proportion that is written $a : b = c : d$, the product of the two values in the middle (the **means**) equals the product of the two values on the outside (the **extremes**).

extremes

$a : b = c : d$

means

$bc = ad$

or

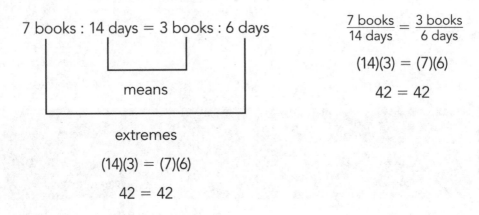

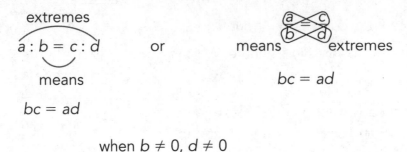

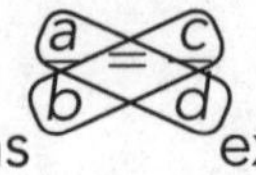

means extremes

$bc = ad$

when $b \neq 0$, $d \neq 0$

To **solve a proportion** means to determine all the values of the variables that make the proportion true.

For example, you can rewrite the proportion $\frac{7 \text{ books}}{14 \text{ days}} = \frac{3 \text{ books}}{6 \text{ days}}$ as the product of the means equal to the product of the extremes.

7 books : 14 days = 3 books : 6 days

means

extremes

$(14)(3) = (7)(6)$

$42 = 42$

$$\frac{7 \text{ books}}{14 \text{ days}} = \frac{3 \text{ books}}{6 \text{ days}}$$

$$(14)(3) = (7)(6)$$

$$42 = 42$$

When you **isolate the variable** in an equation, you perform an operation, or operations, to get the variable by itself on one side of the equals sign. Multiplication and division are inverse operations. **Inverse operations** are operations that "undo" each other.

In the proportion $\frac{a}{b} = \frac{c}{d}$, you can multiply both sides by b to isolate the variable a.

$b \cdot \frac{a}{b} = \frac{c}{d} \cdot b \longrightarrow a = \frac{cb}{d}$

Another strategy is to multiply the means and extremes, and then isolate the variable by performing inverse operations.

$$\frac{a}{b} = \frac{c}{d}$$

$$ad = bc$$

$$\frac{ad}{d} = \frac{bc}{d}$$

$$a = \frac{bc}{d}$$

TOPIC 3

Proportionality

Equivalent ratios and direct variation are vital to chemists. Too much of one solution can result in a smoldering reaction, while too little of a solution may not result in a reaction at all.

Module 1: Thinking Proportionally

TOPIC 3: PROPORTIONALITY

In this topic, students learn about the constant of proportionality: the ratio between the two quantities being compared. They recognize that the constant is determined by the order of the ratio elements, and they use proportions to write and analyze direct variation equations. Students graph proportional relationships and determine the constant of proportionality from the graphs, interpreting this constant, the unit rate, in terms of the problem situation. Students practice determining if relationships are proportional, interpreting the meaning of linear proportional relationships, and determining and interpreting the constant of proportionality.

Where have we been?

In grade 6, students developed a strong understanding of ratio and rate reasoning, including reasoning about equivalent ratios from graphs and tables. In the previous topic, students reviewed some of these basic ideas and developed a formal strategy for solving proportions.

Where are we going?

Students will continue to apply the constant of proportionality to solve multistep ratio and percent problems in the next topic. They will solve percent problems using the constant of proportionality and direct variation and relate the constant of proportionality to the scale factor in scale drawings. The characteristics of proportional relationships, their graphs, and their equations provide the underpinnings of algebra and the study of functions.

Using a Diagram to Represent a Proportional Relationship

The diagram shows that there are 4 times as many dimes as nickels. Also, the total number of coins (40) is 8 times the number of nickels and twice the number of dimes.

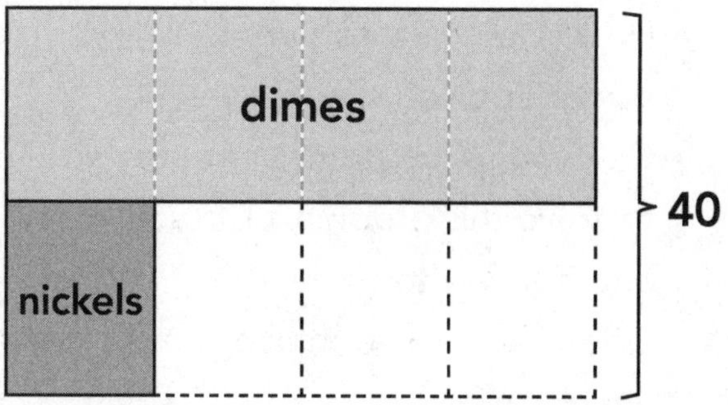

Myth: Asking questions means you don't understand.

It is universally true that, for any given body of knowledge, there are levels to understanding. For example, you might understand the rules of baseball and follow a game without trouble. But there is probably more to the game that you can learn. For example, do you know the 23 ways to get on first base, including the one where the batter strikes out?

Questions don't always indicate a lack of understanding. Instead, they might allow you to learn even more on a subject that you already understand. Asking questions may also give you an opportunity to ensure that you understand a topic correctly. Finally, questions are extremely important to ask yourself. For example, everyone should be in the habit of asking themselves, "Does that make sense? How would I explain it to a friend?"

#mathmythbusted

Talking Points

You can further support your student's learning by asking questions about the work they do in class or at home. Your student is learning to reason using proportions.

Questions to Ask

- How does this problem look like something you did in class?
- Can you show me the strategy you used to solve this problem? Do you know another way to solve it?
- Does your answer make sense? How do you know?
- Is there anything you don't understand? How can you use today's lesson to help?

Key Terms

direct variation

A situation represents a direct variation if the ratio between the *y*-value and its corresponding *x*-value is constant for every point.

constant of proportionality

In a proportional relationship, the ratio of all *y*-values to their corresponding *x*-values is constant. This ratio is called the constant of proportionality.

How Does Your Garden Grow?

1

Proportional Relationships

WARM UP

1. A bus travels 18 miles in 15 minutes. At the same rate, what distance will the bus travel in 50 minutes?
2. A copy machine averages 210 copies in 5 minutes. At the same rate, how many copies can the machine make in 12 minutes?

LEARNING GOALS

- Use tables and graphs to explore proportional relationships.
- Decide whether two quantities are in a proportional relationship by testing for equivalent ratios in a table.
- Decide whether two quantities are in a proportional relationship by graphing on a coordinate plane and observing whether the graph is a straight line through the origin.

KEY TERMS

- origin
- proportional relationship
- direct variation

You have learned about the relationship between ratios, a comparison of two quantities, and proportions. How can you determine if a proportional relationship exists between two quantities?

Getting Started

Keep on Mixing!

Amount of Bluish Green Paint	Amount of Yellow Paint	Amount of Blue Paint
3 pt	1 pt	2 pt
5 pt	2 pt	3 pt
6 pt	2 pt	4 pt
12 pt	4 pt	8 pt
15 pt	6 pt	9 pt
20 pt	8 pt	12 pt

The students in Mr. Raith's art class created various quantities of bluish green paint using pints of yellow and blue paint.

The table shows the different mixtures of paint, in pints, that the students made.

1. How many different shades of paint did the students make? How do you know?

2. Some of the shades of the paint are more yellow than others. Which mixture(s) are the most yellow? Explain your reasoning.

The **origin** is a point on a graph with the ordered pair (0, 0).

3. Plot an ordered pair for each bluish green paint mixture. Draw a line connecting each point to the origin. What do you notice?

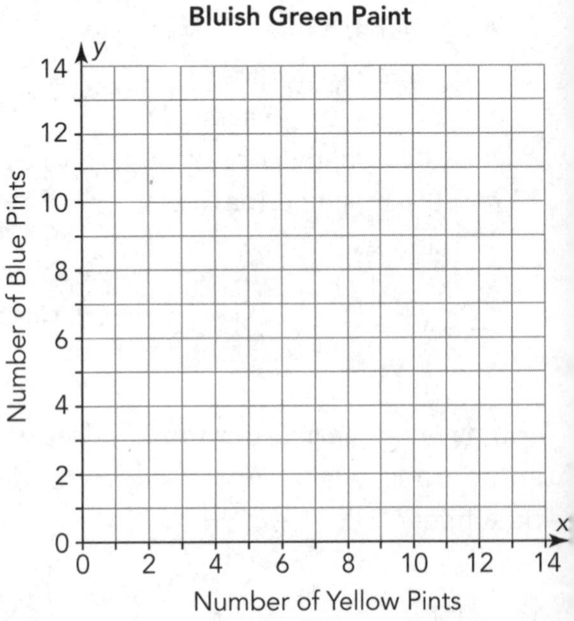

ACTIVITY 1.1 Representations of Varying Quantities

The student government association (SGA) at Radloff Middle School is creating an urban garden at their school for use by their community. They divided up into groups to design different parts of the garden and were asked to (1) describe their project, (2) create an equation to model part of their design or to answer a question about their design, and (3) sketch a graph of their equation.

1. **Isaac, the president of the SGA, mixed up the representations of the projects after they were submitted to him. Help Isaac match the scenarios, equations, and graphs.**

   - **Cut out the scenarios, equations, and graphs at the end of the lesson.**
   - **Sort the scenarios, equations, and graphs into corresponding groups.**
   - **Tape the representations into the table provided.**

When you connect an equation to a graph, you are establishing a dependency between the quantities. Remember, the independent quantity is always represented on the *x*-axis.

The Urban Garden Project

Scenario			
Equation			
Graph			
Table			

ACTIVITY 1.2

Defining Proportional Relationships

NOTES

When looking over the submissions from the urban garden working groups, Isaac notices that there are two different types of graphical relationships represented: linear and non-linear.

1. **Classify each group's graph as representing a linear or a non-linear relationship between quantities.**

Isaac notices that the linear graphs are slightly different but he doesn't know why. He decides to analyze a table of values for each linear graph.

2. **Create a table of at least 4 values for each linear relationship in the urban garden project.**

Isaac knows that simple equations can represent additive or multiplicative relationships between quantities.

3. **Analyze the equations.**

   a. **Based on the equations, which graph represents an additive relationship between the variables and which represents a multiplicative relationship?**

   b. **Which variable represents the independent (input) and which represents the dependent (output).**

One special type of relationship that compares quantities using multiplicative reasoning is a ratio relationship. When two equivalent ratios are set equal to each other, they form a proportion. The quantities in the proportion are in a **proportional relationship**.

You can decide if two quantities are in a proportional relationship by testing that all ratios, $\frac{y}{x}$ or $\frac{x}{y}$, in a table of values are equivalent.

For a relationship to illustrate a proportional relationship, all the ratios $\frac{y}{x}$ or $\frac{x}{y}$, must represent the same constant.

4. Use your tables of values in Question 2 to determine which, if any, of the linear relationships illustrate a proportional relationship. Show the values of the ratios in each relationship.

Isaac says the equation $y = \pi r^2$ represents a proportional relationship between y and r because it includes multiplication between a numerical coefficient and a variable expression.

5. Use a table of values and corresponding ratios in the form of $\frac{y}{x}$ to explain why Isaac is incorrect.

6. Explain to Isaac how the graphs in the urban garden design project are different. Include the terms *linear relationship* and *non-linear relationship, proportional relationship,* and *equivalent ratios.*

ACTIVITY 1.3

Proportional or Not?

In this activity you will analyze three different problem situations and then determine which represents a proportional relationship.

Bob and his little brother Jake want to build bird feeders to sell at a local farmers market. They have enough money to buy materials to build 10 bird feeders.

1. **Complete a table of values by listing possible ways in which they can divide up the work. Assume that each brother only makes whole bird feeders. Then complete the graph.**

Bird Feeders Built by Bob	Bird Feeders Built by Jake

You can draw a line through your points to model the relationship. Then decide if all the points make sense in terms of the problem situation.

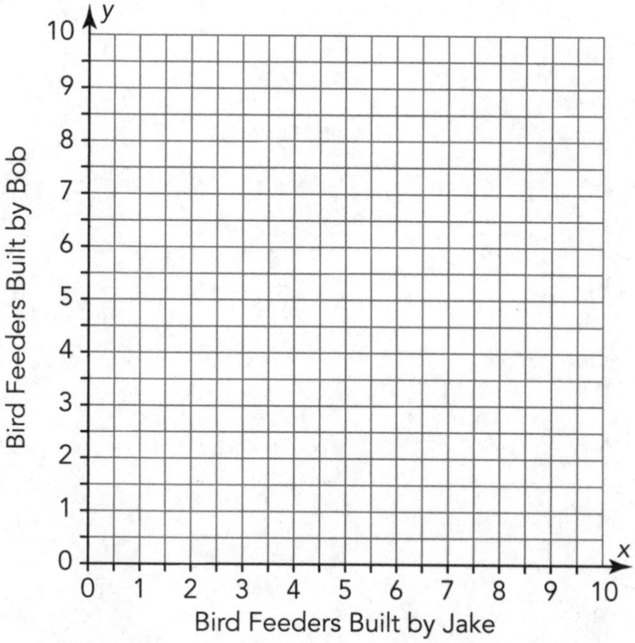

2. Describe how the number of bird feeders built by Bob affects the number Jake builds.

3. What is the ratio of bird feeders that Bob builds to the number that Jake builds? Explain your reasoning.

4. Dontrell claims that the number of bird feeders Bob builds is proportional to the number of bird feeders Jake builds. Do you agree with Dontrell's claim? Explain your reasoning.

Vanessa was given a math problem to determine how many different rectangles can be constructed with an area of 12 square inches.

5. Vanessa thinks that there are only two: one with a width of 2 inches and a length of 6 inches, and another with a width of 3 inches and a length of 4 inches.
Is she correct? Explain your reasoning.

6. Complete a table of values for the width and length of a rectangle with an area of 12 square inches. Then complete the graph.

Width of Rectangle (in.)	Length of Rectangle (in.)

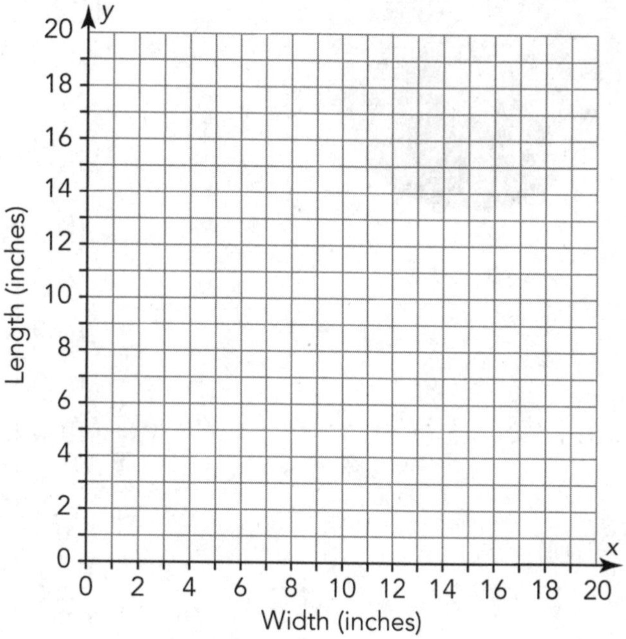

7. Describe how the width of the rectangle affects the length of the rectangle.

8. Do the width and length of a rectangle with an area of 12 square inches form a proportional relationship? Explain your reasoning.

One species of bamboo can grow at an average rate of 60 centimeters per day.

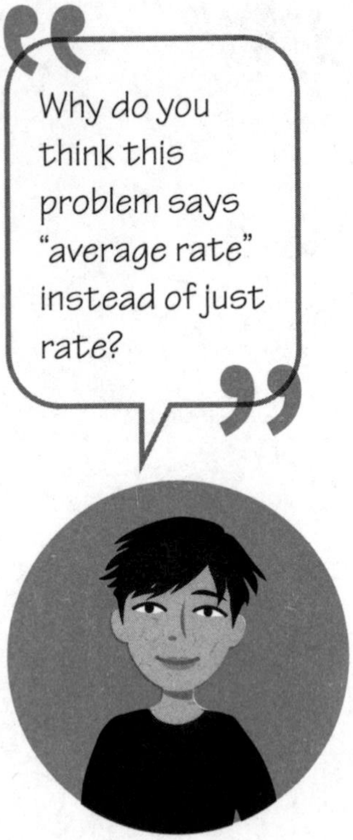

Why do you think this problem says "average rate" instead of just rate?

9. **Complete a table of values using the given growth rate of the bamboo plant. Then complete the graph.**

Time (days)	Height of Bamboo (cm)

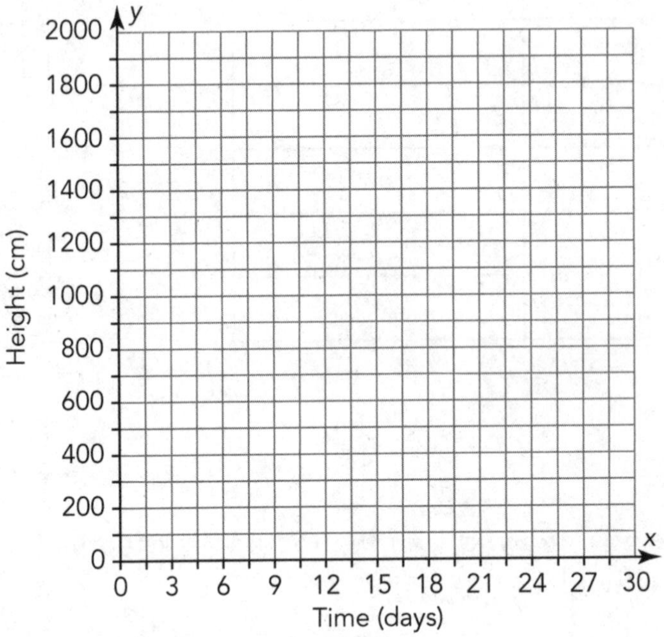

10. **Describe how the time affects the height of the bamboo plant.**

11. **Is the number of days of growth proportional to the height of the bamboo plant? Explain your reasoning.**

ACTIVITY 1.4

Direct Variation

You saw that the height of a bamboo plant varies based on the number of days the bamboo grows. For example, for each increase in one day, the bamboo grows 60 centimeters.

A situation represents a **direct variation** if the ratio between the y-value and its corresponding x-value is constant for every point. If two quantities vary directly, the points on a graph form a straight line, and the line passes through the origin.

You can describe the quantities of a direct variation relationship as directly proportional.

Examine the worked example.

WORKED EXAMPLE

A car driving at a constant rate of 60 miles per hour is an example of direct variation. The distance varies directly as time.

A sketch of a graph that could represent this situation is shown.

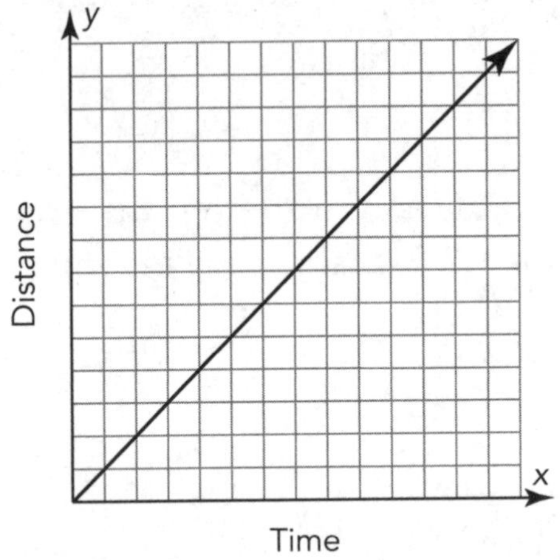

When you sketch a graph, be sure to include the labels for each axis. However, you don't *always* have to show values.

1. Explain how the situation in the worked example is an example of a direct variation.

"Think about how the quantities relate to each other at any given point."

2. Explain how you can use each graph in the previous activity, *Proportional or Not?*, to determine which scenarios represent direct variations.

3. List another example of quantities that vary directly. Then, sketch a graph that could represent the relationship between the quantities.

NOTES

TALK the TALK

Determining Proportionality from Tables and Graphs

Go back and examine the graphs in this lesson. Do you see a pattern?

1. **How are all the graphs that display proportional relationships the same?**

2. **Sketch a graph that displays a proportional relationship.**

NOTES

3. Which tables display linear relationships? Which display proportional relationships? Explain your reasoning.

a.

x	y
1	10
2	11
4	13
5	14

b.

x	y
0	0
1	6
3	18
4	24

c.

x	y
0	4
1	8
2	12
3	16

d.

x	y
1	30
2	15
4	10
5	5

Cutouts for The Urban Garden Project

Group A is designing one section of the garden to include fresh herbs grown in circular beds. The group needs to determine the area of each herb bed given the radius of the bed.	Group B is developing a plan to landscape the perimeter of the urban garden. They could only find a meter stick broken at 6 cm, so they reported the dimensions of the garden based on the measurements read off the meter stick. This group needs to determine the actual side lengths of the garden.	Group C is designing the vegetable patches and have decided that each rectangular vegetable patch will be 5 inches wide for every 8 inches long. This group needs to determine the possible dimensions for the lengths of the vegetable patches.
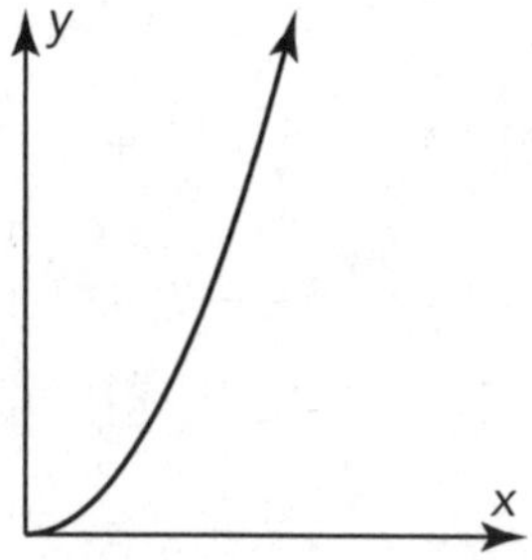	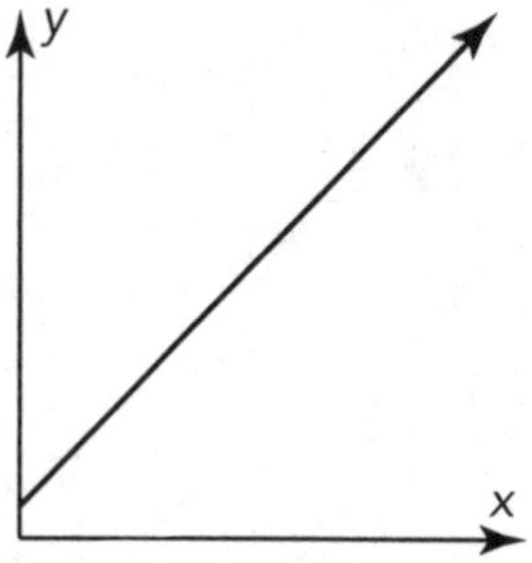	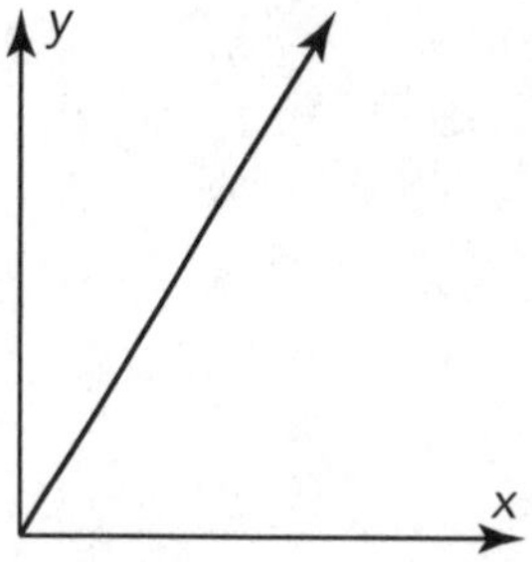
$y = 1.6x$	$y = \pi x^2$	$y = x + 6$

Assignment

Write

Explain how the following terms are related: linear relationship, proportional relationship, equivalent ratios, and direct variation.

Remember

For a graph to represent a proportional relationship, the points of the graph must form a straight line and pass through the origin of the graph.

For a table of values to represent a proportional relationship, all the ratios of corresponding *x*- and *y*-values must be constant.

Practice

1. Analyze each table shown. Determine if the relationship is proportional. If the relationship is proportional, state the constant ratio for the relationship.
   a. Of the 75 boys in the 7th grade class, 25 participate in at least one sport. Of the 120 girls in the 7th grade class, 30 participate in at least one sport.
   b. Of the 210 boys in the 8th grade, 190 have a cell phone. Of the 168 girls in the 8th grade, 152 have a cell phone.

7th Grade Class	Plays Sports	Total
Boys	25	75
Girls	30	120

8th Grade Class	Cell Phones	Total
Boys	190	210
Girls	152	168

2. Match each graph with its scenario. Then state if the scenario represents a linear relationship. If it represents a linear relationship, state if it represents a proportional relationship.
   a. Vanessa and Michelle must decide how to divide 16 marbles among themselves.
   b. The perimeter of a square is 4 times the length of one side of the square.
   c. The area of a square is calculated by squaring the length of one side of the square.
   d. When Tara, a nurse, works on Saturdays, she is paid a $30 bonus plus $40 per hour worked.

Graph A

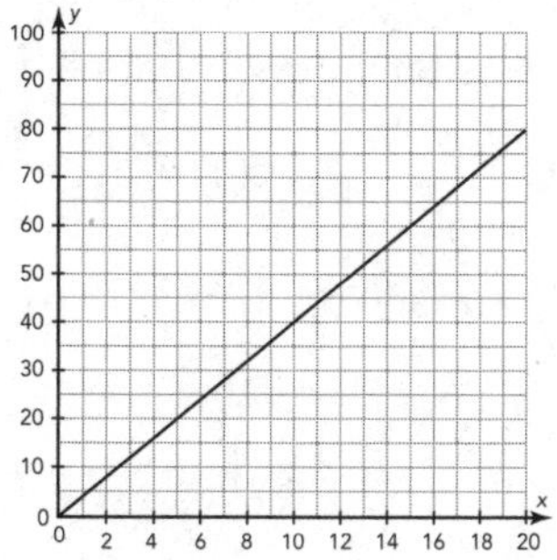

Graph B

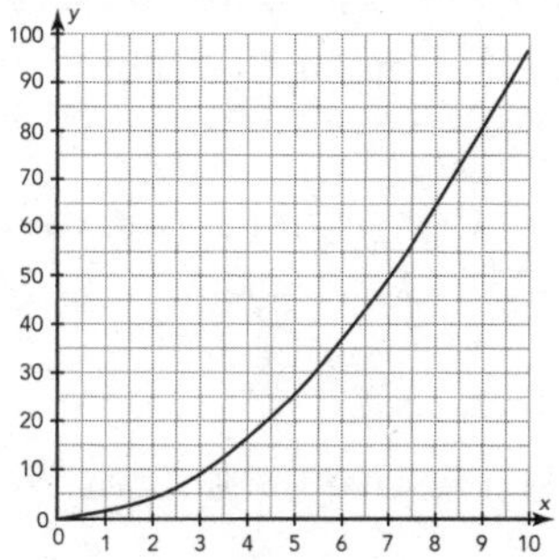

Graph C

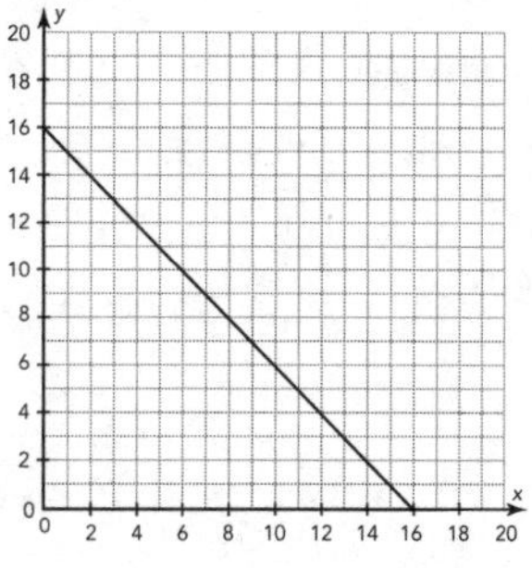

Graph D

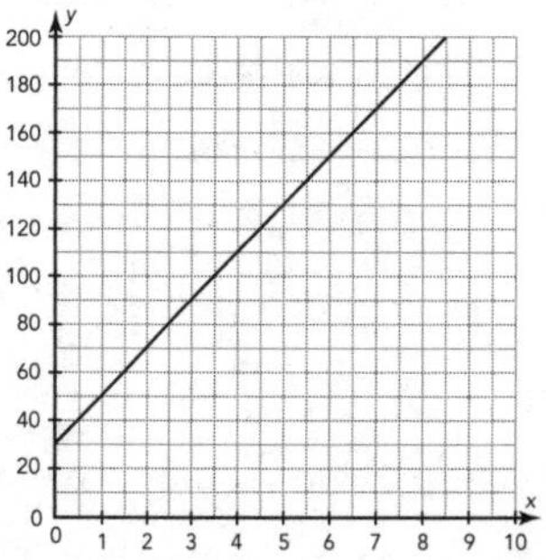

3. In 2010, Chevrolet produced 12,194 Corvettes. That means they made about 34 Corvettes per day.
   a. Create a table to show the number of Corvettes made in at least 5 different numbers of days.
   b. Use the table to determine if this situation represents a proportional relationship.
   c. Use the data in the table to create a graph of the total number of Corvettes produced over time.
   d. Does the number of Corvettes vary directly with the number of days? Explain using the graph.

Stretch

Another way to classify varying quantities is as an inverse variation, or inversely proportional. The tables shown represent inverse variations. Study the tables of values and make a conjecture about the relationship between the quantities that illustrate inverse variation.

Number of Hours	Number of People
2	6
3	4
$\frac{1}{12}$	144

Width of Rectangle	Length of Rectangle
2	18
12	3
0.5	72

Review

Use proportions to solve each.

1. In the town of Clover, 3 out of 5 citizens who are eligible to vote did so in the fall election.
   a. Determine the number of citizens that voted in the fall election if 400 citizens were eligible.
   b. Determine the number of citizens that were eligible to vote in the fall election if 180 actually voted.
2. The student council at Camp Creek Middle School determines that 3 out of 4 students prefer that all school assemblies be held on Friday afternoon.
   a. If 200 students are surveyed, how many will prefer that school assemblies be held on Friday afternoon?
   b. If 747 students prefer the school assemblies be held on Friday afternoon, how many students were surveyed?

Write a unit rate to represent the relationship between the given quantities. Round to the nearest hundredth, if necessary.

3. 2.5 liters ≈ 0.66 gallon

4. 430.6 centimeters ≈ 169.5 inches

Determine each quotient.

5. 67.36 ÷ 3.2

6. 3401.74 ÷ 7.9

Complying with Title IX

2

Constant of Proportionality

Warm Up

Washington Middle School collects canned food for a local community food bank. Last year, there were 180 students enrolled at the school and they collected 102 cans of food.

1. Write the ratio representing the number of cans of food contributed to the total number of students in the school.
2. What is the unit rate of cans contributed per student?
3. This year, 210 students are enrolled in the school. Assume the number of cans of food contributed per student for both years is the same. How many cans of food should the school expect to be contributed this year?

LEARNING GOALS

- Determine if there is a constant ratio between two variables.
- Identify the constant of proportionality in proportional relationships.
- Identify the constant of proportionality in equations.
- Represent proportional relationships by equations.

KEY TERM

- constant of proportionality

You know how to recognize proportional relationships from tables and graphs. How do you represent proportional relationships with equations?

Getting Started

Is It Proportional?

Analyze each table to determine if the relationship is proportional. If the table represents a proportional relationship, state the constant ratio that exists between corresponding values of the two quantities.

Does the order in which you write your ratios, $\frac{x}{y}$ or $\frac{y}{x}$, matter when determining if a proportional relationship exists?

1. A 30-minute television show has 8 minutes of commercials and 22 minutes of the show. A 120-minute television movie has 32 minutes of commercials and 88 minutes of the movie.

Total Program Length (minutes)	Actual Show Length (minutes)	Commercial Length (minutes)
30	22	8
120	88	32

2. There are 250 boys in 6th grade, and 75 are in the band. There are 200 girls in 6th grade, and 60 are in the band.

6th Grade Class	Total	Band
Boys	250	75
Girls	200	60

3. Commuters in McKnight and Mitenridge either drive to work or take public transportation.

Commuters	Drive to Work	Public Transportation to Work
McKnight	175	120
Mitenridge	525	300

4. Of the 250 middle-school boys who have a subscription to *Boys Noise,* 125 access the magazine through the website. Of the 280 middle-school girls who have a subscription to *Girls Rockstar,* 160 access the magazine through the website.

ACTIVITY 2.1

Defining the Constant of Proportionality

In a proportional relationship, the ratio of all *y*-values, or outputs, to their corresponding *x*-values, or inputs, is constant. This specific ratio, $\frac{y}{x}$, is called the **constant of proportionality**. Generally, the variable *k* is used to represent the constant of proportionality.

Let's revisit the television show scenario. This situation represents a proportional relationship.

The input value is known, the output value is what you are trying to determine.

Total Program Length (minutes)	Actual Show Length (minutes)	Commercial Length (minutes)
30	22	8
120	88	32

Suppose you want to determine the actual lengths of your favorite television shows, without commercials, if you know the total program length.

1. **Identify the input and output quantities in this scenario.**

To determine the length of a program, without commercials, you will need to multiply the total program length by a constant of proportionality.

Analyze the different ideas for determining the constant of proportionality.

Jeremiah

We want to know the actual show length and we know the total program length, so

$k = \frac{\text{22 minutes of show}}{\text{30 minutes of total length}}$,

or $k = \frac{11}{15}$.

Keisha

To determine if a proportional relationship exists the order of the ratio doesn't matter, so the constant of proportionality can be

$k = \frac{15}{11}$

or $k = \frac{11}{15}$.

Susan

I think the constant of proportionality is

$k = \frac{\text{22 minutes of show}}{\text{8 minutes of commercials}}$,

or $k = \frac{11}{4}$.

JAMie

JeReMiAH'S CoRReCT ABouT WHiCH NuMBeRS To uSe BuT He HAS THeM MixeD uP. THe CONSTANT oF PRoPoRTioNALiTY iS

$K = \frac{\text{30 MiNUTeS oF ToTAL LeNGTH}}{\text{22 MiNUTeS oF SHoW}}$, oR $K = \frac{15}{11}$.

2. Explain why Susan's solution is incorrect.

3. Explain why Jeremiah is correct but Jamie and Keisha are incorrect.

ACTIVITY 2.2 The Meaning of the Constant of Proportionality

The term proportional *is used often in the Title IX document. What does this mean for sports at schools?*

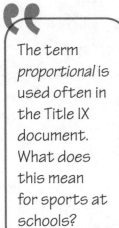

In 1972, the federal government passed Title IX, a law requiring educational institutions that receive federal funds to provide equitable athletic opportunities for boys and girls. One of the requirements for compliance with Title IX is for institutions to provide opportunities for each gender that are *proportional* to their rates of enrollment or show that they are working to increase such opportunities. Similarly, male and female athletes are to receive athletic scholarship dollars *proportional* to their participation.

Let's think about the implications of Title IX at Vista Middle School.

There are 5 girls for every 6 boys enrolled in Vista Middle School.

1. **Set up proportions for each question. Then, solve each proportion to determine the unknown value. Use the information from the ratio given.**

   a. **If there are 300 boys enrolled in the school, how many girls are enrolled in the school?**

   b. **If there are 325 girls enrolled in the school, how many boys are enrolled in the school?**

2. **Define variables for the quantities that are changing in this situation.**

NOTES

3. Set up a proportion using your variables for the quantities to the ratio given for the enrollment of girls to boys enrolled in Vista Middle School.

4. Use your proportion.

   a. Write an equation to determine the number of girls enrolled at Vista Middle School if you know the number of boys enrolled.

   b. What is the constant of proportionality in this situation? Where is the constant of proportionality in the equation?

   c. What does the constant of proportionality mean in this problem situation?

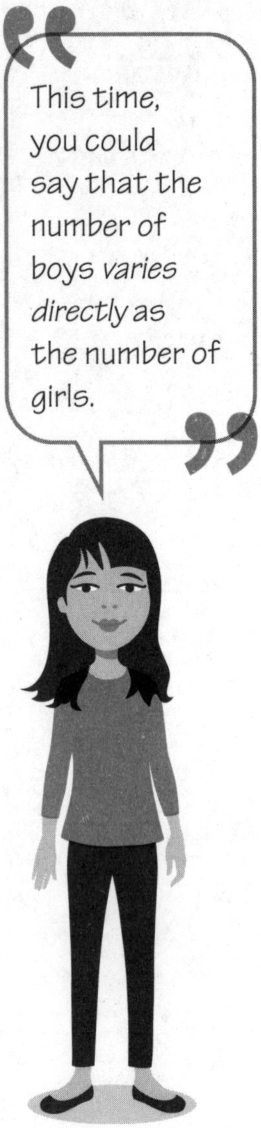

This time, you could say that the number of boys *varies directly* as the number of girls.

5. Use your proportion.

   a. Write an equation to determine the number of boys enrolled at Vista Middle School if you know the number of girls enrolled.

   b. What is the constant of proportionality in this situation? Where do you see the constant of proportionality in the equation?

   c. What does the constant of proportionality mean in this problem situation?

6. What do you notice about the constant of proportionality in each situation?

7. Do you think each constant of proportionality makes sense in terms of the problem situation?

Sometimes, the constant of proportionality is not a whole number. The constant of proportionality can also be a decimal or a fraction. When the constant of proportionality involves whole items, like people, it may seem strange to think about the constant of proportionality in terms of a fraction. Instead, you can think of the constant of proportionality as a way to predict outcomes of a situation.

3. Use your equations and the information about Title IX to answer each question.

a. If there are opportunities for 79 boys to participate in athletics, how many opportunities must be available for girls?

b. If there are opportunities for 119 girls to participate in athletics, how many opportunities must be available for boys?

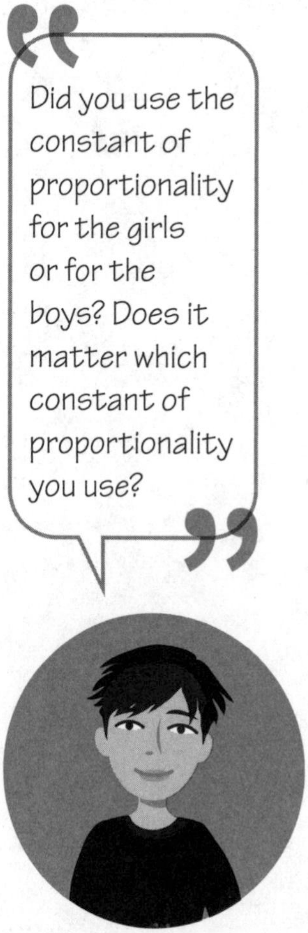

Did you use the constant of proportionality for the girls or for the boys? Does it matter which constant of proportionality you use?

ACTIVITY 2.3

Representing Proportional Relationships with Equations

Title IX addresses the number of athletics opportunities provided to each gender, but the actual participation at schools may differ. Also, the same person may participate in multiple sports.

At Vista Middle School, 5 out of every 7 girls play sports. The guidance counselor, Ms. Shanahan, and the athletics director, Coach Culpepper, are completing reports about the students at Vista Middle School.

Consider the information each person knows and use the constant of proportionality to write equations for each situation.

Guidance Counselor	Athletics Director
Ms. Shanahan knows the number of girls in the school on a given day, and she needs to be able to calculate the expected number of girls who play sports.	Coach Culpepper knows the number of girls participating in sports during a given season, and she needs to be able to calculate the expected number of total girls in the school.

1. Determine the constant of proportionality for each situation.

a. Guidance Counselor

b. Athletics Director

2. Define variables for the quantities that are changing in these situations.

3. Use the constants of proportionality to write equations to determine the information needed by each person.

a. Guidance Counselor

b. Athletics Director

In terms of proportionality, Ms. Shanahan could state that the number of girls who play sports is proportional to the number of total girls in the school at a constant rate equal to the constant of proportionality.

4. Write Coach Culpepper's situation using the language of proportionality and include the value for the constant of proportionality.

5. Consider the given equations, where *y* represents the dependent or output quantity and *x* represents the independent or input quantity.

$$\frac{y}{x} = k$$

$$\frac{y}{x} = \frac{k}{1}$$

$$y = kx$$

a. Describe how the first equation represents the constant of proportionality.

b. Explain how the second equation represents proportional relationships.

c. Describe how the first equation was rewritten to create the third equation.

d. Explain the meaning of the constant of proportionality, *k*, in the third equation.

6. **Identify the constant of proportionality in each equation and describe its meaning.**

   a. **$d = 2r$, where d represents the diameter of a circle and r represents the radius of a circle.**

   b. **$P = 3s$, where P represents the perimeter and s represents the sides of an equilateral triangle.**

ACTIVITY 2.4

Using the Constant of Proportionality to Solve Problems

A chemist must use a solution that is 30% of reagent and 70% of water for an experiment. A solution is a mixture of two or more liquids. A reagent is a substance used in a chemical reaction to produce other substances.

1. **Define variables for the quantities that are changing in this problem situation.**

2. **Write an equation for the amount of water needed based on the amount of reagent. What is the constant of proportionality?**

3. Use your equation from Question 2 to write an equation for the amount of reagent needed based on the amount of water. Explain your reasoning.

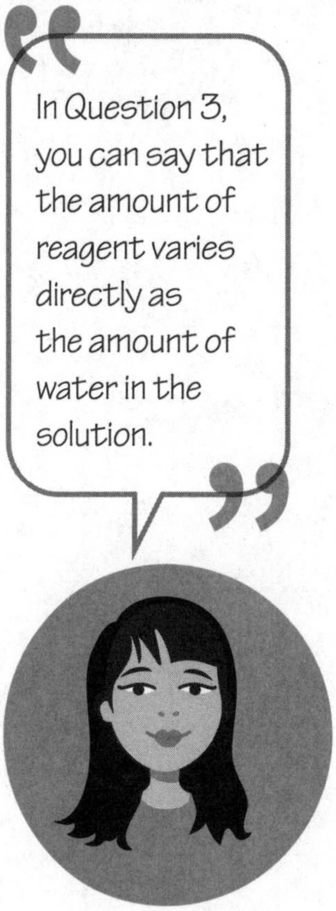

In Question 3, you can say that the amount of reagent varies directly as the amount of water in the solution.

4. Use your equations to answer each question.

   a. If the chemist uses 6 liters of reagent, how many liters of water will she need to make her 30% solution?

   b. If the chemist uses 77 milliliters of water, how many milliliters of reagent will she need to make her 30% solution?

5. Write an equation to show that y is directly proportional to x using the constant of proportionality given. Then solve for the unknown value.

   a. $k = 0.7$ and $y = 4$

   b. $k = \frac{3}{11}$ and $x = 9$

   c. $k = 5$ and $x = 1\frac{1}{2}$

   d. $k = \frac{1}{6}$ and $y = 3\frac{1}{3}$

NOTES

TALK the TALK

Turning the Tables

Consider the equation $y = kx$. Use the value of the constant of proportionality assigned to you to answer the questions. You will present your work to your class.

1. **Write a scenario for a proportional relationship that would be represented by the equation. Clearly define your variables and identify the direction of the proportional relationship.**

2. **Interpret the constant of proportionality in the context of your scenario.**

3. **Write and solve at least 2 questions that could be solved using your equation.**

Assignment

Write

Define *constant of proportionality* in your own words. Provide a specific example with your definition.

Remember

If y is directly proportional to x, the relationship can be represented by the equation $y = kx$, where k is the constant of proportionality.

Practice

1. Analyze each table or problem situation to determine if the relationship is proportional. State a constant of proportionality if possible. Show your work.

a.

Girls	Boys
7	14
9	21
11	22

b. A baby blue whale weighed 5520 pounds at birth. After two days, the baby weighed 5710. After 14 days, the baby weighed 8180 pounds.

2. Maya's construction company builds brick houses. The number of bricks her crew installs varies directly with the number of hours they work.

Hours Worked	Bricks Installed
8	1680
7	1470
6	1260

a. Define variables for the quantities that are changing in this problem situation.
b. Analyze the table to determine the constant of proportionality.
c. What does the constant of proportionality mean in this situation?
d. Write an equation to show the relationship between the number of hours worked, the number of bricks installed, and the constant of proportionality.
e. Use your equation to determine how many bricks Maya's crew can install in 5.5 hours.
f. Use your equation to determine how many hours it will take Maya's crew to install 840 bricks.

3. Given a value for the input variable, x, and the output variable, y, calculate the constant of proportionality.

a. $x = 21$ and $y = 6$
b. $x = 60$ and $y = 18$
c. $x = 2\frac{2}{5}$ and $y = 7\frac{1}{2}$
d. $x = 4\frac{8}{11}$ and $y = 3\frac{6}{11}$

4. The following is the recipe to make 6 cups of Perfect Lemonade:
    - 1 cup sugar
    - 1 cup water (for the simple syrup)
    - 1 cup lemon juice
    - 4 cups cold water (to dilute)

   You want to analyze the relationship between the number of cups of sugar and the number of cups of lemonade.

   a. Define variables for the quantities that are changing in this problem situation.
   b. Set up a proportion using the ratio of cups of sugar to cups of lemonade.
   c. Use your proportion to write an equation for the number of cups of sugar based on the number of cups of lemonade.
   d. What is the constant of proportionality in this equation? What does it mean in this context?
   e. Use your equation in (c) to write an equation for the number of cups of lemonade based on the number of cups of sugar.
   f. What is the constant of proportionality in this equation? What does it mean in this context?

5. Dudley and Bob monitored the distance their pet turtle could walk in a certain amount of time. Their results are shown in the table. The table of values represents a proportional relationship.

Time (minutes)	Distance (inches)
5	14.5
14	40.6
19	55.1
25	72.5

   a. Define variables for the quantities that are changing in this problem situation.
   b. Write an equation for the distance traveled by the turtle based on the number of minutes.
   c. What is the constant of proportionality in this equation? What does it mean in this context?
   d. Use your equation in (b) to write an equation for the time it would take for the turtle to travel a given distance.
   e. What is the constant of proportionality in this equation? What does it mean in this context?

Stretch

If *a* varies inversely as *b*, then the product of *a* and *b* is constant. Use direct and inverse variation to solve this problem.

If x varies inversely as y and varies directly with z, and if y and z are both 3 when $x = 5$, what is the value of $z - y$ when $x = 8$?

Review

1. Sketch a graph that represents a linear, non-proportional relationship. Label your quantities.
2. Sketch a graph that represents a direct variation relationship. Label your quantities.
3. Jonah will be staying a month in one of the cities listed in the table. He wants to determine the average cost of public transportation for each city. He finds the following information.

City	Cost for Unlimited Public Transportation
New York City	\$51.50 for 14 days
Miami	\$100 for 1 month
Los Angeles	\$17 for 1 week
Chicago	\$14 for 3 days

   a. Calculate the unit rate, or per day cost, for unlimited transportation in each city. (Let 1 week = 7 days and 1 month = 30 days.)

   b. If Jonah stays in the city for a month, how much would he spend on transportation in each city?

4. Plot each ordered pair on a coordinate plane.

   a. $A\,(1, 4.75)$
   b. $B\left(\frac{7}{2}, 1\right)$
   c. $C\,(-2, 8)$
   d. $D\left(-4, -\frac{1}{2}\right)$
   e. $E\,(0, 0)$
   f. $F\left(5, -\frac{5}{2}\right)$

Fish-Inches

3

Identifying the Constant of Proportionality in Graphs

WARM UP

Solve each equation for the variable.

1. $\frac{1}{2}a = 5$
2. $\frac{p}{\frac{1}{3}} = 2$
3. $3x = \frac{3}{2}$
4. $\frac{6}{z} = \frac{1}{6}$

LEARNING GOALS

- Determine if relationships represented in words, tables, equations, or graphs are proportional.
- Interpret the meaning of linear proportional relationships represented in words, tables, equations, and graphs.
- Identify and interpret the constant of proportionality for quantities that are proportional and represented in words, tables, equations, and graphs.
- Explain what a point on the graph of a proportional relationship means in terms of the problem situation.
- Explain what the points (0, 0) and (1, *r*) mean on the graph of a proportional relationship, where *r* is the unit rate.

You have determined the constant of proportionality in problem situations and from equations. How can you represent the constant of proportionality in graphs?

Getting Started

The Fish-Inches System of Measurement

You are thinking of purchasing an aquarium. You contact the owner of an aquarium store. You need to know how many fish to purchase for an aquarium, but first you must determine how big the aquarium will be. The owner of the aquarium store tells you his rule of thumb is to purchase "a total length of fish of 3 inches for each 2 gallons of water in the aquarium."

1. How many gallons of water would you need if you had a 4-inch fish and a 2-inch fish? Draw a diagram to explain your reasoning.

Drawing a model would be really helpful here.

2. Define variables for the quantities that are changing in this problem situation.

3. Write an equation for each:

a. fish-inches based on the gallons of water

b. gallons of water based on fish-inches

4. Use one of your equations to solve each problem.

   a. If an aquarium holds 10 gallons of water, how many fish-inches should you purchase?

   b. If you want to purchase a 5-inch fish, two 2-inch fish, and three 3-inch fish, how many gallons of water should the aquarium hold?

5. Determine the constant of proportionality given by each equation and explain what it means in context.

ACTIVITY
3.1

Graphs of Two Constants of Proportionality

Let's graph each equation you wrote in the previous activity.

1. **Create a table of ordered pairs. Then plot the ordered pairs to create a graph of each equation.**

Fish-Inches							
Gallons							

Fish-Inches per Gallon

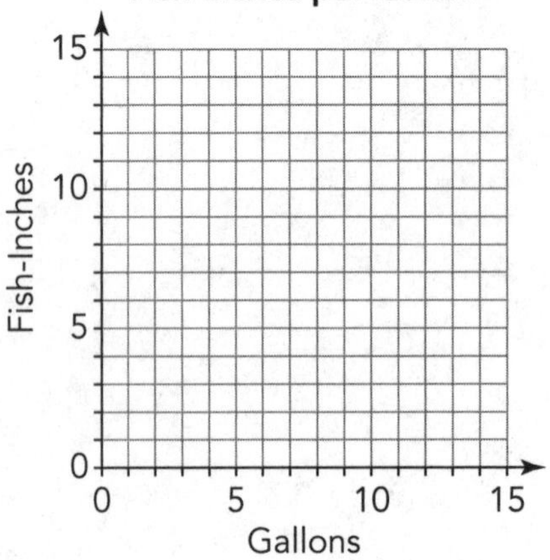

Gallons per Fish-Inch

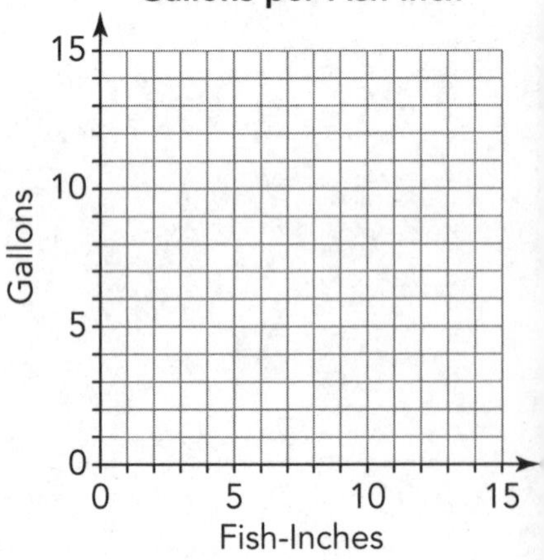

2. **What does the point (0, 0) mean on each graph?**

3. **Determine the meaning of each point.**

   a. **What does the point (6, 9) on the Fish-Inches per Gallon graph represent?**

   b. **What does the point (9, 6) on the Gallons per Fish-Inch graph represent?**

c. What does the point $(1, 1\frac{1}{2})$ on the Fish-Inches per Gallon graph represent?

d. What does the point $(1, \frac{2}{3})$ on the Gallons per Fish-Inch graph represent?

4. What is the unit rate for each graph? Explain how you can determine the unit rate using the graph.

5. Use one of your graphs to determine each answer.

   a. How many inches of fish can fit into 10 gallons of water?

   b. How many gallons are needed for $7\frac{1}{2}$ inches of fish?

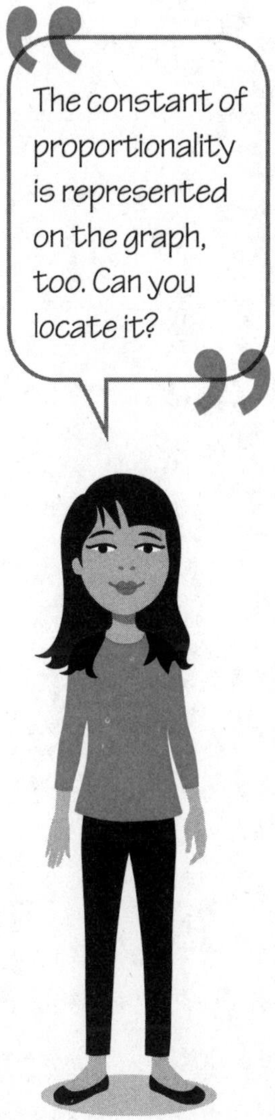

The constant of proportionality is represented on the graph, too. Can you locate it?

6. Use one of the graphs to estimate each answer. Explain how you used the graph to determine your estimate.

   a. How many gallons would be needed for 16 inches of fish?

   b. How many inches of fish would fit into 16 gallons?

NOTES

ACTIVITY 3.2

Constant of Proportionality from a Graph

The graph shown displays the relationship between the time and distance Ella runs.

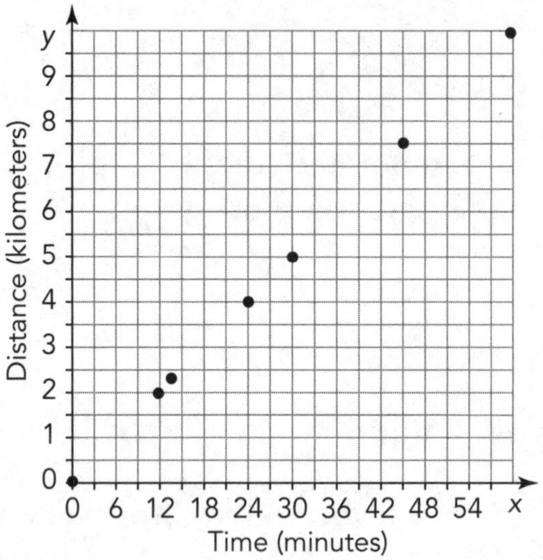

1. **Define variables and write an equation to represent the relationship between Ella's distance and time.**

2. **Use your equation to answer each question.**

   a. **How far can Ella run in 15 minutes?**

b. How long does it take Ella to run 7.5 kilometers?

c. How far can Ella run in one hour?

d. Determine the constant of proportionality in kilometers per hour. Then, write another equation representing Ella's distance (*d*) varies directly with time (*t*).

How can you determine the constant of proportionality from a graph?

e. How is this equation the same as, and different from, the previous equation you wrote?

ACTIVITY
3.3

Determining Proportional Relationships from Graphs

A graph establishes dependency. So, if the graph shows a proportional relationship, then y varies directly as x.

You have seen that proportional relationships can be represented on graphs and that the constant of proportionality can be identified from the graph.

1. Determine if each graph shows a proportional relationship between x and y. If possible, determine the constant of proportionality. Explain how you determined your answer.

a.

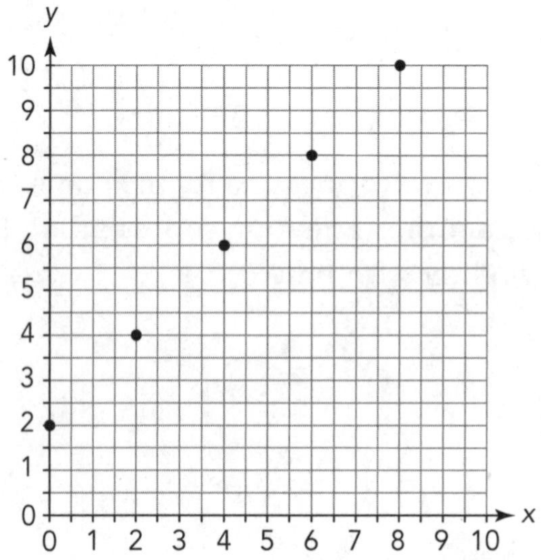

b.

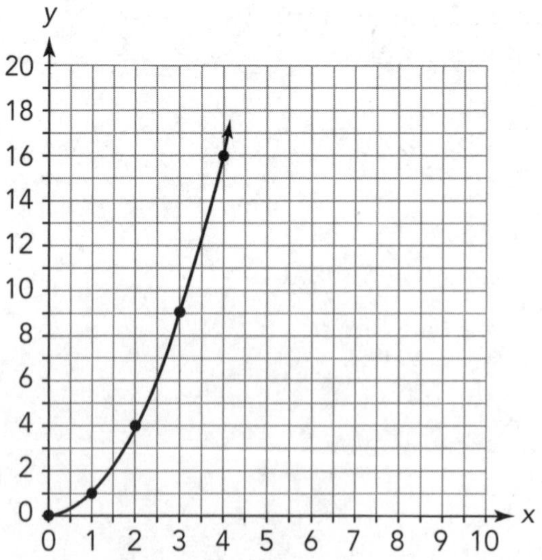

c.

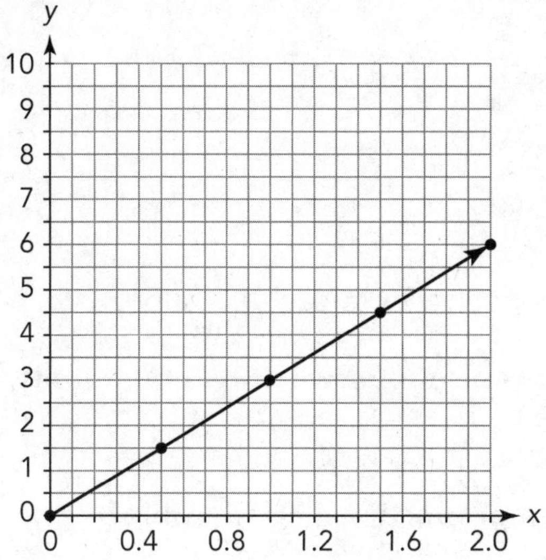

y
10
9
8
7
6
5
4
3
2
1
0
0
0.4
0.8
1.2
1.6
2.0
x

d.

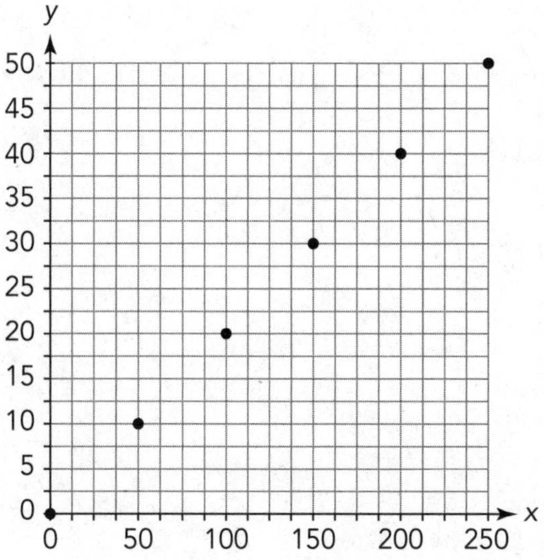

y
50
45
40
35
30
25
20
15
10
5
0
0
50
100
150
200
250
x

NOTES

TALK the TALK

How Do You Know?

Use examples to explain your answer to each question.

1. **Given a graph of a relationship between two quantities, how do you know:**

   a. **if the graph shows a proportional relationship?**

   b. **what the constant of proportionality is?**

   c. **what the unit rate is?**

   d. **what any ordered pair on the graph represents?**

Assignment

Write

Given a graph of a proportional relationship, the quotient of the *y*-value of any ordered pair divided by the *x*-value of that ordered pair is the constant of proportionality. Explain why.

Remember

When the relationship between two quantities is proportional, the graph of the relationship is a straight line that passes through the origin. The point (1, *r*) represents the unit rate and the ratio $\frac{r}{1}$ represents the constant of proportionality, *k*.

Practice

Determine the constant of proportionality *k* and interpret it in the context of each problem.

1. The graph shows the relationship between the distance in miles between you and a storm and the number of seconds between when you see lightning and when you hear thunder.

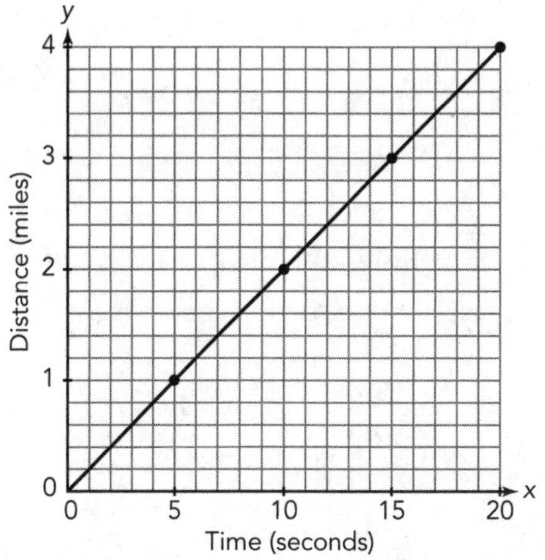

2. The graph shows the relationship between the number of euros Jason received and the number of dollars Jason exchanged during his trip to Spain.

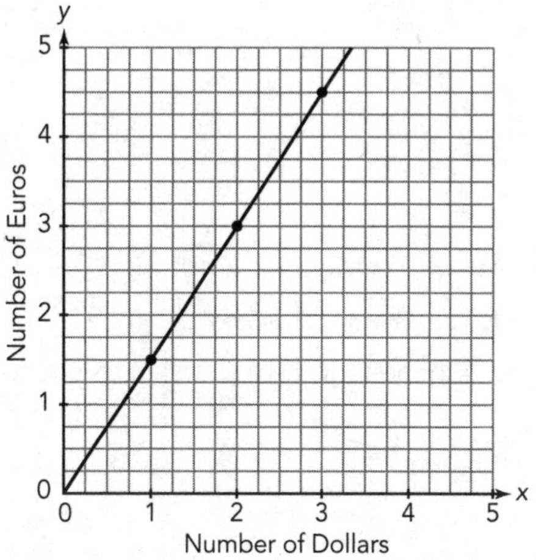

3. The graph shows the relationship between the weight of an object on Earth and the weight of the same object object on Venus.

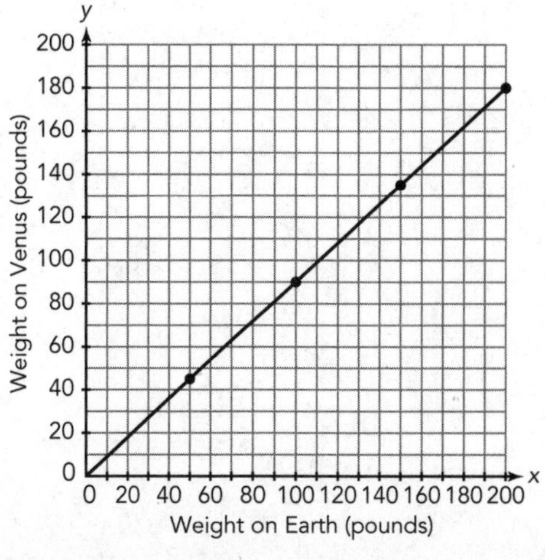

4. The graph shows the relationship between the area of a room in square feet and the cost of covering the floor with new tile.

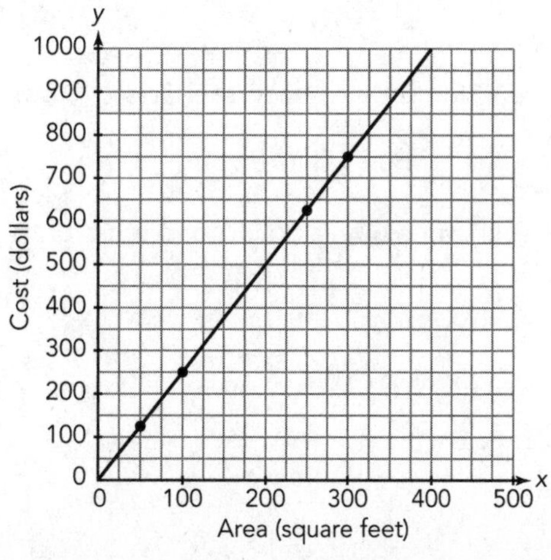

5. The graph shows the relationship between the cups of water and pounds of beef needed for a beef casserole.

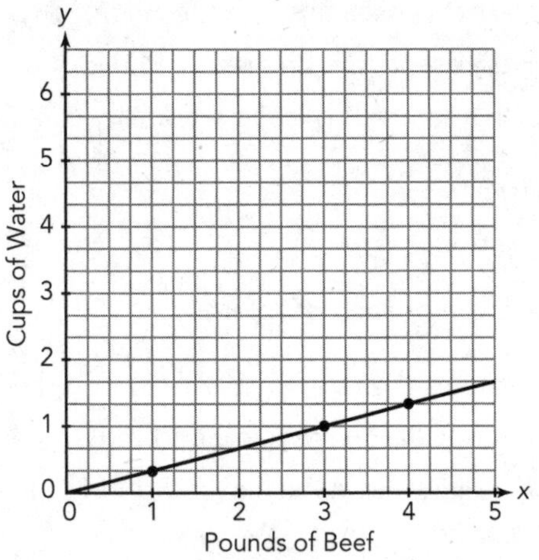

6. The graph shows the relationship between the number of posters in a classroom and the number of thumbtacks used to hold them up.

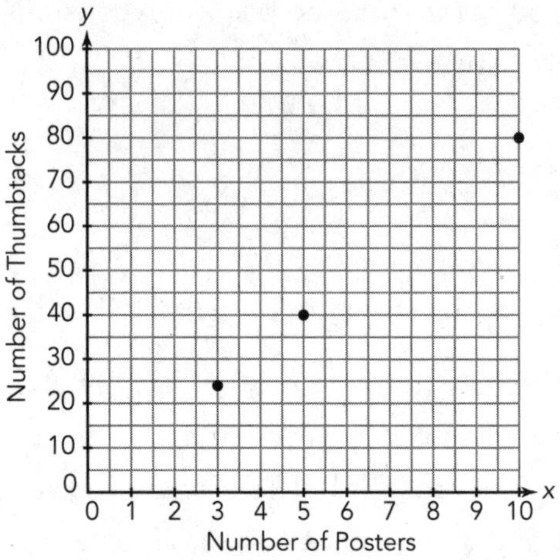

Stretch

At any given time of the day, the length of your shadow is proportional to your height. Suppose a person who is 81 inches tall casts a shadow that is 94.5 inches long. Another person in the same place casts a shadow that is 84 inches long. How tall is the second person?

Review

1. Use the equation for the constant of proportionality, $k = \frac{y}{x}$, to determine each unknown value.

   a. $k = \frac{3}{2}$ and $y = 15$

   b. $k = \frac{1}{4}$ and $y = 5$

2. Determine a unit rate for each scenario.

   a. $\frac{3}{4}$ of an inch of rain fell in $\frac{1}{2}$ hour.

   b. Heather charges a half-dollar for each eighth of a pizza.

3. Simplify each expression.

   a. $8 - 4(5) + 2^4$

   b. $10 \div (1 + 4) - 3^2$

Minding Your Ps and Qs 4

Constant of Proportionality in Multiple Representations

WARM UP

Solve each equation.

1. $5p = 2.5$
2. $\frac{1}{3}j = 9$
3. $0.12k = 10.08$
4. $8k = 0$

LEARNING GOALS

- Determine if relationships represented in words, tables, equations, or graphs are proportional.
- Interpret the meaning of linear proportional relationships represented in words, tables, equations, and graphs.
- Determine and interpret the constant of proportionality for quantities that are proportional and represented in words, tables, equations, and graphs.

You have learned how to determine the constant of proportionality. How can you solve problems using this constant in tables, graphs, and diagrams?

Getting Started

Penny's Nickels Are a Quarter of Her Dimes

Penny collects only nickels and dimes. She has one-quarter as many nickels as dimes.

A diagram can represent this problem situation.

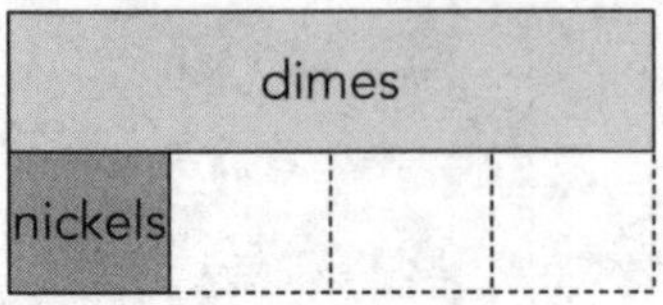

All together she has 40 coins. How much money does she have?

1. **Explain how you can use the diagram to solve the problem. Determine the solution.**

2. **Write an equation to represent the proportional relationship between:**

   a. **the number of nickels and the number of dimes.**

   b. **the number of dimes and the total number of coins.**

   c. **the number of nickels and the total number of coins.**

3. **Identify the constant of proportionality in each proportional relationship described in Question 2.**

ACTIVITY 4.1

Using a Graph to Write an Equation

NOTES

The graph shows Natasha's total number of free throw attempts and the total number of free throws made.

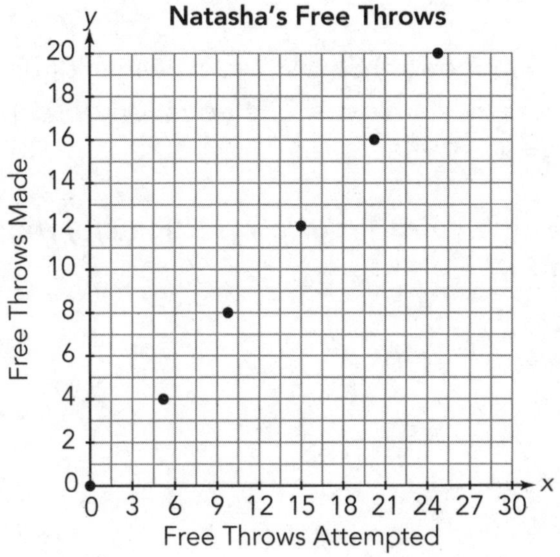

1. Explain how you know the graph represents a relationship that is proportional.

2. Determine the constant of proportionality and describe what it represents in this problem situation.

3. If Natasha attempted 30 free throws, how many would she probably make? First, use your graph to estimate the answer. Then, verify your answer by using an equation.

NOTES

ACTIVITY 4.2 Using an Equation to Create a Table

Another example of a proportional relationship is the relationship between the number of hours a worker works and his or her wages earned in dollars.

The amount of money (m) Shaylah earns varies directly with the number of hours (h) she works. The equation describing this relationship is $m = 9.25h$.

1. What does the constant of proportionality represent in this situation?

2. Complete the table based on the equation given. Include the constant of proportionality in the table.

Hours Worked	Earnings (dollars)
0	
	112.85
40	

NOTES

During the summer, Fernando works as a movie attendant. The number of hours he works varies each week.

3. Write an equation to represent this situation. Then complete the table based on your equation and include the constant of proportionality.

Hours Worked	Earnings (dollars)
3	26.88

4. What is the constant of proportionality? What does it mean in this problem situation?

ACTIVITY 4.3 Using a Table to Create a Scenario

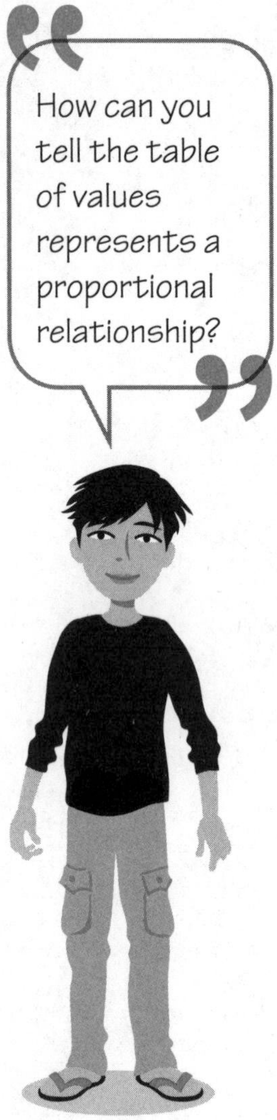

How can you tell the table of values represents a proportional relationship?

Analyze the given table.

Number of Windows	Amount of Window Cleaner (ounces)
0	0
2	16
3	24
4	32
5	40
6	48

1. **Describe one possible situation that could be represented by this table of values. Include how the quantities relate to each other.**

2. **What is the constant of proportionality and what does it represent in your situation?**

3. **If the table values were used to create a graph, how would the points appear?**

ACTIVITY
4.4

Using a Scenario to Write an Equation

A baby elephant nurses for the first two years of its life. It drinks about 10 liters of milk every day.

1. **Define variables and write an equation to represent the relationship between the amounts of milk the baby elephant consumes and the time it spends consuming the milk. Assume the elephant maintains the same rate of consumption.**

2. **Identify the constant of proportionality and describe what it means in this situation.**

3. **Create a graph to represent this situation.**

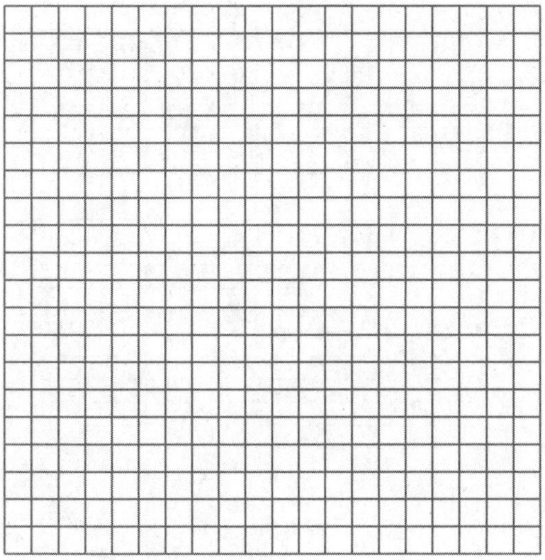

The weight of person on Earth varies directly as the weight of an object on the Moon. A 150-pound person would weigh approximately 25 pounds on the Moon.

4. Define variables and write and equation to represent the relationship between the weight of an object on Earth and the weight of an object on the Moon.

5. Identify the constant of proportionality and describe what it means in this situation.

6. Create a graph to represent this situation.

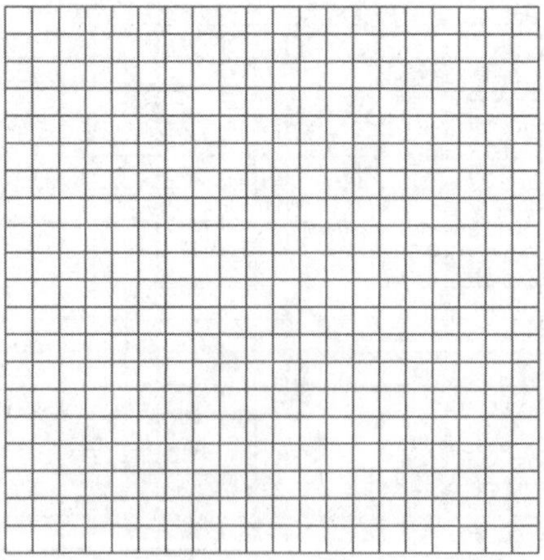

ACTIVITY 4.5

Multiple Representations of Proportional Relationships

Suppose q varies directly as p.

1. Complete the table for variables p and q.

p	q
0	
2	6
4	12
0.25	
	3
1.5	4.5

2. Write an equation that represents the relationship between p and q.

3. Summarize how you can write the equation that represents the relationship between two variables that vary directly if you are given a ratio table.

4. Graph your equation. Label your axes.

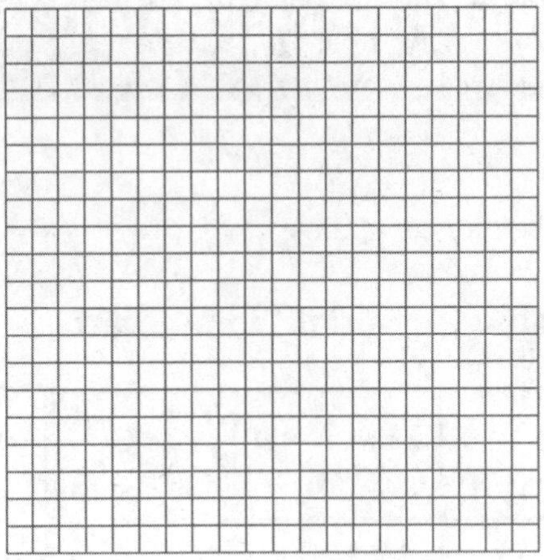

5. Summarize how to draw a graph from the equation representing the relationship between two quantities that vary directly.

6. Summarize how you can write the equation representing the relationship between two quantities that vary directly if you are given a graph.

NOTES

TALK the TALK

Every Which Way

You have seen how to represent proportional relationships in scenarios, on graphs, in tables, and with equations.

1. **Write an equation and sketch a graph to represent each relationship. Label your axes and identify the constant of proportionality on the graph.**

   a. **Suppose the quantity *c* varies directly as the quantity *d*.**

   b. **Suppose the quantity *d* varies directly as the quantity *c*.**

NOTES

2. Write a scenario which describes a proportional relationship between two quantities. Represent this relationship using an equation, a graph, and a table. For each model, identify the constant of proportionality and explain how the model shows that the relationship is proportional.

Scenario	Equation

A PROPORTIONAL RELATIONSHIP

Table	Graph

Assignment

Write

Describe how a table, an equation, and a graph can each represent a direct variation.

Remember

Proportional relationships can be represented in a lot of different ways, including diagrams, tables, equations, graphs, and in scenarios.

Practice

1. The constant of proportionality between the number of children (*c*) on a field trip and the number of teachers (*t*) on the trip is $\frac{14}{3}$.
   a. Write an equation to represent this situation.
   b. Create a graph.
   c. If there are 70 children on a field trip. How many teachers are on the trip?
2. The constant of proportionality between the number of junior varsity players (*j*) on the track team and the number of varsity players (*v*) on the team is $\frac{2}{5}$.
   a. Write an equation to represent this situation.
   b. Create a graph.
   c. If there are 45 varsity players on the track team. How many junior varsity players are on the team?
3. The constant of proportionality between the number of cats (*c*) in a pet shelter and the number of dogs (*d*) in the shelter is 3.
   a. Write an equation to represent this situation.
   b. Create a graph.
   c. If there are 27 cats in the shelter. How many dogs are in the shelter?
4. The constant of proportionality between the height of the water in a sink (*h*) in centimeters and the number of minutes it has been filling (*m*) is 0.95. The sink has been filling for 40 minutes. What is the height of the water in the sink?
5. The constant of proportionality between the number of fiction books (*f*) and the number of nonfiction books (*n*) in a library is $\frac{15}{22}$. There are 3498 nonfiction books in the library. How many fiction books are in the library?
6. The constant of proportionality between the number of markers (*m*) and the number of pencils (*p*) in an art room is $\frac{8}{3}$. There are 304 markers in the art room. How many pencils are in the art room?

Stretch

A map of the United States is drawn such that 1 inch is equal to 600 miles. What is the approximate distance, on the map, between New York and Los Angeles?

Review

1. Suppose the number of pages (p) that Tony can read varies directly with the amount of time (t) in hours he spends reading. Determine the constant of proportionality and describe its meaning.

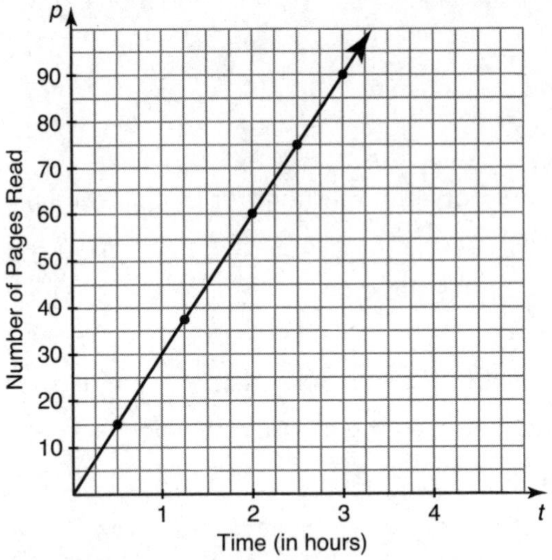

2. In the first quarter (3 months), a store sold 32 limited-edition action figures. If this quarter's sales represent a typical sales pattern, how many action figures should they expect to sell in a year?
3. A recipe calls for $3\frac{1}{2}$ cups of flour and $\frac{3}{4}$ cup of sugar. If you want to make the recipe with 6 cups of flour, how much sugar will you need?

4. Determine the area of each triangle.

a.

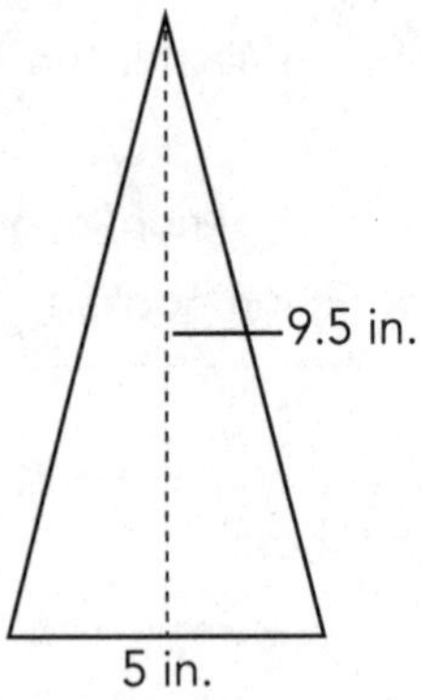

b.

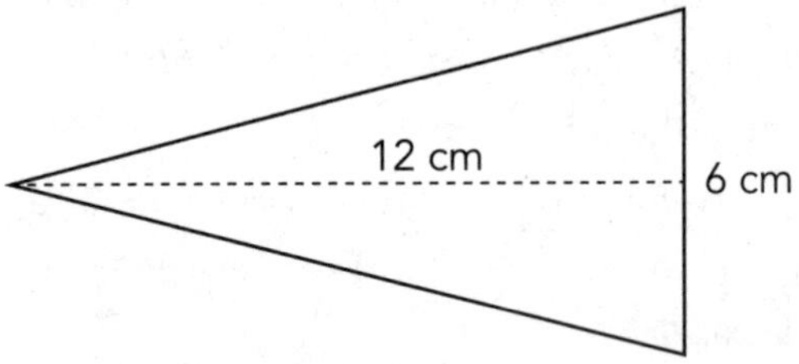

Proportionality Summary

KEY TERMS

- origin
- proportional relationship
- direct variation
- constant of proportionality

LESSON 1

How Does Your Garden Grow?

One special type of relationship that compares quantities using multiplicative reasoning is a ratio relationship. When two equivalent ratios are set equal to each other, they form a proportion. The quantities in the proportion are in a **proportional relationship**.

For a table of values to represent a proportional relationship, all the ratios of corresponding *x*- and *y*-values must be constant.

For example, the table displays the growth rate of a certain species of bamboo by comparing the time in days, *x*, to the height of the bamboo in centimeters, *y*. Does the table show a proportional relationship?

Time (days)	Height of Bamboo (cm)
3	210
10.5	735
18	1260
25.5	1785

$\frac{3}{210} = \frac{1}{70}$ $\frac{10.5}{735} = \frac{1}{70}$ $\frac{18}{1260} = \frac{1}{70}$ $\frac{25.5}{1785} = \frac{1}{70}$

All the values $\frac{x}{y}$ represent the same constant, $\frac{1}{70}$, so the table shows a proportional relationship.

For a graph to represent a proportional relationship, the points of the graph must form a straight line and pass through the origin. The **origin** is the point with the ordered pair (0, 0).

For example, the values from the bamboo situation are graphed here. The graph represents a proportional relationship. It also represents a direct variation. A situation represents a **direct variation** if the ratio between the *y*-value and its corresponding *x*-value is constant for every point. The bamboo grows at a constant rate of 70 centimeters a day. The height varies directly as time.

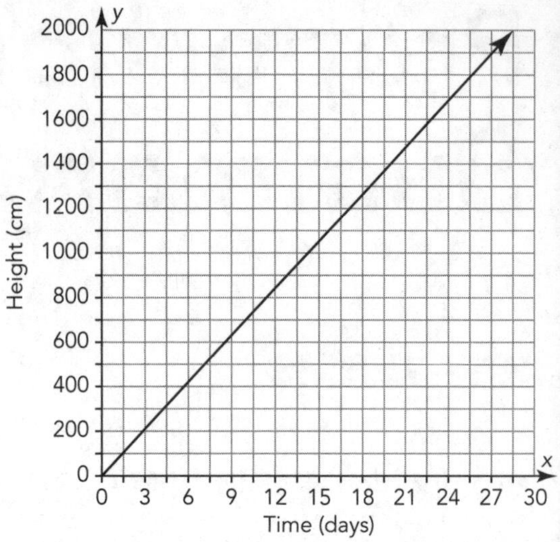

LESSON 2

Complying with Title IX

If *y* is directly proportional to *x*, the relationship can be represented by the equation $y = kx$, where *k* is the **constant of proportionality.** This means that for any value of *x*, the value of *y* is *x* multiplied by *k*.

For example, the table of values represents a proportional relationship. Determine the constant of proportionality.

Girls	Boys
5	6
10	12
15	18

$$y = kx$$
$$6 = k \cdot 5$$
$$\frac{6}{5} = k$$

You can use the constant of proportionality to determine unknown values in proportions.

For example, using the constant of proportionality represented in the previous table, determine how many girls there are if there are 240 boys.

$$\frac{5}{6} = \frac{g}{240}$$
$$(5)(240) = 6g$$
$$1200 = 6g$$
$$200 = g$$

There are 200 girls.

For example, consider the same ratio of 5 girls to 6 boys. If you know the number of boys and need to determine the number of girls, you can use the equation $y = \frac{5}{6}x$. In this equation, the $\frac{5}{6}$ represents the constant of proportionality. For any number of girls, the number of boys is $\frac{5}{6}$ times the number of girls. If you know the number of girls and need to determine the number of boys, you can use the equation $y = \frac{6}{5}x$. In this scenario, the constant of proportionality is $\frac{6}{5}$. You can multiply the number of boys by $\frac{6}{5}$ to determine the number of girls.

LESSON
3 Fish-Inches

The constant of proportionality of a situation can be graphed in two different ways.

For example, Stephen walks at a constant rate of 3 miles per hour.

The first graph shown represents the ratio of distance to time. The point (1, 3) represent the unit rate. The ratio $\frac{3}{1}$ represents the constant of proportionality, $k = 3$.

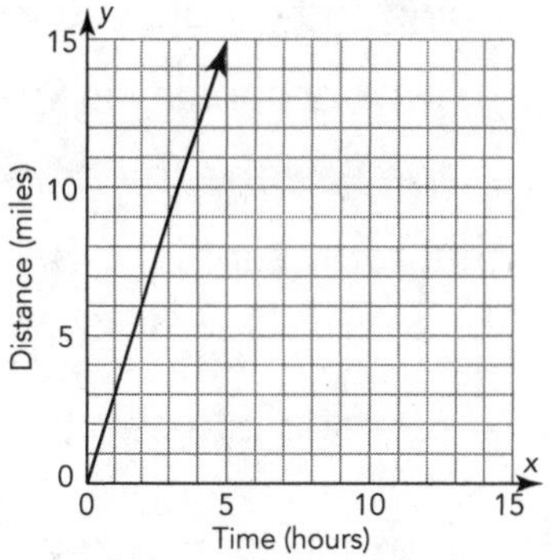

The second graph shown represents the ratio of time to distance. The point $(1, \frac{1}{3})$ represent the unit rate. The ratio $\frac{\frac{1}{3}}{1}$ represents the constant of proportionality, $k = \frac{1}{3}$.

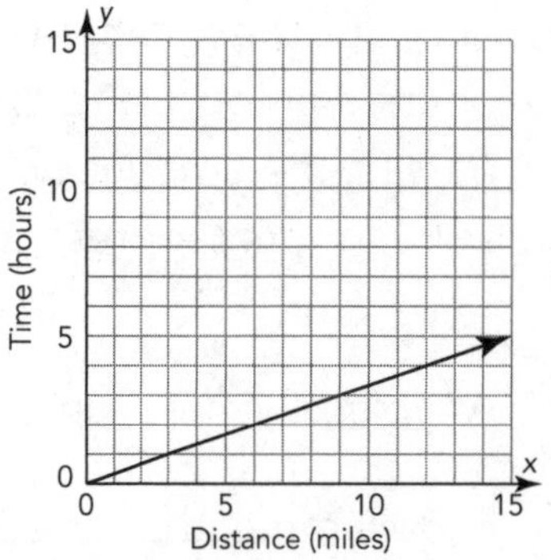

You can determine the constant of proportionality from a graph.

For example, the third graph shown displays the proportional relationship between the time and distance Melanie walks. Determine the constant of proportionality in miles per hour.

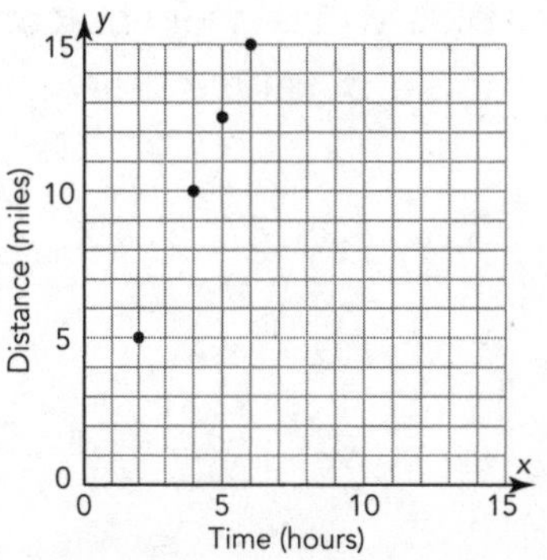

Choose an ordered pair from the graph: (4, 10).

$k = \frac{y}{x}$

$k = \frac{10}{4}$

$k = 2.5$

The constant of proportionality is 2.5.

LESSON 4
Minding Your Ps and Qs

Proportional relationships can be represented in many different ways, including diagrams, tables, equations, and graphs. They can also be described in scenarios.

A graph can be used to write an equation.

For example, the graph shows Patrick's total number of free throw attempts and the total number of free throws made. The graph represents a proportional relationship because it is a straight line that goes through the origin. Using the graph, you can determine that the constant of proportionality is $k = \frac{4}{7}$, which means that Patrick made $\frac{4}{7}$ of the free throws he attempted. The equation that represents this is $y = \frac{4}{7}x$.

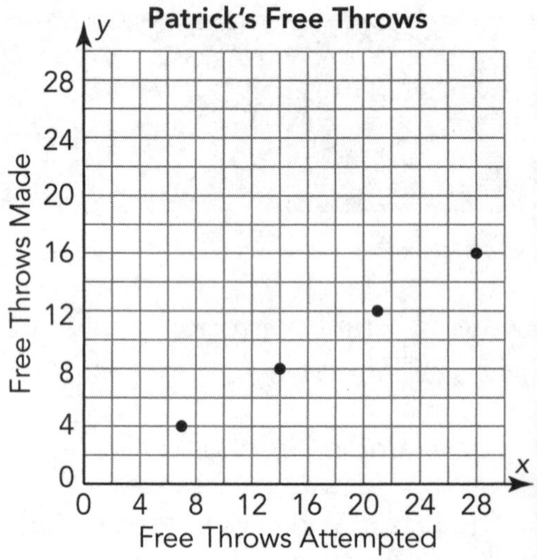

A scenario can also be used to write an equation.

For example, a blue whale eats 8000 pounds of food a day. Let x represent the independent quantity, the number of days, and let y represent the dependent quantity, the number of pounds of food eaten. The constant of proportionality is 8000, meaning that for every day that passes, the amount of food in pounds that the blue whale has eaten increases by 8000. The equation that represents this is $y = 8000x$.

A table of values can be created using an equation.

For example, the equation $y = 8000x$ from the blue whale scenario can be used to create the table of values shown.

Number of Days	Pounds of Food
0	0
1	8000
4	32,000
9	72,000

TOPIC 4

Proportional Relationships

Did you get good service in a restaurant? If you did, it is common to leave a 20% tip for the server that waited on you.

Module 1: Thinking Proportionally

TOPIC 4: PROPORTIONAL RELATIONSHIPS

In this topic, students use their knowledge of proportionality to solve real-world problems about money and scale drawings. They solve a wide variety of multistep ratio and percent problems, including problems about tax, markups and markdowns, gratuities, simple interest, commissions, and scale factors and drawings. Students use percent models, proportions, and the constant of proportionality to solve markup and markdown problems. In addition to considering scenarios involving money, students calculate percent increase and decrease using geometric objects.

Where have we been?

In grade 6, students used ratio strategies, including models and forming equivalent ratios, to solve percent problems involving determining the whole given a part and the percent. In previous lessons in this course, students learned and practiced solving proportions using means and extremes.

Where are we going?

Students learn financial literacy skills related to taxes and fees, commissions, markups and markdowns, tips, simple interest, and percent increase and decrease, including depreciation. They learn how to use proportional reasoning to estimate, calculate, and judge the reasonableness of results of everyday percent problems they will encounter throughout their lives.

Using a Scale Drawing to Solve Problems

The scale drawing is a blueprint for one floor of a new house. Knowing that the scale is the ratio 3 cm : 10 ft can help you determine the actual dimensions of objects in the scale drawing.

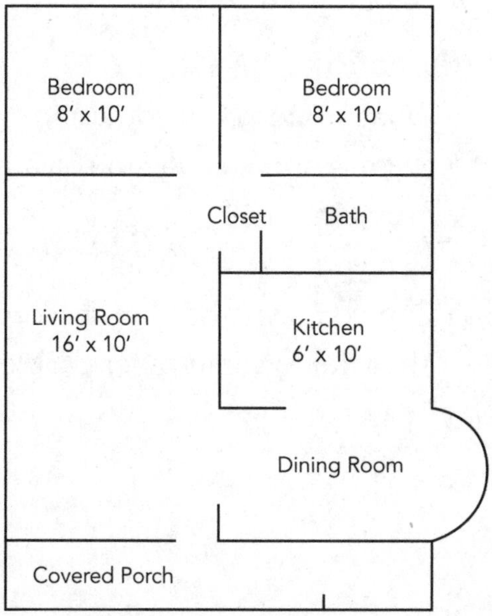

Myth: There is one right way to do math problems.

Employing multiple strategies to arrive at a single, correct solution is important in life. Suppose you are driving in a crowded downtown area. If one road is backed up, then you can always take a different route. If you know only one route, then you're out of luck.

Learning mathematics is no different. There may only be one right answer, but there are often multiple strategies to arrive at that solution. Everyone should get in the habit of saying: Well, that's one way to do it. Is there another way? What are the pros and cons? That way, you avoid falling into the trap of thinking there is only one right way because that strategy might not always work or there might be a more efficient strategy.

Teaching students multiple strategies is important. This helps students understand the benefits of the more efficient method. In addition, everyone has different experiences and preferences. What works for you might not work for someone else.

#mathmythbusted

Talking Points

You can further support your student's learning by asking them to take a step back and think about a different strategy when they are stuck.

Questions to Ask

- What strategy are you using?
- What is another way to solve the problem?
- Can you draw a model?
- Can you come back to this problem after doing some other problems?

Key Terms

percent increase
A percent increase is the ratio of the amount of increase to the original amount, written as a percent.

percent decrease
A percent decrease is the ratio of the amount of decrease to the original amount, written as a percent.

depreciation
Depreciation is decrease in price or value. A car's value depreciates over time.

similar figures
Figures that are proportional in size, or that have proportional dimensions, are called similar figures.

Markups and Markdowns

1

Introducing Proportions to Solve Percent Problems

WARM UP

The regular price of a bathing suit is $89.99. Estimate the sale price of the bathing suit for each of the following sales.

1. 70% off regular price
2. 30% off regular price
3. 50% off regular price
4. 25% off regular price

LEARNING GOALS

- Estimate and calculate the values of percents.
- Use percent models to solve percent problems.
- Use proportional relationships to solve for unknowns in multistep percent problems.
- Solve percent problems using the constant of proportionality.

KEY TERMS

- markdown
- markup

You have used ratio reasoning to solve percent problems. How can you use proportional relationships to solve percent problems involving markdowns and markups?

Getting Started

Need New Kicks?

A marketing department is creating signs for an upcoming shoe sale.

HOLIDAY SHOE SALE 35% OFF the Regular Price	HOLIDAY SHOE SALE 65% Of Regular Price

1. **Compare the two signs. What do you notice?**

2. **Which sign should the store use to advertise the shoe sale? Explain your reasoning.**

3. **The regular price of a pair of shoes is $59.99. Estimate the sale price of the pair of shoes two different ways.**

ACTIVITY

1.1 Percent Models

Three percent scenarios are shown. Match each model to the appropriate scenario.

1. **A shirt costs $20. If it was on sale for 75% off, what is the discount?**

a.

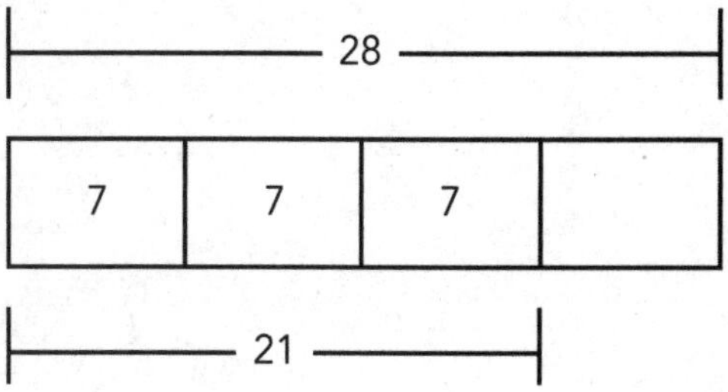

2. **A skirt originally cost $28. Alicia pays $21 for the skirt during a sale. What percent does Alicia save with the sale?**

b.

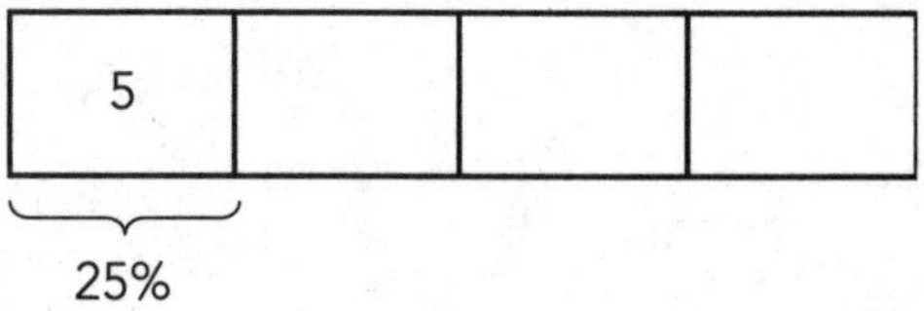

3. **A ski hat is on sale for 25% off, which is $5 off. What is the original price of the ski hat?**

c.

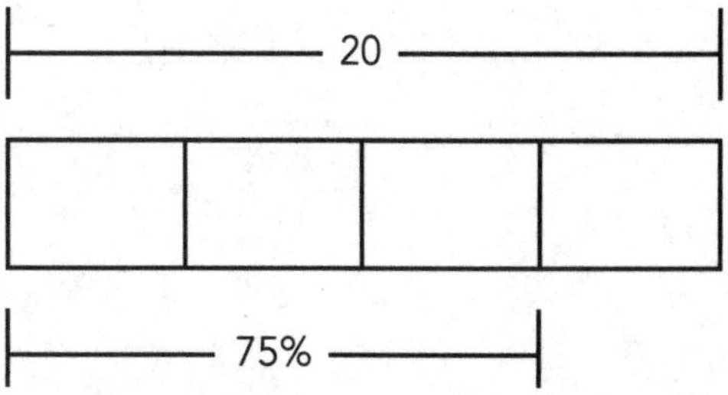

4. **Use the appropriate model to solve each percent problem. Explain how you solved each.**

5. Keisha said that she had developed strategies to solve percent problems, depending on what was given.

   - Case A: If I want to calculate the percent, I can divide the part by the whole and rewrite the decimal as a percent.
   - Case B: If I want to calculate the part, or percent of a number, I can multiply the percent, written in decimal form, by the number.
   - Case C: If I want to calculate the whole, I can divide the percent, written in decimal form, by the part.

   Is Keisha correct?
   Does this always work? Explain your thinking.

ACTIVITY
1.2

Using Proportions to Solve Percent Problems

Corinne, Eduardo, and Adina each set up a proportion to solve four different percent problems.

Remember, you can write a percent as a proportion.

$$\frac{\text{part}}{\text{whole}} = \frac{\text{percent number}}{100}$$

1. **Read each percent problem and analyze the corresponding student's work.**

A shirt costs \$20. If it is on sale for 75% off, what is the discount?

Corinne

$$\frac{75}{100} = \frac{x}{20}$$

$$(75)(20) = 100x$$

$$1500 = 100x$$

$$\frac{1500}{100} = \frac{100x}{100}$$

$$15 = x$$

The discount is \$15.

a. How did Corinne know where to place the 20 in her proportion?

A skirt originally cost \$28. Alicia pays \$21 for the skirt during a sale. What percent does Alicia save with the sale?

Eduardo

$$\frac{x}{100} = \frac{21}{28}$$

$$28x = (100)(21)$$

$$28x = 2100$$

$$\frac{28x}{28} = \frac{2100}{28}$$

$$x = 75$$

Alicia paid 75% of the cost, so Alicia saved 25%.

b. How did Eduardo decide Alicia saved 25%?

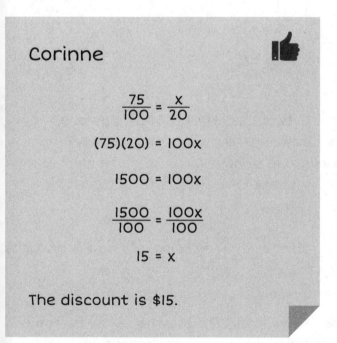

A ski hat is on sale for 25% off, which is $5 off. What is the original price of the ski hat?

Adina

$$\frac{25}{100} = \frac{x}{5}$$

$$(25)(5) = 100x$$

$$125 = 100x$$

$$\frac{125}{100} = \frac{100x}{100}$$

$$1.25 = x$$

c. **Explain what Adina did incorrectly. Then, set up and solve the problem correctly.**

All of the problems in the previous activity involved a sale or a **markdown**. To make money, businesses often buy products from a wholesaler or distributor for one amount and add to that amount to determine the price they use to sell the product to their customers. This is called a **markup**.

The school store is selling spirit wear. They mark up all of the prices by 20% to sell to the community and students.

2. **If the store's cost for a sweatshirt is $25, what is the customer's cost? Analyze the four student responses shown.**

Dean

$$\frac{20}{100} = \frac{x}{25}$$

$$5 = x$$

The customer's cost is $5.

Binh

$$\frac{20}{100} = \frac{x}{25}$$

$$5 = x$$

The customer's cost is $5 + $25 = $30.

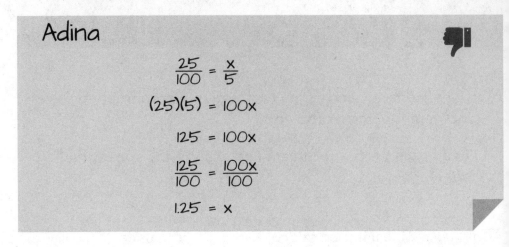

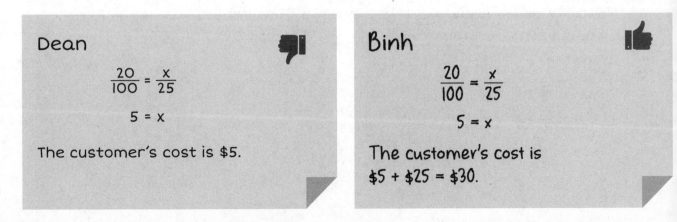

Luke

The new "whole" is the total cost, which is 20% more than the original 100%. I can multiply the store cost by 120%, or 1.20.

$$25(1.20) = 30$$

The customer's cost is $30.

Lahari

The original cost is now the part.

$$\frac{100}{120} = \frac{25}{x}$$

$$30 = x$$

The customer's cost is $30.

a. **Compare Dean's method to Binh's method.**

b. **Compare Luke's method to Lahari's method.**

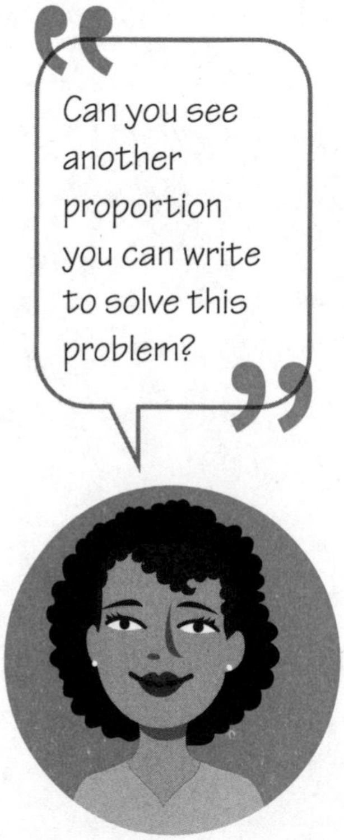

Can you see another proportion you can write to solve this problem?

3. **Use the method(s) of your choice to complete the table of the store's cost and the customer's cost for the spirit wear.**

	Store's Cost	Customer's Cost
T-shirt	$8	
Face Tattoos		$4.50

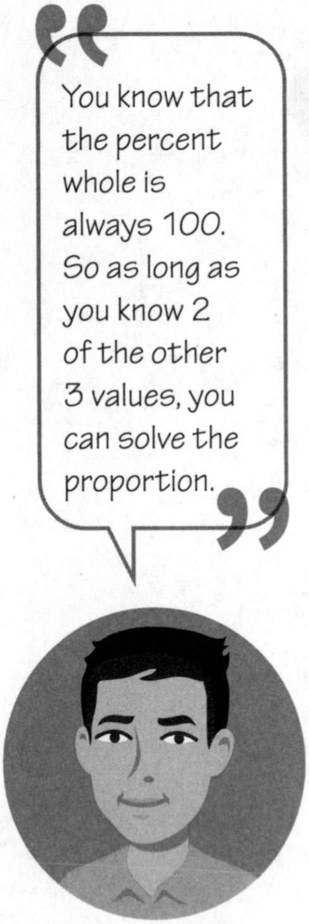

You know that the percent whole is always 100. So as long as you know 2 of the other 3 values, you can solve the proportion.

Solve each percent problem. Show your work.

4. The $199.99 game console Amy purchased was on sale for 10% off. How much did Amy pay?

5. A computer is normally $899 but is discounted to $799. What percent of the original price does Shawn pay?

6. If Fernando paid $450 for a netbook that was 75% of the original price, what was the original price?

7. Fantasy-N-Fun sells gaming cards for $9.99 but they pay only $6.75 per card. What is the percent markup?

8. Dontrelle received 30% off when he purchased a rare book regularly priced at $96.50. How much did Dontrelle pay?

9. Brittany is selling car magnets. She purchases them for $7.50 each and marks up the price by 30%. How much is Brittany planning to charge?

ACTIVITY
1.3

Answering the Question

Chet is planning his vacation. The flight he selected was $229.99 but he got 20% off because he booked it online through a new travel website. What did he pay?

1. **Explain why Katie's answer is incorrect. Then, determine the correct answer.**

Katie

$$\frac{20}{100} = \frac{x}{229.99}$$

$$(20)(229.99) = 100x$$

$$\frac{4599.8}{100} = \frac{100x}{100}$$

$$45.998 = x$$

So, Chet paid about $46.

2. **Explain why Emma's method worked.**

Emma

$$\frac{80}{100} = \frac{x}{229.99}$$

$$(80)(229.99) = 100x$$

$$\frac{18399.2}{100} = \frac{100x}{100}$$

$$183.99 = x$$

Chet paid $183.99 for his flight.

Solve each problem.

3. **Anita sold USB thumb drives for $4.95, which was a 10% markup from what she paid for each. How much did Anita pay for the drives?**

4. **Games that usually sell for $36.40 are on sale for $27.30. What percent off are they?**

5. **Jimmy's new cell phone cost him $49.99 when he signed a 2-year plan, which was 75% off the original price. What was the original price?**

A rebate is a refund of part of the amount paid for an item. Generally, a customer mails a completed form to the company after a purchase, and a rebate check is mailed to the customer.

6. **Liz is shopping for a game system. Two competing stores offer deals on the system that she wants to purchase.**

Game Hut	Fun n Games
• $375 • 15% off sale on all game systems	• $399 • $50 rebate after the purchase

Where should Liz shop? Show all of your work and explain your reasoning.

7. Dante has been shopping around for a new mountain bike. He found two bikes that he likes equally—one is sold at Mike's Bikes for $300, and the other is sold at Cycle Center for $275.

Dante has a coupon for 25% off any bike at Mike's Bikes. However, the manufacturer of the bike at Cycle Center has included a $40 rebate after the purchase of the bike.

Where should Dante purchase his mountain bike? Show all of your work and explain your reasoning.

8. Barry is shopping for a new sweater that originally cost $50.00. The department store has all items marked down by 20%. He also has a coupon for an additional 10% off all purchases.

> Barry
>
> Since all items are marked down by 20%, and I have an additional 10% off, that means I get a 30% discount.
>
> $$\frac{30}{100} = \frac{X}{50}$$
>
> $$2X = 30$$
>
> $$X = 15$$
>
> The cost of the sweater is $50.00 - $15.00 = $35.00.

Describe Barry's mistake. Then calculate how much Barry will pay for the sweater.

ACTIVITY
1.4 Percent and Direct Variation

The Shoe Super Store sells name brand shoes at a price much less than most department stores. The chart hanging in the store displays the normal price of the shoes and the Shoe Super Store price.

Regular Department Store Price	Shoe Super Store Price
$20	$16
$25	$20
$30	$24
$35	$28
$40	$32
$50	$40

Remember, proportions are formed by equivalent ratios.

Alfie

The Shoe Super Store prices do not vary directly with the regular department store prices.

A $20 pair of shoes is only $4 cheaper at the Shoe Super Store, while a $50 pair of shoes is $10 cheaper at Shoe Super Store.

1. **Explain what is wrong with Alfie's reasoning.**

2. What is the constant of proportionality? Interpret the constant of proportionality for this problem situation.

3. Define the variables and write an equation to represent the relationship between the department store price and Shoe Super Store price.

4. What is the Shoe Super Store price for a pair of shoes that cost $28 at the department store? Explain your reasoning.

5. What is the department store price for a pair of shoes that cost $15 at Shoe Super Store? Explain your reasoning.

NOTES

TALK the TALK

Percent and Proportions

Demonstrate how to solve any type of percent problem with proportions.

1. **Write each proportion, with a variable in the appropriate place, to calculate each specific unknown.**

   a. **Calculate the Percent**

   b. **Calculate the Part**

   c. **Calculate the Whole**

Assignment

Write

Explain how to use proportions to solve for the unknown in a percent problem.

Remember

The answer to the percent problem may or may not be the value of the unknown in your proportion. Re-read the problem and ensure that you answer the question being asked.

Practice

1. The cable provider's "triple play" package offers a land line, internet service, and cable TV for one fixed price. If you already subscribe to their cell phone service they offer an additional 12% off the price of the triple play package. If the discounted price of the triple play is $132, what is the price of the package without the discount?
2. The O! Natural Company sells a juice in 1 gallon bottles. The current retail price of the juice is $3.50 for 1 gallon. In order to remain competitive, the company will decrease the price to $3.20.
   a. What percent of the original price are consumers going to pay?
   b. Suppose the company's cost per 1 gallon is $2.70. What is the markup if they sell each gallon at $3.20? What is the markup if they sell each gallon at $3.50?
3. The O! Natural Company is trying to get schools in the state to sell their juice product.
   a. If the sales representative went to 300 schools and convinced 125 to sell their product, what percentage decided to not sell their product? Use two different strategies to calculate the answer.
   b. The sales representative made a deal with the schools for a discount on the individual juice bottles. The company usually sells the bottles to the distributors for $2.25, but they are selling them to the schools for 15% off. For what price will they sell each bottle to the schools?
   c. Suppose the schools pay $2.00 per bottle for the juice and sell it to community members for $2.50 per bottle. What percent markup are they charging?
4. Jillian is shopping for new school supplies. She finds a flyer in the newspaper for her favorite store. They are offering the following coupons.

Office World Sale! All laptops—Buy now and receive a $100 rebate after purchase! *cannot be used with any other coupons	Office World Sale! Receive 20% off any one item!

Jillian needs to buy a new laptop for the school year. The list price for the laptop is $479.99. Is it a better deal to use the coupon for the $100 rebate or the 20% off one item? Explain your reasoning.

Stretch

While Emma is shopping with her friend Jacob, they notice a sign in the front of the store.

BACK-TO-SCHOOL SALE!
• 20% off all purchases • $10.00 student discount

They also notice that the two cashiers are applying the discounts differently. The cashier on their left is taking 20% off the total bill and then subtracting $10.00. The cashier on their right is subtracting $10.00 first and then taking 20% off the total.

In order to get a better deal, should Emma and Jacob go to the cashier on the left or the right? Or does it not matter? Show all of your work and explain your reasoning.

Review

1. Millie is cutting out stars to decorate the gym for the school dance. The number of stars *(s)* she can cut out varies directly with the time *(t)* in minutes she spends cutting out the stars.
   a. Write an equation to show the relationship between *s* and *t*.
   b. Complete the table to show the number of stars Millie is able to cut out for various amounts of time.

Time (*t*) (in minutes)	**Number of Stars (*s*)**	$\frac{s}{t} = k$
	0	……
12	6	
	15	
44		
50		

   c. Write an equation to represent the relationship between *s* and *t* using the value of *k* you determined from the table.
   d. Graph the data. Label the *x*- and *y*-axes and title your graph.
   e. Did the graph turn out as you expected? Explain.
   f. Explain how to determine the constant of proportionality using the graph.
2. Determine if there is a proportional relationship between the two quantities. Explain your reasoning.

a.

A	B
35	92
23	80

b.

C	D
20	8
12.5	5

3. Determine two equivalent ratios for each ratio given.

   a. $\frac{2}{5}$

   b. 6 yellow : 9 blue

Perks of Work

2

Calculating Tips, Commissions, and Simple Interest

WARM UP

Express each percent as a decimal and as a fraction.

1. 47%
2. 3%
3. 12.5%
4. 0.25%
5. 4.99%

LEARNING GOALS

- Use percent equations to solve for unknowns in multistep percent problems.
- Solve multistep percent problems using direct variation.
- Solve multistep percent problems using the constant of proportionality.

KEY TERMS

- percent equation
- simple interest
- commission

You have used proportions to solve percent problems involving markups and markdowns. How can you use proportions and percent equations to solve for the unknown in different types of percent problems?

Getting Started

Make Sure to Tip Your Servers

A patron is another word for a person who eats at a restaurant.

Most restaurant patrons add a tip to the final bill to show their appreciation for the wait staff. Usually, a patron will determine 15% to 20% of the bill, and then add that amount to the total. Many times, patrons will just round off the tip to the nearest dollar.

You can use benchmark percents to estimate the amount of any tip. Common benchmark percents used in calculating tips are 1%, 5%, 10%, and 25%.

WORKED EXAMPLE

One strategy to determine a 20% tip for a restaurant bill that is $38.95 is to first determine 10% of the total and then double that amount. Ten percent of $38.95 is $3.90, or approximately $4. So, a 20% tip should be about $8.

For each bill amount, use benchmark percents to estimate a 15% and 20% tip.

	15% Tip	**20% Tip**
$89.45		
$125.00		
$12.45		

ACTIVITY 2.1

Introduction to Percent Equations

NOTES

Now that many people own phones with built-in calculators, some calculate the exact tip for their restaurant bill rather than use rounding and benchmark fractions.

Suppose you want to determine the recommended 15% tip on a restaurant bill of $45.00. You can use a proportion to determine the amount of a tip based on the restaurant total.

1. **Use a proportion to determine the amount of a tip based on the restaurant total.**

You can also use a *percent equation* to determine the tip amount on a restaurant bill. A **percent equation** can be written in the form percent × whole = part, where the percent is often written as a decimal.

WORKED EXAMPLE

$$\text{percent} = \frac{\text{part}}{\text{whole}}$$

$$\text{percent as decimal} \times \text{whole} = \text{part}$$

$$\text{(tip percent) of (total bill)} = \text{amount of the tip}$$

$$\uparrow \qquad \uparrow \qquad \uparrow$$

$$\frac{15}{100} \text{ or } 0.15 \times 45 = t$$

$$6.75 = t$$

2. Analyze the worked example.

   a. Describe how the percent equation in the form percent × whole = part is equivalent to a proportion in the form percent = $\frac{\text{part}}{\text{whole}}$.

   b. Explain how the variable is isolated. Then, describe how the tip amount is calculated using the percent equation.

3. Use proportions and percent equations to calculate tips on the given restaurant bills. For each, isolate the variable first. Then, determine the tip amount. Finally, write your answer in a complete sentence.

Bill	Percent	Use a Proportion	Use a Percent Equation
$63.89	20%		
Sentence			
$24.40	15%		
Sentence			

4. **Describe how the strategies you used to solve the proportions and the percent equations are similar.**

ACTIVITY 2.2 Strategies for Calculating Percent

Restaurant servers are not the only people provided with tips for a job well done.

Skylar is a hair stylist at a salon. Her clients pay their bills at the front desk but give her cash for her tip. She wondered what her typical tip percent was, so she calculated the tip percent received from each client on a specific day.

WORKED EXAMPLE

Skylar's first client of the day spent $150 to have her hair dyed and cut, and gave Skylar a $30 tip.

Use a Proportion

$$\frac{t}{100} = \frac{30}{150}$$

$$t = \frac{(30)(100)}{150}$$

$$t = 20$$

Use a Percent Equation

$$(t)(150) = 30$$

$$150t = 30$$

$$\frac{150t}{150} = \frac{30}{150}$$

$$t = \frac{30}{150}$$

$$t = 0.2$$

1. **Explain why Skylar's methods result in different values for *t*. What percent tip did Skylar receive from her client?**

NOTES

2. Calculate the tip percent for Skylar's next two clients. Use both proportions and percent equations in the table shown. For each problem, isolate the variable first. Then, calculate the answer. Finally, write your answer in a complete sentence.

Salon Bill	Tip Amount	Use a Proportion	Use a Percent Equation
$80	$15		
Sentence			
$80	$10		
Sentence			

3. Describe the strategies you used to solve each proportion and each percent equation.

ACTIVITY 2.3

Strategies for Calculating the Whole

Tipping for services is not a universal standard, so some business add an automatic gratuity, or tip, onto every bill. Restaurants frequently add an 18% gratuity when the group includes 8 or more people. Some hotels, resorts, and service providers close to tourist areas often add an automatic 18% gratuity to the bill.

An esthetician is someone who is knowledgeable about skin care, particularly the face.

1. **The esthetician, manicurist, and massage therapist at the Sun and Sand Resort earn an automatic 18% gratuity on their services. Determine the value of the services each must provide in a day to earn the desired gratuity. Show your work, and then write a sentence to explain your answer.**

	Desired Gratuity	Use a Proportion	Use a Percent Equation
Esthetician	$100		
Sentence			
Manicurist	$150		
Sentence			
Massage Therapist	$200		
Sentence			

2. Crystal says that when she solved the proportions in Question 1, she could set up her proportions in any way she wanted because ratios can be written in any way. Do you agree with Crystal's statement? Explain your reasoning.

ACTIVITY
2.4 Tips and Direct Variation

A room service waiter or waitress at a hotel receives an automatic gratuity that varies directly with the amount of the food bill.

1. Suppose a room service waitress at the Sun and Sand Resort receives gratuity represented by the equation $g = 0.15b$, where g represents the gratuity and b represents the food bill.

a. What percent gratuity does the room service waitress receive? How do you know?

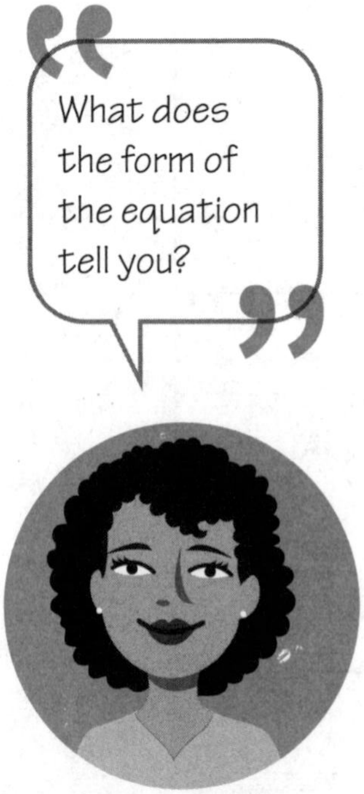

What does the form of the equation tell you?

b. If the food bill is \$19, how much tip did she receive?

c. If the room service waitress receives a \$2.10 gratuity, how much is the food bill?

2. Write an equation to represent the direct proportional relationship between the amount of gratuity (g) received by a room service waitress and the food bill (b). Let k represent the constant of proportionality. What does the constant of proportionality represent in this equation?

3. Gourmet Eatery has a policy of automatically adding an 18% tip to every restaurant bill.

   a. Write an equation to represent the relationship between the tip (t) and the restaurant bill (b).

   b. How much of a tip is added to a restaurant bill of $54? Use your equation to determine the amount of the tip.

   c. Marie receives a tip of $12. How much is the restaurant bill?

   d. If a restaurant bill is $12, how much is the tip?

   e. How much would a restaurant bill be if it had a tip of $3.20 added to it?

NOTES

ACTIVITY 2.5

Simple Interest

When you save money in a bank savings account, the bank pays you money each year and adds it to your account. This additional money is interest, and it is added to bank accounts because banks routinely use your money for other financial projects. They then pay interest for the money they borrow from you.

An original amount of money in your account is called the principal. Interest is calculated as a percent of the principal. One type of interest is **simple interest**, which is a fixed percent of the principal. Simple interest is paid over a specific period of time—either twice a year or once a year, for example. The formula for simple interest is:

$$I = P \times r \times t$$

- I: Interest earned (dollars)
- P: Principal (dollars)
- r: Interest rate (%)
- t: Time that the money earns interest (years)

WORKED EXAMPLE

For example, Kim deposits $300 into a savings account at a simple interest rate of 5% per year.

You can use the formula to calculate the interest she will have earned at the end of 3 years.

Interest = Principal × rate × time

Interest = (300)(0.05)(3)

= $45

Kim will have earned $45 in interest after 3 years.

1. **Complete the table by using your knowledge of the formula for simple interest.**

Principal Amount Saved (dollars)	Interest Rate	Time (years)	Interest Earned (dollars)
425	7%	5	
75	3%	1	
250	2%	8	
340	5%	2	
	4%	3	30.00
456	6%		109.44
500		4	120.00

In the same way that banks pay you interest when they use your money for financial projects, you too pay interest as well.

2. **When you borrow money from a bank, the amount you borrow is the principal, and you pay the interest on that money to the bank. Complete the table shown.**

Principal Borrowed (dollars)	Interest Rate	Time (years)	Interest Paid (dollars)
5000	6%	10	
450	5%	2	
1500	7%	3	
	2%	20	7200

ACTIVITY
2.6 Commissions and Proportionality

A **commission** is an amount of money a salesperson earns after selling a product. Many times, the commission is a certain percent of the product.

A car salesperson makes a 10% *commission* on each sale. A salesperson's commission is proportional to the cost of the products sold.

1. **Complete the table to show the relationship between the price of a car and the commission the salesperson receives.**

Price (dollars)	Commission (dollars)
0	
9000	
15,000	
	1000
18,000	
	2000

To help with sales goal-setting, the salesperson wants to create a visual to display in the office.

2. **Graph the relationship between the price of a car and the commission received.**

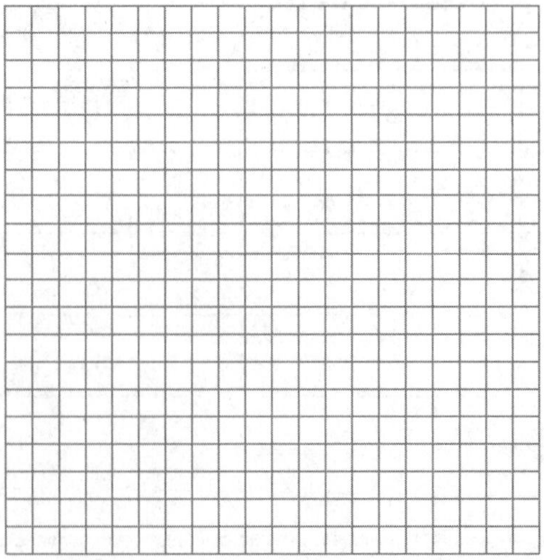

3. Explain how the graph illustrates that the relationship between car price and commission is proportional.

Because commission is proportional to the cost of products sold, you can make all kinds of predictions in these situations.

4. Define the variables and write the equation that represents the relationship between the price of a car and the commission received.

5. How much commission will the salesperson earn for selling a $25,000 car? Determine the commission using your equation.

6. If the salesperson earned a $1250 commission, what was the price of the car? Determine the price of the car using your equation.

For each commission situation, define variables for the varying quantities, write a percent equation to represent the relationship, and then answer the question.

7. **An automobile saleswoman earns 12% on all of her sales. Last month, she sold 3 cars for a total sales amount of $28,950. What is her commission?**

8. **A real estate agent earns 6% of the selling price of each house he sells. If he sells a home for $250,000, how much of a commission will he make?**

9. If a car salesman made $2450 from a 12% commission on a car sale, what is the cost of the car he sold?

10. A real estate agent made $7500 on a $150,000 home sale. What was the percent of her commission?

NOTES

TALK the TALK

Where's Bob?

Each of the restaurant receipts shown includes a missing meal total of a guest who paid a specific percent of the total bill. The tip amount for each table is also provided. Use the receipts to answer the questions.

Table 1

Guest 1:

Guest 2: $18.00

Guest 3: $12.00

Tip: $4.96

Table 2

Guest 1: $38.45

Guest 2: $34.81

Guest 3:

Tip: $14.65

Table 3

Guest 1: $18.22

Guest 2:

Guest 3: $41.00

Tip: $11.74

Table 4

Guest 1: $35.11

Guest 2: $35.05

Guest 3:

Tip: $15.90

1. **Bob ate at a restaurant one night with 2 friends. The cost of his meal was 10% of the total food bill but not clearly shown on the receipt. He knows that his group tipped either 15% or 18%, but he's not sure which. At which table did Bob sit and what was the cost of his meal? What percent did his table tip?**

2. **Assume, instead, that the mystery guest at each table paid 20% of the total bill. Determine the total bill and what percent tip each table gave their waitstaff.**

Assignment

Write

Explain how to solve for any unknown with a percent equation.

Remember

When a tip, gratuity, or commission varies directly with the cost of the product, you can represent the situation using the equation $t = kb$, where t represents the amount of tip, gratuity, or commission, k represents the percent of tip, and b represents the total cost of the product.

Practice

1. Ben recently purchased a new home. In order to be able to afford the home, he came up with a budget that breaks down his monthly income as follows: 30% for housing, 20% for food, 22% for utilities, 10% for savings, 6% for entertainment, and 12% for personal items. Ben has a net income of $4000 per month. Calculations for budget are identical to calculations for tips and commissions. Use what you know about computing tips and commissions to answer each question. For each question,
   - set up and solve a proportion,
   - set up and solve a percent equation, and
   - write a sentence to explain your answer.

   a. Calculate the amount of money that Ben will have each month for his most essential budget items: housing, food, and utilities.
   b. Last month Ben spent $380 on food and $420 on personal items. What percent of his monthly income did he spend on these items?
   c. After 5 years, Ben's income has undergone several increases. Last month, Ben put $600 in savings, which was 10% of his net income. What is Ben's new monthly net income?
   d. Ben would like to purchase a new home. He figures out that his monthly housing costs for the new home will be $2100 per month. If he wants to keep the housing costs as 30% of his budget, what will his monthly net income need to be?
2. Joan receives a 4% commission on the merchandise she sells in a department store.
   a. Write an equation to represent the relationship between the total sales (s) and the commission (c) received.
   b. How much commission would Joan receive if the merchandise she sold totaled $139?
   c. How much would Joan have to sell to earn a commission of $100?
3. Serena deposits $1200 into a savings account that earns simple interest. The interest is applied to her account at the end of each year. Complete the table.

Year	Principal Balance	Interest Rate	Interest Earned
1	$1200	2%	
2	$1224	2%	
3		3%	

4. In the community of Greendale, a local restaurant allows student-based clubs to host fundraising nights. The organizations must hand out flyers ahead of time, and the customers who come to dine at the restaurant must present the flyer with their order. The restaurant will donate 15% of the total sales to the organization.
   a. If the sales total $8000, how much will the organization make?
   b. Write an equation to represent the relationship between the dinner sales *(d)* and the amount *(A)* the organization will receive.
   c. What is the constant of proportionality? Interpret the constant of proportionality for this problem situation.
   d. What were the total dinner sales if the organization was given $885 by the restaurant? Explain your reasoning.
5. A restaurant also donates a percentage of its total sales for the entire day to a local soup kitchen. The table shows the total sales for different days and the amount that was donated to the soup kitchen.

Total Sales (in dollars)	Amount Donated (in dollars)
10,400	416
14,300	572
15,500	620
18,300	732

   a. What percent of the total sales does the restaurant donate to the soup kitchen? How do you know?
   b. Write an equation to represent the relationship between the total sales *(s)* and the amount donated to the soup kitchen *(d)*.
   c. What is the constant of proportionality? Interpret the constant of proportionality for this problem situation.
   d. If the restaurant donated $690 to the soup kitchen, what were the total sales for the day?

Stretch

AnnaMarie goes to dinner at a restaurant where the sales tax on meals is 9%. She leaves a tip that is 175% of the amount of sales tax. If her total bill is $45, what was the cost of her meal and what percent tip did she leave?

Review

1. Lyndi has started a home business making and selling all natural goat milk soaps.
   a. If the cost of the materials for a basic bar of soap is $2.50 and Lyndi sells each bar of soap for $4.50, what is the markup percent?
   b. Lyndi sells intricately shaped holiday soaps for $9 each. After each holiday, she marks the related soaps down to $6.75. What percent discount should she advertise on her social media site?
2. Alexander is selling homemade granola to raise money to support having a pet iguana. He makes a batch of granola and then divides it into 14 individual bags for sale. The total cost of the ingredients is $35.
   a. Alexander sells each bag at a markup of 50%. How much does each bag cost? How much money does Alexander make?
   b. If Alexander has not sold all of the granola after 3 days, he sells the remaining bags for 60% of the cost. What is the sale price of the individual bags of granola?
3. Jameer works in a men's clothing store. The amount of money *(m)* he makes is directly proportional to the number of hours *(h)* he works.
   a. Complete the table to show the amount of money Jameer earns for different amounts of time that he works.
   b. Determine the constant of proportionality.
   c. Write an equation to show the relationship between m and h.
   d. How many hours does Jameer have to work to make $100?
   e. How much money does Jameer earn if he works 40 hours?

Hours (*h*)	Money (*m*) (in dollars)
3	
	56.25
6	75.00
7.5	

4. Determine the volume of the (a) cube and (b) rectangular prism.

a.

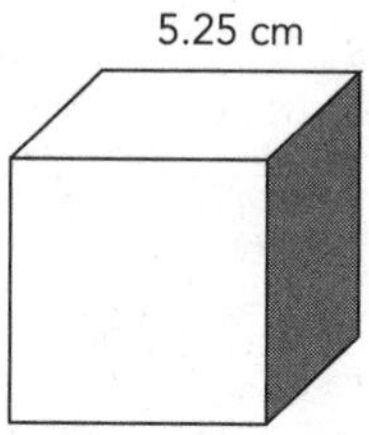

b.

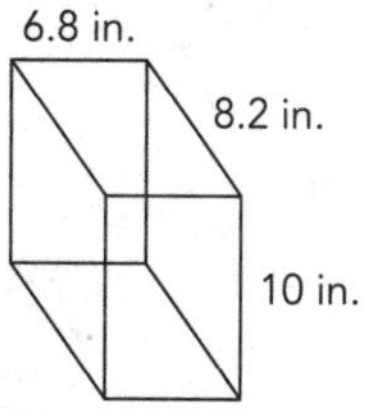

No Taxation Without Calculation

3

Sales Tax, Income Tax, and Fees

WARM UP

Use the Distributive Property to rewrite each product. Then simplify the product. Round to the nearest penny.

1. \$7.80(1 + 0.055)

2. \$36.41(1 + 0.047)

3. \$22(1 + 0.07)

LEARNING GOALS

- Use proportional reasoning to calculate sales tax and income tax amounts.
- Solve sales tax and income tax problems by determining the tax amount, percent, or amount taxed.
- Use proportionality to solve multistep ratio and percent problems involving taxes and fees by writing equations.

KEY TERMS

- sales tax
- income tax

You have used proportionality and percent to solve problems involving price markups and markdowns, tips, and commissions. How can you apply proportional reasoning to solve problems about taxes?

Getting Started

Pay the Piper

If you have ever bought something at the store, you may have noticed that the actual cost of the item ended up being more than what was listed. This is because sales tax is often added to the purchase price. **Sales tax** is a percentage of the selling price of a good or service which is added to the price.

Sales tax percents vary from state to state, though they are usually between 4% and 7%. The percents can also change over time. Sales tax is one of the largest sources of earnings for state governments. Sales taxes fund transportation and public schools.

1. The table shown lists 13 states and the different sales tax added to every dollar of a purchase as of January 2016. Complete the table by determining the tax amount added to each purchase amount. If necessary, round your answer to the nearest penny.

State	Sales Tax (percent)	Tax on $10.00 (dollars)	Tax on $100.00 (dollars)
Indiana	7		
Florida	6		
Arizona	5.6		
Kansas	6.5		
Alabama	4		
Missouri	4.225		
Minnesota	6.875		
Oklahoma	4.5		
Utah	5.95		
Colorado	2.9		
Illinois	6.25		
North Carolina	4.75		
Nebraska	5.5		

ACTIVITY 3.1 Sales Tax

Past sales tax information for California, Maine, and Texas is shown.

California

List Price of an Item ($)	Price Including Sales Tax ($)
12	12.99
30	32.48
117	126.65
200	216.50
250	270.63
369.52	400

Texas

$y = 1.0625x$, where x is the list price and y is the price including sales tax.

Maine

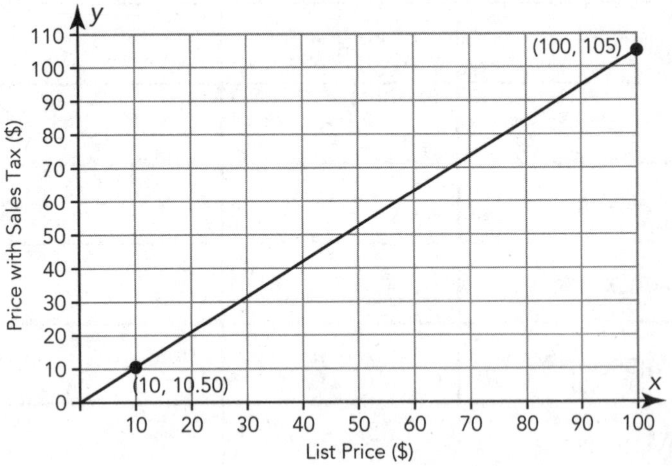

1. **Consider the three state tax representations to answer each question.**

   a. **Determine the cost, including sales tax, of an item which has a list price of $150 for each state. Show all of your work and explain your reasoning.**

   b. **Determine the list price of an item that cost $200 including sales tax for each state. Show all of your work and explain your reasoning.**

c. Which of the three states had the highest sales tax? Explain your reasoning.

d. What was the sales tax percent in each of the three states? Explain your reasoning.

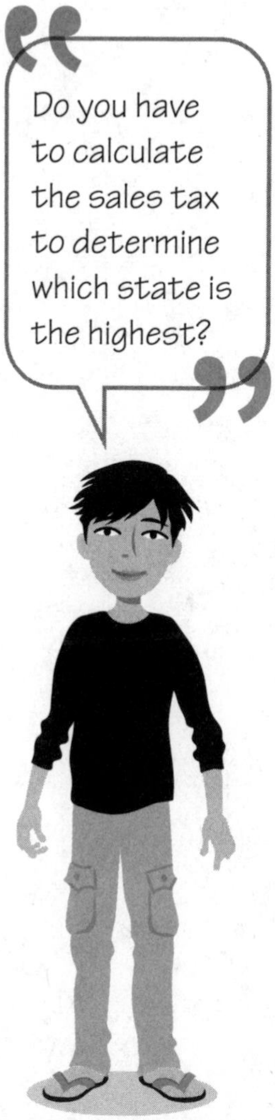

Do you have to calculate the sales tax to determine which state is the highest?

2. Consider the equation for the sales tax in Texas. Why is multiplying the list price by 1.0625 to determine the price including tax the same as calculating the sales tax and then adding it to the list price?

3. The table shows the price of several products and the amount of sales tax added to the price in Pennsylvania.

Cost of Product (dollars)	Sales Tax (dollars)
16	0.96
20	1.20
80	4.80

a. What percent is Pennsylvania's sales tax? How do you know?

b. How much sales tax would there be on a $750 flat screen TV? Show how you determined your answer.

c. If the sales tax on a lawn mower is $48, how much is the cost of the mower?

ACTIVITY

3.2 Income Tax

Income tax is a percent of a person's or company's earnings that is collected by the government. State income tax is defined and applied differently according to the state in which you live. For example, in 2012, New York residents might have paid over 8% of their earnings in state income tax, while residents of Nevada and Texas did not pay state income tax.

Sales tax and income tax are often called rates. This is because they are ratios of amount taxed per dollar spent or earned.

1. If the income tax rate is 4%, determine the amount of income tax paid on an income of:

a. \$40,000.

b. \$60,000.

c. \$75,000.

2. Write an equation to describe the amount of income tax paid on an income of *x* dollars if the income tax rate is 4%.

3. Suppose the income tax rate is 6%. Determine the amount of money remaining after paying income tax on an income of:

   a. $50,000.

   b. $80,000.

   c. $95,000.

4. Write an algebraic equation to describe the amount of money remaining after income tax is paid on an income of x dollars if the income tax rate is 6%.

5. Suppose the income tax rate is 5%. Determine a person's income before taxes if the amount of money taken out in taxes is:

   a. $100.

   b. $500.

   c. $2000.

6. Maxine moved out of state and just got her first job, paying $21.50 per hour. She works 40 hours per week and gets paid every 2 weeks. She pays 4% state income tax. How much does Maxine have remaining after state income tax is deducted from her paycheck?

ACTIVITY

3.3 Graphs and Fees

Tori orders yarn online to make hats for her crochet store. Because she orders her materials from out of the country, she pays a total of 20% in fees, including shipping, on each order.

1. **Identify the constant of proportionality and interpret its meaning.**

2. **Complete the table to determine the amounts Tori paid on each of the four orders shown. Then create a graph.**

Order Amount	Amount with Shipping Fee
\$10	
\$15	
\$20	
\$5	

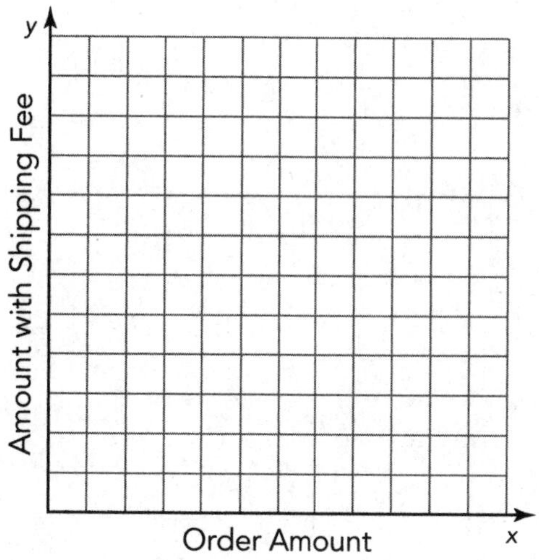

3. **Write an equation to represent the relationship between the order amount and the total amount with shipping fees.**

NOTES

TALK the TALK

Life and Taxes

You have learned about markups and markdowns, tips, discounts, commissions, fees, and taxes.

1. **What similarities and differences can you describe about all of these percent relationships?**

2. **Which of the percent relationships represent an increase from an original amount? Which represent a decrease? Explain your answers.**

Assignment

Write

Write a definition for each in your own words. Provide an example for each definition.

1. sales tax
2. income tax

Remember

When calculating the total cost of a good or service that includes sales tax (x%) multiplying the list price by ($1 + x\%$) is the same as adding the sales tax (x%) to the list price.

Practice

1. Three friends live in three different states. Monica lives in Rhode Island, Anthony lives in Ohio, and Thomas lives in Colorado.

Colorado Sales Tax	
List Price ($)	Price Including Sales Tax ($)
3.50	3.60
8.75	9.00
10.99	11.31

Ohio Sales Tax
$y = 1.055x$, where x is the sales price in dollars and y is the price including sales tax, in dollars.

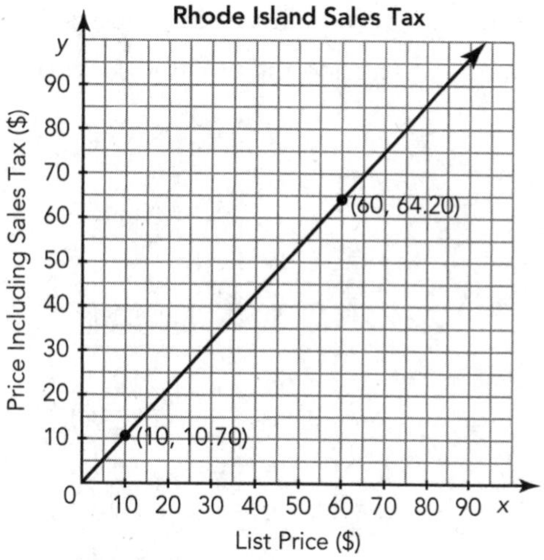

a. Determine the sales tax rate in each state. Show your work.

b. All three friends want to purchase the same gaming system so they can play games together. The list price of the gaming system is $349.99. How much will each friend pay for the gaming system?

2. Jesse earned a total of $75,000 this year. He lives in the District of Columbia where the local income tax rate is 8.5% for all incomes over $40,000.

a. How much will Jesse pay in income tax?

b. How much money will Jesse have after paying his income tax?

Stretch

In 2015, a person working in the United States paid 10% income tax for income up to $9225. Income between $9226 and $37,450 was taxed at 15%. Suppose John earns $9225. How much of his earnings does John take home after taxes? If he were to get a raise, and John's entire check was taxed at 15%, how much more would he need to earn to take home more than his current take-home pay?

Review

1. Determine each total cost, including a 20% tip, for the following bill amounts. Round to the nearest penny.
   a. $45.80
   b. $103.65
2. The graph shows how many centimeters a bamboo plant can grow and the number of hours that the plant has been growing. Determine the constant of proportionality and explain what it means.

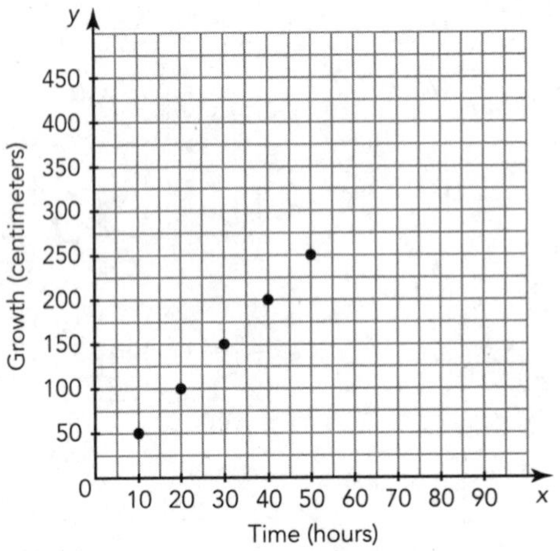

3. In the middle school and high school jazz bands, the number of girls is proportional to the total members. Write a constant of proportionality for this situation and explain what it means.

Jazz Band	Number of Girls	Total Members
Middle School	6	15
High School	8	20

4. Write each as a unit rate.
   a. $180 in 5 hours
   b. $1 in tax for $20 spent

More Ups and Downs

4

Percent Increase and Percent Decrease

WARM UP

Determine each product, rounding to the nearest penny. Describe whether the product represents an increase or decrease.

1. $\$450 \times 1.5 = y$

2. $y = \$36 \times 0.9$

3. $\$100 \times 1.1 = y$

4. $\$250 \times 0.99 = y$

LEARNING GOALS

- Calculate a percent increase and decrease.
- Calculate the depreciation in a value.
- Use proportional reasoning to solve multistep problems involving percent increases and decreases.
- Use proportional reasoning to solve multistep problems involving area, volume, and surface area of two- and three-dimensional objects.

KEY TERMS

- percent increase
- percent decrease
- appreciation
- depreciation

You have used proportional reasoning to solve percent problems, including determining markups and markdowns. How can you apply what you know to determine the percent a value has increased or decreased?

Getting Started

Up or Down?

Tell whether each situation represents an increase or a decrease in spending.

1. **A \$20 shirt is on sale for \$16.**

2. **The cost of a movie ticket in the afternoon is \$6.50, and it is \$8.00 after 5:00 p.m.**

3. **A ride-all-day amusement park ticket last season was \$27, and this season it is \$35.**

4. **The cost of lunch yesterday was \$5.50, and the cost of lunch today is \$5.25.**

ACTIVITY 4.1

Percent Increase and Decrease

NOTES

You have used percents in many different situations. You can also use percents to describe a change in quantities.

A **percent increase** occurs when the new amount is greater than the original amount, such as when stores mark up the price they pay for an item to make a greater profit.

1. **All That Glitters Jewelry Store marks up its prices so it can maximize its profits. What is the percent increase for each item? Use the formula shown to complete the table.**

$$\text{Percent Increase} = \frac{\text{Amount of Increase}}{\text{Original Amount}}$$

All That Glitters Accounting Sheet				
Item	Cost (dollars)	Customer's Price (dollars)	Difference (dollars)	Percent Increase
Initial ring	60	90		
ID bracelet	120	240		
Earrings	25	50		
Pin	36	45		

A **percent decrease** occurs when the new amount is less than the original amount. An example of a percent decrease is the amount water evaporates over time. Water evaporates at different rates, depending on the size and shape of the container it is in and the air temperature.

Evaporation is the process by which a liquid changes into a gas or vapor.

2. A science class is conducting an experiment to determine how fast water evaporates. They fill 4 differently shaped containers with water and measure the level once at the beginning of the experiment and once at the end. Use the formula shown to complete the table.

$$\text{Percent Decrease} = \frac{\text{Amount of Decrease}}{\text{Original Amount}}$$

Container	Starting Height (cm)	Ending Height (cm)	Difference (cm)	Percent Decrease
A	7.1	4.5		
B	2.3	0.9		
C	3.8	2.9		
D	9.2	7.6		

3. How do you know if the percent is a decrease or increase?

Sometimes people incorrectly use "200% increase" to mean a 100% increase.

4. How would you describe a 50 percent decrease?

5. How would you describe a 100 percent increase?

6. Jake was doing a great job at work, so his boss gave him a 20 percent raise. But then he started coming to work late and missing days, so his boss gave him a 20 percent pay cut. Jake said, "That's okay. At least I'm back to where I started."

Is Jake correct in thinking he is making the same amount of money when he received a pay cut? If you agree, explain why he is correct. If you do not agree, explain to Jake what is incorrect with his thinking and determine what percent of his original salary he is making now.

7. Analyze each student's percent reasoning.

Brett

If you multiply a number n by 0.5, that's a 50% increase, because 0.5 = 50%.

Brendon

If you multiply a number n by 1.2, that's a 20% increase:

$n \times 1.2 = n(1 + 0.2)$

$= n + 0.2n$

The expression $n + 0.2n$ means a 20% increase from n.

Martina

If you multiply a number n by 0.9, that's a 10% decrease:

$n \times 0.9 = n(1 - 0.1)$

$= n - 0.1n$

The expression $n - 0.1n$ means a 10% decrease from n.

Explain what Brett did incorrectly. What expression correctly represents a 50% increase over a number n?

8. Use Brendon's and Martina's methods to determine each percent increase or decrease.

   a. A ticket originally cost $20, but its price decreases by 20%.

   b. Shawna is making $12 per hour. She gets a 6% increase in pay.

   c. This month's rainfall is 30% less than last month's total of 3.5 inches.

   d. Yvette's family home is 1600 square feet. They hope to increase the area by 10%.

ACTIVITY
4.2

Depreciation and Proportionality

Generally, things like homes and savings accounts gain value, or appreciate over time. Other things, like cars, depreciate every year. New cars depreciate about 12% of their value each year.

Appreciation is an increase in price or value.

Depreciation is a decrease in price or value.

1. How much would a new car depreciate the first year if it costs:

a. $35,000?

b. $45,000?

c. $20,000?

2. If a car lost $3600 in depreciation in the first year, what is the original cost of this car?

3. Complete the table to record the value of a car that costs $50,000 and depreciates at the rate of 12% per year for the first five years.

Time (years)	Value of the Car (dollars)
0	50,000
1	
2	
3	
4	
5	

4. Complete the graph.

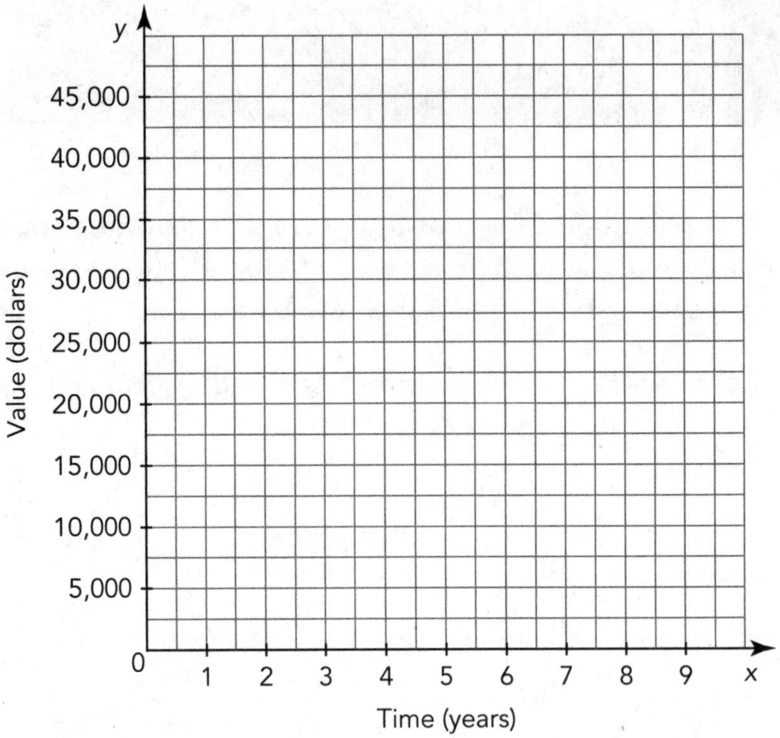

5. Would it make sense to connect the points on the graph? If so, connect the points. Explain your reasoning.

6. Describe how the value of the car decreases over time.

7. Is the relationship between time and the car's value proportional? Explain how you know using the graph and the completed table of values.

ACTIVITY 4.3

Percent Increase and Decrease with Geometry

NOTES

It is common to talk about percent increases and percent decreases when talking about money. But you can also use them when thinking geometrically.

1. **Consider the cubes shown. The side lengths of Cube B are each 20% greater than the side lengths of Cube A.**

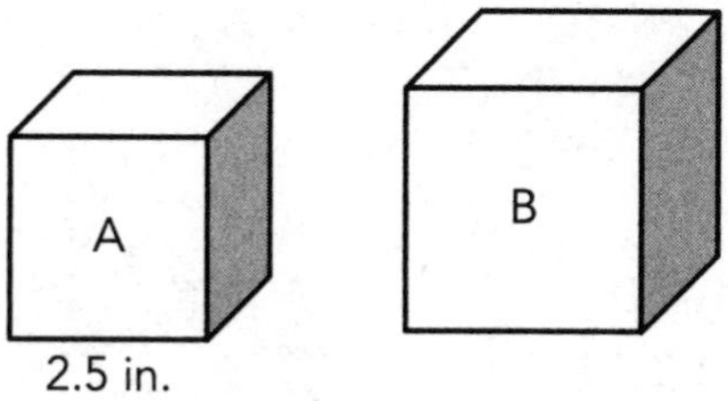

   a. **Determine the surface area of each cube. Show your work.**

   b. **Determine the volume of each cube. Show your work.**

2. What is the percent decrease in the amount of pizza, from the extra large to the large? Round to the nearest percent. Explain how you determined your answer.

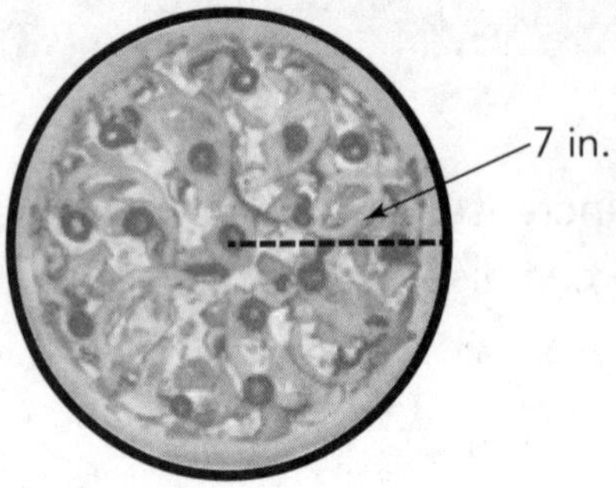

Large

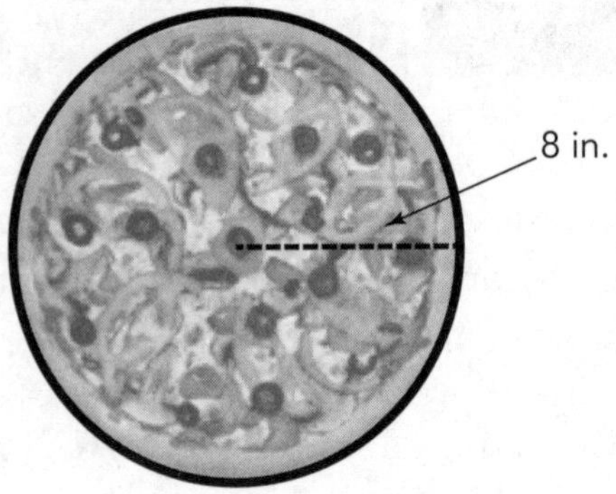

X Large

3. Elinor wanted to order an 18-inch hoagie, which cost $7.99. The sandwich shop is out of 18-inch buns. They only have 12-inch buns.

   a. What should be the percent decrease in cost of the hoagie?

   b. What should the new cost be?

NOTES

TALK the TALK

Gas Prices

The table shows the average price of gasoline per gallon in the U.S. for the years 2000 through 2015.

Year	Price ($ per gallon)	% Increase or Decrease
2000	2.02	
2001	1.91	
2002	1.75	
2003	2.01	
2004	2.32	
2005	2.74	
2006	3.00	
2007	3.16	
2008	3.61	
2009	2.58	
2010	3.02	
2011	3.75	
2012	3.80	
2013	3.62	
2014	3.40	
2015	2.45	

1. Complete the table by determining each yearly percent increase or decrease in the price of gasoline. Round to the nearest percent.

NOTES

2. Casey added together all of the increases from 2000 to 2005 and subtracted the decreases. She concluded that there was about a 35% increase in gas price from 2000 to 2005. Is Casey correct? Explain why or why not.

Assignment

Write

Write a definition for *depreciation* in your own words. Use an example in your definition.

Remember

A percent increase is calculated as a ratio of the amount of increase to the original amount.

A percent decrease is calculated as a ratio of the amount of decrease to the original amount.

Practice

Calculate each percent increase or percent decrease. Round to the nearest whole percent if necessary.

1. original amount: 30, new amount: 45
2. original amount: 12, new amount: 16
3. original amount: 17, new amount: 21
4. original amount: 85, new amount: 56
5. original amount: 48, new amount: 37
6. original amount: 124, new amount: 76

Use the given information to answer each question.

7. A dress that normally sells for $72 is on sale for $45. What is the percent decrease in the price?
8. A home purchased for $120,000 in 2012 is sold for $156,000 in 2015. What is the percent increase in the price?
9. The CD Warehouse purchases CDs for $6 each and sells them for $9 each. What is the percent increase in the price?
10. The CD Warehouse is having a clearance sale. A CD player that originally sells for $60 is now priced at $36. What is the percent decrease in the price?
11. The local high school sold 1914 tickets this year to its spring musical. That was 174 more tickets sold than last year. What is the percent increase in the number of tickets sold?
12. Ken's heart rate went from 74 beats per minute while resting to 148 beats per minute while exercising. What is the percent increase in his heart rate?

Stretch

Can you write a percent decrease as a negative ratio? Provide an example of a percent decrease written as a negative ratio and describe what it means in context.

Review

1. A T-shirt that costs \$14 without tax costs \$14.98 with tax. What is the sales tax percent?
2. A car that costs \$14,000 without tax costs \$14,700 with tax. What is the sales tax percent?
3. Identify the constant of proportionality in each situation.
   a. The temperature rises 4 degrees each hour for 10 hours.
   b. Two thirds of the floats in the parade have flowers.
4. Rewrite each algebraic expression with fewer terms.
   a. $9.5(a + 4) - a$
   b. $8 + h - 2 \times 5$

5

Pound for Pound, Inch for Inch

Scale and Scale Drawings

WARM UP

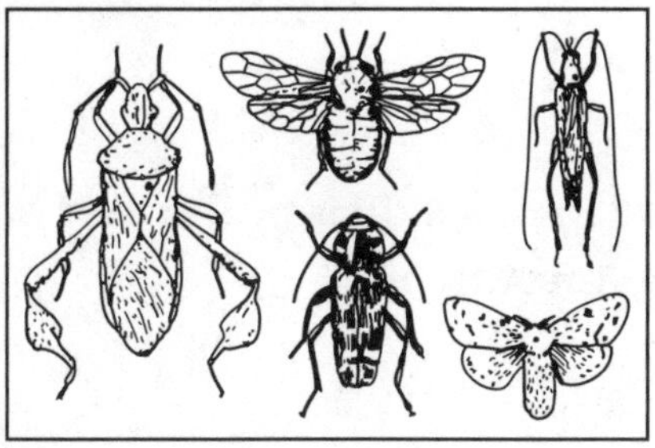

1. These bugs are not drawn to scale. What does that mean?

2. Is it possible that the leftmost bug is the smallest bug in real life? Explain your reasoning.

LEARNING GOALS

- Identify the scale of a drawing as the ratio of drawing length to actual length.
- Compute actual lengths and areas given a scale and a scale drawing.
- Reproduce a scale drawing at a different scale.
- Use concepts of proportionality to determine the scale factor used to produce a scale drawing.

KEY TERMS

- corresponding
- scale
- scale factor
- scale drawing
- similar figures

You have learned a lot about proportional relationships. You can use proportionality to solve problems with geometric figures too. How can you use proportions to investigate real-world and mathematical objects at different scales?

Getting Started

Triangle Drawings

The triangle given, Triangle *A*, is an equilateral triangle—all of its sides are the same length. Each side has a length of 4 units.

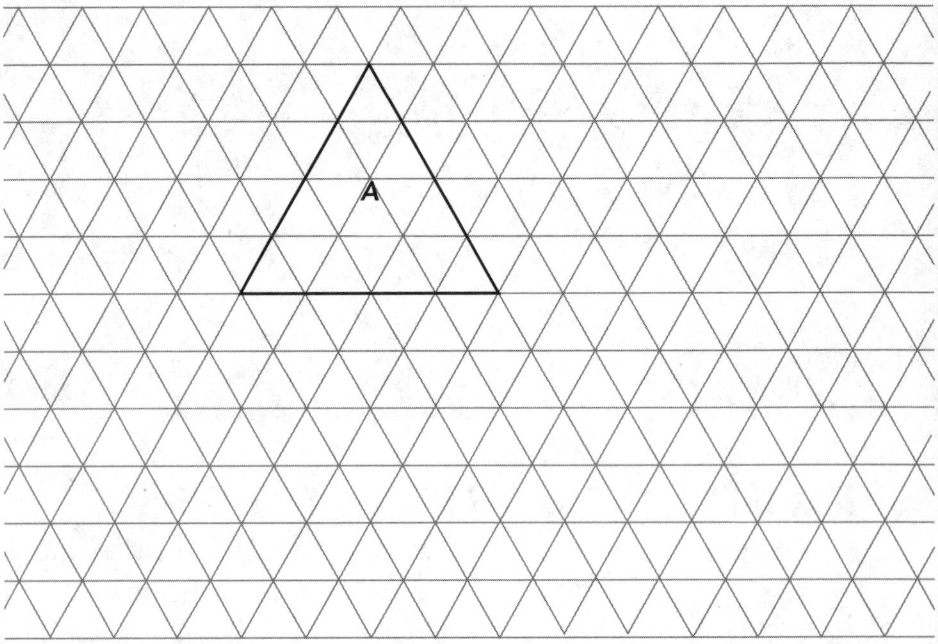

1. **Draw a new triangle, Triangle *B*, which has side lengths that are 50% the length of Triangle *A*'s side lengths.**

2. **Write each ratio to compare Triangle *B* to Triangle *A* in fraction form and as a percent. Describe the meaning of each ratio.**

   a. **Determine the ratio of corresponding side lengths for each side of the triangles.**

   b. **Determine the ratio of the triangle perimeters.**

The bottom side of the original triangle and the bottom side of the new triangle are **corresponding** sides.

ACTIVITY 5.1

Scales, Scale Factors, and Scale Drawings

A **scale** is a ratio that compares two measures. The ratios that you wrote to compare the measures of the triangles are scales.

When you multiply a measure by a scale to produce a reduced or enlarged measure, the scale is called a **scale factor**. You can multiply each of Triangle *A*'s lengths by the scale factor 1 : 2, or 50%, or $\frac{1}{2}$, to produce the side lengths for Triangle *B*.

WORKED EXAMPLE

Triangle *A*			**Triangle *B***
side length → 4 units	× 1 : 2, or $\frac{1}{2}$, or 50%	=	2 units ← side length
	↑ scale, scale factor		

1. **What scale factor is used to produce Triangle *A*'s lengths, given Triangle *B*'s lengths? Explain your reasoning.**

Triangle *A*'s side lengths are 200% of Triangle *B*'s side lengths. But they are 100% larger.

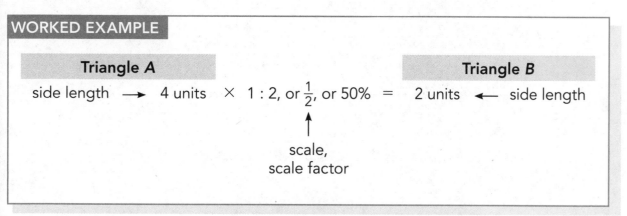

2. Draw a triangle, Triangle *C*, whose side lengths are 150% of Triangle *B*'s side lengths.

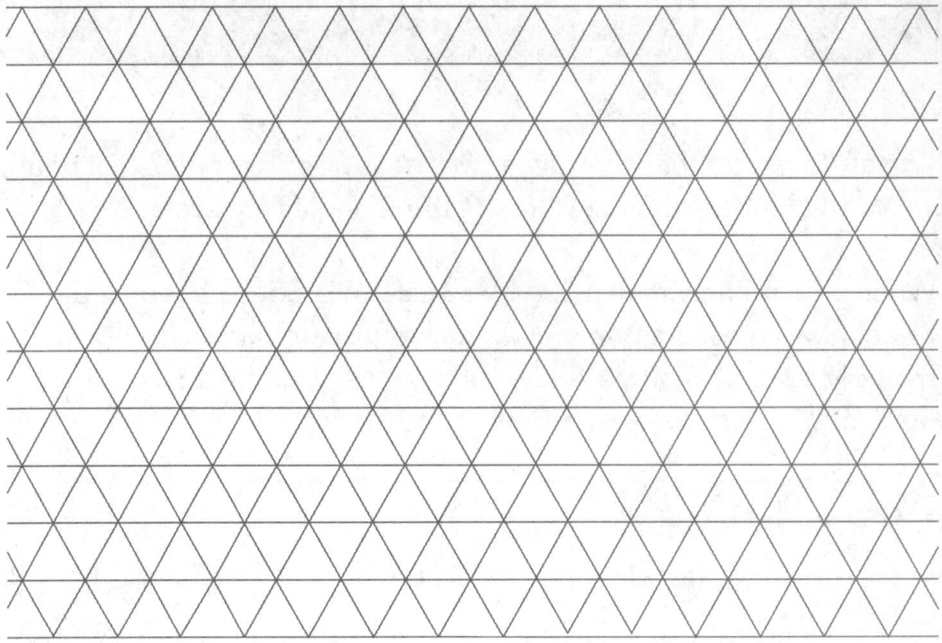

3. What scale factor is used to produce:

   a. Triangle *C*'s lengths given Triangle *B*'s lengths?

   b. Triangle *B*'s lengths given Triangle *C*'s lengths?

   c. Triangle *C*'s lengths given Triangle *A*'s lengths?

4. Compare the perimeters of Triangles *A*, *B*, and *C*. How did the scale factors affect the perimeters? Explain your reasoning.

A **scale drawing** is a representation of a real object or place that is in proportion to the real object or place it represents. The purpose of a scale drawing is to represent either a very large or very small object. The scales on scale drawings often use different units of measure.

NOTES

WORKED EXAMPLE

The scale of a drawing might be written as:

1 cm : 4 ft

↗ Drawing Length ↖ Actual Length

This scale means that every 1 centimeter of length in the drawing represents 4 feet of the length of the actual object.

The scale of a map might look like this:

1 in. : 200 mi

↗ Map Distance ↖ Actual Distance

This scale means that every 1 inch of distance on the map represents 200 miles of actual distance.

5. Study the worked example. What scale factor is used to produce:

a. the drawing length given the actual length?

b. the map distance given the actual distance?

6. Write a sentence to describe the meaning of each.

   a. A scale on a map is 1 in. : 2 mi.

   b. A scale on a drawing is 1 cm : 4 cm.

   c. A scale on a drawing is 2 in. : 1 in.

   d. A scale on a drawing is 1 cm : 1 cm.

7. The scale factor for a model car is 1 : 24. What does this mean?

8. The scale factor for a model train is 1 : 87. What does this mean?

ACTIVITY
5.2 Creating Scale Drawings

In this activity you will reproduce two different scale drawings at a different scale.

A grid length can be anything you want. But make it the same for both grids.

1. The rectangle shown is drawn at a scale of 1 in. : 2 ft.

1 in. : 2 ft

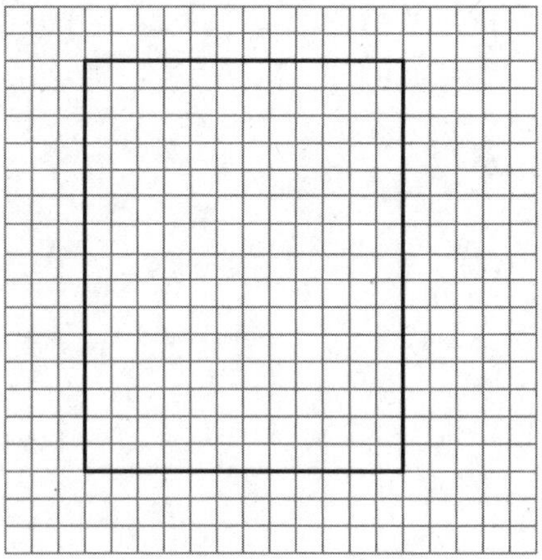

1 in. : 3 ft

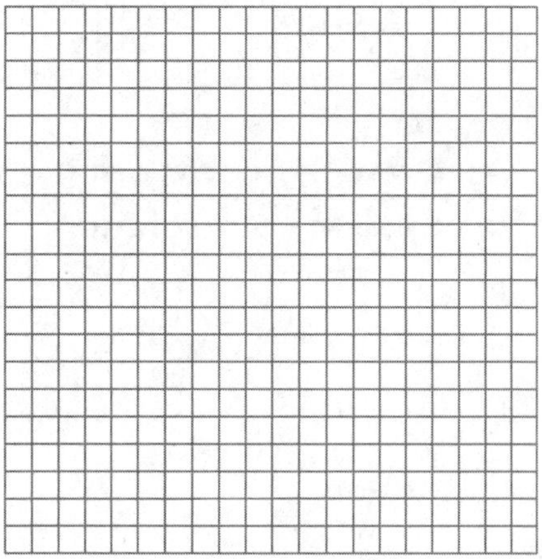

a. Draw the rectangle using a scale of 1 in. : 3 ft. Explain your solution.

b. Did you enlarge the rectangle or reduce the rectangle?

c. Show how to calculate the actual dimensions of the rectangle using each scale.

2. The circle shown is drawn at a scale of 2 cm : 3 mi.

2 cm : 3 mi

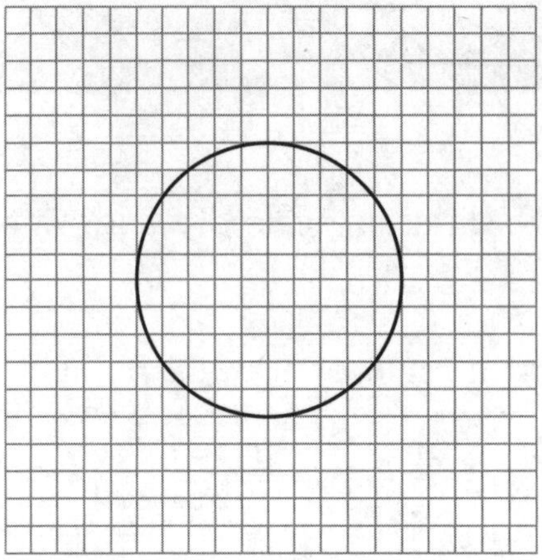

4 cm : 5 mi

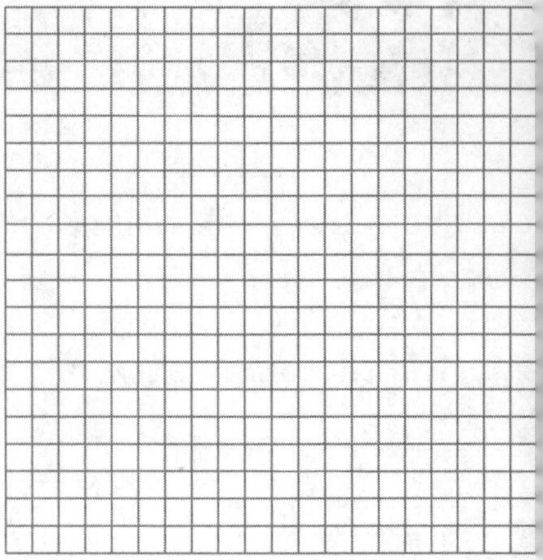

a. Draw the circle using a scale of 4 cm : 5 mi. Explain your solution.

b. Did you enlarge the circle or reduce the circle?

c. Show how to calculate the actual diameter of the circle using each scale.

ACTIVITY
5.3 Similar Figures

Figures that are proportional in size, or that have proportional dimensions, are called **similar figures**.

When Timmons Photo Company prints photo packages, they include several sizes of photos that are all mathematically similar. The largest size is 12 in. × 16 in. This is read as "12 inches by 16 inches." The first measure is the width of the photo, and the second measure is the height of the photo.

Fran and Joe determined the width of a mathematically similar photo that has a height of 8 inches.

Fran

To determine the unknown width of the smaller photo, I wrote ratios using the measurements from within each photo. The ratio on the left contains the measurements of the large photo. The ratio on the right contains the measurements of the smaller photo.

$$\frac{\text{width of larger photo}}{\text{height of larger photo}} = \frac{\text{width of smaller photo}}{\text{height of smaller photo}}$$

$$\frac{12 \text{ inches}}{16 \text{ inches}} = \frac{x \text{ inches}}{8 \text{ inches}}$$

$$(12)(8) = (16)(x)$$

$$96 = 16x$$

$$6 = x$$

I calculated that the width of the smaller photo is 6 inches.

Joe

To determine the unknown width of the smaller photo, I wrote ratios using the measurements between the two photos. The ratio on the left contains the width measurements of both photos. The ratio on the right contains the height measurements of both photos.

$$\frac{\text{width of larger photo}}{\text{width of smaller photo}} = \frac{\text{height of larger photo}}{\text{height of smaller photo}}$$

$$\frac{12 \text{ inches}}{x \text{ inches}} = \frac{16 \text{ inches}}{8 \text{ inches}}$$

$$(12)(8) = (x)(16)$$

$$96 = 16x$$

$$6 = x$$

I calculated that the width of the smaller photo is 6 inches.

NOTES

1. What is similar about the two solution methods? What is different about the two solution methods?

2. Determine other possible photo sizes that are mathematically similar.

a. 2 in. × ______

b. 3 in. × ______

c. ______ × 2 in.

d. 4 in. × ______

e. ______ × 3.5 in.

ACTIVITY
5.4

Calculating with Map Scales

A map of the United States is shown. A scale is included on the map.

Determine the approximate distances between the locations. Write the distances in miles and kilometers.

1. Washington, D.C., to San Francisco, California

2. Washington, D.C., to Seattle, Washington

3. Washington, D.C., to your state capital ______________

4. Chicago, Illinois, to Los Angeles, California

5. Augusta, Maine, to Austin, Texas

6. Which is longer, a mile or a kilometer? How can you tell?

7. How many kilometers make one mile? Explain how you determined your answer.

8. How many days would it take to travel from Washington, D.C., to San Francisco, California, traveling at 60 miles per hour for 8 hours per day? Show your work.

9. Does your response to Question 8 seem realistic? Explain your reasoning.

ACTIVITY 5.5

Calculating the Scale for a Blueprint

A blueprint is an example of a scale drawing that represents a larger structure. The blueprint shown represents a plan for a new house.

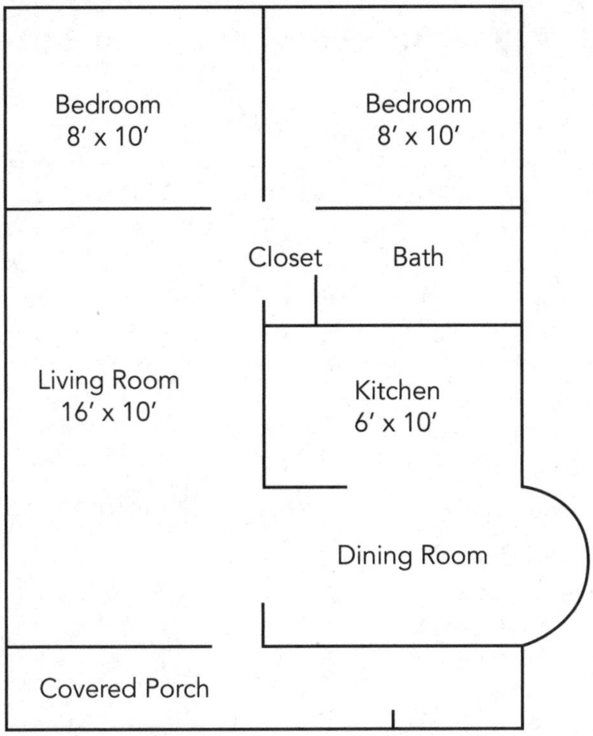

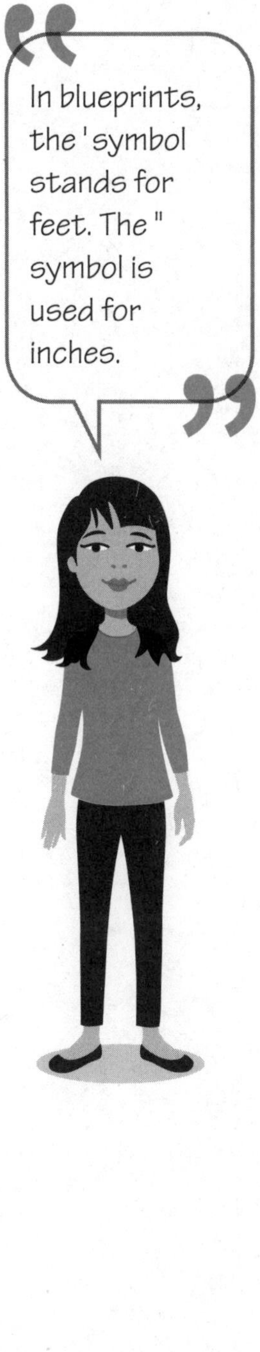

In blueprints, the ' symbol stands for feet. The " symbol is used for inches.

1. Use a centimeter ruler to determine the scale factor used to create the blueprint. Show your work.

2. **Explain why Marty's reasoning is incorrect. Then, determine the actual area of the covered porch.**

> **Marty**
>
> The covered porch measures approximately 2.8 cm by 6 cm.
>
> $2.8 \times 6 = 16.8 \text{ cm}^2$
>
> $16.8 \times \frac{10}{3} = 56$, so the actual area of the covered porch is 56 ft^2.

3. **Determine the approximate area of the dining room. Show your work.**

NOTES

TALK the TALK

Interpreting Scales

1. Which scale would produce the largest scale drawing of an object when compared to the actual object? Explain your reasoning.

   1 in. : 25 in.
   1 cm : 1 m
   1 in. : 1 ft

2. Which scale would produce the smallest scale drawing of an object when compared to the actual object? Explain your reasoning.

   1 in. : 10 in.
   1 cm : 10 cm
   1 mm : 1 m

NOTES

3. The scale of a drawing is 6 cm : 1 mm. Is the scale drawing larger or smaller than the actual object or place? Explain your reasoning.

4. Given a scale of $\frac{5}{4}$, explain how you can tell whether the drawing is bigger or smaller than the actual object.

Assignment

Write

Write the term that best completes each sentence.

1. The purpose of a(n) ______________ is to create an accurate drawing of either a very large or very small object.
2. Two geometric figures that are proportional in size are ______________ figures.
3. The "bottom" sides of two similar triangles are ______________ sides.

Remember

A scale is a ratio that compares two measures.

When you multiply a measure by a scale to produce a reduced or enlarged measure, the scale is called a scale factor.

Practice

1. Brent and Margaret are planning a trip to the city of Chicago. The map shown includes several destinations they would like to visit while they are there. A scale is included on the map.

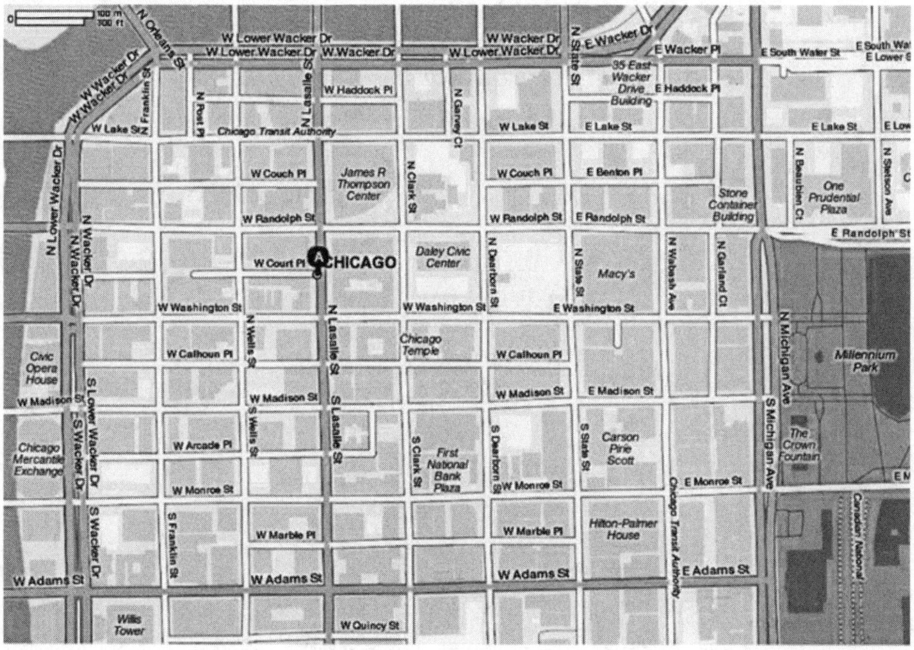

a. According to the map, which is longer, a meter or a foot? How can you tell?

b. By following the shortest route along the roads, determine the distance from the Civic Opera House to the Chicago Temple. Write your answer in meters and in feet.

c. Use the distances you approximated from the Opera House to the Temple to determine the approximate number of feet that are in one meter. Explain your answer.

d. By following the shortest route along the roads, determine the distance from the Crown Fountain to the James R. Thompson Center. Write your answer in meters and in feet.

e. By following the shortest route along the roads, determine the distance from the Chicago Mercantile Exchange to Macy's. Write your answer in meters and in feet.

f. Use the distances you approximated from the Chicago Mercantile Exchange to Macy's to determine the approximate number of meters that are in one foot. Explain your answer.

2. While in Chicago, Brent and Margaret plan on visiting the Willis Tower, built as and still commonly referred to as the Sears Tower.
   a. In the lobby, there is a model of the Sears Tower that has an observation deck with a height of 4 meters. If the actual height of the observation deck is 412 meters, what is the scale of the model?
   b. Brent and Margaret decide to buy a toy replica of the Sears Tower in the gift shop to take home to their neighbors. The toy replica has a scale of 1 inch : 200 feet. Is this replica larger or smaller than the model in the lobby?
   c. If the toy replica from the gift shop is 7.25 inches tall, what is the height in feet of the actual Sears Tower? Show your work.

Stretch

You may have seen the star Betelgeuse (BEETLE juice) in the night sky. It is a red giant star, which has a radius of 821.3 million kilometers. By comparison, our Sun has a radius of 0.5 million kilometers.

Suppose the circle shown represents our Sun. How big would the model of Betelgeuse be if you drew it to scale?

Review

1. Determine each percent increase or decrease.
   a. Original: \$340 New: \$34
   b. Original: 75 New: 225
2. Solve each proportion.
   a. $\frac{4}{x} = 9$
   b. $\frac{7.5}{26} = \frac{75}{p}$
3. Graph each inequality on a number line.
   a. $x > 7$
   b. $-12 \leq x$

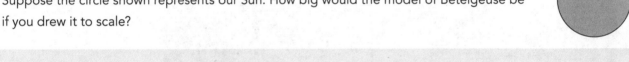

Proportional Relationships Summary

KEY TERMS

- markdown
- markup
- percent equation
- simple interest
- commission
- sales tax
- income tax
- percent increase
- percent decrease
- appreciation
- depreciation
- corresponding
- scale
- scale factor
- scale drawing
- similar figures

LESSON 1 Markups and Markdowns

A percent scenario can be represented by a model.

For example, suppose a dress originally cost \$36. Annika pays \$27 for the dress during a sale. What percent does Annika save with the sale?

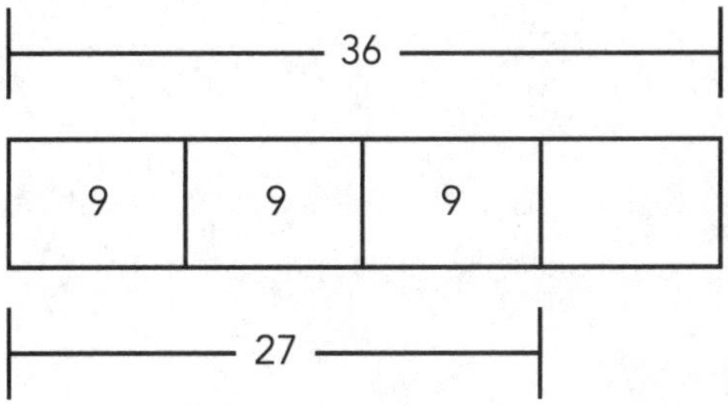

The model represents the scenario and can be used to solve the problem. The amount Annika saves is one-fourth the total amount of the dress, so she saves 25%.

You can write a percent as a proportion.

For example, using the same scenario above, you can set up the proportion $\frac{\text{part}}{\text{whole}} = \frac{\text{percent number}}{100}$.

$$\frac{x}{100} = \frac{27}{36}$$

$$36x = (100)(27)$$

$$\frac{36x}{36} = \frac{2700}{36}$$

$$x = 75$$

Annika paid 75% of the cost, so she saved 25%.

When businesses sell an item at lower price than the original price, the reduction in price is called a **markdown**. To make money, businesses often buy products from a wholesaler or distributor for one amount and add to that amount to determine the price they use to sell the product to their customers. This increase in price is called a **markup**.

For example, a store marks up all of its prices by 25% to sell to its customers. If the store's cost for an item is $16, what is the customer's cost?

$$\frac{25}{100} = \frac{x}{16}$$

$$x = 4$$

The customer's cost is $16 + $4 = $20.

The answer to the percent problem may or may not be the value of the unknown in your proportion. Re-read the problem and ensure that you answer the question being asked.

LESSON 2

Perks of Work

You can use a percent equation to determine the percent of a whole. A **percent equation** can be written in the form percent × whole = part, where the percent is often written as a decimal.

For example, suppose you want to leave a 15% tip on a restaurant bill of $45.

The amount of tip you should leave is $6.75.

$$\text{percent} = \frac{\text{part}}{\text{whole}}$$

percent	×	whole	=	part
(tip percent)	of	(total bill)	=	amount of tip
↑		↑		↑
$\frac{15}{100}$ or 0.15	×	45	=	t
		6.75	=	t

Simple interest is a fixed percent of an original amount of money called the principal. The formula for simple interest is:

$$I = P \times r \times t$$

- I: Interest earned (dollars)
- P: Principal (dollars)
- r: Interest rate (%)
- t: Time that the money earns interest (years)

A **commission** is an amount of money a salesperson earns after selling a product. Many times, the commission is a certain percent of the product.

For example, a car salesperson's commission varies directly with the cost of the products sold. Determine the percent commission the salesperson makes.

Price (dollars)	Commission (dollars)
0	0
7000	700
12,000	1200
23,000	2300

In this scenario, the constant of proportionality is equal to the percent commission, and $k = \frac{700}{7000} = 0.1$. The salesperson makes 10% commission.

When a tip, gratuity, or commission varies directly with the cost of the product, you can represent the situation using the equation $t = kb$, where t represents the amount of tip, gratuity, or commission, k represents the percent, and b represents the total cost of the product.

LESSON 3 No Taxation Without Calculation

A percent relationship can represent an increase or decrease from an original amount.

Sales tax is a percent of the selling price of a good or service that is added to the price. When calculating the total cost of a good or service that includes sales tax (x%), multiplying the list price by (1 + x%) is the same as adding the sales tax (x%) to the list price.

Income tax is a percent of a person's or company's earnings that is collected by the government. When calculating the total income after income tax (x%) is taken out, multiplying the income by (1 − x%) is the same as subtracting the income tax (x%) from the income.

Sales Tax	Income Tax
Rick wants to buy a pair of shoes for \$60. The sales tax in his state is 6%. What is the total price Rick will pay for the shoes, including sales tax?	Gia earned an income of \$40,000 this year. The income tax rate in her state is 5%. How much will Gia keep after income tax is taken out?
Multiply the list price by (1 + 0.06). \$60 × 1.06 = \$63.60	Multiply the income by (1 − x%). S40,000 × 0.95 = \$38,000
Rick will pay \$63.60 in total.	Gia will keep \$38,000.

LESSON 4

More Ups and Downs

A **percent increase** occurs when the new amount is greater than the original amount, such as when stores mark up the price they pay for an item to make a greater profit. A percent increase is calculated as a ratio of the amount of increase to the original amount.

For example, if you multiply a whole amount n by 1.2, that is a 20% increase.

$$n \times 1.2 = n(1 + 0.2) = n + 0.2n$$

The expression $n + 0.2n$ means a 20% increase from n.

A **percent decrease** occurs when the new amount is less than the original amount. A percent decrease is calculated as a ratio of the amount of decrease to the original amount.

For example, if you multiply a whole amount n by 0.9, that is a 10% decrease.

$$n \times 0.9 = n(1 - 0.1) = n - 0.1n$$

The expression $n - 0.1n$ means a 10% decrease from n.

Generally, things such as homes and savings accounts gain value, or appreciate, over time. **Appreciation** is an increase in price or value. Other things, such as cars, depreciate every year. **Depreciation** is a decrease in price or value.

You can use percent increases and decreases when thinking geometrically.

For example, what is the percent decrease in the area from Circle *A* to Circle *B*?

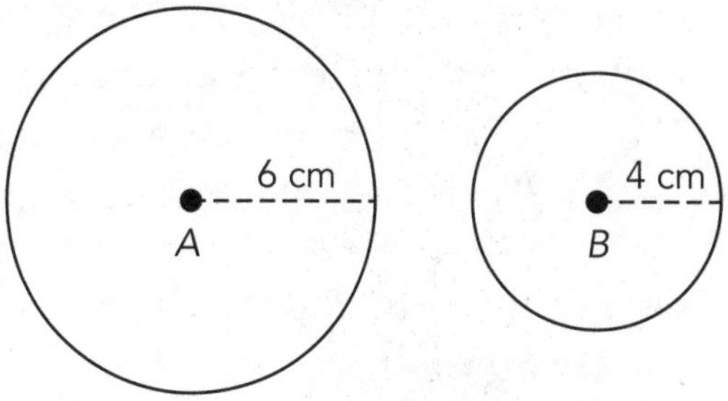

The area of Circle $A = 36\pi$ square units.

The area of Circle $B = 16\pi$ square units.

$36\pi - 16\pi = 20\pi$

$\frac{20\pi}{36\pi} \approx 0.56$

The percent decrease in the area is about 56%.

LESSON
5

Pound for Pound, Inch for Inch

A **scale** is a ratio that compares two measures. When you multiply a measure by a scale to produce a reduced or enlarged measure, the scale is called a **scale factor**.

For example, Triangle *A* is an equilateral triangle with side lengths of 4 units. If Triangle *A* is reduced by 50% to create Triangle *B*, what will be the side lengths of Triangle *B*? You can multiply each of Triangle *A*'s lengths by the scale factor 1 : 2, or 50%, or $\frac{1}{2}$, to produce the side lengths for Triangle *B*.

Triangle *A*				Triangle *B*
side length → 4 units	×	1 : 2, or $\frac{1}{2}$, or 50%	=	2 units ← side length
		↑ scale, scale factor		

If you draw Triangle *A* and Triangle *B*, the bottom sides of the triangles are **corresponding** sides.

A **scale drawing** is a representation of a real object or place that is in proportion to the real object or place it represents. The scales on scale drawings often use different units of measure.

For example, the scale of a drawing might be written: 1 cm : 4 ft. This scale means that every 1 centimeter of length in the drawing represents 4 feet of length of the actual object or place. The scale of a map might be written: 1 in. : 200 mi. This scale means that every 1 inch of distance on the map represents 200 miles of actual distance.

Figures that are proportional in size, or that have proportional dimensions, are called **similar figures**.

For example, a rectangle has a height of 20 inches and a width of 15 inches. Determine the width of a mathematically similar rectangle that has a height of 16 inches.

$$\frac{\text{height of larger rectangle}}{\text{height of smaller rectangle}} = \frac{\text{width of larger rectangle}}{\text{width of smaller rectangle}}$$

$$\frac{20 \text{ inches}}{16 \text{ inches}} = \frac{15 \text{ inches}}{x \text{ inches}}$$

$$(20)(x) = (15)(16)$$

$$20x = 240$$

$$x = 12$$

The width of the similar rectangle is 12 inches.

MODULE 2

OPERATING WITH SIGNED NUMBERS

The lessons in this module build on your experiences with signed numbers and absolute value in grade 6. You will use physical motion, number line models, and two-color counters to develop an understanding of the rules for operating with positive and negative numbers. You will then solve real-world and mathematical problems involving positive and negative rational numbers.

TOPIC 1

Adding and Subtracting Rational Numbers

Death Valley has some very high and very low elevations: Badwater Basin is the point of the lowest elevation in North America, at 282 feet below sea level, while Telescope Peak in the Panamint Range has an elevation of 11,043 feet.
Photo by Tuxyso / Wikimedia Commons, CC BY-SA 3.0, https://commons.wikimedia.org/w/index.php?curid=28603629

Module 2: Operating with Signed Numbers

TOPIC 1: ADDING AND SUBTRACTING RATIONAL NUMBERS

In this topic, students use number lines and two-color counters to model addition and subtraction of integers before developing rules for determining the sum and difference of signed numbers. Students are expected to make connections among the representations used. After they understand what it means to add and subtract integers, students apply the rules to the set of rational numbers.

Where have we been?

In grade 6, students learned how to represent positive and negative rational numbers on a number line. They also know that $-p$ is p units from 0 on the number line and that $|p| = |-p| = p$. Students used number lines to model the distance from 0 and to model the distance between two rational numbers represented on vertical or horizontal number lines.

Where are we going?

Students will develop a strong conceptual foundation for adding and subtracting with rational numbers to provide the foundation for manipulating and representing increasingly complex numeric and algebraic expressions in later lessons and future courses and grades.

Using a Number Line to Model Adding and Subtracting Integers

A number line can be used to model adding and subtracting negative numbers. This number line models the sum $5 + (-8)$.

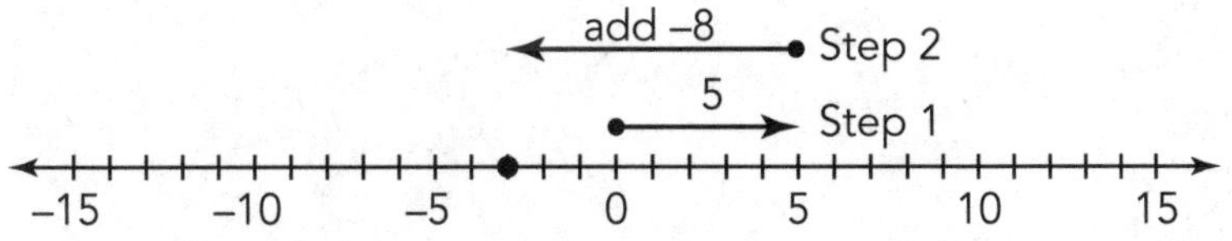

Myth: Students only use 10% of their brains.

Hollywood is in love with the idea that humans only use a small portion of their brains. This notion formed the basis of the movies *Lucy* (2014) and *Limitless* (2011). Both films ask the audience: Imagine what you could accomplish if you could use 100% of your brain!

Well, this isn't Hollywood, and you're stuck with an ordinary brain. The good news is that you **do** use 100% of your brain. As you look around the room, your visual cortex is busy assembling images; your motor cortex is busy moving your neck; and all of the associative areas recognize the objects that you see. Meanwhile, the corpus callosum, which is a thick band of neurons that connect the two hemispheres, ensures that all of this information is kept coordinated. Moreover, the brain does this automatically, which frees up space to ponder deep, abstract concepts...like mathematics!

#mathmythbusted

Talking Points

You can further support your student's learning by asking questions about the work they do in class or at home. Your student is learning to reason using signed numbers.

Questions to Ask

- How does this problem look like something you did in class?
- Can you show me the strategy you used to solve this problem? Do you know another way to solve it?
- Does your answer make sense? How do you know?
- Is there anything you don't understand? How can you use today's lesson to help?

Key Terms

absolute value

The absolute value of a number is its distance from 0 on a number line.

additive inverse

The additive inverse of a number is the opposite of the number: $-x$ is the additive inverse of x. Two numbers with the sum of zero are called additive inverses.

zero pair

A zero pair is a pair of numbers whose sum is zero. The value of negative 1 plus positive 1 is zero. So, negative 1 and positive 1 together are a zero pair.

1

Math Football

Using Models to Understand Integer Addition

WARM UP

Sketch a number line and plot each value.

1. -3
2. 0
3. 1
4. $\frac{1}{2}$
5. 3

LEARNING GOALS

- Represent numbers as positive and negative integers.
- Use a number line diagram to represent the sum of positive and negative integers.

You have learned about negative numbers and can plot locations on a number line. Does addition and subtraction work the same with negative numbers as with positive numbers?

Getting Started

Hut! Hut! Hike!

The playing field and footballs are located at the end of the lesson. You also need two number cubes, one red and one black.

You and a partner are going to play **Math Football**. You will take turns rolling two number cubes to determine how many yards you can advance the football toward your end zone.

Player 1 will be the Home Team and Player 2 will be the Visiting Team. In the first half, the Home Team will move toward the Home end zone, and the Visiting Team will move toward the Visiting end zone.

Rules
Players both start at the zero yard line and take turns. On your turn, roll two number cubes, one red and one black. The number on each cube represents a number of yards. Move your football to the left the number of yards shown on the red cube. Move your football to the right the number of yards shown on the black cube. Start each of your next turns from the ending position of your previous turn.

Scoring
When players reach their end zone, they score 6 points. If players reach their opponent's end zone, they lose 2 points. An end zone begins on either the +10 or −10 yard line.

Example:

	Player	Starting Position	Results of the Number Cubes Roll	Ending Position
First Turn	Home Team	0	Red 3 and Black 5	+2
	Visiting Team	0	Red 5 and Black 6	+1
Second Turn	Home Team	+2	Red 1 and Black 6	+7
	Visiting Team	+1	Red 6 and Black 2	−3

1. **Read through the table. After two turns, which player is closest to their end zone?**

ACTIVITY 1.1

Signed Numbers as Values with Directions

NOTES

Let's play Math Football. Begin by selecting the home or visiting team. Your teacher will set the length of time for each half. You will play two halves. Make sure to switch ends at half-time with the Home Team moving toward the Visiting end zone, and the Visiting Team moving toward the Home end zone. Good luck!

1. **Once your game is finished, answer each question.**

   a. **When you are trying to get to the Home end zone, which number cube do you want to show the greater value? Explain your reasoning.**

   b. **When you are trying to get to the Visiting end zone, which number cube do you want to show the greater value? Explain your reasoning.**

   c. **Did you ever find yourself back at the same position you ended on your previous turn? Describe the values on the cubes that would cause this to happen.**

   d. **Describe the roll that causes you to move your football the greatest distance either left or right.**

ACTIVITY
1.2

Writing Equations with Signed Numbers

You can write equations to describe the results of number cube rolls. Think of the result of rolling the red number cube as a negative number and the result of rolling the black number cube as a positive number.

	Player	Starting Position	Results of the Number Cubes Roll	Ending Position	Number Sentence
First Turn	Home Team	0	Red 3 and Black 5	+2	$0 + (-3) + 5 = +2$
	Visiting Team	0	Red 5 and Black 6	+1	$0 + (-5) + 6 = +1$
Second Turn	Home Team	+2	Red 1 and Black 6	+7	$+2 + (-1) + 6 = +7$
	Visiting Team	+1	Red 6 and Black 2	−3	$+1 + (-6) + 2 = -3$

1. Describe each part of the number sentence for the second turn of the Visiting Team player.

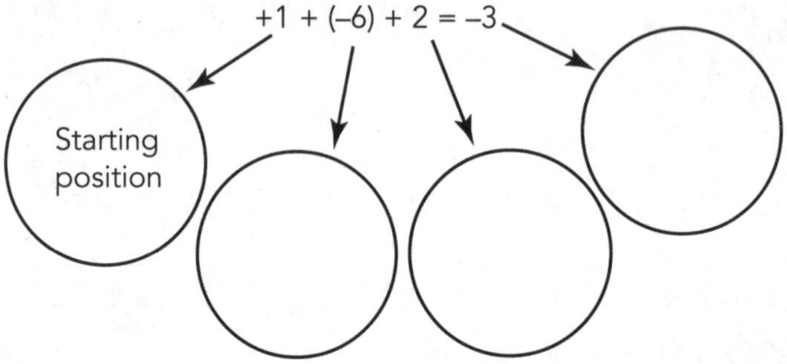

Play Math Football again. But this time, work with your partner to get to the Home end zone together in the first half and the Visiting end zone in the second half. Write equations to record your moves.

2. Think about the number cube rolls you made in the game.

a. What kind of rolls move you closer to the Home end zone?

b. What kind of rolls move you closer to the Visiting end zone?

3. Write an equation for each situation. Use the game board for help.

a. The Home Team player starts at the zero yard line and rolls a red 6 and a black 2. What is the ending position?

Equation: ______________________________

b. The Visiting Team player starts at the zero yard line and rolls a red 5 and a black 4. What is the ending position?

Equation: ______________________________

c. The Home Team player starts at the 5 yard line and rolls a red 2 and a black 2. What is the ending position?

Equation: ______________________________

d. The Visiting Team player starts at the −5 yard line and rolls a red 4 and a black 6. What is the ending position?

Equation: ______________________________

e. Suppose the Home Team player is at the +8 yard line. Complete the table and write two equations that will put the player into the Home end zone.

Starting Position	Roll of the Red Number Cube	Roll of the Black Number Cube	Equation
+8			
+8			

f. Suppose the Visiting Team player is at the −8 yard line. Complete the table and write two equations that will put the player into the Visiting end zone.

Starting Position	Roll of the Red Number Cube	Roll of the Black Number Cube	Equation
−8			
−8			

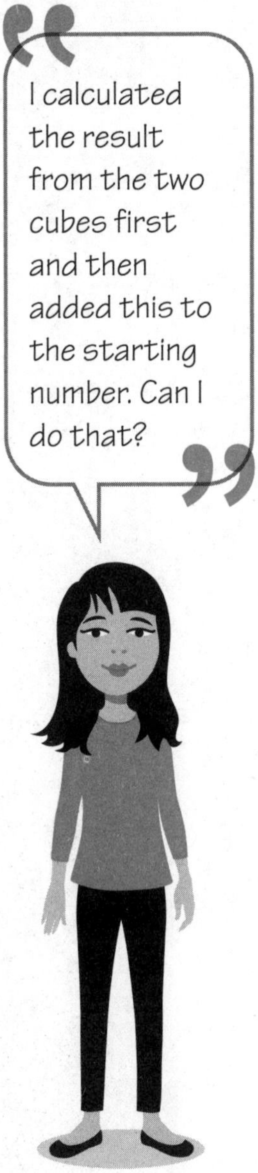

"I calculated the result from the two cubes first and then added this to the starting number. Can I do that?"

NOTES

TALK the TALK

Mission: Possible, and Impossible

Consider the moves you made in the Math Football game.

1. In which direction would you move if you roll:

a. a larger number on the black cube than on the red cube?

b. a larger number on the red cube than on the black cube?

c. two black cubes?

d. a black cube and a red cube?

e. two red cubes?

2. Is it possible to decrease in value if rolling two black cubes? Explain your reasoning.

3. Is it possible to increase in value if rolling two red cubes? Explain your reasoning.

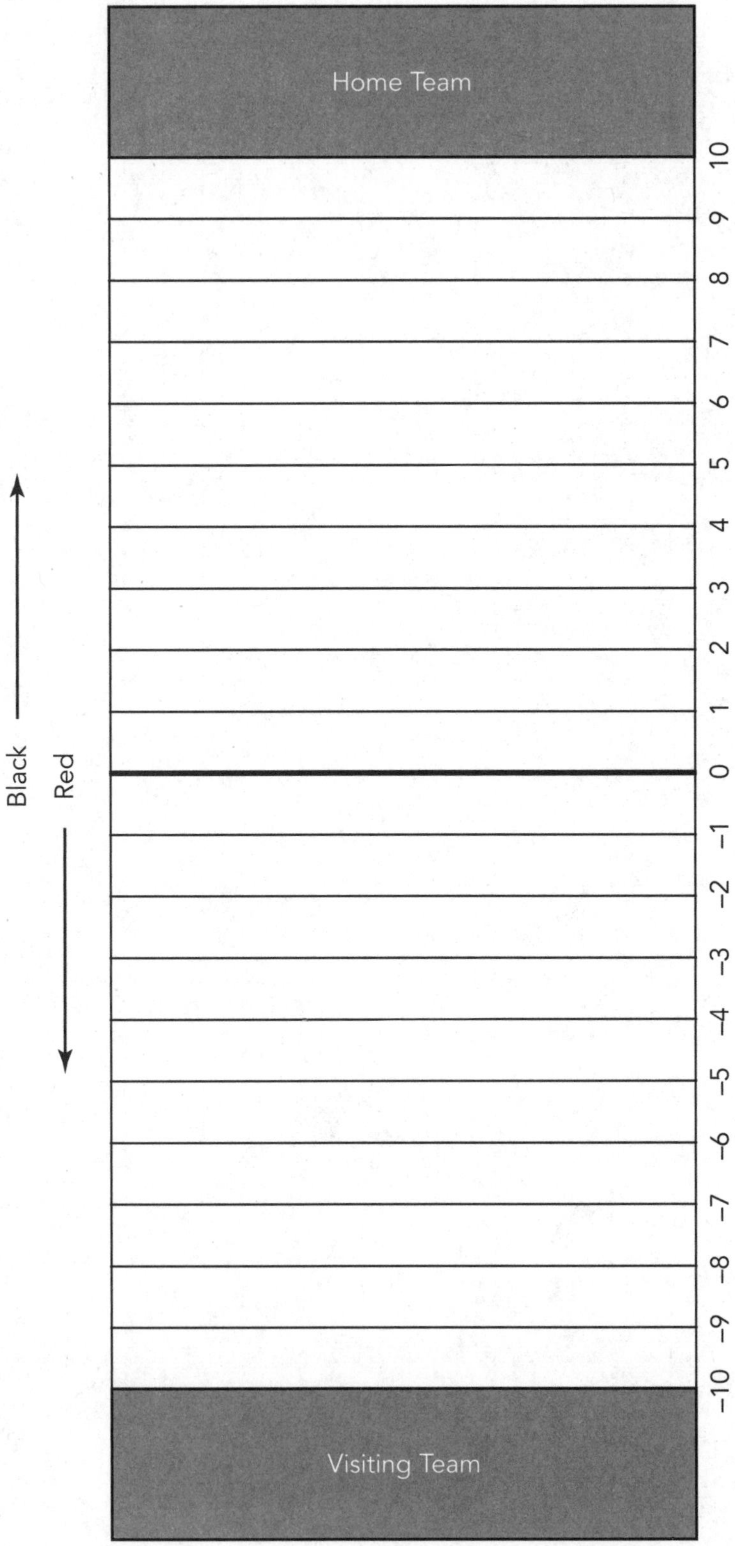
Home Team
Visiting Team
Black
Red
10
9
8
7
6
5
4
3
2
1
0
–1
–2
–3
–4
–5
–6
–7
–8
–9
–10

Assignment

Write

In your own words, explain how to decide whether the sum of two numbers is less than, equal to, or greater than 0.

Remember

Combining positive and negative moves together on a line results in a move to the left, a move to the right, or staying in the same position, depending on the size of the positive and negative values.

Practice

1. Determine the ending position by adding and subtracting the indicated steps from each starting position.

Starting Position	Steps Backward	Steps Forward	Ending Position
+3	4	5	
+7	6	2	
+5	2	4	
0	5	8	
−4	3	7	
+1	7	9	
−6	1	5	
−2	5	6	
8	3	1	
−9	2	4	

2. Write an equation to represent the movement indicated by the starting point, steps backward, and steps forward.

Starting Position	Steps Backward	Steps Forward	Equation
+2	4	7	
−7	3	5	
+6	9	4	
+4	6	1	
−5	2	9	
0	5	3	
−3	1	4	
−8	2	6	
0	8	2	
+9	7	8	

Stretch

Draw a model to represent the addition problem $-3\frac{1}{2} + (-1\frac{1}{4})$. Then determine the solution.

Review

1. Solve each proportion.

   a. $\frac{6.6}{p} = \frac{9}{12.15}$

   b. $\frac{8}{10.5} = \frac{c}{6.5625}$

2. Describe which method (scaling, unit rate, or means and extremes) you would use to solve for each variable and explain why.

   a. $\frac{2}{3} = \frac{20}{x}$

   b. $\frac{16}{4} = \frac{100}{x}$

3. Determine if each rectangle is a scale drawing of the given rectangle. Explain why or why not.

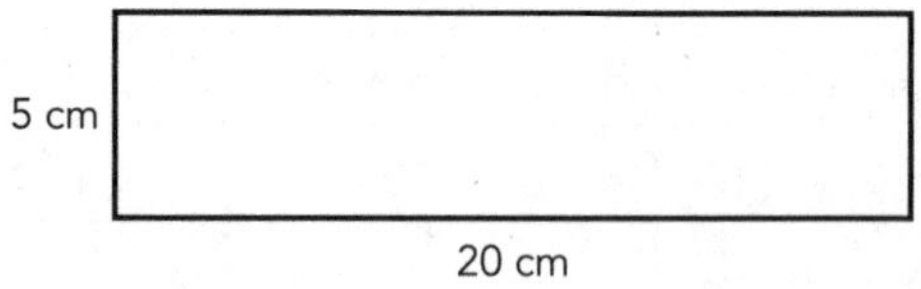

   a.

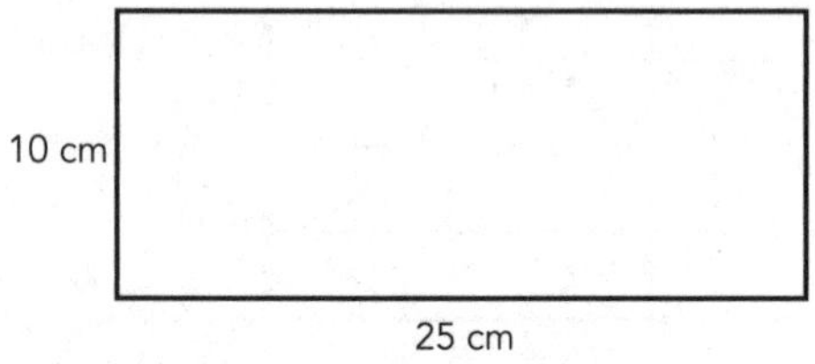

   b.

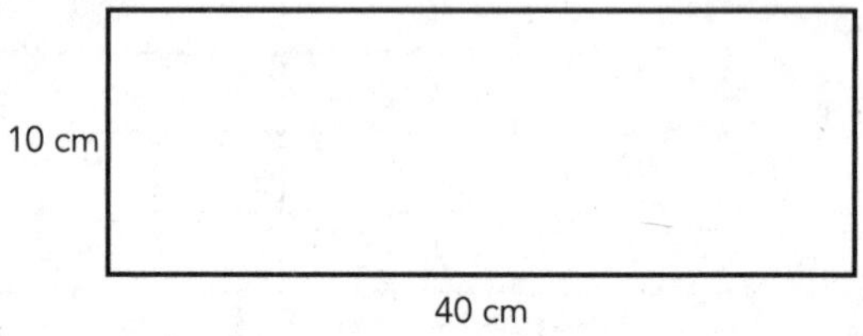

Walk the Line

2

Adding Integers, Part I

WARM UP

A large hotel has a ground floor (street level) and 26 floors of guest rooms above street level, which can be modeled by positive integers. There are 5 floors of parking below street level, which can be modeled by negative integers. In this hotel, street level is represented by zero.

Write an integer addition problem that models the hotel elevator's motion in each case.

1. The elevator starts at street level, goes up 7 floors, and then goes down 3 floors.
2. The elevator starts at street level, goes up 10 floors, and then goes down 12 floors.
3. The elevator starts at street level, goes down 4 floors, and then goes up 11 floors.
4. The elevator starts at street level, goes down 2 floors, goes up 5 floors, and finally goes down 3 floors.

LEARNING GOALS

- Model the addition of integers on a number line.
- Develop a rule for adding integers.
- Identify $p + q$ as the number located a distance of $|q|$ from p.

KEY TERM

- absolute value

You have been adding and subtracting positive numbers most of your life. In elementary school, you learned how to add numbers using a number line. How can a number line be a helpful tool in adding positive and negative numbers?

Getting Started

Getting on Line

Use the number line and determine the number described by each. Explain your reasoning.

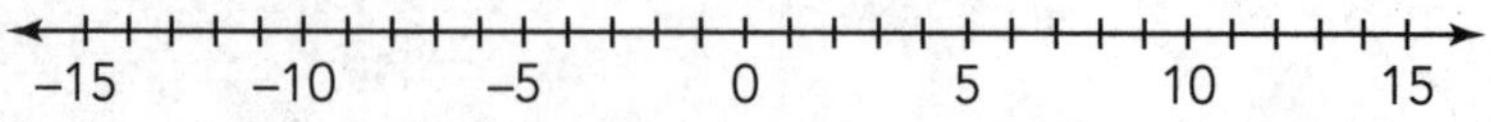

1. the number that is 7 more than −9

2. the number that is 2 more than −6

3. the number that is 10 more than −8

4. the number that is 10 less than 6

5. the number that is 5 less than −4

6. the number that is 2 less than −4

ACTIVITY
2.1

Walking the Number Line

Walking a number line can help you to add positive and negative numbers.

Walk the number line for an addition sentence:

- Start at zero and walk to the value of the first term of the expression.
- To indicate addition, turn to face up the number line, towards the greater positive numbers.
- Walk forward if adding a positive number or walk backward if adding a negative number.

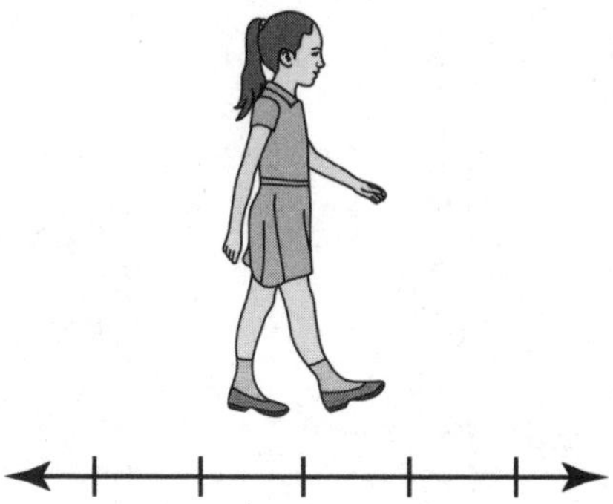

Your teacher will select a classmate to walk the line for each of the given problems. Help your classmate by preparing the directions that are needed.

1. Complete the table.

	Where You Start	Direction You Face	Walk Backwards or Forwards	Final Location
1 + 3				
0 + (−4)				
−3 + 5				
−1 + (−4)				

This worked example represents the movement created by walking the number line.

WORKED EXAMPLE

A number line can be used to model integer addition.
When adding a positive integer, move to the right on a number line.
When adding a negative integer, move to the left on a number line.

Example 1: The number line shows how to determine 5 + 8.

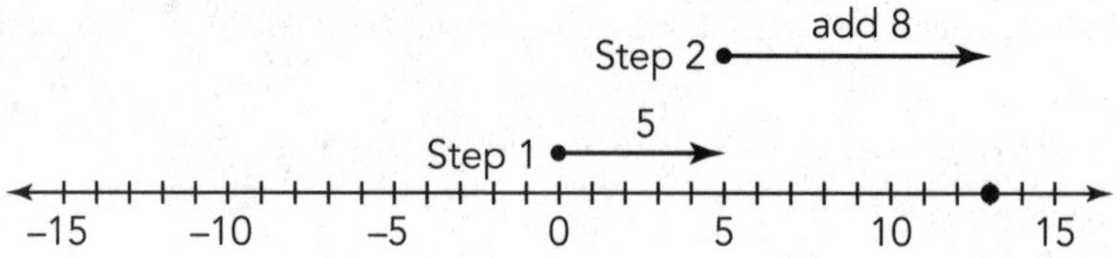

Example 2: The number line shows how to determine 5 + (–8).

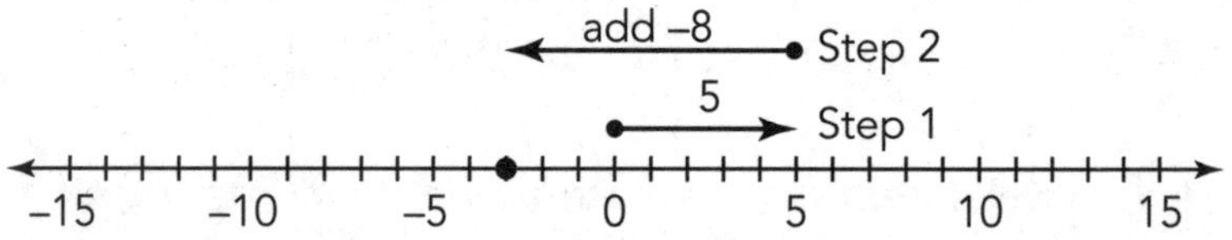

Compare the first steps in each example.

2. What distance is shown by the first term in each example?

Remember that the **absolute value** of a number is its distance from 0.

3. Describe the graphical representation of the first term. Where does it start and in which direction does it move? How does this movement represent walking the line?

4. What is the absolute value of the first term in each example?

Compare the second steps in each example.

5. What distance is shown by the second term in each example?

6. Why did the arrows for the second terms both start at the endpoints of the first terms but then continue in opposite directions? Explain your reasoning.

7. What is the absolute value of the second term in each example?

8. Use the number line to determine each sum. Show your work.

Think about walking the line as you model these sums on the number line.

a. $-3 + 7 =$ ________

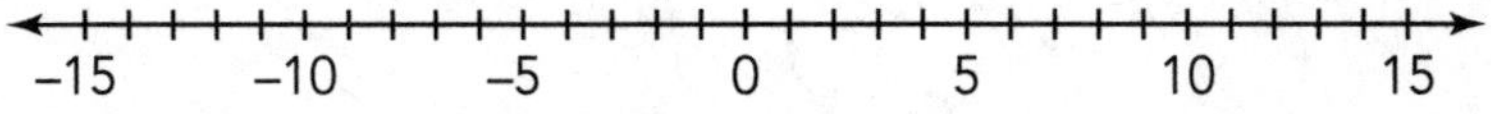

b. $3 + (-7) =$ ________

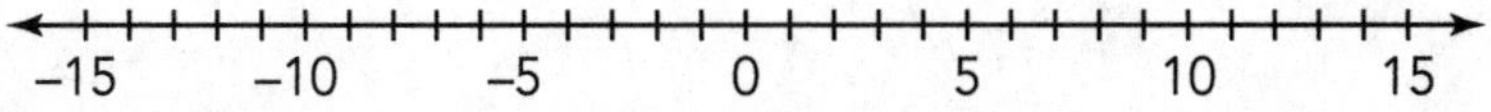

NOTES

c. $-3 + (-7) =$ ________

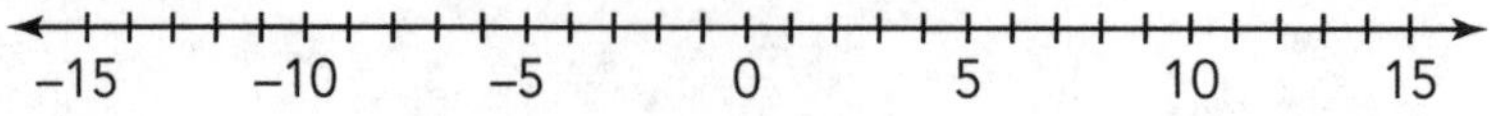

d. $3 + 7 =$ ________

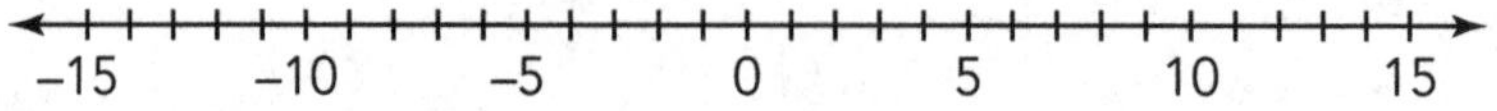

Notice that the first term in each expression in parts (a) through (d) was either 3 or (–3).

9. **What do you notice about the distances shown by these terms on the number lines?**

10. **What is the absolute value of each term?**

Notice that the second term in each expression was either 7 or (–7).

11. **What do you notice about the distances shown by these terms on the number lines?**

12. **What is the absolute value of each term?**

ACTIVITY
2.2 Adding on Number Lines

Now that you have the feel for how to move on the number line when adding negative numbers, it is time to practice with more examples.

Use the number line to determine each sum. Show your work.

1. $-9 + 5 =$ ________

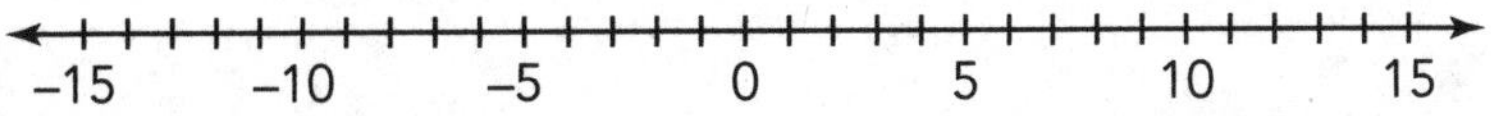

2. $9 + (-5) =$ ________

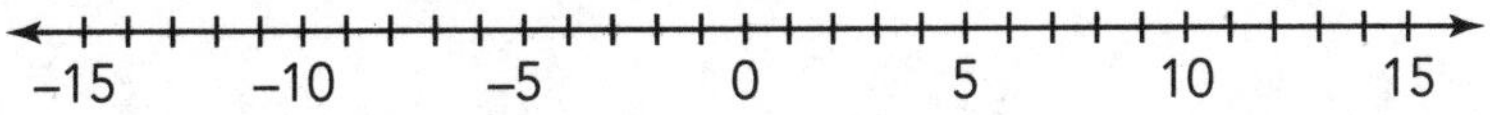

3. $-9 + (-5) =$ ________

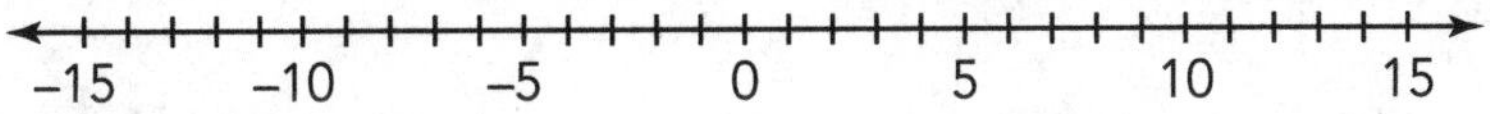

4. $9 + 5 =$ ________

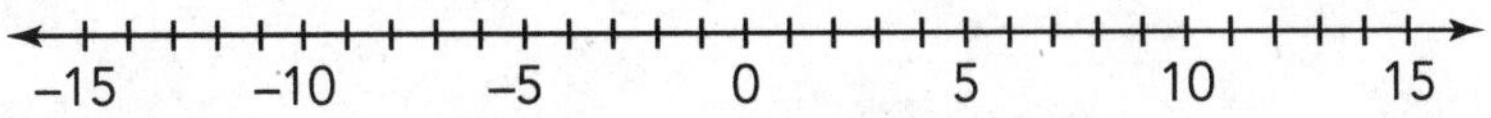

Notice that the first term in each expression in Questions 1 through 4 was either 9 or (−9).

5. What do you notice about the distances shown by these terms on the number lines?

6. What is the absolute value of each term?

How is knowing the absolute value of each term important?

Notice that the second term in each expression was either 5 or (−5).

7. What do you notice about the distances shown by these terms on the number lines?

8. What is the absolute value of each term?

Jse the number line to determine each sum. Show your work.

9. $-8 + 2 =$ ____________

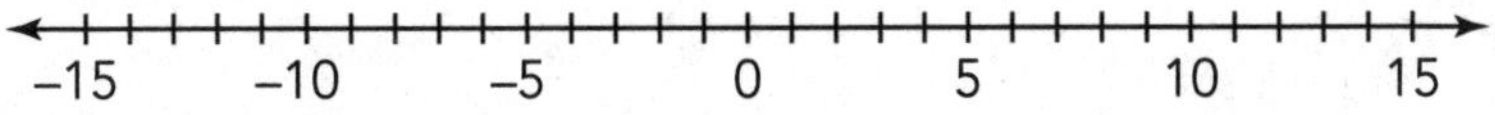

10. $8 + (-2) =$ ____________

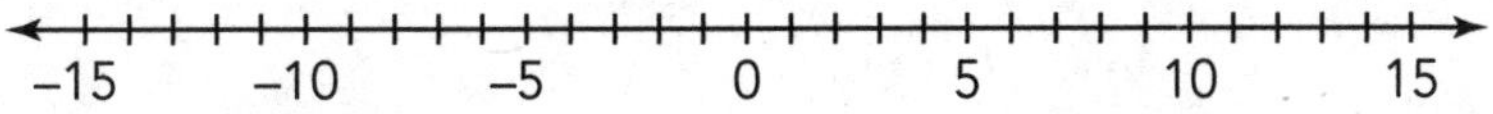

11. $-8 + (-2) =$ ____________

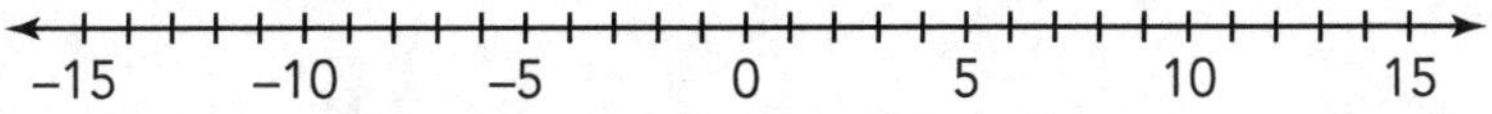

12. $8 + 2 =$ ____________

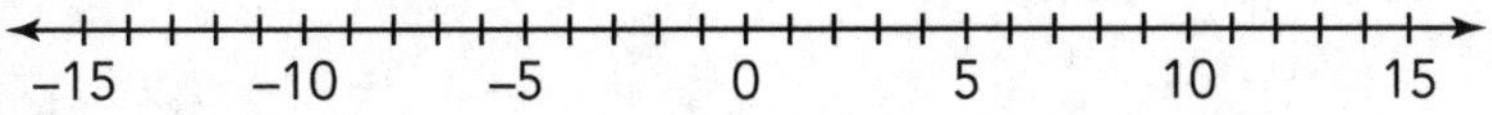

13. $-4 + 11 =$ ___________

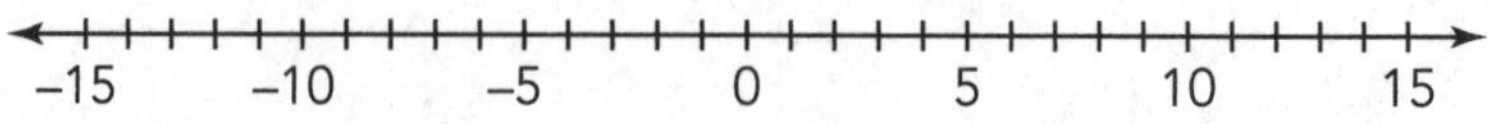

14. $4 + (-11) =$ ___________

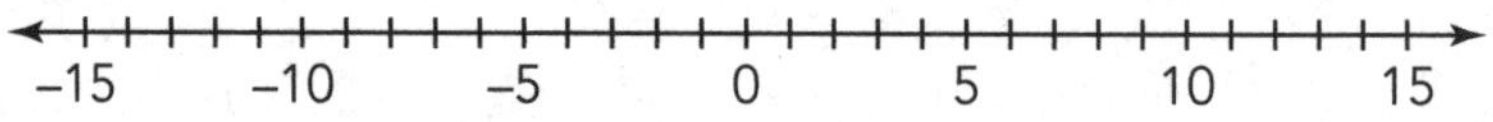

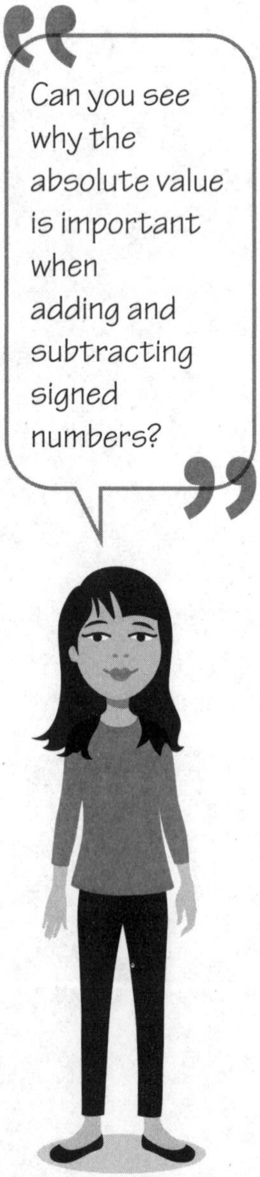

Can you see why the absolute value is important when adding and subtracting signed numbers?

15. $-4 + (-11) =$ ___________

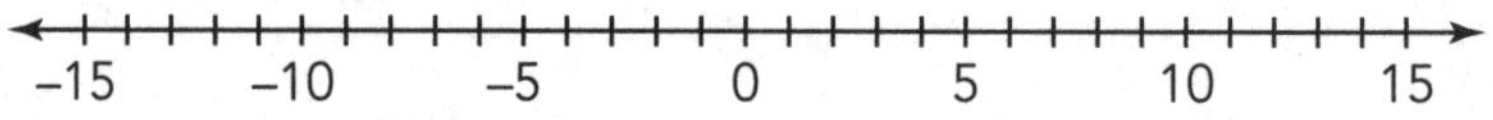

16. $4 + 11 =$ ___________

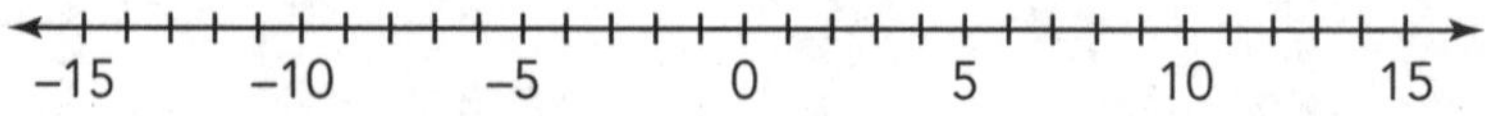

NOTES

TALK the TALK

Patterns on the Line

Demonstrate what you have learned about adding two numbers using a number line.

1. **Describe the patterns from the *Adding on Number Lines* activity, when you:**

   a. **add two positive numbers.**

   b. **add two negative numbers.**

   c. **add a negative and a positive number.**

2. **Do you think these patterns will hold true for all numbers, even fractions and decimals? Explain your reasoning.**

NOTES

3. **Complete each number line model and number sentence.**

a. 4 + ________ = 12

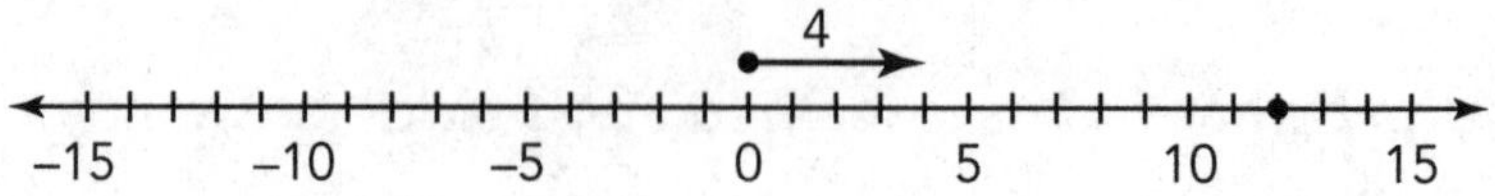

b. –3 + ________ = 2

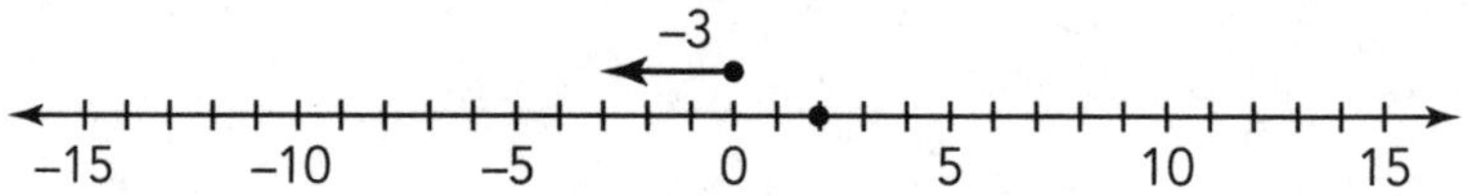

c. 7 + ________ = –2

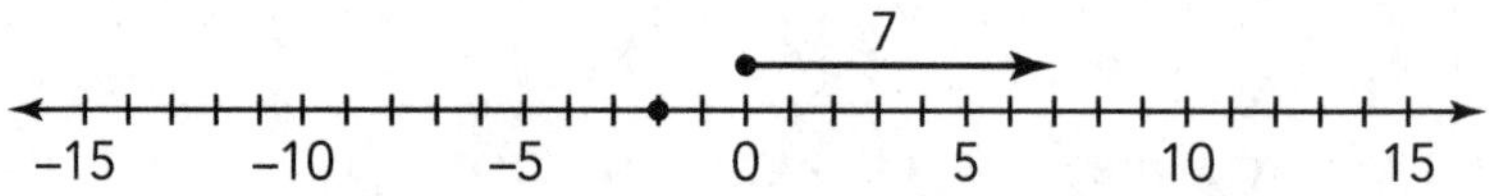

d. –6 + ________ = –11

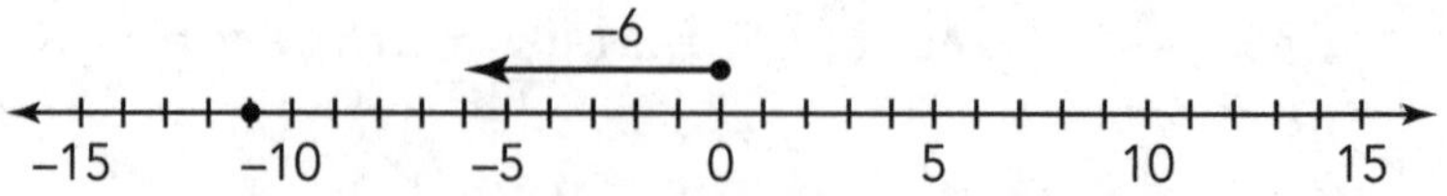

Assignment

Write

Explain how walking the line is the same as representing addition and subtraction on the number line.

Remember

When adding a positive integer on a number line, move to the right on the number line. When adding a negative integer, move to the left on the number line.

Practice

Use the number line to determine each sum. Show your work.

1. $-6 + 4$

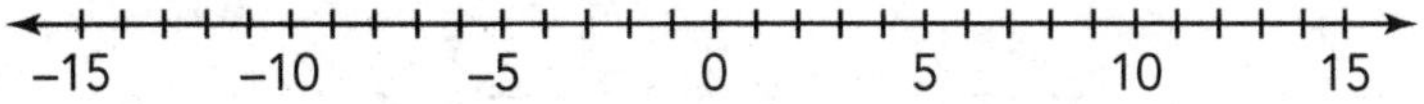

2. $-9 + (-2)$

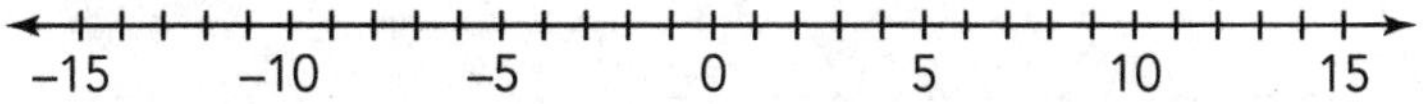

3. $13 + (-12)$

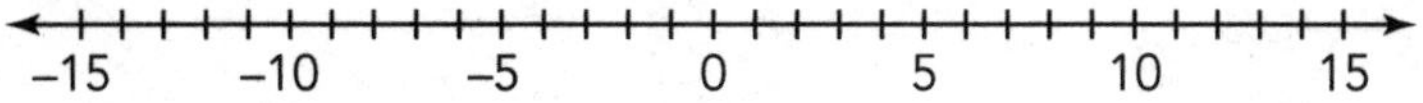

4. $7 + (-14)$

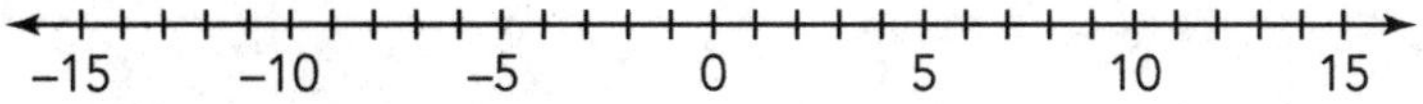

5. $7 + (-1)$

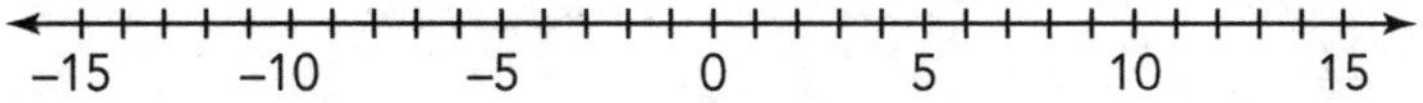

6. $3 + (-13)$

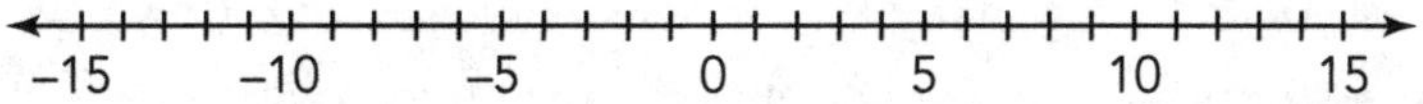

7. $8 + (-8)$

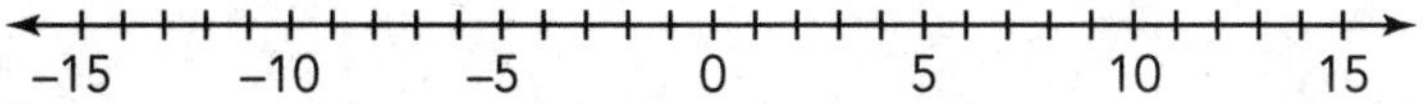

8. $-2 + 8$

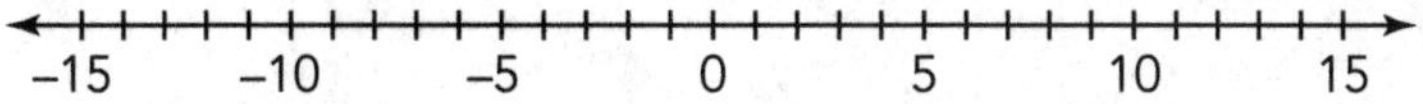

9. $-13 + 3$

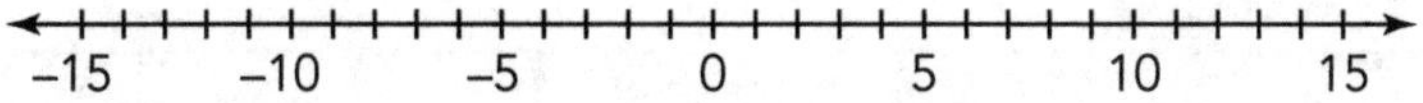

10. $0 + (-12)$

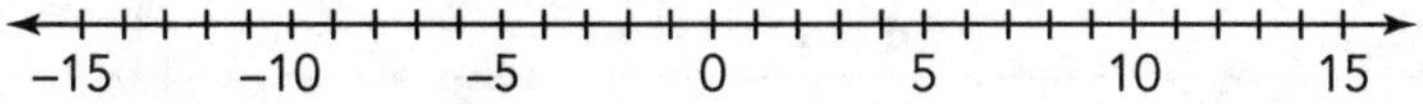

Complete each number line model and number sentence.

1. −4 + ______ = 0

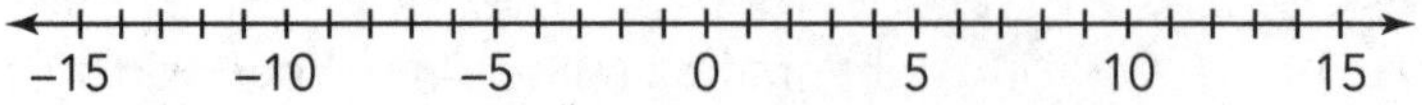

2. −15 + ______ = −9

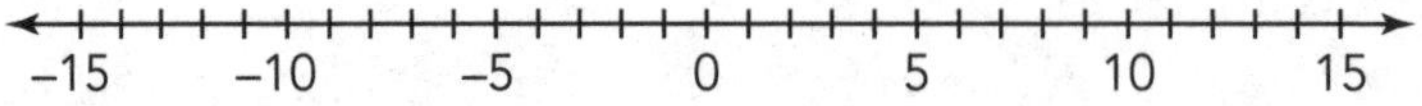

3. ______ + 10 = −2

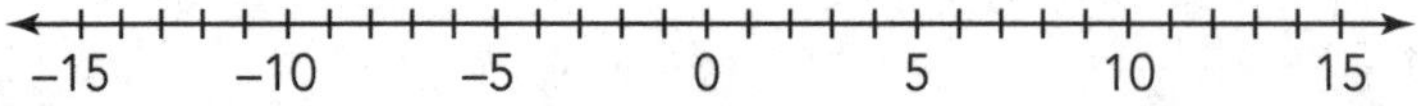

4. ______ + (−11) = −4

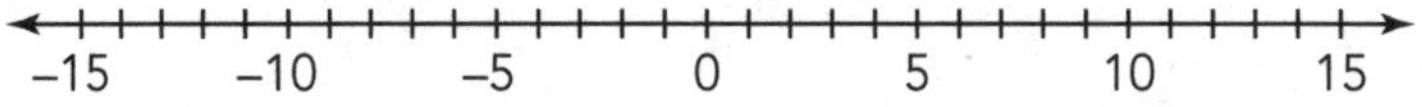

5. −12 + ______ = −14

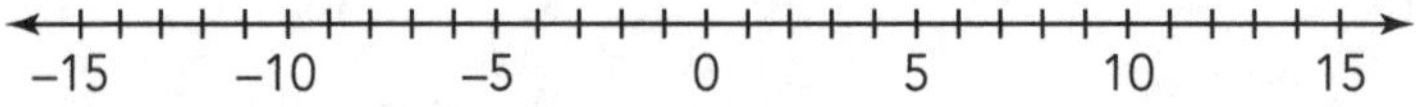

Stretch

Draw a number line model to determine each sum.

1. −1.6 + −0.7

2. −2.1 + 0.8

3. 2.2 + −4.1

Review

Northern Tier Gardens has hired you for a summer job installing water gardens. They have circular water garden pools available in a variety of sizes. The manager has asked you to create a table to show the circumference and area of the company's various water garden pools. Use 3.14 for π and round each answer to the nearest hundredth.

Garden Name	Radius (feet)	Diameter (feet)	Area (square feet)	Circumference (feet)
Atlantic	2.5	5		
Pacifica	6	12		
Mediterranean	1.75	3.5		
Baltica	1	2		
Japanesque	2.25	4.5		
Floridian	3.25	6.5		

Two-Color Counters

3

Adding Integers, Part II

WARM UP

Use a number line to determine each sum. Then write a sentence to describe the movement you used on the number line to compute the sum of the two integers.

1. $-2 + 1$

2. $-5 + 8$

3. $-2 + (-3)$

4. $4 + (-6)$

LEARNING GOALS

- Describe situations in which opposite quantities combine to make 0.
- Model the addition of integers using two-color counters.
- Develop a rule for adding integers.
- Apply previous understandings of addition and subtraction to add rational numbers.

KEY TERM

- additive inverses

You know how to use a number line to model adding positive and negative numbers. Do the patterns you noticed from the number line model apply to other models for adding positive and negative numbers?

Getting Started

Creating Zero

Use a number line to illustrate how the sum of two numbers can be zero.

How can you end at zero if you start at zero?

1. Write 3 examples of number sentences that sum to zero and draw the number line models to support your solutions.

2. What pattern do you notice?

3. Describe a real-life situation in which two numbers would sum to zero. Write the number sentence that could be used to represent the situation.

ACTIVITY
3.1 Additive Inverses

Addition of integers can also be modeled using two-color counters that represent positive (+) charges and negative (–) charges. One color, usually red, represents the negative number, or negative charge. The other color, usually yellow, represents the positive number, or positive charge. In this book, gray shading will represent the negative number, and no shading will represent the positive number.

Two numbers with the sum of zero are called **additive inverses.**

⊖ = −1 ⊕ = +1

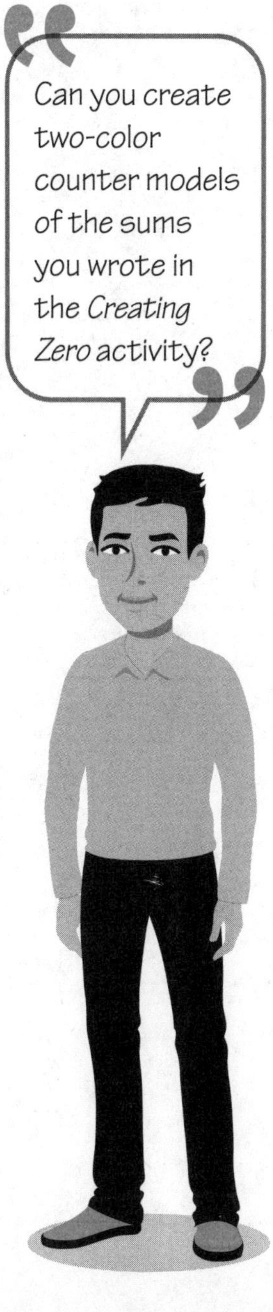

Can you create two-color counter models of the sums you wrote in the *Creating Zero* activity?

WORKED EXAMPLE

You can model the expression 3 + (−3) in different ways using two-color counters:

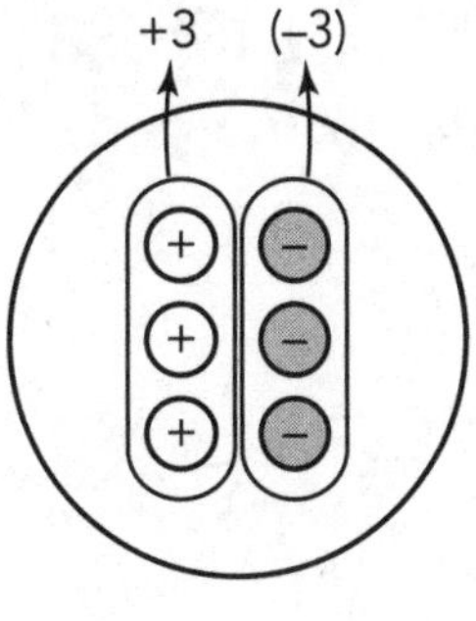

Three positive charges and three negative charges have no charge.

3 + (−3) = 0

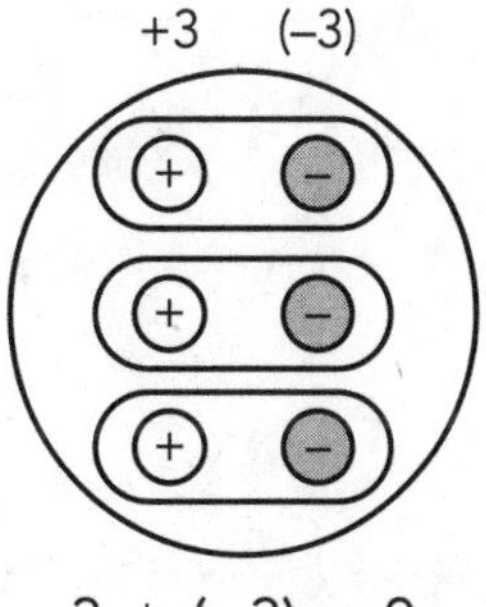

Each positive charge is paired with a negative charge.

Each pair of positive and negative charges has no charge.

3 + (−3) = 0

NOTES

1. What is the value of each ⊕ and ⊖ pair in the second model?

2. Describe how you can change the numbers of ⊕ and ⊖ counters in the model but leave the sum unchanged.

ACTIVITY 3.2

Adding Integers with Two-Color Counters

Let's consider two examples where integers are added using two-color counters.

WORKED EXAMPLE

Example 1: 5 + 8

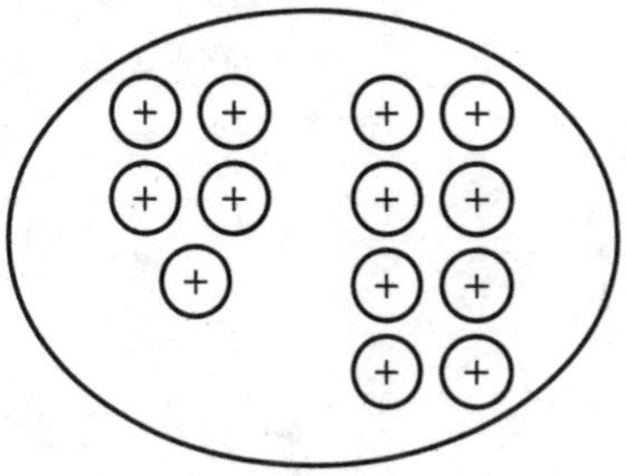

There are 13 positive counters in the model. The sum is 13.

Example 2: 5 + (−8)

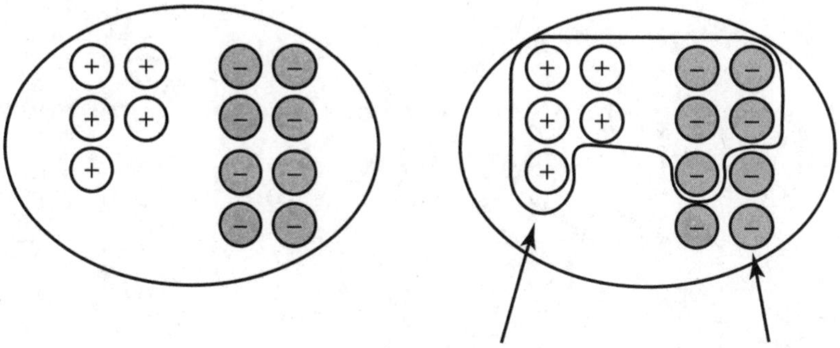

There are five (+) (−) pairs. The value of those pairs is 0.

There are 3 (−), or negative counters, remaining.

There are 3 negative counters remaining. The sum of 5 + (−8) is −3.

1. **Create another model to represent a sum of −3. Write the appropriate number sentence.**

2. **Share your model with your classmates. How are they the same? How are they different?**

In an addition sentence, the terms being added together are called addends.

3. **Write a number sentence to represent each model.**

a.

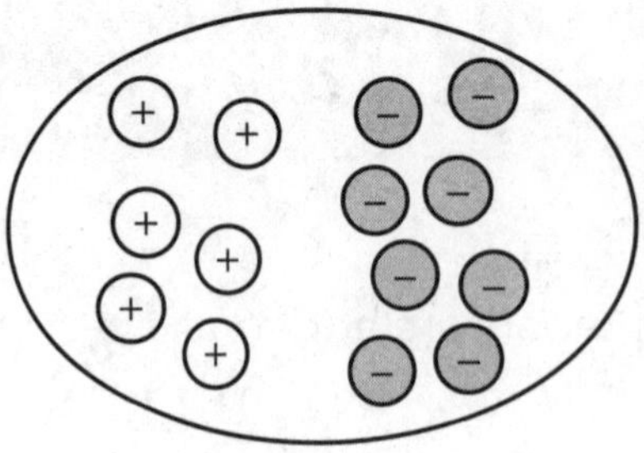

b.

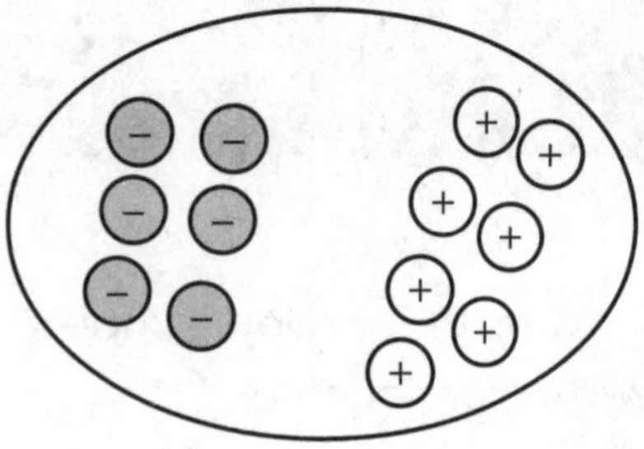

c.

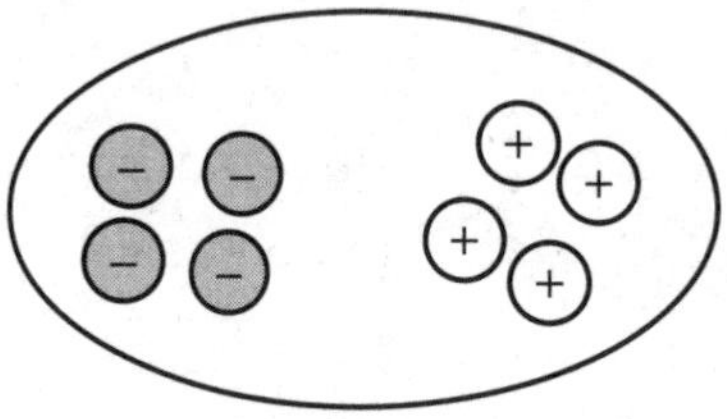

d.

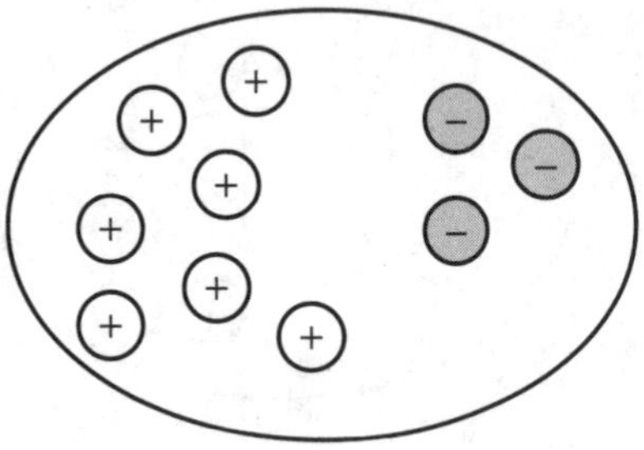

4. **Does the order in which you wrote the integers in your number sentence matter? How do you know?**

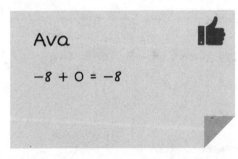

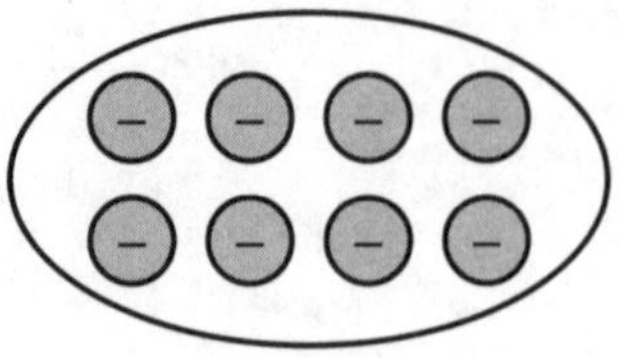

The students were then asked to write a number sentence for the given model.

Ava

$-8 + 0 = -8$

Landon

$-1 + (-7) = -8$

5. Analyze the number sentences written by Ava and Landon.

   a. Explain why both number sentences are correct.

   b. Write an additional number sentence that could describe the model.

6. Write each number sentence in Question 5 a second way.

Ava and Landon used two-color counters to represent the number sentence $3 + (-5)$.

7. The students placed the same counters on their desks, but they reported different sums. Ava reported the sum as 8 and Landon said the sum was -2. Use the model to explain who is correct. What was the error made by the incorrect student?

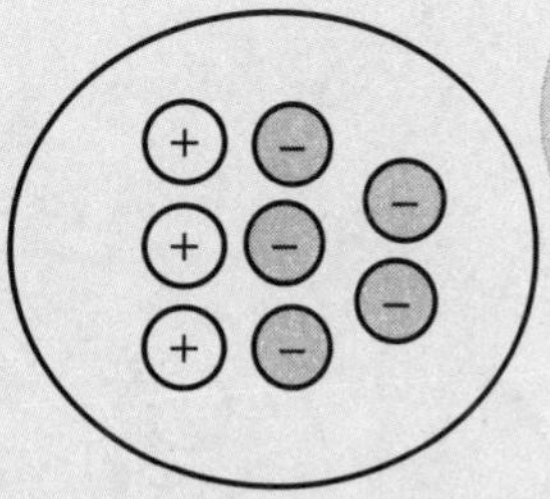

NOTES

8. Draw a model for each, and then complete the number sentence.

a. $-9 + (-4) =$ ______

b. $-9 + 4 =$ ______

c. $9 + (-4) =$ ______

d. $9 + 4 =$ ______

9. Complete the model to determine the unknown integer.

a. $1 +$ ______ $= -4$

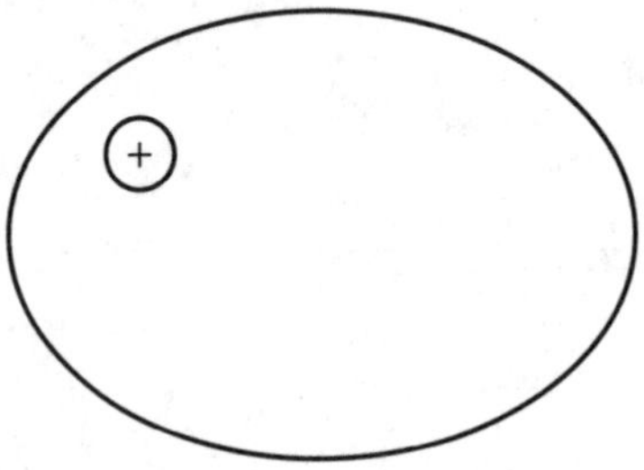

b. $-3 +$ ______ $= 7$

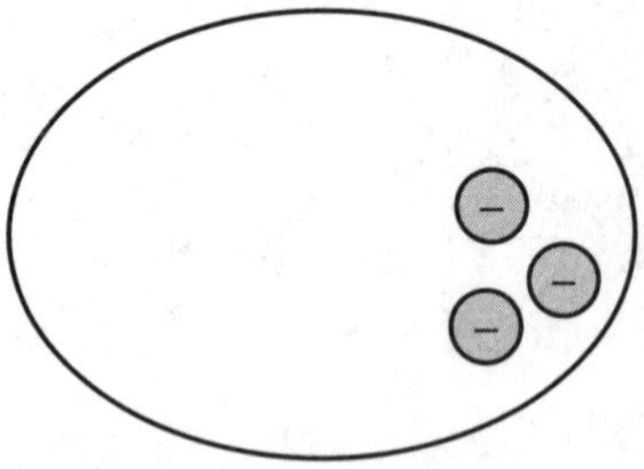

c. $7 +$ ______ $= -1$

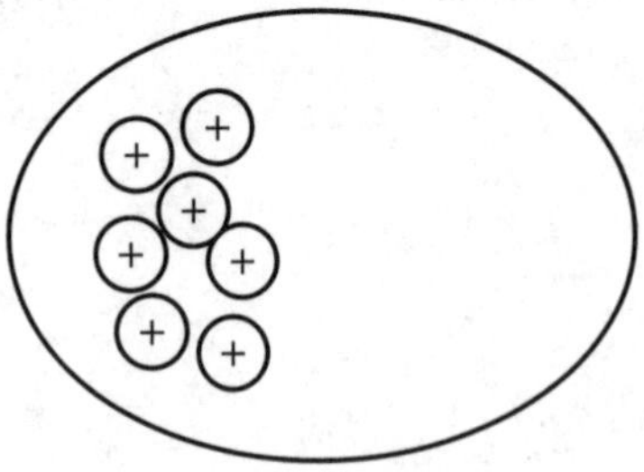

10. **Describe the set of integers that makes each sentence true.**

    a. **What integer(s) when added to −7 give a sum greater than 0?**

    b. **What integer(s) when added to −7 give a sum less than 0?**

    c. **What integer(s) when added to −7 give a sum of 0?**

You have now used two models to represent adding integers.

11. **For each problem, draw both models to represent the number sentences and determine the sums.**

    a. (−6) + 13

    b. 8 + (−13)

    c. (−3) + (−7)

    d. 2 + 9

Think about how the absolute values of the addends compare with each other.

12. **Explain the similarities and differences of the models in helping you determine the sum of two integers.**

ACTIVITY
3.3 Rules for Adding Integers

Visual models provide concrete representations of new ideas, like adding signed numbers. But you probably do not want to draw visual models when you have large numbers, lots of addends, fractions, or decimals.

Look back over the activities in this lesson and write rules for adding integers.

1. When adding two integers, what will the sign of the sum be if:

a. both integers are positive?

b. both integers are negative?

c. one integer is positive and one integer is negative?

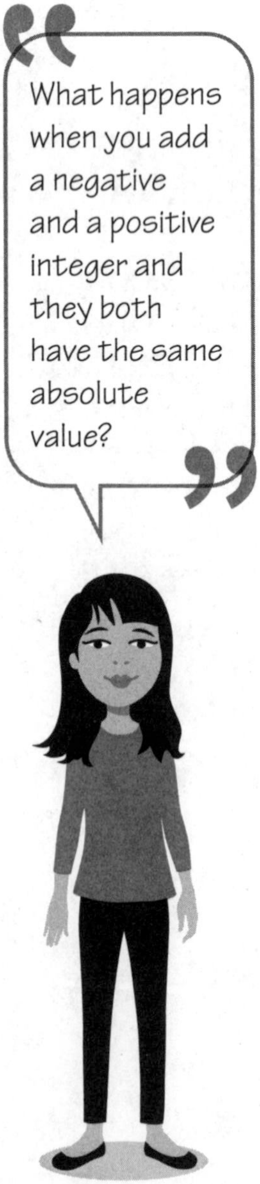

What happens when you add a negative and a positive integer and they both have the same absolute value?

2. Write a rule that states how to determine the sum of any two integers that have the same sign.

3. Write a rule that states how to determine the sum of any two integers that have opposite signs.

NOTES

Cut out the sums provided at the end of the lesson.

4. **Without computing the sums, sort the number sentences into two piles: those that have a positive sum and those that have a negative sum.**

   a. **How can you decide which number sentences have a positive sum and which have a negative sum?**

   b. **Tape or glue the number sentences in the space provided.**

   Positive Sums **Negative Sums**

   c. **Use your rules to determine the sum of each number sentence.**

What reasoning are you using to determine the missing addends?

5. Determine each unknown addend.

a. _______ + (−25) = 34

b. _______ + 26 = 12

c. 8 + _______ = −24

d. −12 + _______ = −24

e. −15 + _______ = −28

f. _______ + 18 = −3

TALK the TALK

Summarizing Sums

1. Use the graphic organizer provided to represent additive inverses. Write an example, using both a number sentence and a real-life situation. Then represent your number sentence in words, using a number line model, and using a two-color counter model.

EXAMPLE: NUMBER SENTENCE AND REAL-LIFE SITUATION

IN WORDS

ADDITIVE INVERSES AND ZERO

NUMBER LINE MODEL

TWO-COLOR COUNTER MODEL

NOTES

2. Write a number sentence that meets the given conditions. If it is not possible to create the number sentence, explain why not.

   a. Two positive addends with a positive sum.

   b. Two positive addends with a negative sum.

   c. Two negative addends with a positive sum.

   d. Two negative addends with a negative sum.

   e. A positive addend and a negative addend with a positive sum.

   f. A positive addend and a negative addend with a negative sum.

Rules for Adding Integers Cutouts

$-58 + 24$	$-35 + (-15)$
$-33 + (-12)$	$-48 + 60$
$26 + (-13)$	$67 + 119$
$-105 + 25$	$153 + (-37)$
$21 + (-56)$	$18 + (-17)$

Assignment

Write

Define the term *additive inverse* in your own words.

Remember

When two integers have the same sign and are added together, the sign of the sum is the sign of both integers.
When two integers have opposite signs and are added together, the absolute values of the integers are subtracted and the sign of the sum is the sign of the integer with the greater absolute value.

Practice

1. Write a number sentence for each two-color counter model. Then determine the sum.

   a.

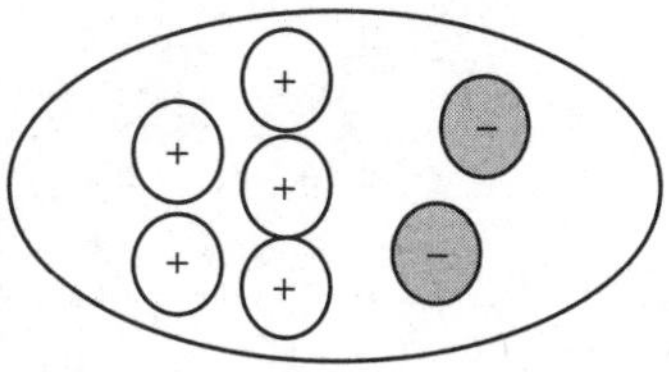

   b.

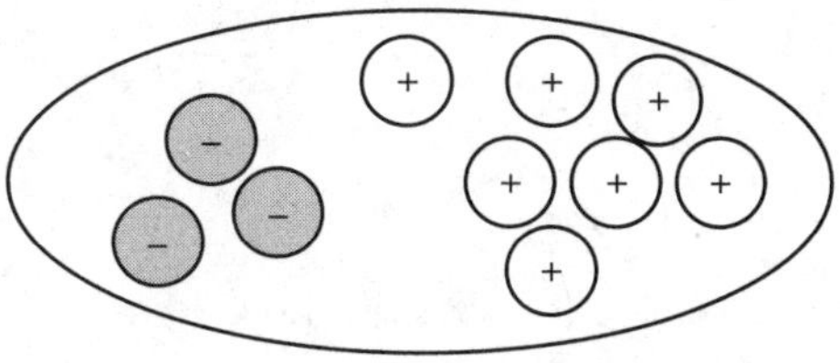

2. Draw a two-color counter model for each number sentence. Then determine the sum.

   a. 3 + (−6)

   b. −7 + (−4)

   c. 2 + 5

   d. 10 + (−8)

3. An atom is made up of protons, neutrons, and electrons. The protons carry a positive (+) charge and make up the nucleus of an atom with the neutrons. Neutrons do not carry a charge. The electrons carry a negative (−) charge and circle the nucleus. Atoms have no positive or negative charge. This means that they must have the same number of protons and electrons. A partial model of a nitrogen atom is shown.

Atom

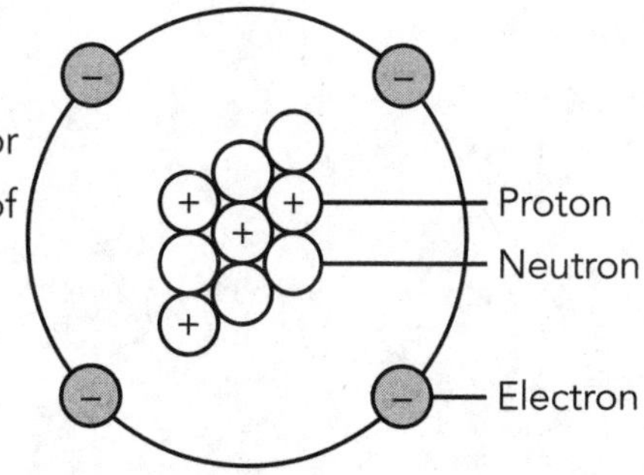

   a. How many electrons should be drawn on the model of a nitrogen atom so that it has the same number of protons and electrons? How did you know?

   b. Complete the model of the nitrogen atom by drawing in the electrons.

   c. Write a number sentence to represent the sum of the number of protons and electrons in a nitrogen atom.

   d. Use a number line to show the sum of the number of protons and electrons in the nitrogen atom.

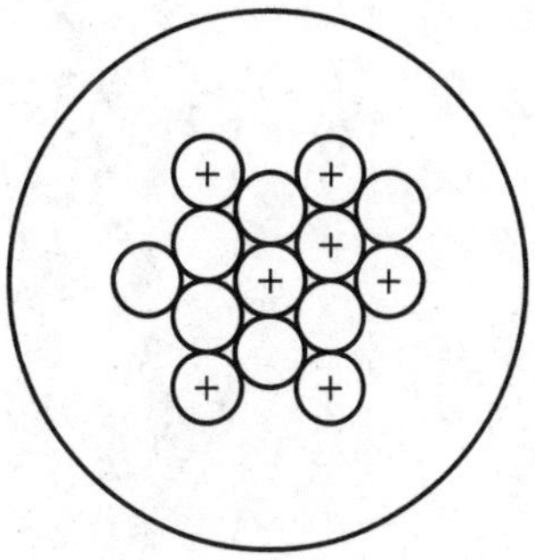

Determine each sum.

4. 45 + (−27)
5. 32 + (−98)
6. −153 + 74
7. −63 + (−41)
8. 527 + (−289)
9. −32 + 98
10. −47 + (−95)
11. −51 + 134

Stretch

Determine each sum.

1. $21\frac{3}{8} + \left(-51\frac{1}{4}\right)$

2. $-65\frac{2}{5} + 103$

3. $-34.528 + 78.12$

4. $863.78 + (-1024.01)$

Review

Use a number line to determine each sum.

1. $-3 + 4$
2. $-3 + (-4)$

Calculate the sale price of each item.

3. A pair of headphones is on sale for 15% off the original price of $305.
4. A hoverboard is on sale for 10% off the original price of $247.50.

Solve each proportion.

5. $\frac{3}{4} = \frac{x}{18}$
6. $\frac{5}{8} = \frac{21}{x}$

What's the Difference?

4

Subtracting Integers

WARM UP

For each number line model, write the number sentence described by the model and draw a two-color counter model to represent the number sentence.

1. 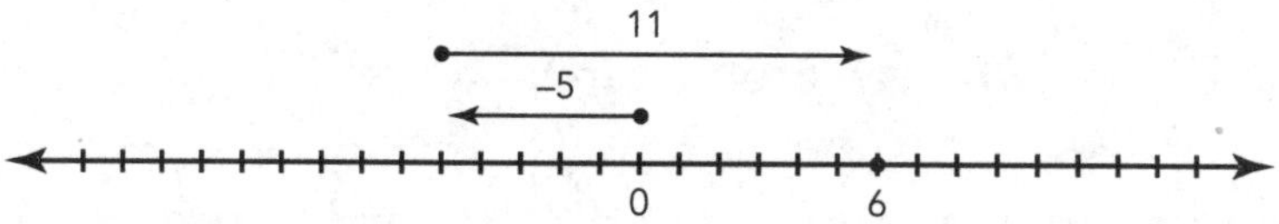

2. 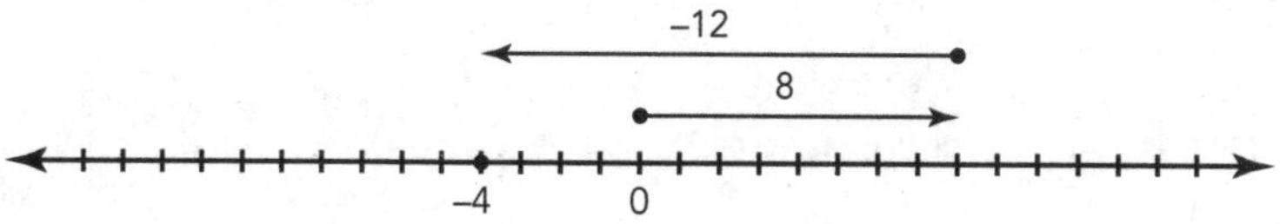

3. 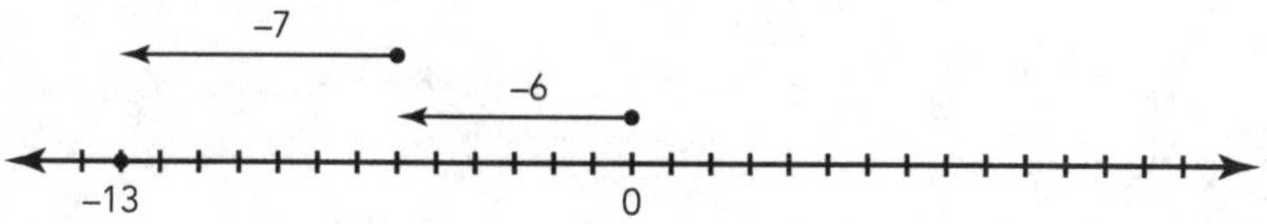

LEARNING GOALS

- Model subtraction of integers on a number line.
- Model subtraction of integers using two-color counters.
- Develop a rule for subtracting integers.
- Apply previous understandings of addition and subtraction to subtract rational numbers.

KEY TERM

- zero pair

You have added integers using number lines and two-color counter models. How can you use these models to subtract integers?

Getting Started

Take It Away

Each situation described has two different conclusions. Describe how you might model each on a number line.

1. You owe your friend $10.

a. You borrow an additional $5.

b. Your friend takes away $5 of that debt.

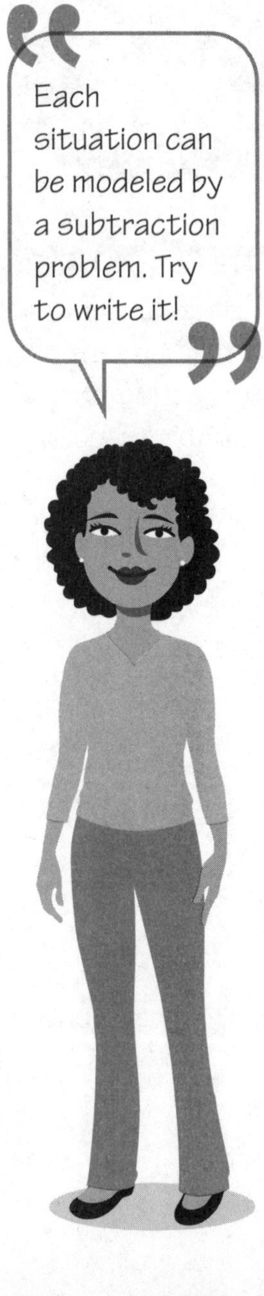

Each situation can be modeled by a subtraction problem. Try to write it!

2. The temperature is −7°.

a. Overnight it gets 12° colder.

b. During the day, it gets 12° warmer.

3. You have charged $65 on a credit card.

a. You return an item purchased with that card that cost $24.

b. You purchase an additional item with that card that cost $24.

4. You dug a hole in the ground that is 20 inches deep. Your dog sees the pile of dirt and thinks it's a game.

a. He knocks 6 inches of dirt back into the hole.

b. He digs the hole another 4 inches deeper.

ACTIVITY 4.1

Subtracting Integers on a Number Line

Think about how you moved on the number line when you were learning to add positive and negative numbers in the previous lesson. Let's walk the line to generate rules for subtracting integers.

Walk the number line for a subtraction sentence:

- Start at zero and walk to the value of the first term of the expression.
- To indicate subtraction, turn to face down the number line, towards the lesser negative numbers.
- Walk forward if subtracting a positive number or walk backward if subtracting a negative number.

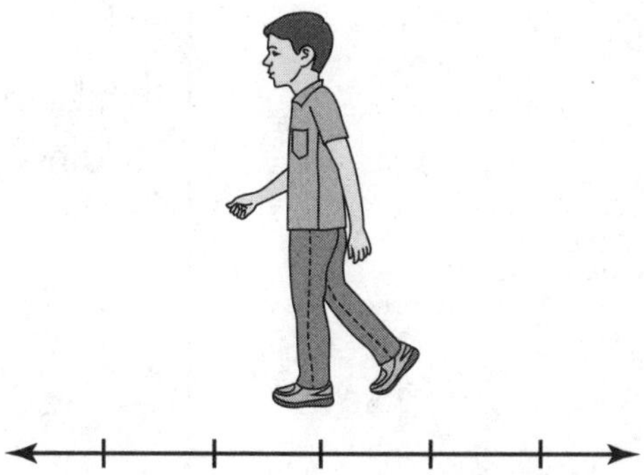

Your teacher will select a classmate to walk the line for each of the given problems. Help your classmate by preparing the directions that are needed.

1. Complete the table.

	Where You Start	Direction You Face on the Number Line	Walk Backwards or Forwards	Final Location
1 − 3				
0 − (−4)				
−3 − 5				
−1 − (−4)				

Cara thought about how she could take what she learned from walking the line and create a number line model on paper. She said, "Subtraction means to move in the opposite direction."

Analyze Cara's examples.

WORKED EXAMPLE

Example 1: $-6 - (+2)$

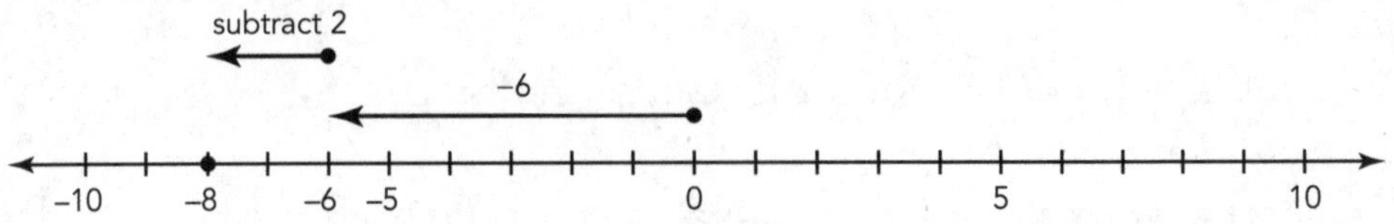

First, I moved to −6. Then, I went in the opposite direction of adding (+2) because I am subtracting (+2). So, I went two units to the left and ended up at −8.

$-6 - (+2) = -8$

Example 2: $-6 - (-2)$

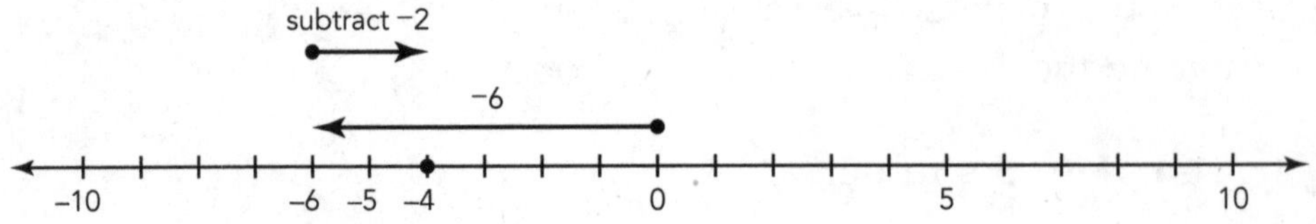

In this problem, I started by moving to −6. Because I am subtracting (−2), I went in the opposite direction of adding −2. So, I moved right two units and ended up at −4.

$-6 - (-2) = -4$

Example 3: $6 - (-2)$

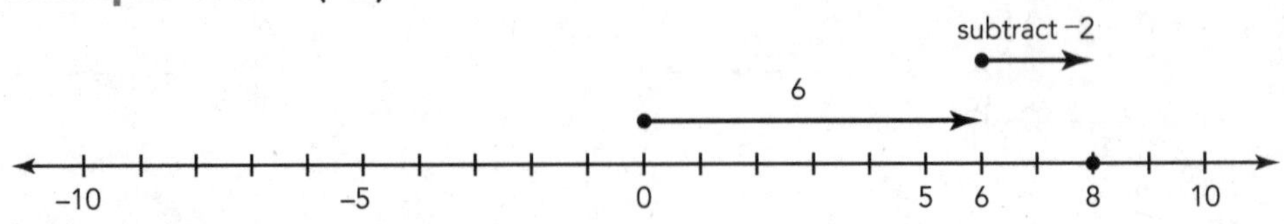

2. $6 - (-2) =$ ______

Explain the movement Cara modeled on the number line to determine the answer.

Example 4: 6 − (+2)

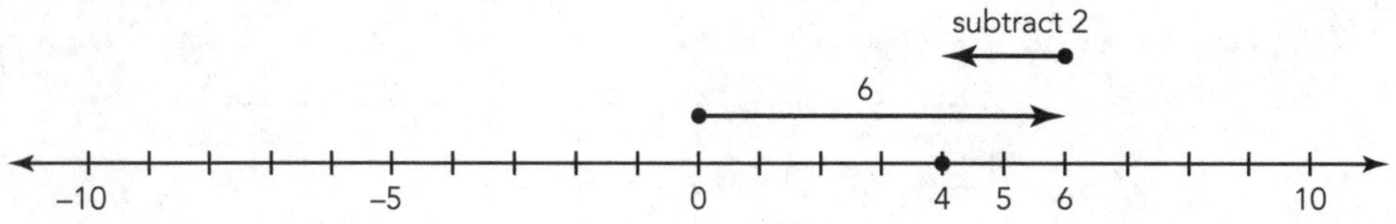

3. **6 − (+2) = ______**

   Explain the movement Cara modeled on the number line to determine the answer.

4. **Use the number line to complete each number sentence.**

   a. **−4 − (−3) = ______**

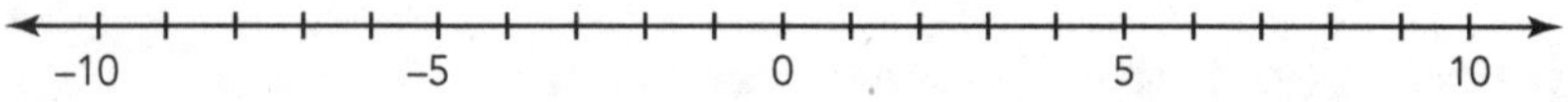

   b. **−4 − (−4) = ______**

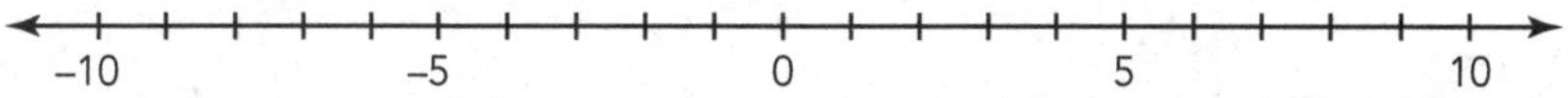

   c. **−4 − 3 = ______**

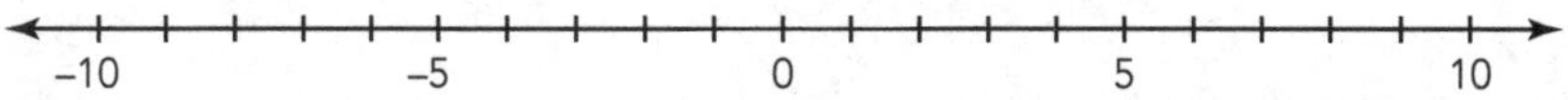

   d. **−4 − 4 = ______**

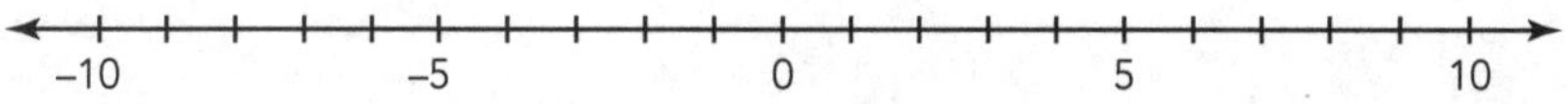

   e. **4 − (−3) = ______**

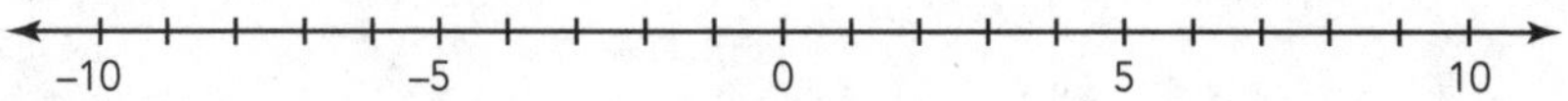

f. $4 - 4 =$ ______

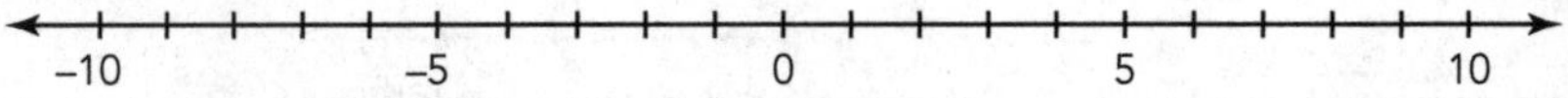

g. $4 - 3 =$ ______

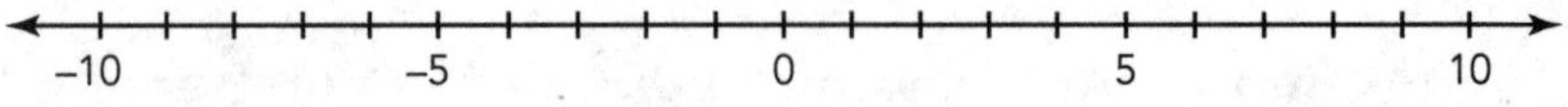

h. $4 - (-4) =$ ______

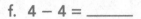

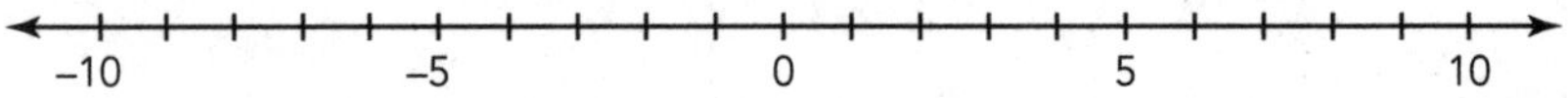

5. **What patterns did you notice when subtracting the integers in Question 4? Describe an addition problem that is similar to each subtraction problem.**

   a. **Subtracting two negative integers**

   b. **Subtracting two positive integers**

   c. **Subtracting a positive integer from a negative integer**

   d. **Subtracting a negative integer from a positive integer**

ACTIVITY
4.2
Subtracting Integers with Two-Color Counters

Subtraction can mean to "take away" objects from a set. Subtraction can also mean a comparison of two numbers, or the "difference between them."

The number line model and the two-color counter model used in the addition of integers can also be used to investigate the subtraction of integers.

WORKED EXAMPLE

Using just positive or just negative counters, you can show subtraction using the "take away" model.

Example 1: $7 - 5$
First, start with seven positive counters.

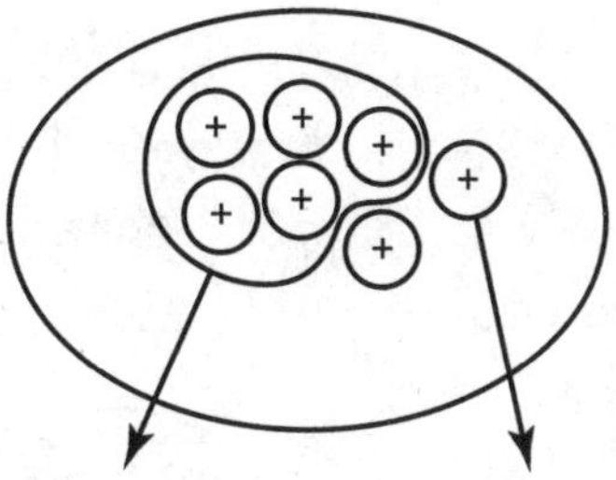

Then, take away five positive counters. Two positive counters remain.

$$7 - 5 = 2$$

Example 2: $-7 - (-5)$
First, start with seven negative counters.

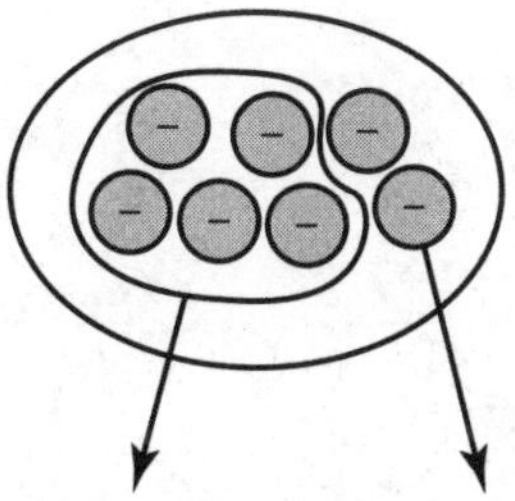

Then, take away five negative counters. Two negative counters remain.

$$-7 - (-5) = -2$$

1. **How are Examples 1 and 2 similar? How are these examples different?**

To subtract integers using both positive and negative counters, you will need to use *zero pairs*.

+ = 0

Recall that the value of a ⊖ and ⊕ pair is zero. So, together they form a **zero pair**. You can add as many pairs as you need and not change the value.

WORKED EXAMPLE

Example 3: 7 − (−5)

Start with seven positive counters.

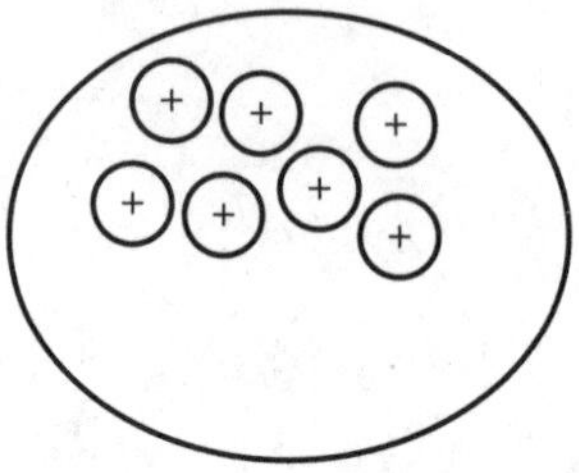

The expression says to subtract five negative counters, but there are no negative counters in the first model. Insert five negative counters into the model. So that you don't change the value, you must also insert five positive counters.

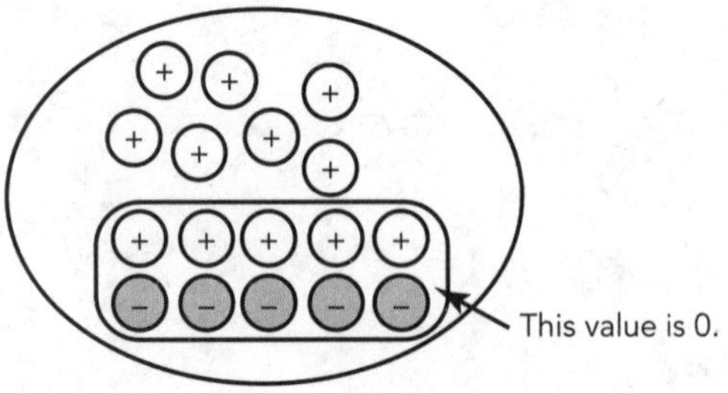
This value is 0.

Now, you can subtract, or take away, the five negative counters.

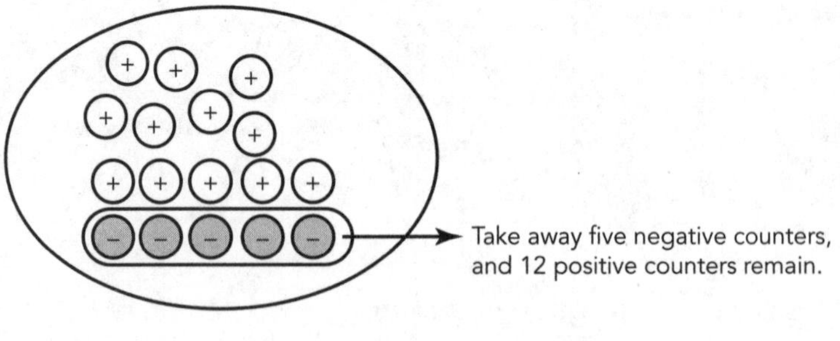
Take away five negative counters, and 12 positive counters remain.

7 − (−5) = 12

2. Why is the second model equivalent to the original model?

Example 4: $-7 - 5$

Start with seven negative counters.

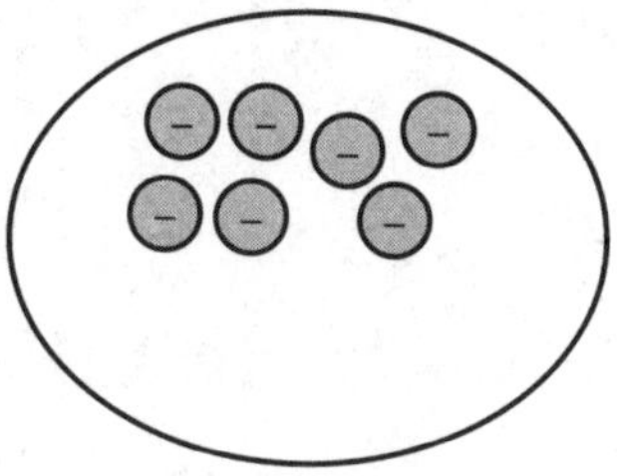

3. The expression says to subtract five positive counters, but there are no positive counters in the first model.

a. How can you insert positive counters into the model and not change the value?

b. Complete the model.

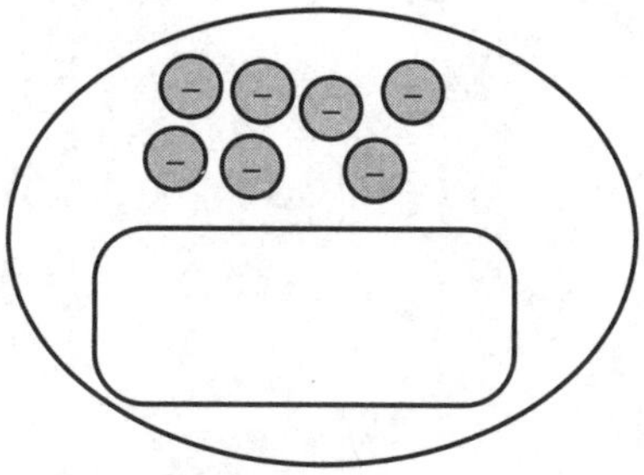

This is a little bit like regrouping in subtraction.

c. Now, subtract, or take away, the five positive counters. Determine the difference.

4. Draw a representation for each subtraction problem. Then, calculate the difference.

a. $4 - (-5)$

b. $-4 - (-5)$

c. $-4 - 5$

d. $4 - 5$

5. How could you model $0 - (-7)$?

   a. Draw a sketch of your model. Then, determine the difference.

   b. In part (a), does it matter how many zero pairs you add? Explain your reasoning.

6. Does the order in which you subtract two numbers matter? Draw models and provide examples to explain your reasoning.

7. Are the rules you wrote at the end of the previous activity true for the two-color counter models? What else did you learn about subtracting integers?

NOTES

ACTIVITY 4.3 Analyzing Integer Subtraction

You probably have noticed some patterns when subtracting signed numbers on the number line and with two-color counters. Let's explore these patterns to develop a rule.

$-8 - 5 = -13$

$-8 - 4 = -12$

$-8 - 3 = -11$

$-8 - 2 = -10$

$-8 - 1 = -9$

$-8 - 0 = -8$

1. Analyze the number sentences shown.

a. What patterns do you see? What happens as the integer subtracted from -8 decreases?

b. From your pattern, predict the answer to $-8 - (-1)$.

Consider the subtraction expression $-8 - (-2)$.

Cara's Method

Start at -8. Since I'm subtracting, you go in the opposite direction of adding (-2), which means I go to the right 2 units. The answer is -6.

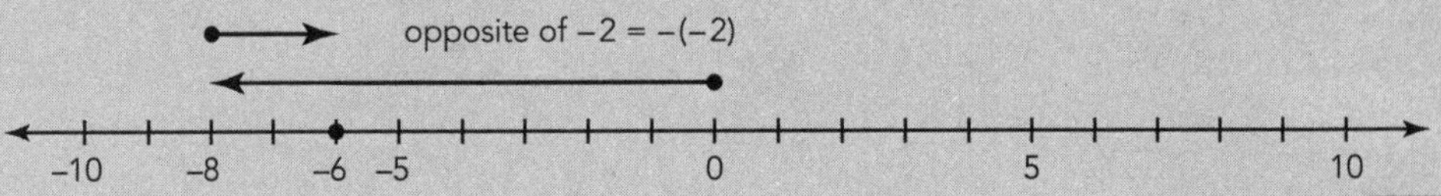

Neveah's Method

I see another pattern. Since subtraction is the inverse of addition, you can think of subtraction as adding the opposite number.

$-8 - (-2)$ is the same as $-8 + (+2)$

$-8 + 2 = -6$

2. How is Neveah's method similar to Cara's method?

3. Use Neveah's method to fill in each blank.

$10 - (-4) = 10 + (______) = ______$

4. Determine each difference.

a. $-9 - (-2) =$

b. $-3 - (-3) =$

c. $-7 - 5 =$

d. $24 - 8 =$

e. $-4 - 2 =$

f. $5 - 9 =$

g. $-20 - (-30) =$

h. $-10 - 18 =$

5. Determine the unknown integer in each number sentence.

a. $3 + _________ = 7$

b. $2 + _________ = -7$

c. $_________ + -20 = -10$

d. $_________ - 5 = 40$

e. $_________ - (-5) = 40$

f. $_________ + 5 = 40$

g. $6 + _________ = 52$

h. $-6 + _________ = 52$

i. $-6 + _________ = -52$

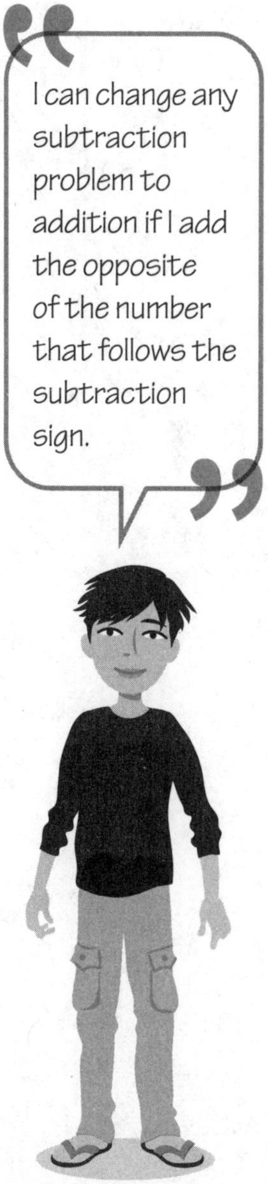

I can change any subtraction problem to addition if I add the opposite of the number that follows the subtraction sign.

ACTIVITY 4.4 Distance Between Rational Numbers

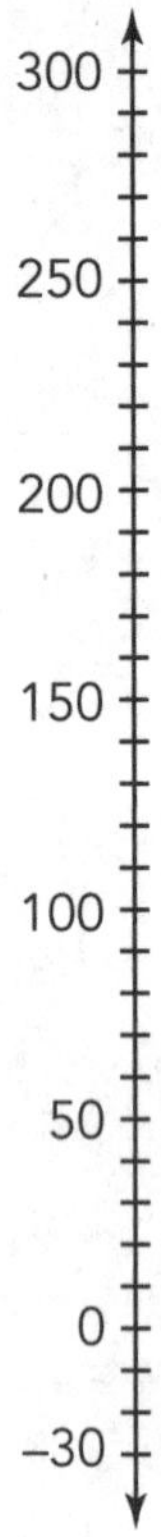

Amusement parks are constantly trying to increase the level of thrills on their rides. One way is to make the roller coasters drop faster and farther. A certain roller coaster begins by climbing a hill that is 277 feet above ground. Riders go from the top of that hill to the bottom, which is in a tunnel 14 feet under ground, in approximately 3 seconds!

Determine the vertical distance from the top of the roller coaster to the bottom of the tunnel.

1. **Plot the height and depth of the first hill of the roller coaster on the number line.**

Consider Christian's and Mya's methods for determining the vertical distance.

Christian

In sixth grade, I learned that you could add the absolute values of each number to calculate the distance.

$$|277| + |-14| = 277 + 14$$

$$= 291$$

The vertical distance is 291 feet.

Mya

I learned in elementary school that the difference between two numbers on a number line can be determined with subtraction. Because absolute value measures distance, I need the absolute value of the difference.

$$|277 - (-14)| = |277 + (+14)|$$
$$= |291|$$
$$= 291$$

The vertical distance is 291 feet.

2. Describe how Christian and Mya used absolute value differently to determine the vertical distance from the top of the roller coaster to the bottom of the tunnel.

3. Carson wonders if order matters. Instead of calculating the distance from the top to the bottom, he wants to calculate the vertical distance from the bottom to the top. Is Carson correct? Determine if Carson is correct using both Christian's strategy and Mya's strategy.

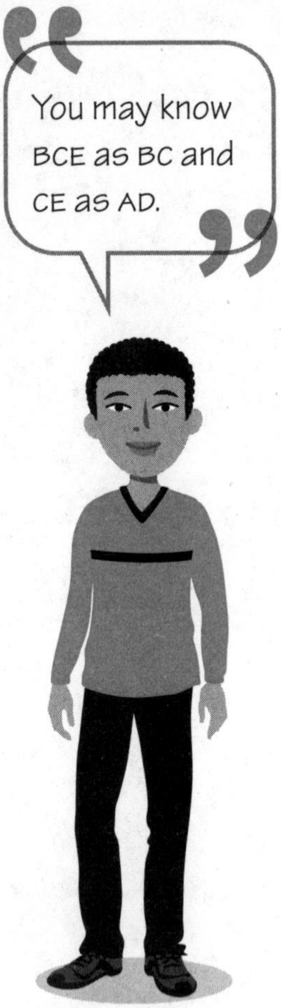

You may know BCE as BC and CE as AD.

As demonstrated in Mya's strategy, the distance between two numbers on the number line is the absolute value of their difference. Use Mya's strategy to solve each problem.

4. **The first recorded Olympic Games began in 776 BCE. Called the *Ancient Olympics*, games were held every four years until being abolished by Roman Emperor Theodosius I in 393 CE.**

   a. **Represent the start and end years of the Ancient Olympic Games as integers.**

   b. **Determine the length of time between the start and end of the Ancient Olympic Games.**

   c. **Determine the length of time between the start of the Ancient Olympics and the Modern Olympics, which began in 1896.**

   d. **If you research the ancient calendar, you will learn that there actually was no Year 0. The calendar went from −1 BCE to 1 CE. Adjust your answer from part (c) to account for this.**

5. **On February 10, 2011, the temperature in Nowata, OK, hit a low of −31°. Over the course of the next week, the temperature increased to a high of 79°. How many degrees different was the low from the high temperature?**

NOTES

TALK the TALK

Determining the Difference

Use what you have learned about adding and subtracting with integers to think about patterns in addition and subtraction.

1. **Determine whether these subtraction sentences are always true, sometimes true, or never true. Give examples to explain your thinking.**

   a. **positive − positive = positive**

   b. **negative − positive = negative**

   c. **positive − negative = negative**

   d. **negative − negative = negative**

2. **If you subtract two negative integers, will the answer be greater than or less than the number you started with? Explain your thinking.**

3. **What happens when a positive number is subtracted from zero?**

NOTES

4. What happens when a negative number is subtracted from zero?

5. Just by looking at the problem, how do you know if the sum of two integers is positive, negative, or zero?

6. How are addition and subtraction of integers related?

7. Write a rule for subtracting positive and negative integers.

Assignment

Write

Define the term *zero pair* in your own words.

Remember

You can change any subtraction problem to an addition problem without changing the answer. Subtracting two integers is the same as adding the opposite of the subtrahend, the number you are subtracting.

Practice

1. Draw both a model using two-color counters and a model using a number line to represent each number sentence. Then, determine the difference.
   a. $-8 - (-5)$
   b. $-4 - 9$
   c. $2 - (-8)$
   d. $3 - 12$
2. Determine each difference without using a number line.
   a. $7 - (-13)$
   b. $10 - (-1)$
   c. $-16 - 3$
   d. $-9 - 7$
   e. $-1 - (-2)$
   f. $-5 - (-5)$
   g. $19 - (-19)$
   h. $-8 - (-8)$
   i. $40 - (-20)$
   j. $-800 - (-300)$
3. The highest temperature ever recorded on Earth was 136° F at Al Aziziyah, Libya, in Africa. The lowest temperature ever recorded on Earth was −129° F at Vostok Station in Antarctica. Plot each temperature as an integer on a number line, and use absolute value to determine the difference between the two temperatures.
4. The highest point in the United States is Mount McKinley, Alaska, at about 6773 yards above sea level. The lowest point in the United States is the Badwater Basin in Death Valley, California, at about 87 yards below sea level. Plot each elevation as an integer on a number line, and use absolute value to determine the number of yards between in the lowest and highest points.

Stretch

1. Determine each difference without using a number line.
   a. $3.1 - (-3.3)$
   b. $-8.3 - 8.8$
   c. $42.5 - 45.6$
   d. $-28.4 - (-79.5)$
2. The deepest point in the ocean is the Marianas Trench in the Pacific Ocean at about 6.9 miles below sea level. The highest point in the world is Mount Everest in the Himalayan Mountains at about 5.5 miles. Plot each elevation as an rational number on a number line, and use absolute value to determine the number of miles between the deepest point in the ocean and the highest point in the world.

Review

1. The city of Nashville, Tennessee, constructed an exact replica of the Parthenon. In 1982, construction began on a sculpture of Athena Parthenos, which stands 41 feet 10 inches tall.
   a. The sculptor first made a 1 : 10 model from clay. This means that 1 inch on the model is equal to 10 inches on the real statue. What was the height of the clay model?
   b. Later the sculptor made a 1 : 5 model. This means that 1 inch on the model is equal to 5 inches on the real statue. What was the height of the model?
2. Write and solve a proportion to answer each problem. Show all your work.
   a. Tommy types 50 words per minute, with an average of 3 mistakes. How many mistakes would you expect Tommy to make if he typed 300 words? Write your answer using a complete sentence.
   b. Six cans of fruit juice cost $2.50. Ned needs to buy 72 cans for a camping trip for the Outdoor Club. How much will he spend?
3. Solve each equation for x.
   a. $72 = 55 + x$
   b. $\frac{4}{5}x = 60$

All Mixed Up 5

Adding and Subtracting Rational Numbers

WARM UP

Determine each sum.

1. $\frac{1}{6} + \frac{1}{3}$

2. $\frac{2}{7} + \frac{2}{5}$

3. $\frac{1}{2} + \frac{3}{5}$

4. $\frac{1}{3} + \frac{4}{5}$

LEARNING GOALS

- Interpret and determine sums and differences of rational numbers in real-world contexts.
- Represent and apply the additive inverse in real-world contexts.
- Determine distance as the absolute value of the difference between two signed numbers in real-world contexts.
- Solve real-world and mathematical problems involving operations with rational numbers.

You have learned how to add and subtract with signed numbers using models and rules. How can you solve real-world problems by adding and subtracting signed numbers?

Getting Started

No Matter the Number

Consider this addition problem: $-3\frac{3}{4} + 4\frac{1}{4} = ?$

1. **Draw a model to add the two numbers and determine the sum. Explain how your model represents the addition problem.**

Remember, addends are the numbers being added.

2. **How would your model be different if the addends were integers? How would the model be the same?**

3. **Describe how you can apply the rules you have learned about adding signed numbers to determine the sum of $-3\frac{3}{4}$ and $4\frac{1}{4}$.**

ACTIVITY 5.1

Sum of Rational Numbers Problems

You can use what you know about adding and subtracting positive and negative integers to solve problems with positive and negative fractions and decimals.

Yesterday, Katrina was just $23.75 below her fundraising goal. She got a check today for $12.33 to put toward the fundraiser. Describe Katrina's progress toward the goal.

WORKED EXAMPLE

You can model this situation using addition:

–$23.75 + $12.33

–$23.75: currently below the goal

$12.33: got a check for this amount

- Estimate.

  Katrina will still be below her goal, because $-23.75 + 12.33 < 0$.

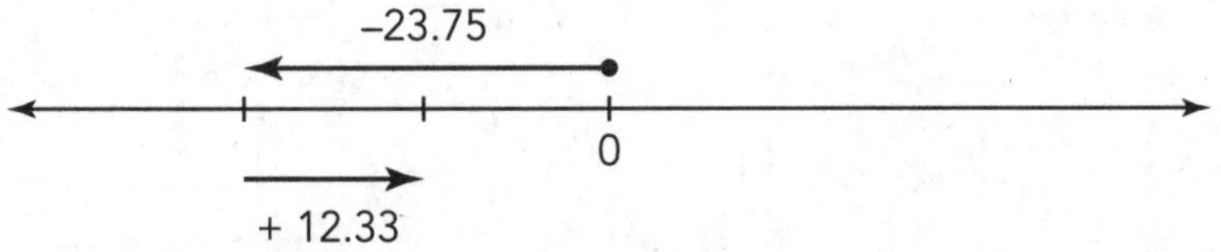

- Determine the sum.

  $-23.75 + 12.33 = -11.42$

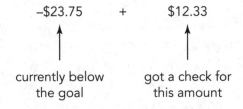

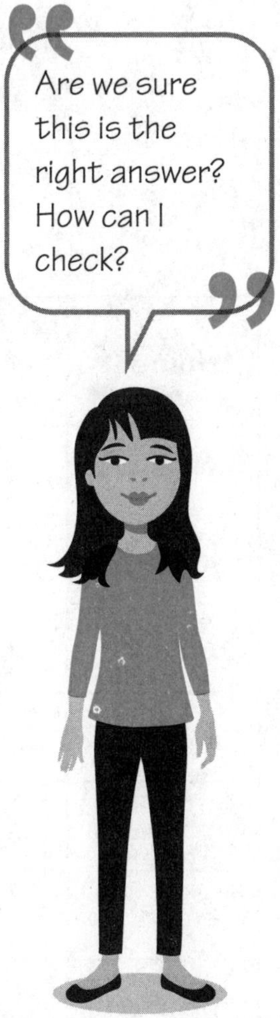

Are we sure this is the right answer? How can I check?

1. Explain how the final sum was calculated.

2. What does the sum mean in terms of the problem situation?

3. Explain how you can know that addition is the correct operation to use to solve this problem.

Sketch a model to estimate each sum or difference. Then determine each solution and write an equation.

4. The table shows the freezing points of some of the elements in the periodic table.

Element	Freezing Point (°F)
Helium	−458
Hydrogen	−434
Oxygen	−368.77
Nitrogen	$-345\frac{3}{4}$
Chlorine	−149.51
Mercury	$-37\frac{7}{10}$
Phosphorus	111.7

a. Patricia and Elliott are trying to figure out how much the temperature would have to increase from the freezing point of hydrogen to reach the freezing point of phosphorus. Patricia says the temperature would have to increase 545.7°, and Elliott says the temperature would have to increase 322.3°. Who is correct?

b. Francine and Lisa are trying to figure out how much the temperature would have to increase from the freezing point of nitrogen to reach the freezing point of mercury. Francine says the temperature would have to increase $308\frac{1}{20}$°, and Lisa says the temperature would have to increase $383\frac{9}{20}$°. Who is correct?

5. A drilling crew dug to a height of $-45\frac{1}{4}$ feet during their first day of drilling. On the second day, the crew dug down $9\frac{1}{3}$ feet more than on the first day. Describe the height of the bottom of the hole after the second day.

6. The ancient Babylonians were writing fractions in 1800 BCE. But they did not have a concept of zero until about 1489 years later. In what year did the Babylonians develop the concept of zero?

The abbreviation BCE means "before the common era," or before Year 0.

7. Ben purchased lunch today at the school cafeteria for $2.75. Before today, Ben owed $9.15 on his lunch account. What is the status of his lunch account after today?

8. The highest mountain in the world is Mt. Everest, whose peak is 29,029 feet above sea level. But the tallest mountain is Mauna Kea. The base of Mauna Kea is 19,669 feet below sea level, and its peak is 33,465 feet above its base. How much higher above sea level is Mt. Everest than Mauna Kea?

ACTIVITY
5.2

Rational Number Difference Problems

The freezing point of chlorine is –149.51° Fahrenheit. The element zinc freezes at much higher temperatures. The freezing point of zinc is 787.51° Fahrenheit. How many more degrees is the freezing point of zinc than the freezing point of chlorine?

WORKED EXAMPLE

You can model this situation using subtraction:

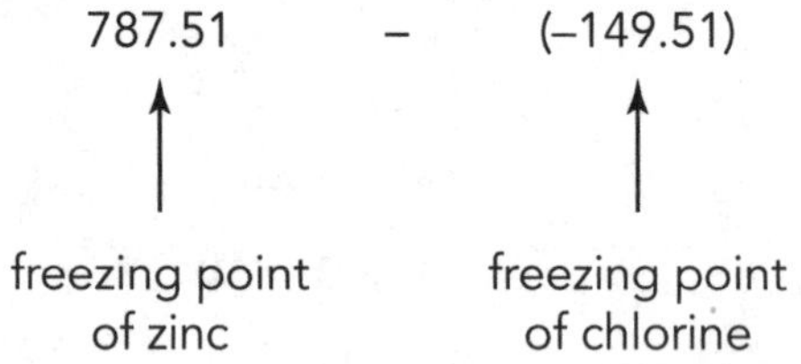

- Estimate.

  The answer is greater than 787.51, because 787.51−(−149.51) = 787.51 + 149.51.

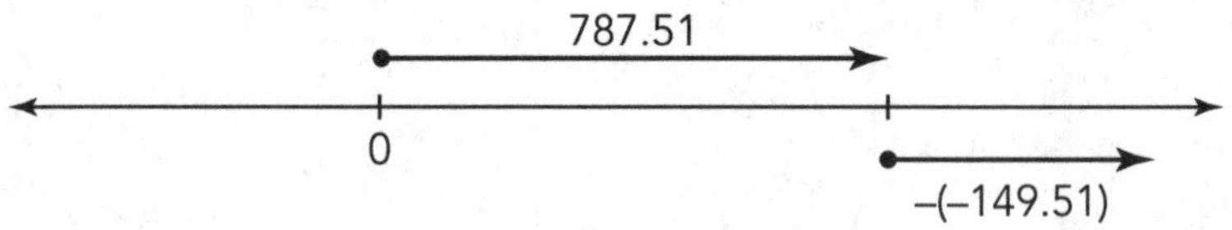

- Determine the difference. Write an equation.

  787.51−(−149.51) = 937.02

1. What does the difference mean in terms of the problem situation?

2. Explain how you can check the answer.

Sketch a model to estimate. Then determine each solution and write an equation.

3. **The temperature in Wichita, Kansas, is -3°C. The temperature in Ryan's hometown is 18° colder than that. What is the temperature in Ryan's hometown?**

4. **To qualify to compete in the high jump finals, athletes must jump a certain height in the semi-finals. Clarissa jumped $2\frac{3}{8}$ inches below the qualifying height, but her friend Anika made it to $1\frac{5}{6}$ inches over the qualifying height. How much higher was Anika's semi-final jump compared with Clarissa's?**

5. **The Down Under roller coaster rises up to 65.8 feet above the ground before dropping 90 feet into an underground cavern. Describe the height of the roller coaster at the bottom of the cavern.**

NOTES

ACTIVITY 5.3 Adding and Subtracting Rational Numbers

Determine each sum or difference.

1. $4.7 + (-3.65)$

2. $-\frac{2}{3} + \frac{5}{8}$

3. $3.95 + (-6.792)$

4. $2\frac{5}{7} + \left(-1\frac{1}{3}\right)$

5. $-\frac{3}{4} + \frac{5}{8}$

6. $-7.38 - (-6.2)$

7. $-\frac{3}{4} - \frac{5}{8}$

8. $-2\frac{5}{6} + 1\frac{3}{8}$

9. $-\frac{7}{12} - \frac{5}{6}$

10. $-37.27 + (-13.2)$

11. $-0.8 - (-0.6)$

12. $2\frac{3}{7} + \left(-1\frac{3}{4}\right)$

NOTES

13. $0.67 + (-0.33)$

14. $-42.65 - (-16.3)$

15. $-7300 + 2100$

16. $-3\frac{5}{8} - \left(-2\frac{1}{3}\right)$

17. $-4.7 + 3.16$

18. $26.9 - (-3.1)$

19. $-325 + (-775)$

20. $-2\frac{1}{5} - 1\frac{3}{10}$

NOTES

TALK the TALK

Mixing Up the Sums

Represent each number as the sum of two rational numbers. Use a number line to explain your answer.

1. -2.1

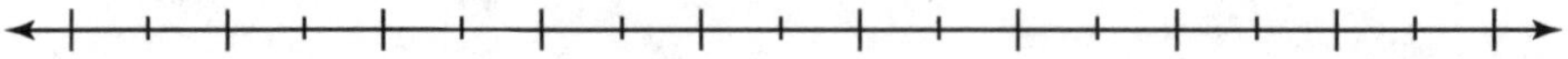

2. $-5\frac{2}{3}$

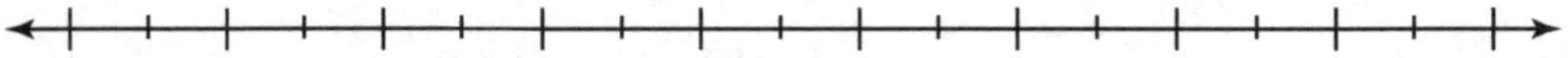

3. $4\frac{7}{9}$

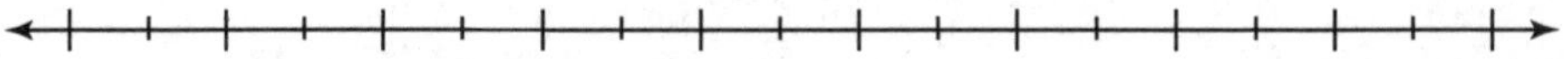

4. 5.8

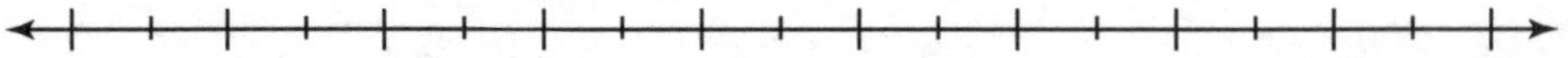

5. $-1\frac{4}{7}$

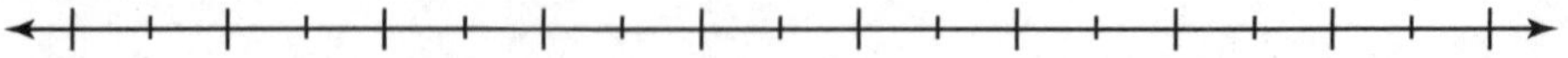

Assignment

Write

Explain in your own words how adding and subtracting positive and negative numbers with fractions and decimals is different from and similar to adding and subtracting with whole numbers.

Remember

The opposite of a number is called the additive inverse of the number. The absolute value of the difference between two numbers is a measure of the distance between the numbers.

Practice

Consider the subtraction expression $-1.3 - (-2.4)$.

1. Use a number line to solve the problem.
2. Use a two-color counter model to solve the problem.

Calculate each sum. Be sure to estimate first.

3. $12\frac{2}{5} + \left(-3\frac{1}{4}\right)$
4. $5.3 + (-7.45)$
5. $-\frac{5}{8} + 8\frac{3}{8}$

Calculate each difference. Estimate before calculating.

6. $-8.38 - 11.29$
7. $7\frac{2}{3} - \left(-4\frac{1}{4}\right)$
8. $-4\frac{5}{6} - 6\frac{2}{3}$

Stretch

Determine each solution. Let $-3 = x$, $-5 = y$, and $-4 = k$.

1. $|x - y - y - k + y + x|$
2. $k - y - k + x + k$
3. $-k - y + x - y$

Review

1. Determine each difference. Then, write a sentence that describes the movement on the number line that you could use to solve the problem.
   a. $7 - (-6)$
   b. $-5 - 13$
2. Shilo is riding her bicycle across the state of Georgia to raise money for her favorite charity. The distance in miles that she can travel varies directly with the length of time in hours she spends riding. Assume that her constant of proportionality is 18. What does the constant of proportionality represent in this problem?
3. The constant of proportionality between the number of children on a field trip and the number of teachers on the trip is $\frac{14}{3}$. There are 70 children on a field trip. How many teachers are on the trip?
4. Determine two unit rates for each given rate.
   a. 12 students ate 4.5 pizzas.
   b. Shae painted $\frac{1}{3}$ of the wall in $\frac{1}{4}$ hour.

Adding and Subtracting Rational Numbers Summary

KEY TERMS

- absolute value
- additive inverses
- zero pair

LESSON 1 Math Football

Combining positive and negative moves together on a line results in moving to the left, moving to the right, or staying in the same position, depending on the size of the positive and negative values. For example, the table shows possible moves in the game of Math Football.

	Player	Starting Position	Results of the Number Cubes Roll	Ending Position
First Turn	Home Team	0	Red 3 and Black 5	+2
	Visiting Team	0	Red 5 and Black 6	+1
Second Turn	Home Team	+2	Red 1 and Black 6	+7
	Visiting Team	+1	Red 6 and Black 2	−3

LESSON 2 Walk the Line

A number line can be used to model integer addition. When adding a positive integer, move to the right on a number line. When adding a negative integer, move to the left on a number line.

For example, this number line model shows how to determine 5 + (−8).

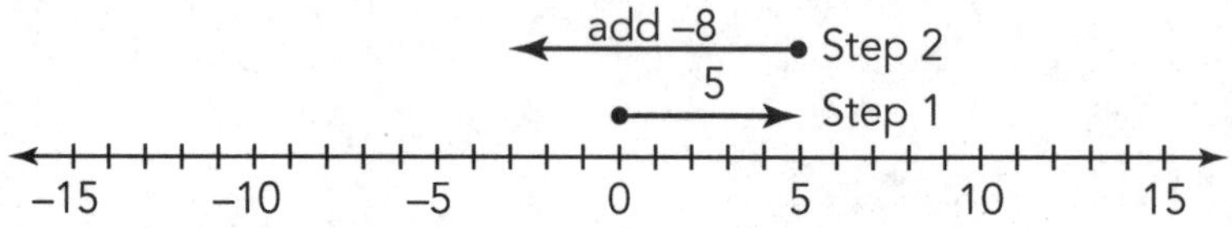

The **absolute value** of a number is its distance from 0. The absolute value of 5 is 5, and the absolute value of −8 is 8.

LESSON 3 Two-Color Counters

You can model the addition of integers using two-color counters that represent positive (+) charges and negative (−) charges.

The expression 3 + (−3) can be modeled in different ways.

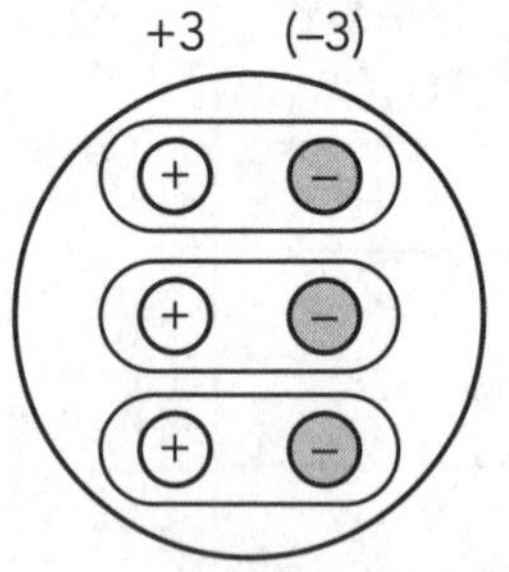

3 + (−3) = 0

Each positive charge is paired with a negative charge.

Each pair of positive and negative charges has no charge.

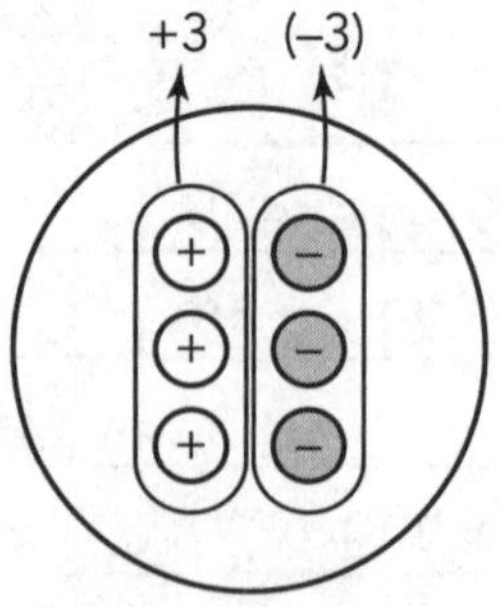

3 + (−3) = 0

Three positive charges and three negative charges have no charge.

Two numbers with the sum of zero are called **additive inverses.** You can use additive inverses to model adding integers with different absolute values.

For example, the expression 5 + (−8) is modeled here using two-color counters. There are 3 negative charges remaining. The sum of 5 + (−8) is −3.

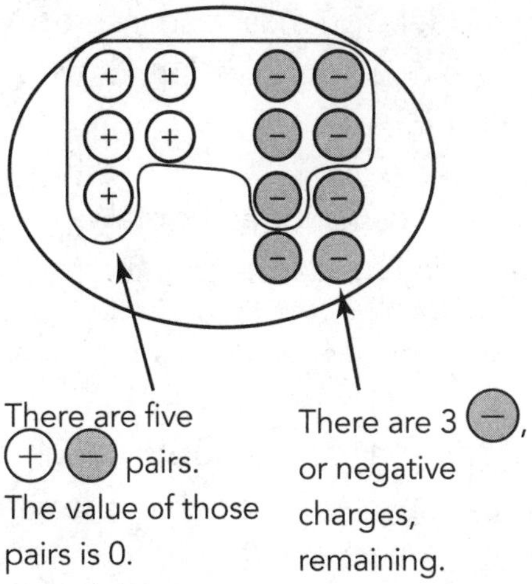

There are five (+)(−) pairs. The value of those pairs is 0.
There are 3 (−), or negative charges, remaining.

These are the rules for adding integers:

- When two integers have the same sign and are added together, the sign of the sum is the sign of both integers.
- When two integers have opposite signs and are added together, the absolute values of the integers are subtracted and the sign of the sum is the sign of the integer with the greater absolute value.

LESSON 4

What's the Difference?

A number line can be used to model integer subtraction. When subtracting an integer, you move in the opposite direction.

For example, the number line model shows how to determine −6 − (+2).

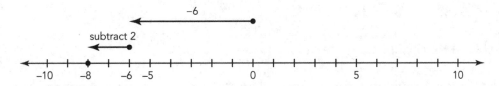

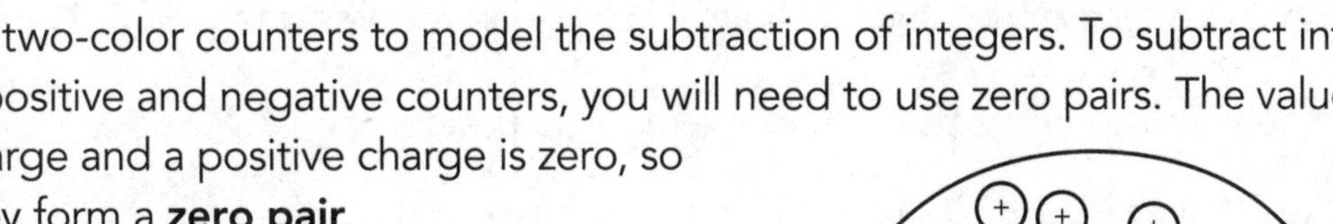

First, move to −6. Then, move in the opposite direction of adding (+2).

You can use two-color counters to model the subtraction of integers. To subtract integers using both positive and negative counters, you will need to use zero pairs. The value of a negative charge and a positive charge is zero, so together they form a **zero pair**.

For example, the expression 7 − (−5) is modeled here using two-color counters.

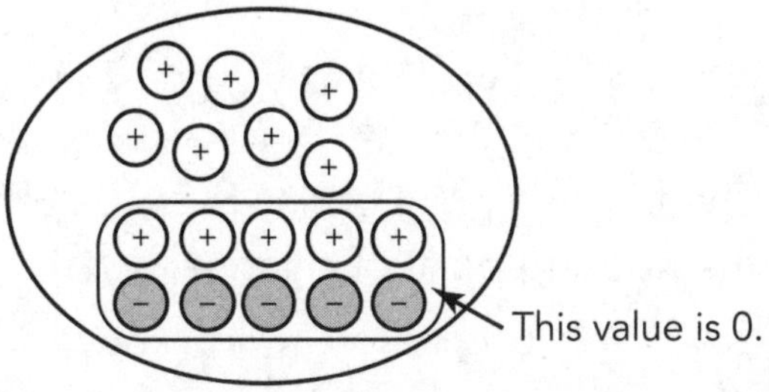

Start with 7 positive counters. There are no negative counters to subtract, so insert 5 negative counters into the model. You must also insert 5 positive counters in order not to change the value.

Now you can subtract, or take away, the 5 negative counters.

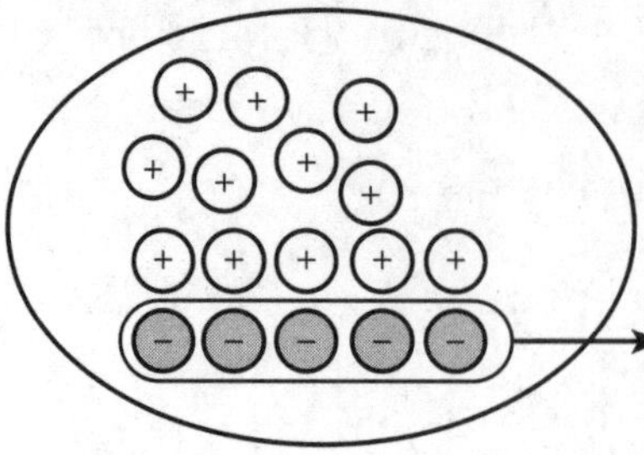

Take away 5 negative counters, and 12 positive counters remain.

$7 - (-5) = 12$

You can change any subtraction problem to an addition problem without changing the answer. Subtracting two integers is the same as adding the opposite of the subtrahend, the number you are subtracting.

LESSON 5

All Mixed Up

You can use what you know about adding and subtracting integers to solve problems with positive and negative fractions and decimals.

For example, yesterday, Katrina was just \$23.75 below her fundraising goal. She got a check today for \$12.33 to put toward the fundraiser. Describe Katrina's progress toward the goal.

$-\$23.75 + \$12.33 = -\$11.42$

Katrina will still be below her goal, because $-11.42 < 0$.

The difference between two numbers is a measure of the distance between the numbers.

For example, the freezing point of chlorine is −149.51°F. The freezing point of zinc is 787.51°F. How many more degrees is the freezing point of zinc than the freezing point of chlorine?

A model can help you estimate that the answer will be greater than 787.51.

$787.51 - (-149.51) = 937.02$

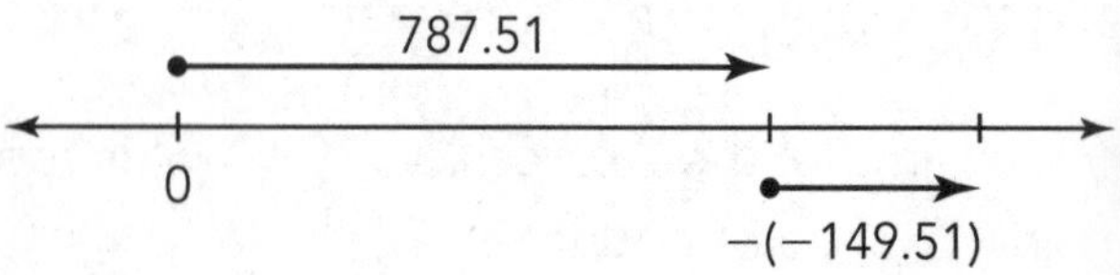

The freezing point of zinc is 937.02°F more than the freezing point of chlorine.

TOPIC 2

Multiplying and Dividing Rational Numbers

Multiplying and dividing are all about equal groups. Five each of four kinds of chocolate makes 20 total chocolates.

Module 2: Operating with Signed Numbers

TOPIC 2: MULTIPLYING AND DIVIDING RATIONAL NUMBERS

In this topic, students use number lines and two-color counters to model the multiplication of integers before developing rules for determining the product of signed numbers. Students use patterns and multiplication fact families to develop the rules for the quotient of signed numbers, namely that the same rules apply to quotients as products. After students understand multiplying and dividing integers, they apply the rules to the set of rational numbers in the context of problem solving.

Where have we been?

Students have learned to use number lines and two-color counters to represent and model operations with integers. Even earlier, in elementary school, students learned that multiplication can be viewed as repeated addition and as equal groups of objects. Fact families, a familiar concept from elementary school, are used to help students generalize the rules for the signs of the products and quotients.

Where are we going?

It is essential that students develop a strong conceptual foundation for multiplying and dividing with rational numbers, as a basis for manipulating and representing increasingly complex numeric and algebraic expressions. In high school, students will focus more on expressions and equations than on numbers, including rational expressions, equations, and functions.

Modeling Integer Products with Two-Color Counters and Number Lines

Both the number line and counter models represent the product $3 \times (-4)$, or 3 groups of -4.

Consider the expression $3 \times (-4)$. As repeated addition, it is represented as $(-4) + (-4) + (-4)$.

You can think of $3 \times (-4)$ as three groups of (-4).

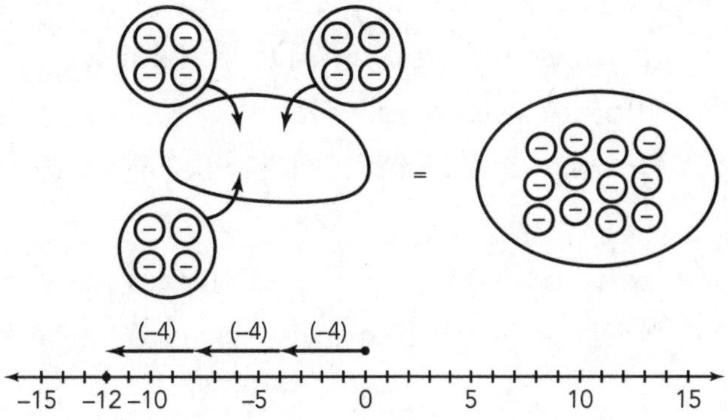

Myth: Just watch a video, and you will understand it.

Has this ever happened to you? Someone explains something, and it all makes sense at the time. You feel like you get it. But then, a day later when you try to do it on your own, you suddenly feel like something's missing? If that feeling is familiar, don't worry. It happens to us all. It's called the illusion of explanatory depth, and it frequently happens after watching a video.

How do you break this illusion? The first step is to try to make the video interactive. Don't treat it like a TV show. Instead, pause the video and try to explain it to yourself or to a friend. Alternatively, attempt the steps in the video on your own and rewatch it if you hit a wall. Remember, it's easy to confuse familiarity with understanding.

#mathmythbusted

Talking Points

You can further support your student's learning by asking questions about the work they do in class or at home. Your student is learning to multiply and divide with negative integers and rational numbers.

Questions to Ask

- How does this problem look like something you did in class?
- Can you show me the strategy you used to solve this problem? Do you know another way to solve it?
- Does your answer make sense? How do you know?
- Is there anything you don't understand? How can you use today's lesson to help?

Key Terms

terminating decimals

A terminating decimal has a finite number of digits, meaning that after a finite number of decimal places, all following decimal places have a value of 0.

repeating decimals

A repeating decimal is a decimal in which a digit or a group of digits repeat infinitely.

bar notation

Bar notation is used to indicate the digits that repeat in a repeating decimal. In the quotient of 1 and 7, the sequence 142857 repeats. The digits that lie underneath the bar are the digits that repeat.

$\frac{1}{7} = 0.142857142857... = 0.\overline{142857}$

Equal Groups

Multiplying and Dividing Integers

1

WARM UP

Determine each sum.

1. $-2\frac{3}{4} + \left(-2\frac{3}{4}\right)$

2. $-9.502 - 4.239$

3. $-3 + 8 + (-2)$

4. $5 - 16 + 7 + (-1)$

LEARNING GOALS

- Multiply integers using models.
- Develop rules for multiplying integers.
- Develop rules for dividing integers.

You know the reasoning and rules to add and subtract integers. How do you multiply and divide integers?

Getting Started

Addition or Multiplication?

Consider the addition problem $(-8) + (-8) + (-8) + (-8)$.

1. **Rewrite the addition problem as a multiplication problem.**

2. **Is the product from Question 1 positive or negative? Explain your reasoning.**

Consider the addition problem $(-1) + (-1) + (-1) + (-1) + (-1)$.

3. **Rewrite the addition problem as a multiplication problem.**

4. **Is the product from Question 3 positive or negative? Explain your reasoning.**

5. **What relationship helped you answer Questions 2 and 4?**

ACTIVITY 1.1

Modeling the Multiplication of Integers

NOTES

When thinking about multiplying integers, remember that multiplication can be represented as repeated addition.

WORKED EXAMPLE 1

Consider the expression 3×4.

As repeated addition, it is representented as $4 + 4 + 4$.

You can think of 3×4 as three groups of 4.

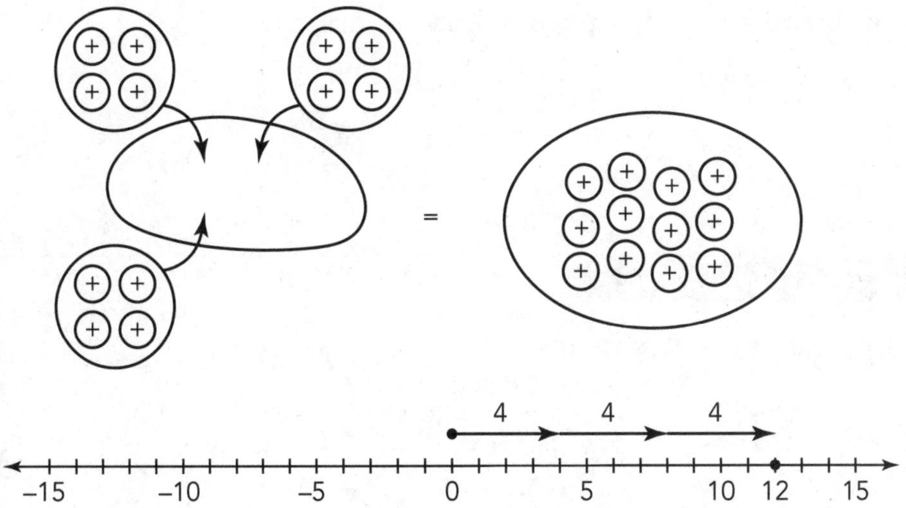

1. **Explain how the number line in Worked Example 1 illustrates 3×4.**

WORKED EXAMPLE 2

Consider the expression $3 \times (-4)$. As repeated addition, it is represented as $(-4) + (-4) + (-4)$.

You can think of $3 \times (-4)$ as three groups of (-4).

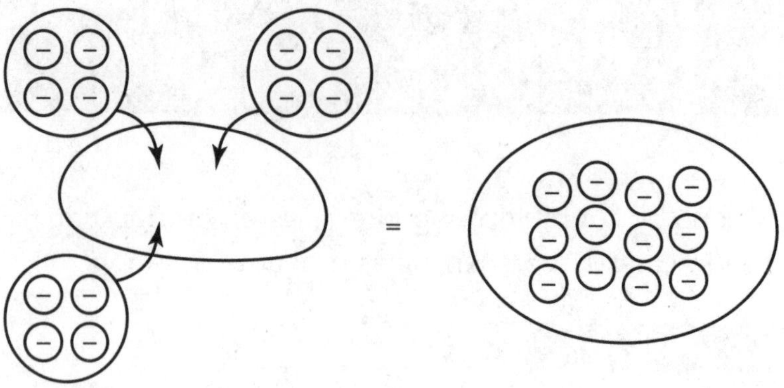

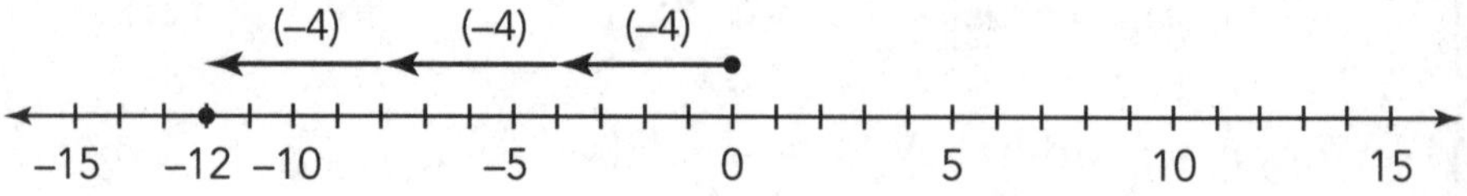

2. Explain how each model in Worked Example 2 can be interpreted as three groups of *the opposite of 4*.

WORKED EXAMPLE 3

Consider the expression $4 \times (-3)$.

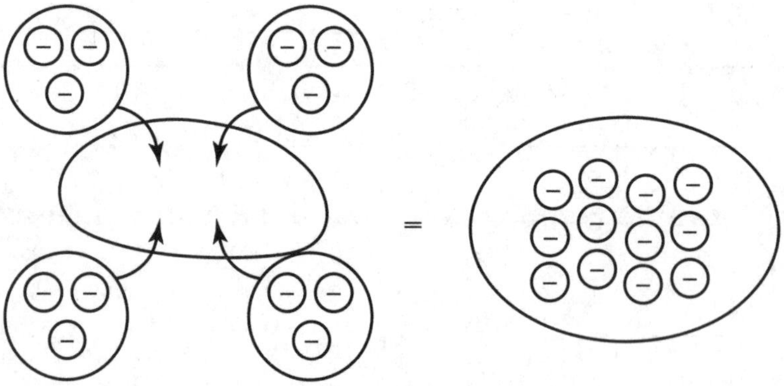

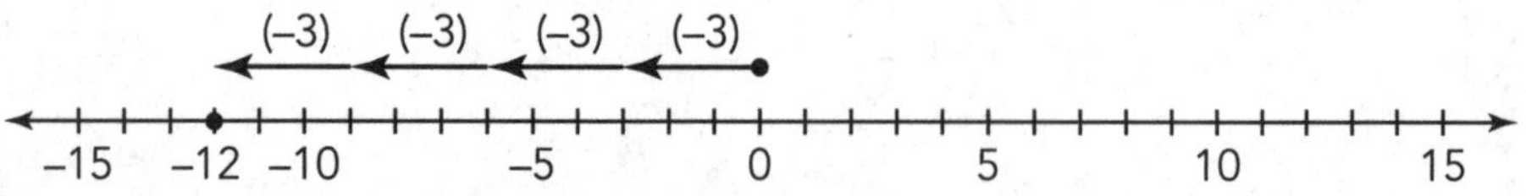

How is the number line model similar to models you have used to add positive numbers?

3. Interpret each model in Worked Example 3.

WORKED EXAMPLE 4

Consider the expression $(-3) \times (-4)$.

You know that $3 \times (-4)$ means "three groups of (-4)" and that -3 means "the opposite of 3." So, $(-3) \times (-4)$ means "the opposite of 3 groups of (-4)."

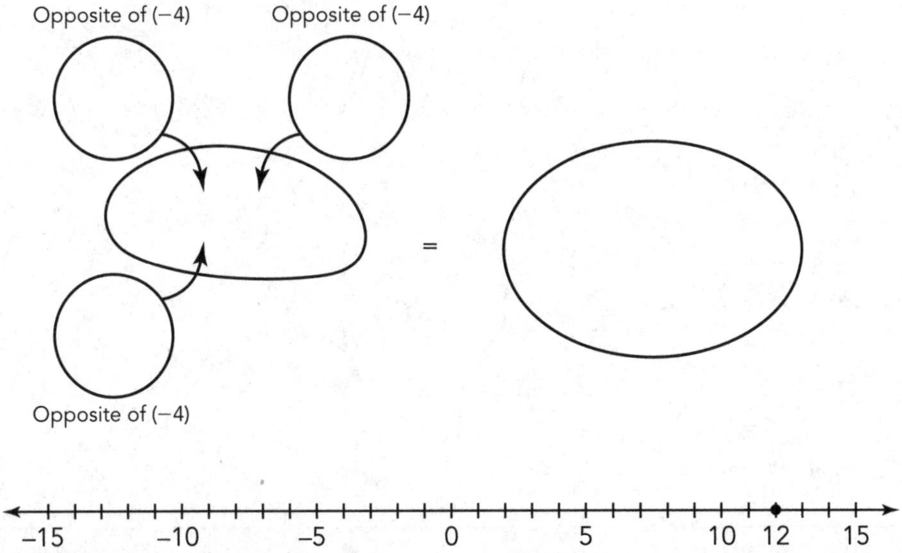

Think about how the 4 worked examples are alike and how they are different.

4. Complete the model by drawing in the appropriate counters and the appropriate rays in Worked Example 4.

a. Determine the product and explain how your models illustrate this product.

b. This expression can be written as $-((-4) + (-4) + (-4))$. Rewrite the expression as the opposite of a number: $-($______$)$.

c. How does the expression you wrote in part (b) relate to the product? Explain why this makes sense.

Use the examples if you need help.

5. Draw either a number line or two-color counter model to determine each product. Describe the expression in words.

a. 2×3

b. $2 \times (-3)$

c. $(-2) \times 3$

d. $(-2) \times (-3)$

6. Complete the table.

Expression	Description	Addition Sentence	Product
3×5	Three groups of 5	$5 + 5 + 5 = 15$	15
$(-3) \times 5$			
$3 \times (-5)$			
$(-3) \times (-5)$			

7. What do you notice about the products and their signs across the problems in this activity?

ACTIVITY
1.2 Signed Multiplication Facts

Analyze the sequence of products with 4.

$4 \times 5 = 20$
$4 \times 4 = 16$
$4 \times 3 = 12$
$4 \times 2 = 8$
$4 \times 1 = 4$
$4 \times 0 = 0$

1. What pattern do you notice in the products as the numbers multiplied by 4 decrease?

2. Continue the pattern to determine each product.

a. $4 \times (-1) =$ ____________ **b.** $4 \times (-2) =$ ____________

c. $4 \times (-3) =$ ____________

3. Describe the pattern(s) that you notice in the new products.

Analyze the sequence of products with −5.

$-5 \times 5 = -25$
$-5 \times 4 = -20$
$-5 \times 3 = -15$
$-5 \times 2 = -10$
$-5 \times 1 = -5$
$-5 \times 0 = 0$

4. Describe the pattern and then extend it by writing the next three number sentences.

5. How do these products change as the numbers multiplied by −5 decrease?

Look back at the products you have determined in this lesson to answer each question.

6. Describe the sign of the product of two integers when:

a. they are both positive.

b. they are both negative.

c. one is positive and one is negative.

d. one is zero.

7. If you know that the product of two integers is negative, what can you say about the two integers? Give examples.

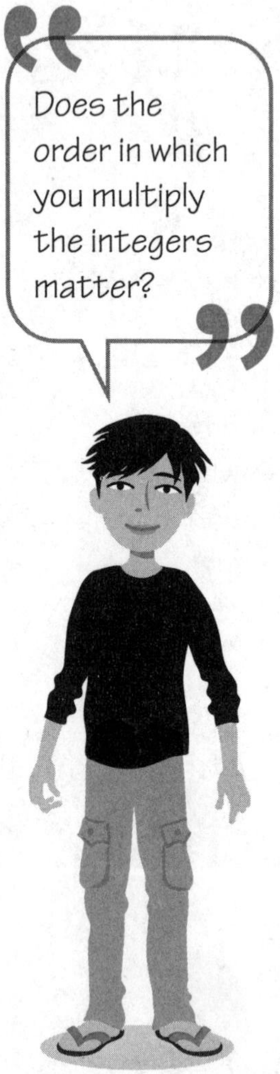

Does the order in which you multiply the integers matter?

8. Describe a rule that will help you multiply any two integers.

9. Use your rule to evaluate each expression.

a.

$6 \times 5 =$ ______

$6 \times (-5) =$ ______

$-6 \times 5 =$ ______

$-6 \times (-5) =$ ______

b.

$-8 \times 7 =$ ______

$-8 \times (-7) =$ ______

$8 \times (-7) =$ ______

$8 \times 7 =$ ______

c.

$-3 \times 2 \times (-4) =$ ______

$-3 \times (-2) \times (-4) =$ ______

$3 \times (-2) \times 4 =$ ______

$-3 \times (-2) \times 4 =$ ______

$3 \times 2 \times (-4) =$ ______

$-3 \times 2 \times 4 =$ ______

10. Describe the sign of each product and how you know.

    a. the product of three negative integers

    b. the product of four negative integers

    c. the product of seven negative integers

    d. the product of ten negative integers

Create some examples to test if you are not sure how to answer these questions.

11. What is the sign of the product of any odd number of negative integers? Explain your reasoning.

12. What is the sign of the product of three positive integers and five negative integers? Explain your reasoning.

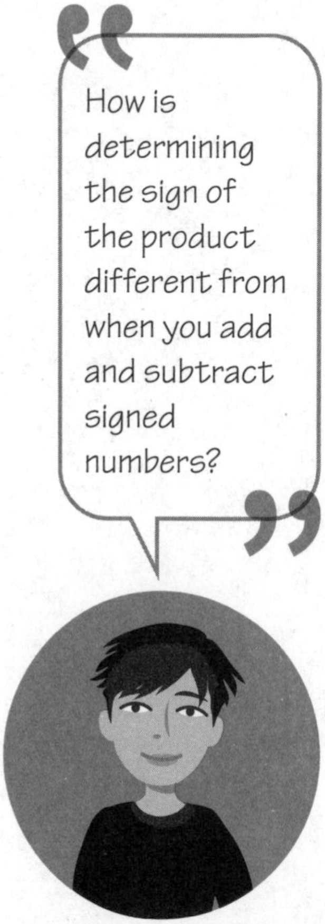

How is determining the sign of the product different from when you add and subtract signed numbers?

NOTES

ACTIVITY
1.3 Signed Fact Families

When you studied division in elementary school, you learned that multiplication and division were inverse operations. For every multiplication fact, you can write a corresponding division fact.

WORKED EXAMPLE

Consider the fact family for 4, 5, and 20.

$$4 \times 5 = 20$$
$$5 \times 4 = 20$$
$$20 \div 4 = 5$$
$$20 \div 5 = 4$$

Similarly, you can write fact families for integer multiplication and division.

EXAMPLES:

$-7 \times 3 = -21$	$-8 \times (-4) = 32$
$3 \times (-7) = -21$	$-4 \times (-8) = 32$
$-21 \div (-7) = 3$	$32 \div (-8) = -4$
$-21 \div 3 = -7$	$32 \div (-4) = -8$

1. What pattern(s) do you notice in each fact family?

2. Write a fact family for −6, 8, and −48.

3. Fill in the unknown numbers to make each number sentence true.

Use fact families to help you determine each answer.

a. $56 \div (-8) =$ ______
b. $28 \div (-4) =$ ______

c. $-63 \div$ ______ $= -7$
d. $24 \div$ ______ $= -8$

e. ______ $\div (-8) = -4$
f. $-105 \div$ ______ $= -5$

g. ______ $\div (-8) = 0$
h. $-26 \div$ ______ $= -1$

4. Describe the sign of the quotient of two integers when:

a. both integers are positive.

b. one integer is positive and one integer is negative.

c. both integers are negative.

d. the dividend is zero.

Remember that a quotient is the answer to a division problem.

5. How do the answers to Question 4 compare to the answers to the same questions about the multiplication of two integers? Explain your reasoning.

NOTES

TALK the TALK

What's Your Sign?

Think about patterns in the signs of sums, differences, products, and quotients of integers.

1. Determine two different sets of single-digit integers that make each number sentence true.

a. ____ × ____ = −42

b. ____ × ____ = 56

c. ____ × ____ = 63

d. ____ × ____ = −48

2. Complete the table by writing the sign (+, −, or +/−) to describe each sum, difference, product, or quotient.

Description of Integers	Addition (Sum)	Subtraction (Difference)	Multiplication (Product)	Division (Quotient)
two positive integers				
two negative integers				
one positive and one negative integer				

3. Create a true multiplication or division number sentence that meets the given condition.

a. positive product

b. negative product

c. positive quotient

d. negative quotient

Assignment

Write

Explain how you determine the sign of the product or quotient of three of integers.

Remember

To multiply and divide integers, perform the usual multiplication and division algorithms and then apply the correct sign to the product or quotient.

Practice

Draw a two-color counter model to determine each product. Describe the expression in words.

1. $6 \times (-3)$
2. -2×5
3. $-4 \times (-2)$

Complete a number line model to determine each product.

4. -2×7
5. $-5 \times (-3)$
6. $3 \times (-3)$

Determine each product.

7. 5×11
   $5 \times (-11)$
   -5×11
   $-5 \times (-11)$

8. $3 \times 4 \times 5$
   $-3 \times (-4) \times 5$
   $-3 \times 4 \times 5$
   $-3 \times (-4) \times (-5)$
   $3 \times 4 \times (-5)$
   $3 \times (-4) \times (-5)$

Determine the integer that makes each number sentence true.

9. ______ $\times (-9) = -36$

10. $3 \times$ ______ $= -24$

11. $14 \times$ ______ $= 56$

12. ______ $\times (-6) = 30$

13. $9 = (-63) \div$ ______

14. $-40 \div$ ______ $= -8$

15. $16 \div$ ______ $= -8$

16. ______ $\div (-6) = -4$

Stretch

Multiplication can be represented as repeated addition. Repeated multiplication leads to exponents. Use what you know about multiplying signed numbers to evaluate each expression.

1. $(-3)^3$
2. $(-4)^2$
3. $(-2)^5$
4. $\left(-\frac{1}{2}\right)^2$

What do you notice?

Review

1. The Baby Shop sells baby supplies for new families. They offer different brands of the same items. James and his mom are shopping for his new baby brother. It is James' job to make sure that his mom is making wise purchases. Their first item to purchase is diapers. There are 3 different options for newborn-sized diapers.

   Stay-Dry: 108 diapers for $25.18
   UberSoft: 180 diapers for $39.14
   Cuddlies: 160 diapers for $38.77

   a. What is a unit rate for the Stay-Dry diapers?
   b. What is a unit rate for the UberSoft diapers?
   c. What is a unit rate for the Cuddlies diapers?
   d. Which kind of diapers should James advise his mom to purchase?

2. Calculate each sum.

   a. $2\frac{1}{2} + \left(-3\frac{3}{4}\right) + 5\frac{2}{5}$

   b. $5\frac{1}{3} + \left(-4\frac{1}{6}\right) + \left(-2\frac{1}{2}\right)$

3. Determine each unit rate.

   a. $1\frac{1}{4}$ teaspoons baking powder per $\frac{3}{8}$ cup flour

   b. $2\frac{2}{5}$ parts ammonia per $1\frac{1}{3}$ parts vinegar

Be Rational! 2

Quotients of Integers

WARM UP

Classify each number into as many categories as it belongs: natural number, whole number, integer, rational number.

1. -3
2. $\frac{1}{2}$
3. 0
4. 5

LEARNING GOALS

- Know that the decimal form of a rational number terminates in 0s or eventually repeats.
- Represent rational numbers as terminating or repeating decimals.
- Use long division to represent quotients of integers as rational numbers.
- Write equivalent forms of signed rational numbers.
- Determine that every quotient of integers is a rational number, provided the divisor is not zero.

KEY TERMS

- terminating decimals
- non-terminating decimals
- repeating decimals
- bar notation
- non-repeating decimals

You have learned the rule to determine the sign of a quotient. Does a quotient change if the negative sign is on the divisor instead of the dividend?

Getting Started

Are You a Terminator?

1. For each pair of numbers, use long division to calculate the quotient. Write quotients in fractional and decimal form.

   a. 5 ÷ 8

   b. 5 ÷ 11

   c. 7÷ 9

   d. 6 ÷ 2

2. What types of numbers are the quotients in Question 1? Use the definitions of the different number classifications to explain why this makes sense.

3. How many decimal places did you need to go to in the long division for each quotient? Why?

ACTIVITY
2.1 Classifying Decimals

Decimals can be classified into two categories: *terminating* and *non-terminating.*

A **terminating decimal** has a finite number of digits, meaning that after a finite number of decimal places, all following decimal places have a value of 0. Terminating decimals are rational numbers.

A **non-terminating decimal** is a decimal that continues on infinitely without ending in a sequence of zeros.

1. **Classify the decimals in Question 1 as terminating or non-terminating decimals.**

2. **Determine which unit fractions are terminating and which are non-terminating? Explain your reasoning for each.**

   $\frac{1}{2}$ $\frac{1}{3}$ $\frac{1}{4}$ $\frac{1}{5}$ $\frac{1}{6}$ $\frac{1}{7}$ $\frac{1}{8}$ $\frac{1}{9}$ $\frac{1}{10}$

Pi (π) is one of the most well-known non-repeating decimals.

The bar is called a vinculum.

Non-terminating decimals can be further divided into two categories: *repeating* and *non-repeating*.

A **repeating decimal** is a decimal in which a digit, or a group of digits, repeat(s) infinitely. Repeating decimals are rational numbers.

Bar notation is used to indicate the digits that repeat in a repeating decimal. In the quotient of 3 and 7, the sequence 428571 repeats. The numbers that lie underneath the bar are the numbers that repeat.

$$\frac{3}{7} = 0.4285714285714\ldots = 0.\overline{428571}$$

A **non-repeating decimal** continues without terminating and without repeating a sequence of digits. Non-repeating decimals are not rational numbers.

3. **Classify the non-terminating decimals in Question 1 as repeating or non-repeating decimals. If they are repeating decimals, rewrite them using bar notation.**

If you can find a counterexample to your conjecture, revise your conjecture.

4. **Use your results in Question 2 to make a conjecture about other fractions. Which fractions will have repeating decimal representations? Use examples to support your conjecture.**

ACTIVITY 2.2 Equivalent Rational Numbers

Cut out the numbers at the end of the lesson. There are four possible representations of each rational number, but not all of the rational numbers have all four representations provided.

Think about how you determine the sign of a quotient. What is special about each of these representations?

1. **Sort the numbers into their equivalent representations. For any numbers that do not have four representations, create the missing representation using the blank cards. Tape or glue the sets of representations in the space provided.**

Consider how you can use positive and negative signs to write an equivalent form of $\frac{3}{5}$.

2. **What do you notice about the negative sign in the fraction form of the representations?**

NOTES

TALK the TALK

It's All the Same to Me

Any quotient of two integers is a rational number, so long as the divisor is not 0.

For each rational number,

- write two equivalent representations in fractional form,
- convert to a decimal,
- classify the decimal as terminating or non-terminating and, if applicable, repeating or non-repeating.

1. $\frac{-11}{25}$

2. $\frac{-1}{6}$

3. $\frac{27}{-50}$

4. $\frac{-3}{7}$

$-\frac{2}{3}$	$\frac{-4}{5}$	$\frac{11}{-4}$	$\frac{-13}{15}$
$\frac{-39}{60}$	$\frac{-7}{22}$	$\frac{2}{-3}$	$-0.8\overline{6}$
$-\frac{11}{4}$	$\frac{4}{-5}$	$\frac{13}{-15}$	$-0.\overline{6}$
$-\frac{39}{60}$	$\frac{7}{-22}$	$\frac{-2}{3}$	$-\frac{4}{5}$

Assignment

Write

Explain how the three different fractional representations of a rational number are related to determining the sign of the quotient of two integers.

Remember

The sign of a negative rational number in fractional form can be placed in front of the fraction, in the numerator of the fraction, or in the denominator of the fraction.

Practice

Convert each fraction to a decimal. Classify the decimal as *terminating*, *non-terminating*, *repeating*, or *non-repeating*. If the decimal repeats, rewrite it using bar notation.

1. $\frac{3}{8}$
2. $\frac{5}{6}$
3. $\frac{7}{25}$
4. $\frac{2}{11}$
5. $\frac{5}{12}$

Write each rational number as an equivalent fraction by changing the placement of the negative sign(s).

6. $-\frac{4}{7}$
7. $\frac{-5}{3}$
8. $\frac{1}{2}$
9. $\frac{9}{-2}$
10. $-\frac{8}{5}$

Stretch

Use what you know about multiplying signed numbers to evaluate each expression.

1. $\left(-\frac{1}{2}\right)^2$
2. $-\left(\frac{1}{2}\right)^2$
3. $\left(-\frac{1}{2}\right)^3$
4. $-\left(\frac{1}{2}\right)^3$

What do you notice?

Review

Represent each scenario as a multiplication or division problem. Then, solve the problem.

1. The temperature changed $-2°$ per hour for 5 hours. How many degrees did the temperature drop during that time period.
2. Lina missed 8 questions on her science final, which changed her final score by -32 points. If each question is weighted equally, how many points did she lose for each question?

Determine each product.

3. $2\frac{1}{2} \times \left(-3\frac{3}{4}\right)$
4. $-5\frac{1}{3} \times \left(-2\frac{1}{2}\right)$

Determine an 18% gratuity for each restaurant bill.

5. \$29.50
6. \$56.70

3

Building a Wright Brothers' Flyer

Simplifying Expressions to Solve Problems

WARM UP

Simplify each expression.

1. $-20 \div 2\left(7\frac{2}{3}\right)$

2. $-20 - 2\left(-7\frac{2}{3}\right)$

3. $-7\left(\dfrac{-\frac{3}{4}}{-\frac{2}{3}}\right)$

LEARNING GOALS

- Model situations using expressions with rational numbers.
- Evaluate expressions with rational numbers and variables.
- Solve real-world problems using operations with signed rational numbers.

KEY TERM

- percent error

You have learned how to operate with signed numbers, including integers and other rational numbers. How can you use what you know to solve problems?

Getting Started

Orville and Wilbur

In the middle of December 1903, two brothers—Orville and Wilbur Wright—became the first two people to make a controlled flight in a powered plane. They made four flights on December 17, the longest covering only 852 feet and lasting just 59 seconds.

The table shows information about the flights made that day.

	Pilot	Flight Time (s)	Distance (ft)
A	Orville	12	120
B	Wilbur	13	175
C	Orville	15	200
D	Wilbur	59	852

1. Determine the approximate speed of all four flights, in miles per hour.

Human flight progressed amazingly quickly after those first flights. In the year before Orville Wright died, Chuck Yeager had already piloted the first flight that went faster than the speed of sound: 767.269 miles per hour!

2. What is the speed of sound in feet per second?

ACTIVITY 3.1

Operating with Rational Numbers to Solve Problems

In order to build a balsa wood model of the Wright brothers' plane, you would need to cut long lengths of wood spindles into shorter lengths for the wing stays, the vertical poles that support and connect the two wings. Each stay for the main wings of the model needs to be cut $3\frac{1}{4}$ inches long.

Show your work and explain your reasoning.

1. **If the wood spindles are each 10 inches long, how many stays could you cut from one spindle?**

2. **How many inches of the spindle would be left over?**

3. **If the wood spindles are each 12 inches long, how many stays could you cut from one spindle?**

4. **How many inches of the spindle would be left over?**

You also need to cut vertical stays for the smaller wing that are each $1\frac{5}{8}$ inches long.

5. **If the wood spindles are each 10 inches long, how many of these stays could you cut from one spindle?**

6. **How many inches of the spindle would be left over?**

7. **If the wood spindles are each 12 inches long, how many stays could you cut from one spindle?**

8. **How many inches of the spindle would be left over?**

9. **Which length of spindle should be used to cut each of the different stays so that there is the least amount wasted?**

ACTIVITY
3.2

Using Rational Numbers in Equations

There are longer spindles that measure 36 inches.

Remember, a stay is $3\frac{1}{4}$ inch.

1. **How much of a 36-inch-long spindle would be left over if you cut one of the stays from it?**

2. **How much of this spindle would be left over if you cut two of the stays from it?**

3. **Define variables and write and equation for the number of $3\frac{1}{4}$-inch stays and the amount of the 36-inch spindle left over.**

4. **Use your equation to calculate the amount of the spindle left over after cutting 13 stays.**

ACTIVITY
3.3 Calculating Percent Error

Airline travel has come a long way since the days of Orville and Wilbur Wright. In 2015, there were approximately 9.1 million flights that took off from U.S. airports carrying approximately 895.5 million passengers. To transport this many passengers to and from their destinations, airlines have to make good estimations about the number of flights passengers will book, the size of the airplanes to use for a given route, and the approximate arrival time for each flight.

Tracking the accuracy of these estimations is important for airlines. Calculating **percent error** is one way to compare an estimated value to an actual value. To compute percent error, determine the difference between the estimated and actual values and then divide by the actual value.

$$\text{Percent Error} = \frac{\text{actual value} - \text{estimated value}}{\text{actual value}}$$

When planning which airplanes to use for a given route, airlines have to estimate how many people they think will book that particular flight. They want to be able to have enough seating to meet the demand but not have too big of a plane and waste the extra fuel needed.

1. **An airline estimates that they will need an airplane that sits 224 passengers for the 6 A.M. flight from Washington, D.C., to Boston. Calculate the percent error for each number of actual passengers booked. Show your work.**

   a. **186 booked tickets**

   b. **250 booked tickets**

Another challenge is accurately estimating the travel time for each flight. Having minimal error in these estimations allows airlines to keep their schedules accurate and passengers happy.

Airlines use historical data on how long the flight has taken in the past, but these estimates are often impacted by weather issues, airport traffic, and earlier flight delays.

2. An airline estimates that the flight from Washington, D.C., to Boston takes 1 hour and 27 minutes. Calculate the percent error for each actual flight time. Show your work.

a. 1 hour and 11 minutes

b. 2 hours

3. What does a negative value for percent error indicate?

4. Vernice is told that the DC to Boston flight took 10 minutes longer than estimated. She calculated the percent error and got 10.3%. She later learns that she had been given the wrong information. The flight took 10 minutes *less* than estimated. Vernice thinks that the percent error should just be −10.3%. Is she correct? Explain why or why not.

NOTES

ACTIVITY

3.4 Evaluating Expressions with Rational Numbers and Variables

Recall that to evaluate an expression with a variable, substitute the value for the variable and then perform the operations.

WORKED EXAMPLE

Evaluate the expression $-12\frac{1}{2} - 3v$ for $v = -5$.

Estimate:

$$-12 - 3(-5) = -12 + 15 = 3$$

Substitute -5 for v and solve:

$$-12\frac{1}{2} - 3(-5) = -12\frac{1}{2} - (-15)$$

$$= -12\frac{1}{2} + 15$$

$$= 2\frac{1}{2}$$

1. Evaluate the expression for $v = -\frac{6}{7}$.

Evaluate each expression for the given value.

2. Evaluate $-3.25 - 2.75z$ for $z = -4$.

3. Evaluate $\left(-1\frac{1}{4}\right)x - 8\frac{7}{8}$ for $x = -\frac{2}{5}$.

4. Evaluate $-0.75(p - 1.2)$ for $p = 2$.

I'll TRY to remember to check my work. How can I do that?

5. Evaluate $\dfrac{m}{-\frac{6}{5}}$ for $m = 6\frac{3}{4}$.

NOTES

TALK the TALK

Rational Thinking

Write each problem as a product or quotient of rational numbers and then solve. Show your work.

1. **Carey and Patrick both borrowed money from Melinda. Carey owes Melinda $25.00. Patrick owes Melinda $\frac{3}{4}$ the amount that Carey owes. How much does Patrick owe Melinda?**

2. **Therese is measuring how fast water evaporates in a bucket in her backyard. In 6 hours in direct sunlight, the water level changes $-\frac{3}{8}$ inch. How fast is the water level changing per hour?**

3. **A meteorologist forecasts that the temperature is going to change $-1\frac{1}{2}^\circ$ per hour from 11:00 P.M. to 7:00 A.M. What is the total expected temperature change over the time period?**

Assignment

Write

Write the steps you would follow to evaluate an expression for a variable. Use an example in your description.

Remember

Percent error is one way to report the difference between estimated values and actual values.

$$\text{Percent error} = \frac{\text{actual value} - \text{estimated value}}{\text{actual value}}$$

Practice

Write an expression with rational numbers to represent each situation and then solve. Show your work.

1. Jaxon's start-up business makes a profit of \$450 during the first month. However, the company records a profit of −\$60 per month for the next four months and profit of \$125 for the final month. What is the total profit for the first six months of Jaxon's business?
2. A diver is exploring the waters of the Great Barrier Reef.
   a. She is currently −5 feet from the surface of the water and plans to explore a shipwreck that is at −75 feet from the surface. If she moves at a rate of −8 feet per minute, how many minutes does it take the diver to reach the shipwreck?
   b. When she is done exploring the reef, she ascends at a rate of 5 feet per minute. Once she reaches a height of −30 feet, she must rest for 15 minutes to allow her body to adapt to the changing water pressure. She then continues to the surface at the same rate. How long will it take the diver to reach the surface?
3. The drain in your 45-gallon bathtub is partially clogged, but you need to take a shower. The showerhead had a flow rate of 2.25 gallons per minute, but the bathtub only drains at a rate of −0.5 gallons per minute. What is the longest shower you can take?
4. Tesha withdrew \$22.75 each week for four weeks from her savings account to pay for her piano lessons. By how much did these lessons change her savings account balance?

Calculate the percent error.

5. Jerri estimated that 30 people would attend the dinner event, but only 25 people attended.
6. Gene estimated the length of the fence to be 150 feet, but the actual measurement was 142 feet.

Evaluate each expression for the given value.

7. $\frac{5}{6}x$ for $x = -8$
8. $9\frac{1}{3} - m$ for $m = -1\frac{2}{3}$
9. $t \div \frac{3}{4}$ for $t = 9\frac{3}{4}$
10. $\frac{2}{5}k - 3\frac{1}{2}$ for $k = 15$

Stretch

Solve each equation.

1. $x + 4.5 = 9.125$

2. $\frac{4}{5}(p + 1) = 1$

3. $\frac{g}{8} - 5 = 1\frac{1}{2}$

Review

Convert each fraction to a decimal. Classify the decimal as terminating or non-terminating and, if applicable, repeating or non-repeating.

1. $\frac{11}{12}$

2. $\frac{11}{14}$

Determine each absolute value. Show your work.

3. $|-5 - (-7)|$

4. $\left|-\frac{3}{8} + \frac{1}{6}\right|$

Determine each quotient.

5. $\frac{3}{4} \div \frac{4}{3}$

6. $\frac{1}{8} \div \frac{1}{5}$

Properties Schmoperties

4

Using Number Properties to Interpret Expressions with Signed Numbers

WARM UP

Use the Order of Operations to simplify each expression.

1. $18 + 6 \times (-3) - 4$

2. $5 \div (1 - 6) \times 10$

3. $8 + (-3) \times 9 \times 0$

LEARNING GOALS

- Use the Commutative, Associative, and Distributive Properties, Additive and Multiplicative Inverses, Identity, and Zero Properties to rewrite numeric expressions with signed numbers in order to interpret their meanings and solve problems.
- Apply the properties of operations to add, subtract, multiply, and divide with rational numbers.
- Use number properties to solve mathematical problems involving signed numbers and other rational numbers more efficiently.

You have learned how to add, subtract, multiply, and divide with signed numbers and other rational numbers. How can you use number properties with rational numbers to solve problems?

Getting Started

All in Your Head

You have used mental math before to solve problems without calculating on paper. Now try it with signed numbers!

1. **Determine each sum or difference using mental math.**

   a. $-8 + 5 + 8$

   b. $-\frac{1}{2} + \frac{3}{5} + -\frac{1}{2}$

   c. $\frac{3}{8} + \left(\frac{5}{8} + \left(-\frac{5}{6}\right)\right)$

The Commutative Property says that you can add or multiply in any order without changing the sum or product.

The Associative Property says that you can group addends or factors without changing the sum or product.

2. **Explain how you can use the Commutative and Associative Properties to help you solve the problems in your head.**

ACTIVITY 4.1 Distributing and Factoring with −1

When first learning about negative numbers, you reflected a positive value across 0 to determine the opposite of the value.

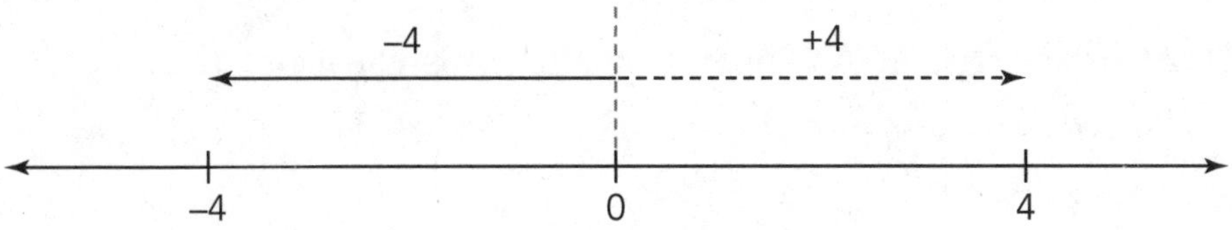

This illustrates that the opposite of 4 is -4, or $(-1)(4) = -4$.

In the same way, you can use reflections across 0 on the number line to determine the opposite of an expression.

WORKED EXAMPLE

Consider the expression $-7 + 2$. When the model of $-7 + 2$ is reflected across 0 on the number line, the result is $7 - 2$.

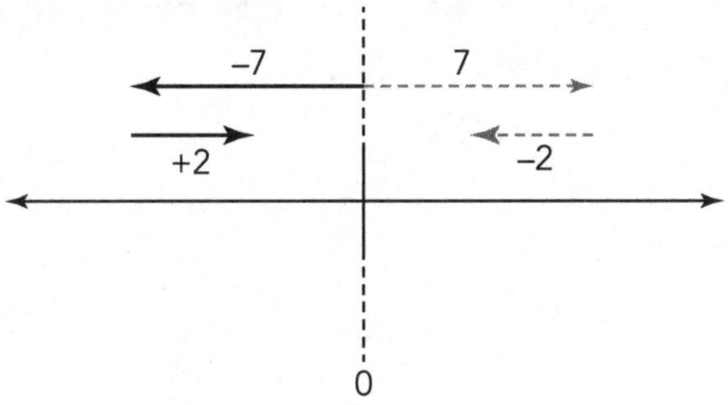

So, $(-7 + 2)$ is the opposite of $(7 - 2)$.

This means that $-7 + 2 = -(7 - 2)$.

1. Draw models like the ones in the worked example to show the opposite of each expression. Rewrite each as an opposite of a different expression.

a. $-1 - 6$ **b.** $2 + (-3)$ **c.** $-4 + 5$

How would your answer be different if the expression were -4×5?

Adam

To reflect an expression across 0 on the number line, multiply the expression by -1.

$$-1(2 + 3) = (-1)(2) + (-1)(3)$$
$$= -2 + -3$$

2. What property did Adam use to show his reasoning?

3. Does Adam's expression, $-1(2 + 3)$, mean the same thing as $-(2 + 3)$? Draw a model and explain your reasoning.

4. Rewrite each expression as an addition or subtraction expression using a factor of -1.

Rewriting an expression as a product with -1 is also called *factoring out a* -1.

a. $-2 + (-4) = -1(\_\_\_\_\_\_\_\_)$

b. $-5 - 8 = -1(\_\_\_\_\_\_\_\_)$

c. $-9 - (-9) = -1(\_\_\_\_\_\_\_\_)$

5. Use the Distributive Property to show that your expressions in Question 4 are correct.

ACTIVITY **4.2**

Subtraction as Adding the Opposite

You know that subtracting a number is the same as adding the opposite of that number. Rewriting subtraction as addition allows you to apply the Commutative Property to any expression involving addition and subtraction.

For example, $-4.5 - 3 + 1.5 = -4.5 + 1.5 + (-3)$. Rewriting expressions helps you to see patterns and use mental math to make solving simpler.

You can use what you know about adding opposites to help you solve problems more efficiently.

1. Simplify each expression.

a. $10.5 + 6 + 2 - 0.5$

b. $-\frac{1}{2} + \left(\frac{1}{2} - \frac{4}{5}\right)$

c. $3\frac{7}{8} - 4\frac{1}{2}$

2. Explain how you can use the Commutative, Associative, and Distributive Properties to help you simplify the expressions in Question 1.

"You can rewrite a mixed number as the sum of a whole number and a fraction.
$7\frac{1}{2} = 7 + \frac{1}{2}$
How can you rewrite $-7\frac{1}{2}$?"

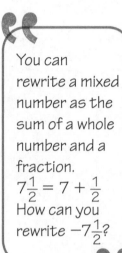

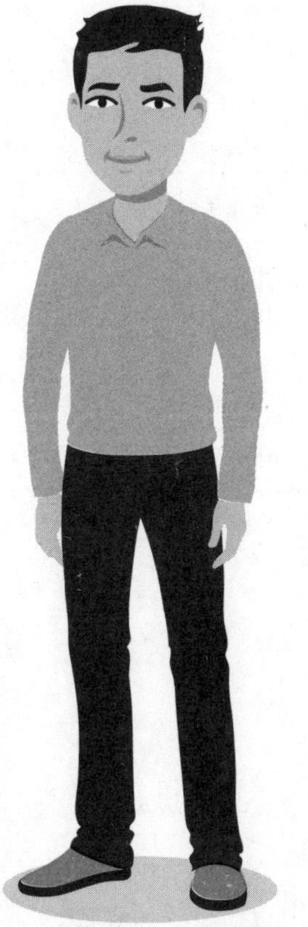

NOTES

ACTIVITY 4.3

Practice with the Properties

1. **For each equation, identify the number property or operation used.**

Equation	Number Property
a. $-3\frac{1}{2} + 5 = 5 + \left(-3\frac{1}{2}\right)$	
b. $\left(3\frac{1}{2}\right)\left(2\frac{1}{5}\right)5 = 3\frac{1}{2}\left(2\frac{1}{5}\right)(5)$	
c. $-3\frac{1}{2} + \left(-2\frac{1}{2} + 5\right) = \left(-3\frac{1}{2} + \left(-2\frac{1}{2}\right)\right) + 5$	
d. $-\left(-3\frac{1}{2} + 2\frac{1}{4}\right) = -1\left(-3\frac{1}{2}\right) + -1\left(2\frac{1}{4}\right)$	
e. $\dfrac{-3\frac{1}{2} - 2\frac{1}{4}}{4} = \dfrac{-3\frac{1}{2}}{4} - \dfrac{2\frac{1}{4}}{4}$	
f. $(-7.02)(-3.42) = (-3.42)(-7.02)$	

Evaluate each expression. Describe your strategy.

2. $-2\left(2\frac{1}{4}\right) + -2\left(-\frac{3}{4}\right)$

3. $\left(-3\frac{1}{4} - 2\frac{1}{5}\right) + \left(-6\frac{3}{5}\right)$

4. $\frac{7}{8}\left(-\frac{4}{5}\right)\left(-\frac{8}{7}\right)$

5. $\dfrac{\frac{8}{9} + \left(-\frac{4}{5}\right)}{4}$

6. $(-11.4)(6.4) + (-11.4)(-12.4)$

NOTES

NOTES

TALK the TALK

What's It All About?

When you rewrite addition and subtraction expressions using a factor of −1, you are "factoring out" a −1. Here are some other examples.

$-8 + 5 = -1(8 - 5)$ $-2 - 9 = -1(2 + 9)$ $3 - (-4) = -1(-3 - 4)$

1. **Describe how you can factor out a −1 from any addition or subtraction expression.**

2. **How is factoring out a negative 1 from an addition or subtraction expression different from factoring out a negative 1 from a multiplication or division expression?**

3. **Demonstrate using words and models why the product of −1 and any expression is the opposite of that expression.**

Assignment

Write

Describe in your own words how to factor a −1 out of an addition or subtraction expression.

Remember

When you multiply any expression by −1, the result is the opposite of that expression.

Practice

Factor out a negative 1 from each expression.

1. $7 + (-6)$
2. $-4 - (5 + 3)$
3. $-9 - 1$
4. Use the Distributive Property to show that your answers to Questions 1 through 3 are correct.

Use a number property to solve each problem efficiently. Show your work and list the property or properties used.

5. $-9.9 + 5.2 + 3.9 + 1$
6. $-\frac{3}{5} + \left(\frac{1}{5} - \frac{3}{2} + 0\right)$

Stretch

The rectangle shown is formed by a reflection of points *C* and *D* across the *y*-axis of the coordinate plane. Point *C* has the coordinates (4, 4). Determine *a* and *b* and then calculate the perimeter of the rectangle.

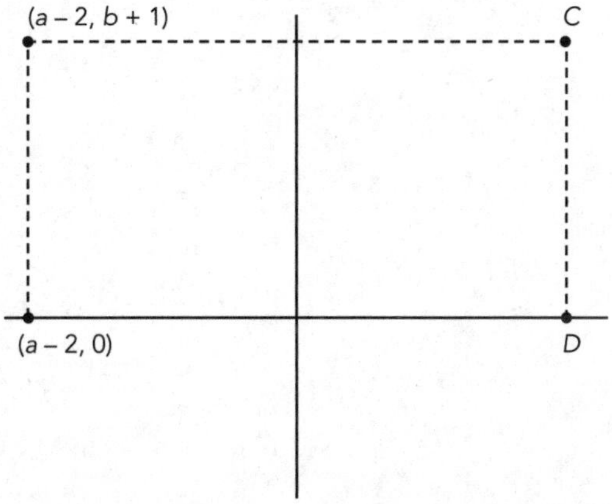

Review

1. Carl and Joe recorded how fast they ran 1 mile and 2 miles. Carl recorded his times using fractions, and Joe recorded his times using decimals.

Distance	Carl	Joe
1 mi	$10\frac{1}{2}$ min	10.4 min
2 mi	$22\frac{1}{4}$ min	22.3 min

   a. Who ran the mile faster, Carl or Joe? How much faster?

   b. Who ran 2 miles faster, Carl or Joe? How much faster?

2. A small submarine is at an elevation of −30 feet compared to sea level. What is its elevation after it ascends 9 feet?
3. On Tuesday, Marissa was $45 short of her fundraising goal. The next day, she was $5 over her goal. Write an equation to show how much she raised in one day.
4. What is 12% of 350?
5. What is 35% of 120?

Multiplying and Dividing Rational Numbers Summary

KEY TERMS

- terminating decimals
- non-terminating decimals
- repeating decimals
- bar notation
- non-repeating decimals
- percent error

LESSON 1 Equal Groups

When thinking about multiplying integers, remember that you can think about multiplication like repeated addition.

For example, consider the expression 3 × (−4). As repeated addition, it is represented as (−4) + (−4) + (−4).

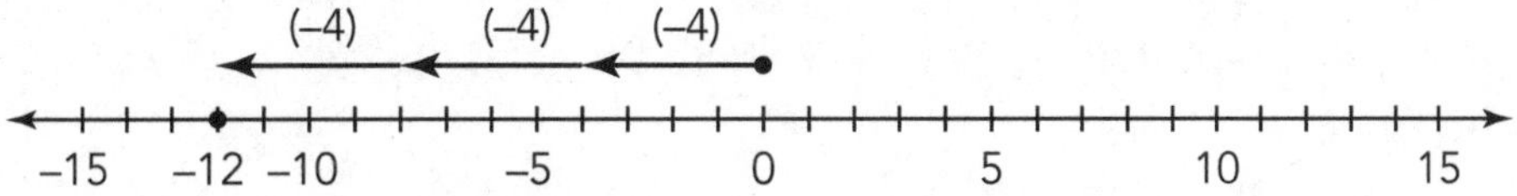

You can think of 3 × (−4) as three groups of (−4).

Now consider the expression (−3) × (−4).

You know that 3 × (−4) means "three groups of (−4)" and that −3 means "the opposite of 3." So, (−3) × (−4) means "the opposite of 3 groups of (−4)."

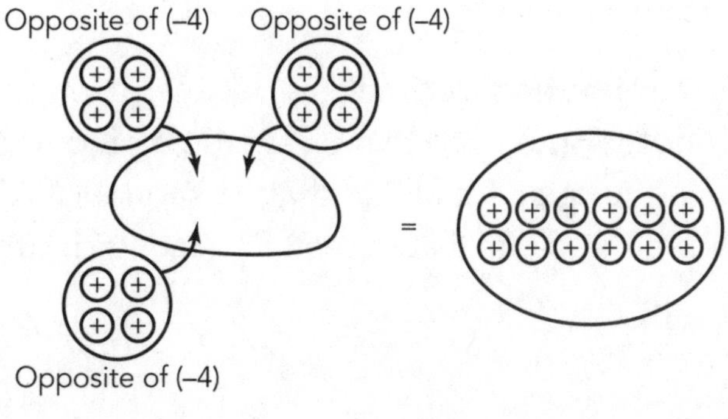

To multiply and divide integers, perform the usual multiplication and division algorithms, and then apply the correct sign to the product or quotient. An odd number of negative signs in the expression gives a negative product or quotient. An even number of negative signs in the expression gives a positive product or quotient.

When you studied division in elementary school, you learned that multiplication and division were inverse operations. For every multiplication fact, you can write a corresponding division fact. Similarly, you can write fact families for integer multiplication and division.

For example, consider these two fact families.

$-7 \times 3 = -21$	$-8 \times (-4) = 32$
$3 \times (-7) = -21$	$-4 \times (-8) = 32$
$-21 \div (-7) = 3$	$32 \div (-8) = -4$
$-21 \div 3 = -7$	$32 \div (-4) = -8$

LESSON 2

Be Rational!

Decimals can be classified into two categories: terminating and non-terminating. A **terminating decimal** has a finite number of digits, meaning that after a finite number of decimal places, all following decimal places have a value of 0. A **non-terminating decimal** is a decimal that continues infinitely, without ending in a sequence of zeros.

For example, 0.375 is a terminating decimal. The decimal 0.454545... is a non-terminating decimal.

Non-terminating decimals can be further divided into two categories: repeating and non-repeating.

A **repeating decimal** is a decimal in which a digit or a group of digits repeat infinitely. **Bar notation** is used to indicate the digit or digits that repeat in a repeating decimal. For example, in the quotient of 3 and 7, the sequence 428571 repeats. The digits that lie underneath the bar are the digits that repeat. Repeating decimals are rational numbers.

$$\frac{3}{7} = 0.4285714285714\ldots = 0.\overline{428571}$$

A **non-repeating decimal** continues without terminating and without repeating a sequence of digits. Non-repeating decimals are not rational numbers.

The sign of a negative rational number in fractional form can be placed in front of the fraction, in the numerator of the fraction, or in the denominator of the fraction.

$$-\frac{3}{5} = \frac{-3}{5} = \frac{3}{-5}$$

LESSON 3

Building a Wright Brothers' Flyer

You can use the rules you have learned to operate with rational numbers in order to solve problems and equations.

Percent error is one way to report the difference between estimated values and actual values.

$$\text{Percent error} = \frac{\text{actual value} - \text{estimated value}}{\text{actual value}}$$

For example, an airline estimates that they will need an airplane that sits 416 passengers for the 8 A.M. flight from Austin to Orlando. Calculate the percent error if 380 actual passengers are booked.

$$\frac{380-416}{380} = \frac{-36}{430} \approx -9.5\%$$

The airline served 9.5% fewer passengers than they expected.

Expressions with variables can be evaluated for rational numbers.

For example, evaluate the expression $-12\frac{1}{2} - 3v$ for $v = -5$.

Substitute -5 for v and solve:

$$\begin{aligned} -12\tfrac{1}{2} - 3(-5) &= -12\tfrac{1}{2} - (-15) \\ &= -12\tfrac{1}{2} + 15 \\ &= 2\tfrac{1}{2} \end{aligned}$$

When $v = -5$, the value of the expression is $2\frac{1}{2}$.

LESSON 4

Properties Schmoperties

You can use reflections across 0 on the number line to determine the opposite of an expression.

For example, consider the expression −7 + 2. When the model of −7 + 2 is reflected across 0 on the number line, the result is 7 − 2.

Therefore, (−7 + 2) is the opposite of (7 − 2).

This means that −7 + 2 = −(7 − 2).

When you multiply any expression by −1, the result is the opposite of that expression.

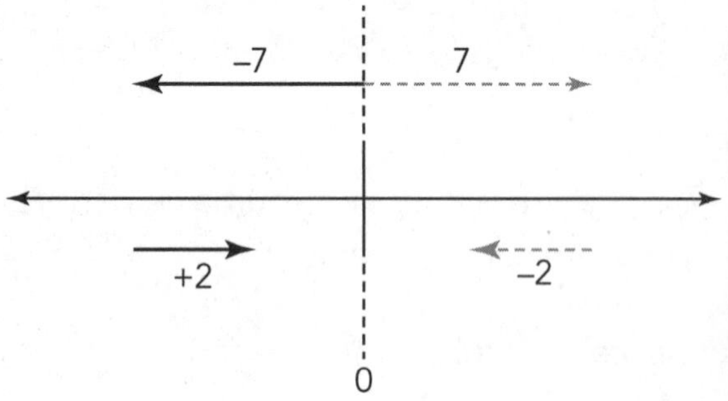

Using number properties can help you to solve problems involving signed numbers more efficiently.

Rewriting subtraction as addition allows you apply the Commutative Property to any expression involving addition and subtraction. For example, −4.5 − 3 + 1.5 = −4.5 + 1.5 + (−3).

You can apply what you know about the Zero Property of Addition and the Associative Property to expressions with positive and negative integers. For example, $-\frac{3}{4} + \left(\frac{3}{4} - \frac{1}{5}\right) = \left(-\frac{3}{4} + \frac{3}{4}\right) - \frac{1}{5} = 0 - \frac{1}{5} = -\frac{1}{5}$.

MODULE 3

REASONING *algebraically*

The lessons in this module build on your experiences with algebraic expressions and one-step equations in grade 6. The expressions, equations, and inequalities you encounter will involve a wide range of rational numbers and require two steps rather than one. You will write equations and inequalities for problem situations, interpret the meanings of quantities in the problems, create tables of values, graph problem situations, and make connections across the representations.

TOPIC 1

Algebraic Expressions

Number lines are so useful. You can use number lines and double number lines to reason with algebraic expressions.

Module 3: Reasoning Algebraically

TOPIC 1: ALGEBRAIC EXPRESSIONS

In this topic, students represent variable expressions on a number line and evaluate algebraic expressions. Then they apply the Distributive Property as a strategy to write equivalent expressions, and they use it to factor linear expressions in a variety of ways. Finally, students combine like terms, including like linear terms, and use properties of operations to add and subtract expressions.

Where have we been?

This topic combines students' knowledge of expressions and negative numbers on a number line to develop number line models for variable expressions. Students are then expected to evaluate algebraic expressions, as they did in grade 6, with rational numbers, using operations they learned in previous lessons in this course.

Where are we going?

Visualizing simple variable expressions on a number line will carry through the entire topic to help students develop a concrete idea of operating on and with algebraic expressions. Students will need this fluency throughout the remainder of this course, as they solve equations in grade 8, and as they expand and factor polynomial expressions in high school.

Using Number Lines to Compare Variable Quantities

Algebraic expressions can be represented on number lines. Knowing the location of $1(x + 1)$, which is simply $x + 1$, for example, allows us to determine the locations of all the other expressions shown. The expression $0(x + 1)$, or just 0, would be between $-1(x + 1)$ and $1(x + 1)$.

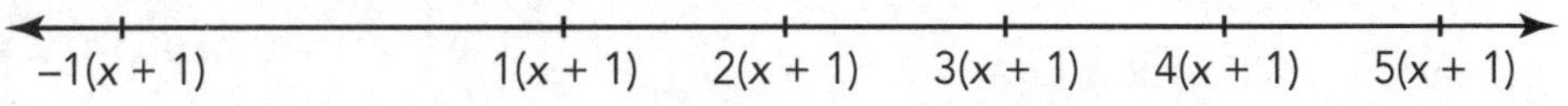

Myth: "I learn best when the instruction matches my learning style."

If asked, most people will tell you they have a learning style – the expressed preference in learning by seeing images, hearing speech, seeing words, or being able to physically interact with the material. Some people even believe that it is the teacher's job to present the information in accordance with that preference.

However, it turns out that the best scientific evidence available does not support learning styles. In other words, when an auditory learner receives instruction about content through a visual model, they do just as well as auditory learners who receive spoken information.

Students may have a preference for visuals or writing or sound, but sticking to their preference doesn't help them learn any better. Far more important is ensuring the student is engaged in an interactive learning activity and that the new information connects to the student's prior knowledge.

#mathmythbusted

Talking Points

You can support your student's learning by resisting the urge, as long as possible, to get to the answer in a problem that your student is working on. Students will learn the algebraic shortcuts that you may know about, but only once they have experience in mathematical reasoning. This may seem to take too long at first. But if you practice asking good questions instead of helping your student arrive at the answer, they will learn to rely on their own knowledge, reasoning, patience, and endurance when struggling with math.

Key Terms

algebraic expression

An algebraic expression is a mathematical phrase that has at least one variable, and it can contain numbers and operation symbols.

linear expression

A linear expression is any expression in which each term is either a constant or the product of a constant and a single variable raised to the first power.

coefficient

A coefficient is a number that is multiplied by a variable in an algebraic expression.

like terms

Like terms are parts of an algebraic expression that have the same variable raised to the same power.

No Substitute for Hard Work

1

Evaluating Algebraic Expressions

WARM UP

Perform each operation.

1. $(-3)(6.6)$

2. $-3 + 6.6$

3. $-3 - 6.6$

4. $6.6 \div (-3)$

LEARNING GOALS

- Compare unknown quantities on a number line.
- Define linear expressions.
- Evaluate algebraic expressions.
- Solve real-life and mathematical problems using algebraic expressions.

KEY TERMS

- variable
- algebraic expression
- linear expression
- constraint
- evaluate an algebraic expression

You have written and evaluated algebraic expressions with positive rational numbers. How do you evaluate algebraic expressions over the set of rational numbers?

The Empty Number Line

In algebra, a **variable** is a letter or symbol that is used to represent an unknown quantity.

Consider the list of six *variable* expressions:

x $2x$ $3x$ $\frac{1}{2}x$ $-x$ $-\frac{1}{2}x$

1. With your partner, think about where you would place each expression and sketch your conjecture.

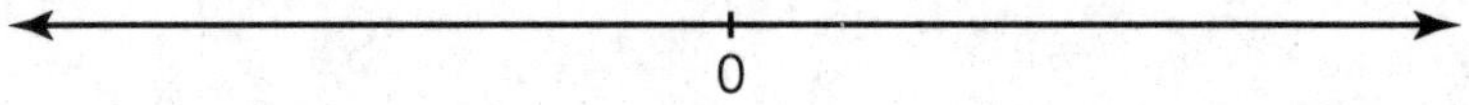

2. Compare your number line with another group's number line. What is the same? What is different?

3. Your teacher will select students to place an index card representing each expression on the number line on the board. Record the locations agreed upon by the class.

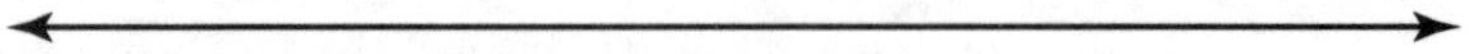

ACTIVITY

1.1 Algebraic Expressions

In this lesson, you will explore the relationship between unknown quantities by writing and evaluating *algebraic expressions*. An **algebraic expression** is a mathematical phrase that has at least one variable, and it can contain numbers and operation symbols.

Each of the expressions in the *Empty Number Line* activity is an algebraic expression. They are also *linear expressions*. A **linear expression** is any expression in which each term is either a constant or the product of a constant and a single variable raised to the first power.

How could you verify the placement of the expressions on the number line?

Additional examples of linear expressions include:
$\frac{1}{2}x + 2$, $-3 + 12.5x$, $-1 + 3x + \frac{5}{2}x - \frac{4}{3}$, or $4y$.

The expressions $3x^2 + 5$ and $-\frac{1}{2}xy$ are examples of expressions that are not linear expressions.

1. **Provide a reason why each expression does not represent a linear expression.**

Let's revisit how you may have plotted the expressions in the previous activity. The directions did not specify the possible values for x. When you graphed each expression, did you think about the set of all possible values of x or just the set of positive x-values?

In mathematics, it is sometimes necessary to set *constraints* on values. A **constraint** is a condition that a solution or problem must satisfy. A constraint can be a restriction set in advance of solving a problem or a limit placed on a solution or graph so the answer makes sense in terms of a real-world scenario.

Analyze the number lines created by Bella and Tito using the expressions from the *Empty Number Line* activity.

Bella

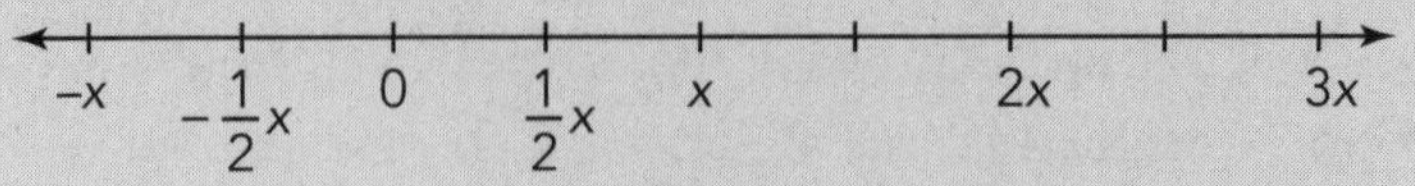

Tito

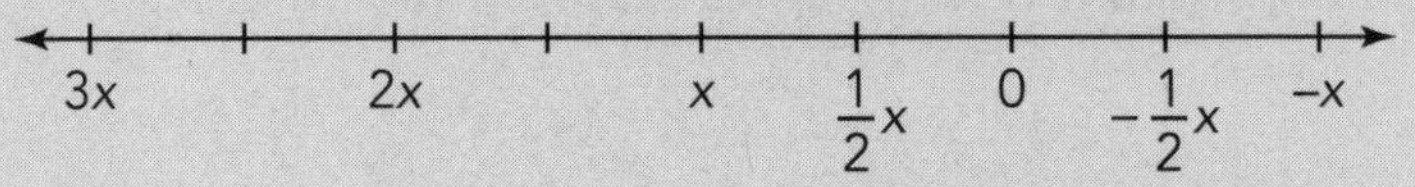

2. Compare and contrast each representation.

a. What are the constraints on each representation? Identify the set of *x*-values that make each number line true.

b. Select a value for *x* from your set of possible values and substitute that value for *x* in each expression to verify the plotted locations are correct.

c. Compare your values from part (b) with your classmates. Do you have the same values? If not, what does that mean?

One strategy to verify your placement of the cards is to substitute values for the variable *x* into each expression.

ACTIVITY 1.2

Substitution with Rational Numbers

To earn money for a summer mission trip, Levi is working as a handyman around his neighborhood. Levi has been hired to build a wooden fence. He plans to use a post hole digger to dig the holes for the posts.

Levi starts the project on Saturday morning but because of the type of soil, he only starts the holes, fills them with water, and then plans to return Sunday to finish the job. When Levi starts on Sunday, each hole is 3 inches deep. Each time he uses the post hole diggers, he extracts 2 inches of soil. The height of the soil in the hole with respect to ground level can be modeled by the linear expression $-3 - 2n$, where n is the number of times Levi extracted soil with the post hole diggers.

A depth of 3 inches is equivalent to a height of −3 inches.

1. Determine the height of the soil in the hole as Levi works.

Number of Soil Extractions	Height of the Soil (inches)
0	
1	
2	
5	
10	
15	
20	

Use the Order of Operations to evaluate the expressions.

2. From his research about digging post holes, Levi knows that each pole must be placed at a depth that is 2 feet below the frost level, and the frost level is 16 inches beneath ground level.

   a. How deep must Levi dig each hole?

   b. Determine the minimum number of soil extractions for each hole.

Cable drilling, also known as percussion drilling, is a method used to drill a borehole.

Levi's mom, Maggie, uses a cable tool rig to dig wells during the mission trip. Her rig can dig 12.4 meters of hard rock per day. When Maggie starts working on one well, the hole is already 33 meters deep.

3. Write a linear expression for the height of the hole with respect to ground level for the number of days that Maggie runs the rig.

4. Use your expression to determine the height of the hole after each number of days.

   a. 2 days after Maggie starts

   b. 5 days after Maggie starts

   c. 2 days before Maggie started

ACTIVITY 1.3 Evaluating Expressions

Previously, you evaluated algebraic expressions with positive rational numbers. Now you can evaluate expressions with negative rational numbers. To **evaluate an algebraic expression**, you replace each variable in the expression with a number or numeric expression and then perform all possible mathematical operations.

1. Evaluate each algebraic expression.

a. $x - 7$

- for $x = -8$
- for $x = -11$
- for $x = 16$

b. $-6y$

- for $y = -3$
- for $y = 0$
- for $y = 7$

Use parentheses to show multiplication like −6(−3).

c. $3b - 5$

- for $b = -2$
- for $b = 3$
- for $b = 9$

d. $-1.6 + 5.3n$

- for $n = -5$
- for $n = 0$
- for $n = 4$

Sometimes, it is more convenient to use a table to record the results when evaluating the same expression with multiple values.

2. Complete each table.

a.

h	$-2h - 7$
2	
−1	
8	
−7	

b.

a	−12	−10	−4	0
$\frac{a}{4} + 6$				

c.

x	$x^2 - 5$
1	
3	
6	
−2	

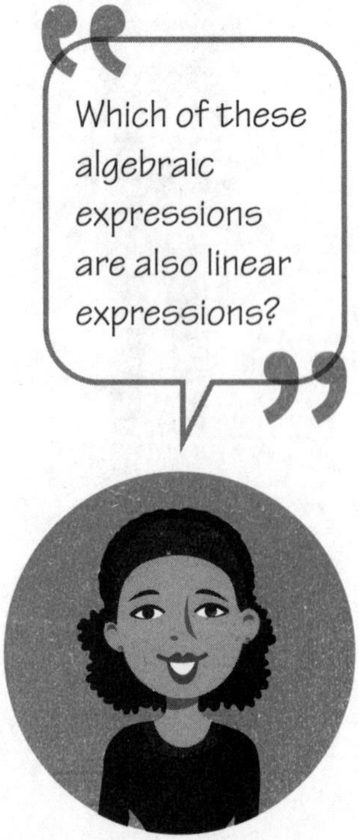

Which of these algebraic expressions are also linear expressions?

d.

y	−5	−1	0	15
$-\frac{1}{5}y + 3\frac{2}{5}$				

3. Evaluate each algebraic expression for $x = 2, -3, 0.5$, and $-2\frac{1}{3}$.

a. $-3x$

b. $5x + 10$

c. $6 - 3x$

d. $8x + 75$

4. Evaluate each algebraic expression for $x = 23.76$ and $-21\frac{5}{6}$.

a. $2.67x - 31.85$

b. $11\frac{3}{4}x + 56\frac{3}{8}$

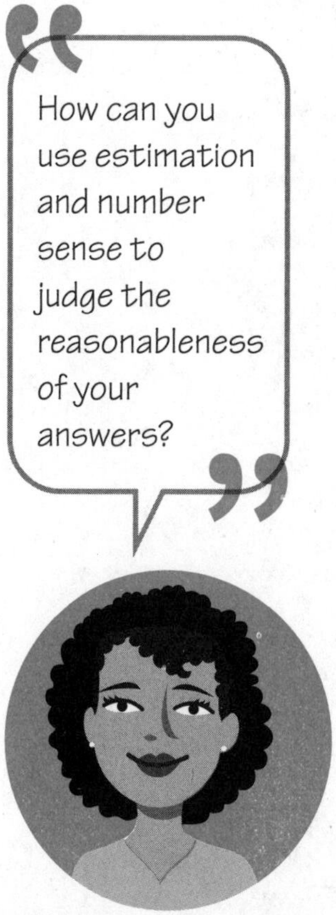

How can you use estimation and number sense to judge the reasonableness of your answers?

NOTES

TALK the TALK

Strategies

Write a 1–2 paragraph summary of this lesson. Be sure to address each question.

1. **Describe your basic strategy for evaluating any algebraic expression.**

2. **How are tables helpful when evaluating expressions?**

Assignment

Write

Explain the difference between an algebraic expression and a linear expression.

Remember

To evaluate an algebraic expression, replace each variable in the expression with a number or numeric expression and then perform all possible mathematical operations.

Practice

Evaluate each algebraic expression.

1. $64 - 9p$ for $p = 4, 9, -3$
2. $-w + 8.5$ for $w = 12, -1.5, 5.3$
3. $46 + (-2k)$ for $k = 3, 23, -2$

Complete each table.

4.

b	$3b + 14$
-5	
-3	
0	
4	

5.

v	1	2	5	-3.25
$6.75 - 6v$				

6.

f	4	8	-12	-1
$\frac{f}{4} + 3f$				

Evaluate each algebraic expression for the given quantity.

7. $-6.2x + 1.4x$, $x = -9.3$

8. $3\frac{1}{2}x - 5\frac{1}{3}x$, $x = \frac{2}{5}$

Stretch

Evaluate each algebraic expression for the given quantity.

1. $-3(2.1x - 7.9)$ for $x = -18.1, -0.3, 14.4$
2. $-9.8t^2 + 20t + 8$ for $t = -2, 0, 3.5$

Review

Rewrite each numeric expression by factoring out (−1).

1. $-7 + 5$
2. $3 + 8$

Determine each quotient.

3. $-8.9 \div -0.1$
4. $-4\frac{1}{3} \div \frac{2}{5}$

Write two unit rates for each given ratio.

5. $\frac{3}{4}$ inch : $\frac{1}{2}$ hour
6. $\frac{4}{5}$ gallon : $\frac{1}{4}$ cup

Mathematics Gymnastics 2

Rewriting Expressions Using the Distributive Property

WARM UP

Write a numeric expression for the opposite of each given expression.

1. $-7 - 2$

2. $3 - 9$

3. $-3 + 2$

4. $3 - (-7)$

LEARNING GOALS

- Write and use the Distributive Property.
- Apply the Distributive Property to expand expressions with rational coefficients.
- Apply the Distributive Property to factor linear expressions with rational coefficients.

KEY TERMS

- factor
- coefficient
- common factor
- greatest common factor (GCF)

You have used the Distributive Property to expand and factor algebraic expressions with positive numbers. How can you apply the property to all rational numbers?

Getting Started

Where Are They?

Consider the list of linear expressions.

$x + 1$ $2x + 2$ $3x + 3$ $4x + 4$

1. On the empty number line, plot each algebraic expression by estimating its location.

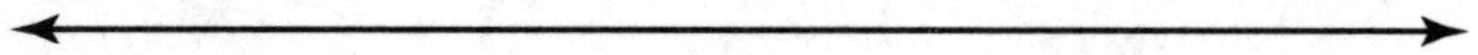

2. Explain your strategy. How did you decide where to plot each expression?

3. What assumptions did you make to plot the expressions? Does everyone's number line look the same? Why or why not?

ACTIVITY
2.1 Algebraic Expressions on the Number Line

To **factor** an expression means to rewrite the expression as a product of factors.

Consider the four expressions plotted in the previous activity. How can you prove that you are correct?

Graham

I can use an example by evaluating all four expressions at the same value of x and plot the values.

Let $x = 4$.

$x + 1 = 4 + 1 = 5$

$2x + 2 = 2(4) + 2 = 10$

$3x + 3 = 3(4) + 3 = 15$

$4x + 4 = 4(4) + 4 = 20$

I can plot the expressions at 5, 10, 15, and 20.

Meaghan

The expressions look similar.
I can factor out the coefficient of each expression.

$x + 1$

$2x + 2 = 2(x + 1)$

$3x + 3 = 3(x + 1)$

$4x + 4 = 4(x + 1)$

So, I can plot $x + 1$ and use that expression to plot the other expressions.

1. **Use Graham's strategy with a different positive value for x to accurately plot the four expressions.**

A **coefficient** is a number that is multiplied by a variable in an algebraic expression.

2. **Use Graham's strategy with a negative value for x to accurately plot the four expressions. How is your number line different from the number line in Question 1?**

Often, writing an expression in a different form reveals the structure of the expression. Meaghan saw that each expression could be rewritten as a product of two factors.

Meaghan's expressions

$x + 1$

$2x + 2 = 2(x + 1)$

$3x + 3 = 3(x + 1)$

$4x + 4 = 4(x + 1)$

3. What are the two factors in each of Meaghan's expressions? What is common about the factors of each expression?

4. Use Meaghan's work to accurately plot the four expressions. Explain your strategy.

If a variable has no coefficient, the understood coefficient is 1.

5. Meaghan noticed that the expressions formed a sequence. Write and plot the next two terms in the sequence. Explain your strategy.

6. What property did Meaghan use when she factored out the coefficient of the expressions?

ACTIVITY
2.2

Applying the Distributive Property

NOTES

Recall that the Distributive Property states that if *a*, *b*, and *c* are any real numbers, then $a(b + c) = ab + ac$. The property also holds if addition is replaced with subtraction, then $a(b - c) = ab - ac$.

Dominique remembers that the Distributive Property can be modeled with a rectangle. She illustrates with this numeric example.

Dominique

Calculating 230 × 7 is the same as determining the area of a rectangle by multiplying the length by the width.

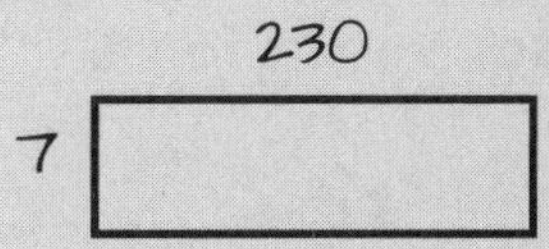

But I can also decompose the rectangle into two smaller rectangles and calculate the area of each. I can then add the two areas to get the total.

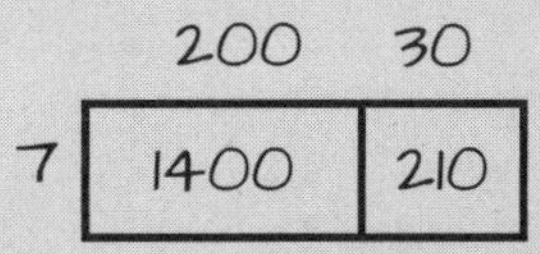

$1400 + 210 = 1610$

So, $7(230) = 1610$.

1. Write Dominique's problem in terms of the Distributive Property.

You can also use area models with algebraic expressions.

2. Draw a model for each expression, and then rewrite the expression with no parentheses.

a. $6(x + 9)$

b. $7(2b - 5)$

c. $-2(4a + 1)$

d. $\frac{x + 15}{5}$

3. Use the Distributive Property to rewrite each expression in an equivalent form.

a. $3(4y + 2)$

b. $12(x + 3)$

c. $-4a(3b - 5)$

d. $-7(2y - 3x + 9)$

e. $\frac{6m + 12}{-2}$

f. $\frac{22 - 4x}{2}$

Be careful with the signs of the products and quotients.

4 Simplify each expression. Show your work.

a. $-6(3x + (-4y))$

b. $-4(-3x - 8) - 34$

c. $\frac{-7.2 - 6.4x}{-0.8}$

d. $\left(-2\frac{1}{2}\right)\left(3\frac{1}{4}\right) + \left(-2\frac{1}{2}\right)\left(-2\frac{1}{4}\right)$

e. $\frac{\left(-7\frac{1}{2}\right) + 5y}{2\frac{1}{2}}$

5. **Evaluate each expression for the given value. Then, use properties to simplify the original expression. Finally, evaluate the simplified expression.**

a. $2x(-3x + 7)$ for $x = -1\frac{2}{3}$

b. $\frac{4.2x - 7}{1.4}$ for $x = 1.26$

c. **Which form—simplified or not simplified—did you prefer to evaluate? Why?**

6. A student submitted the following quiz. Grade the paper by marking each correct item with a √ or incorrect item with an X. Correct any mistakes.

Name Alicia Smith

Distributive Property Quiz

a. $2(x + 5) = 2x + 10$

b. $2(3x - 6) = 6x - 6$

c. $-3x(4y - 10) = -12xy + 30$

d. $5x(3x + 2y) = 15x + 10xy$

e. $\frac{15x + 10}{5} = 3x + 2$

f. $\frac{8x - 4}{4} = 2x + 1$

g. $12x + 4 = 3(4x + 1)$

h. $-2x + 8 = -2(x - 4)$

ACTIVITY
2.3 Factoring Linear Expressions

You can use the Distributive Property to expand expressions, as you did in the previous activity, and to factor linear expressions, as Meaghan did. Consider the expression:

$$7(26) + 7(14)$$

Since both 26 and 14 are being multiplied by the same number, 7, the Distributive Property says you can add 26 and 14 together first, and then multiply their sum by 7 just once.

$$7(26) + 7(14) = 7(26 + 14)$$

You have factored the original expression.

The number 7 is a *common factor* of both 7(26) and 7(14).

A **common factor** is a number or an algebraic expression that is a factor of two or more numbers or algebraic expressions.

1. Factor each expression using the Distributive Property.

a. 4(33) − 4(28)

b. 16(17) + 16(13)

The Distributive Property can also be used to factor algebraic expressions. For example, the expression $3x + 15$ can be written as $3(x) + 3(5)$, or $3(x + 5)$. The factor, 3, is the *greatest common factor* to both terms.

The **greatest common factor (GCF)** is the largest factor that two or more numbers or terms have in common.

When factoring algebraic expressions, you can factor out the greatest common factor from all the terms.

WORKED EXAMPLE

Consider the expression $12x + 42$.

The greatest common factor of $12x$ and 42 is 6. Therefore, you can rewrite the expression as $6(2x + 7)$.

How can you check to make sure you factored correctly?

It is important to pay attention to negative numbers. When factoring an expression that contains a negative leading coefficient it is preferred to factor out the negative sign.

WORKED EXAMPLE

Consider the expression $-2x + 8$. You can think about the greatest common factor as being the coefficient of -2.

$$
\begin{aligned}
-2x + 8 &= (-2)x + (-2)(-4) \\
&= -2(x - 4)
\end{aligned}
$$

2. Rewrite each expression by factoring out the greatest common factor.

a. $7x + 14$

b. $9x - 27$

c. $10y - 25$

d. $8n + 28$

e. $-3x - 27$

f. $-6x + 30$

So, when you factor out a negative number all the signs will change.

Often, especially in future math courses, you will need to factor out the coefficient of the variable, so that the variable has a coefficient of 1.

3. Rewrite each expression by factoring out the coefficient of the variable.

a. $10x - 45$

b. $-2x + 3$

c. $-x + 4$

d. $-x - 19$

NOTES

4. Rewrite each expression by factoring out the GCF.

a. $-24x + 16y$

b. $-4.4 - 1.21z$

c. $-27x - 33$

d. $-2x - 9y$

e. $4x + (-5xy) - 3x$

5. Evaluate each expression for the given value. Then factor the expression and evaluate the factored expression for the given value.

a. $-4x + 16$ for $x = 2\frac{1}{2}$

b. $30x - 140$ for $x = 5.63$

c. Which form—simplified or not simplified—did you prefer to evaluate? Why?

NOTES

TALK the TALK

Flexible Expressions

As you have seen, you can rewrite expressions by factoring out a GCF or by factoring out the coefficient of the variable. You can also rewrite expressions by factoring out any value. For example, some of the ways $6x + 8$ can be rewritten are provided.

$2(3x + 4)$ $\quad$ $6\left(x + \frac{4}{3}\right)$ $\quad$ $-2(-3x - 4)$

$-6\left(-x - \frac{4}{3}\right)$ $\quad$ $\frac{1}{2}(12x + 16)$ $\quad$ $-\frac{1}{2}(-12x - 16)$

Rewrite each expression in as many ways as you can by factoring the same value from each term.

1. $4x - 12$

2. $-3x + 15$

3. $10 - 20y$

4. $-8y + 9$

Assignment

Write

Match each term to the correct example.

1. factor — a. the 6 in $6(x) + 6(3)$
2. coefficient — b. $-6x - 18 = -6(x + 3)$
3. common factor — c. the 4 in $4x + 3$

Remember

The Distributive Property states that if a, b, and c are any real numbers, then $a(b + c) = ab + ac$.

The Distributive Property makes it possible to write numeric and algebraic expressions in equivalent forms by expanding and factoring expressions.

Practice

Use the Distributive Property to rewrite each expression in its equivalent form.

1. $4(x + 3)$
2. $-7(4 - y)$
3. $6(3x + 5y - 4)$
4. $\frac{9a - 3}{3}$
5. $\frac{0.4(0.3m + 0.6n)}{1.2}$
6. $-9\frac{2}{3}(-2\frac{1}{4}a + b + 8\frac{1}{4})$

Rewrite each linear expression by factoring out the greatest common factor.

7. $64x + 24$
8. $-5y - 35$
9. $36 - 8z$
10. $54n - 81$

Rewrite each linear expression by factoring out the coefficient of the variable.

11. $-2x + 5$
12. $3x - 8$
13. $\frac{-1}{2}x + 6$
14. $-x - 10$

Stretch

1. Jack decides to grow and sell bean plants. Let p represent the number of plants he will grow and sell. After considering his expenses, the expression $-3p(p - 10) - 6p(p - 10)$ represents his profit.
   a. Rewrite and simplify the profit expression by factoring out the greatest common factor.
   b. Rewrite the expression in simplest form with no parentheses.

Review

Evaluate each expression for the given value.

1. $-20a - 65$ for $a = 2.7$

2. $-6x + 52$ for $x = 1\frac{1}{6}$

Determine each product.

3. $(-3.472)(0.89)$

4. $\left(-2\frac{7}{8}\right)\left(-4\frac{4}{5}\right)$

Identify the constant of proportionality in each graph and use it to write an equation in the form $y = kx$.

5.

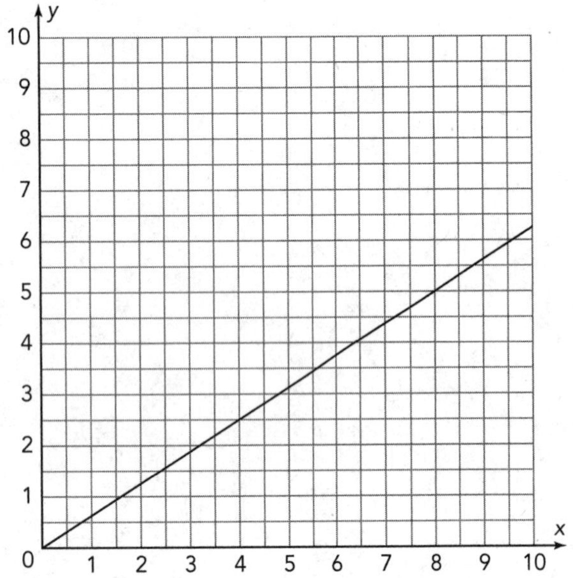

6.

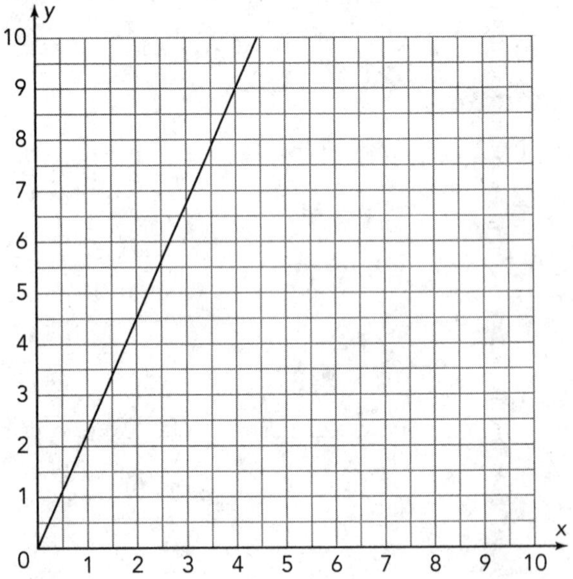

All My Xs

Combining Like Terms

3

WARM UP

Simplify each expression using the Order of Operations.

1. $10 + 8 \div 2(4 + 3)$

2. $21 \div (1)(3) + 0 - 14$

3. $18.2 + 6.1(5) - 3.5$

4. $\frac{3}{4} - \frac{4}{5}(2 - 10)$

LEARNING GOALS

- Model adding and subtracting linear expressions on the number line.
- Determine sums and differences of linear algebraic expressions with rational coefficients.
- Combine like terms to simplify linear expressions and determine sums and differences.
- Write and evaluate algebraic expressions to model situations.
- Rewrite expressions in different forms in context to shed light on how quantities in a problem are related.

KEY TERMS

- like terms

You have evaluated algebraic expressions and determined equivalent expressions using the Distributive Property. How can you add and subtract algebraic expressions?

Getting Started

Find X

The number line shows the locations of two values, represented by linear algebraic expressions.

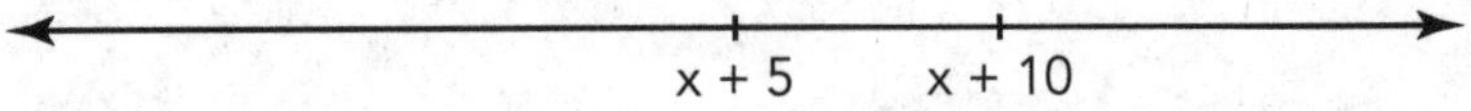

1. **Draw and label a tick mark on the number line to locate each expression given. Explain the reasoning you used to determine the location.**

   a. x

   b. $x + 15$

   c. $x - 5$

ACTIVITY 3.1

Combining Like Terms in Linear Expressions

NOTES

The number line shows the locations of six values, represented by linear expressions.

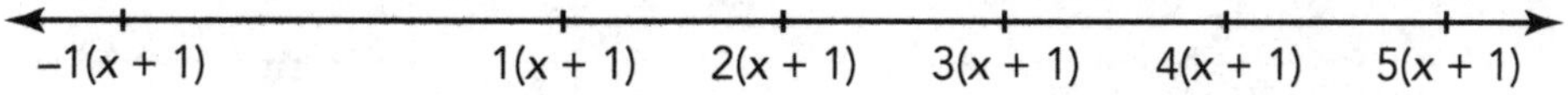

1. Determine the distance between $3(x + 1)$ and $1(x + 1)$ on the number line. Describe the reasoning you used to determine the distance.

Like terms are parts of an algebraic expression that have the same variable expression. For example, in the expression $5(x + 2) + 3 - 2(x + 2)$, the terms $5(x + 2)$ and $2(x + 2)$ are like terms. The coefficients, 5 and 2, are different, but the variable expression is the same $(x + 2)$.

NOTES

When you operate with like terms, you can combine like terms before doing other operations.

WORKED EXAMPLE

Rewrite the expression $5(x + 2) + 3 - 2(x + 2)$ by combining like terms.

$3 + 5(x + 2) - 2(x + 2)$	You can rewrite the expression using the Commutative Property of Addition.
$3 + 3(x + 2)$	Combine the like terms.

2. Use the worked example to answer each question.

a. How is the Commutative Property used to rewrite the expression?

b. How are the like terms in the expression combined?

3. Consider the expressions $3(x + 1)$ and $1(x + 1)$ from Question 1.

a. Explain how these two expressions can be "like terms."

b. How did you combine like terms to determine the distance between the expressions? Use the number line to explain your reasoning.

4. **First, use the number line to determine the distance between the given expressions. Then write an expression and show how combining like terms produces the same result.**

The number line given is separated into intervals of $(x + 1)$.

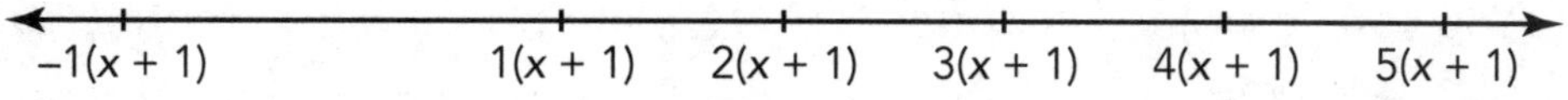

a. **Determine the distance between $5(x + 1)$ and $2(x + 1)$.**

b. **Determine the distance between $1(x + 1)$ and $-1(x + 1)$.**

5. **Explain why Kaitlyn's reasoning is incorrect. Then rewrite the expression correctly.**

Kaitlyn

$7 - 5(x + 1)$ is the same as $2(x + 1)$, because $7 - 5 = 2$.

6. **Simplify each expression by combining like terms.**

a. $5(x + 2) + 2(x + 2)$

b. $5(x + 2) - 2(x + 2)$

ACTIVITY
3.2

Combining Like Terms with Decimal and Fractional Coefficients

You can combine like terms to determine prices with discounts and with sales tax.

For example, suppose a new toy that is regularly priced at \$26.99 is on sale for $\frac{3}{4}$ off.

1. **Write an expression to represent the price of the toy, *p*, minus $\frac{3}{4}$ of the price. Then, combine like terms to simplify the expression.**

2. **Explain what the simplified expression means in terms of the original price of the toy.**

A new shirt costs \$18.99. The sales tax is 5%.

3. **Write an expression to represent the cost of the shirt, *s*, plus 5% of the cost. Then, combine like terms to simplify the expression.**

4. **Explain what the simplified expression means in terms of the original cost of the shirt.**

5. Write and simplify an algebraic expression to represent each situation.

   a. An 18% tip is given for a meal. What expression represents the total cost with tip?

   b. A pair of shoes is advertised as $\frac{1}{4}$ off. What expression represents the total cost after the discount?

   c. A new bike is discounted 35%. What expression represents the total cost?

Make sure you define your variables for each expression.

ACTIVITY 3.3

Adding the Opposite to Subtract

Sasha was able to combine like terms to determine the distance between 3(x + 1) and (x + 1) on the number line. She knew that the distance was 2(x + 1).

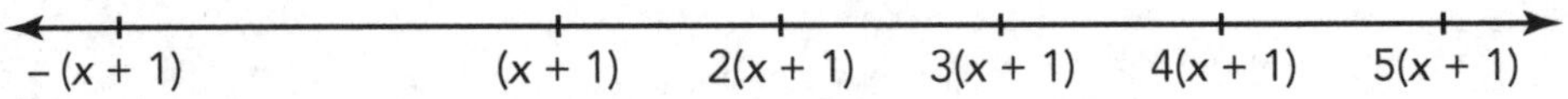

But when she showed her work using the Distributive Property, she got the wrong answer.

Sasha

$3(x + 1) - (x + 1)$

$3x + 3 - x + 1$

$3 + 3x - x + 1$

$3 + 2x + 1$

$2x + 4 = 2(x + 2)$

1. Julian said that Sasha made a mistake when subtracting (x + 1). He said that subtracting (x + 1) is the same as adding the opposite of (x + 1).

a. What is the opposite of (x + 1)? Write your answer without parentheses.

b. Show Sasha how adding the opposite produces the correct answer.

Simplify each expression. Use the Order of Operations.

2. $30x - 140 - (x - 4)$

3. $10 - 5(-2r - 13) - 7r$

4. $-4x - 5(2x - y) - 3y$

5. $7.6p - 3.2(3.1p - 2.4)$

6. $3\frac{2}{3}p - 1\frac{3}{4}(4p - 2\frac{1}{7})$

2*x* and 2*y* are not like terms because they don't have the same variable.

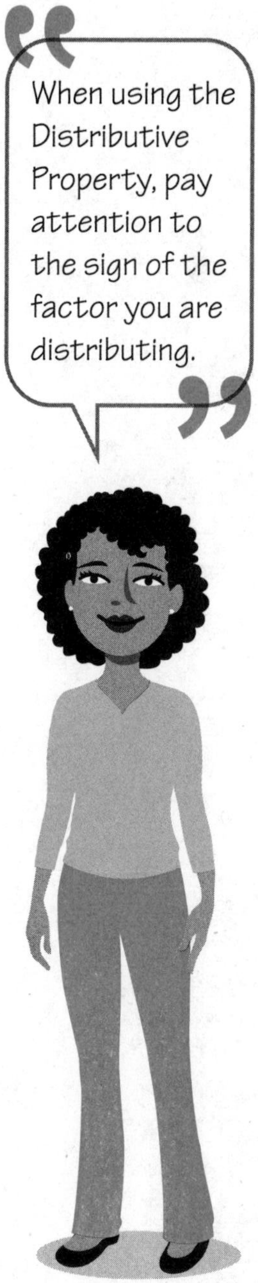
When using the Distributive Property, pay attention to the sign of the factor you are distributing.

NOTES

TALK the TALK

Business Extras

Katie is starting a limousine rental company. As part of her research, Katie discovers that she must charge a 7% sales tax to her customers in addition to her rental fees.

1. **Write an algebraic expression that represents how much tax Katie should collect for any amount of rental fee.**

Katie also discovers that most limousine rental companies collect a flat gratuity from customers in addition to the rental fee. Katie decides to collect a gratuity of $35 from her customers.

2. **Write an expression that represents the total amount of additional money to be collected for tax and gratuity.**

3. **Write an expression that represents the total cost of any rental.**

4. **Use one of your expressions to calculate the amount of tax and gratuity Katie should collect if the rental fee is $220.**

5. **Use one of your expressions to calculate the total cost of a rental if the rental fee is $365.**

Assignment

Write

Write a definition of *like terms* in your own words. Use an example to illustrate your definition.

Remember

Use the Order of Operations to simplify expressions.

1. Simplify expressions in parentheses.
2. Simplify powers.
3. Multiply and divide from left to right.
4. Add and subtract from left to right.

Practice

Simplify each expression by combining like terms.

1. $6x + 4x$
2. $-5y + 2y$
3. $-3m - 8(m + 1)$
4. $-8(r - 2) + 6(r - 2)$
5. $9m - 7m + 13$
6. $4a + 8b$
7. $2(x + 3) + 4(x - 3)$
8. $6 - 2(3x + 4)$
9. $4.5x + 2.5(x - 4)$
10. $3.1 - 4.9(x + 1)$

11. Identify the expression or expressions equivalent to $-5 + 4(-2x + 6) - 3x$.
    a. $-8x + 19 - 3x$
    b. $5x - 29$
    c. $-11x + 19$
    d. $-5x - 19$

Stretch

Sonya is renting a car. She pays a fee of \$50 for the rental plus \$20 each day she has the car. Suppose she pays a total of \$130. For how many days did she rent the car?

Review

Rewrite each expression using the Distributive Property.

1. $5x + 11x$
2. $-2(x - 5)$

Determine each product or quotient.

3. $-\frac{2}{3} \times \frac{1}{5}$
4. $-\frac{1}{8} \div 4$

Solve for the unknown in each proportion. Round to the nearest tenth.

5. $\frac{4.1}{42} = \frac{x}{12}$
6. $\frac{9.7}{1.4} = \frac{5.2}{y}$

Algebraic Expressions Summary

KEY TERMS

- variable
- algebraic expression
- linear expression
- constraint
- evaluate an algebraic expression
- factor
- coefficient
- common factor
- greatest common factor (GCF)
- like terms

LESSON 1 No Substitute for Hard Work

In algebra, a **variable** is a letter or symbol that is used to represent an unknown quantity. An **algebraic expression** is a mathematical phrase that has at least one variable, and it can contain numbers and operation symbols. A **linear expression** is any expression in which each term is either a constant or the product of a constant and a single variable raised to the first power.

Examples of linear expressions include $\frac{1}{2}x + 2$, $-3 + 12.5x$, $-1 + 3x + \frac{5}{2}x - \frac{4}{3}$, and $4y$.

In mathematics, it is sometimes necessary to set constraints on values. A **constraint** is a condition that a solution or problem must satisfy. A constraint can be a restriction set in advance of solving a problem or a limit placed on a solution or graph so that the answer makes sense in terms of a real-world scenario.

To **evaluate an algebraic expression**, you replace each variable in the expression with a number or numeric expression and then perform all possible mathematical operations.

For example, evaluate $-\frac{1}{2}b + 2$ for $b = -8$.

Substitute the value for the variable. → $-\frac{1}{2}(-8) + 2$

Use the Order of Operations to simplify. → $4 + 2 = 6$

LESSON 2

Mathematics Gymnastics

To **factor** an expression means to rewrite the expression as a product of factors. A **coefficient** is a number that is multiplied by a variable in an algebraic expression. If a variable has no coefficient, the understood coefficient is 1.

For example, you can factor the expression $2x + 2$ and rewrite it as the product of two factors.

$2x + 2 = 2(x + 1)$

The Distributive Property states that if a, b, and c are real numbers, then $a(b + c) = ab + ac$. The property also holds if addition is replaced with subtraction: $a(b - c) = ab - ac$.

For example, use the Distributive Property to rewrite the expression $-3a(5b - 2)$ in an equivalent form.

$$-3a(5b - 2) = (-3a)(5b) - (-3a)(2) = -15ab + 6a$$

You can use the Distributive Property to expand expressions and to factor linear expressions. For example, in the expression $7(26) + 7(14)$, the number 7 is a common factor of both $7(26)$ and $7(14)$. A **common factor** is a number or an expression that is a factor of two or more numbers or algebraic expressions. The expression $7(26) + 7(14)$ can be factored and rewritten as $7(26 + 14)$.

The Distributive Property can also be used to factor algebraic expressions. When factoring algebraic expressions, you can factor out the greatest common factor from all the terms. The **greatest common factor** is the largest factor that two or more numbers or terms have in common.

For example, consider the expression $12x + 42$. The greatest common factor of $12x$ and 42 is 6. Therefore, you can rewrite the expression as $6(2x + 7)$.

When factoring an expression, examine the structure of the expression first. If the expression contains a negative leading coefficient, you can factor out the negative factor.

For example, consider the expression $-2x + 8$. You can think about the greatest common factor as being the coefficient -2.

$$\begin{aligned} -2x + 8 &= (-2)x + (-2)(-4) \\ &= -2(x - 4) \end{aligned}$$

LESSON 3

All My Xs

Like terms are parts of an algebraic expression that have the same variable expression. For example, in the expression $5(x + 2) + 3 - 2(x + 2)$, the terms $5(x + 2)$ and $2(x + 2)$ are like terms. The coefficients, 5 and 2, are different, but the variable expression, $(x + 2)$, is the same.

When you operate with like terms, you can combine like terms before doing other operations.

For example, rewrite the expression $5(x + 2) + 3 - 2(x + 2)$ by combining like terms.

$3 + 5(x + 2) - 2(x + 2)$	Rewrite the expression using the Commutative Property of Addition.
$3 + 3(x + 2)$	Combine the like terms.

You can combine like terms with decimal and fractional coefficients, such as in problems determining prices with discounts and with sales tax.

For example, a toaster is on sale for 20% off. An expression to represent the price of the toaster, t, minus 20% of the price is $t - 0.2t$. You can combine like terms to simplify the expression to $0.8t$.

Use the Order of Operations to simplify algebraic expressions.

1. Simplify expressions in parentheses.
2. Simplify powers.
3. Multiply and divide from left to right.
4. Add and subtract from left to right.

When simplifying expressions, remember that subtracting is the same as adding the opposite.

For example, simplify the expression $20x - 8 - 2(x - 3)$.

$20x - 8 - (2x - 3)$	Use the Distributive Property.
$20x + (-8) + (-2x) + 3$	Add the opposite.
$20x + (-2x) + (-8) + 3$	Use the Commutative Property.
$18x - 5$	Combine like terms.

TOPIC 2

Two-Step Equations and Inequalities

For many kinds of rentals – e.g., limos or taxis – there is a fixed charge plus a variable charge, which is an amount charged per mile..

Module 3: Reasoning Algebraically

TOPIC 2: TWO-STEP EQUATIONS AND INEQUALITIES

Students begin this topic by reasoning with bar models to write and solve equations from problem situations. Next, they use a double number line with variable expressions. Throughout these reasoning exercises, the meaning of a solution to an equation is reinforced. Students check their solutions with substitution and write equations from solutions. Students then use inverse operations to solve equations. Students extend their understanding of solving equations to solving one- and two-step inequalities and graphing the solution sets on number lines.

Where have we been?

Students first encountered variable equations and used models to solve one-step equations in grade 6. Work in this topic builds on students' knowledge of expressions and equations to introduce two-step equations.

Where are we going?

In grade 8 and beyond, students will be expected to solve a wide variety of linear equations and inequalities, eventually using their knowledge of equations, inequalities, and solutions to solve nonlinear equations and inequalities. Reasoning about solutions to equations will continue to build students' number sense, an important goal of mathematics education.

Using Number Lines to Compare Variable Quantities

Double number lines were used in grades 6 and 7 to generate equivalent ratios. They are used in this topic to model and solve a two-step equation. This model shows the steps for solving the equation $2j + 10 = 46$. The expression $2j$ must be located 10 to the left of $2j + 10$, and this location must be equal to 36, which is 10 to the left of 46. The value of $1j$ is half the value of $2j$ and also half the value of 36. Therefore, $j = 18$.

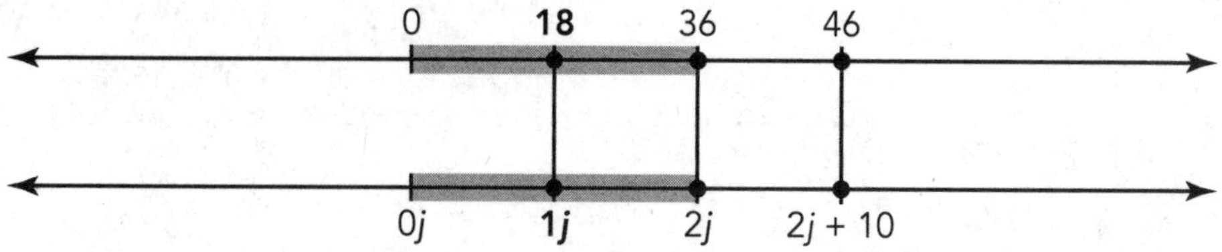

Myth: "Just give me the rule. If I know the rule, then I understand the math."

Memorize the following rule: *All quars are elos.* Will you remember that rule tomorrow? Nope. Why not? Because it has no meaning. It isn't connected to anything you know. What if we change the rule to: *All squares are parallelograms.* How about now? Can you remember that? Of course you can, because now it makes sense.

Learning does not take place in a vacuum. It ***must be*** connected to what you already know. Otherwise, arbitrary rules will be forgotten.

#mathmythbusted

Talking Points

You can further support your student's learning by making sure they eat right and get enough sleep. Healthy bodies make for healthy minds, and both diet and sleep have significant effects on learning.

Key Terms

equation

An equation is a mathematical sentence you create by placing an equals sign, =, between two expressions to show that the expressions have the same value.

literal equation

A literal equation is an equation in which the variables represent specific measures. Common literal equations occur in measurement and geometry concepts.

inequality

An inequality is any mathematical sentence that has an inequality symbol. The solution set of an inequality is all values that make the inequality statement true.

Picture Algebra

1

Modeling Equations as Equal Expressions

WARM UP

Write each phrase as a mathematical expression.

1. the sum of 6 less than a number and 3

2. the distance between a number and 2 on the number line

3. half as many as 7 more than a number

4. an amount, shared equally with 5 people

LEARNING GOALS

- Create and interpret pictorial models to represent equal expressions.
- Write an equation to represent a situation and interpret the parts of the equation.
- Solve word problems leading to equations of the form $px + q = r$.

KEY TERM

- equation

You have learned about both numeric expressions and algebraic expressions. How can you model situations using equal algebraic expressions?

Getting Started

In the Dog House

To build a dog house, you and your friends cut a 10-foot board into two boards. One of the boards is 4 feet longer than the other. How long is each board?

You can draw a bar model to represent a situation like this.

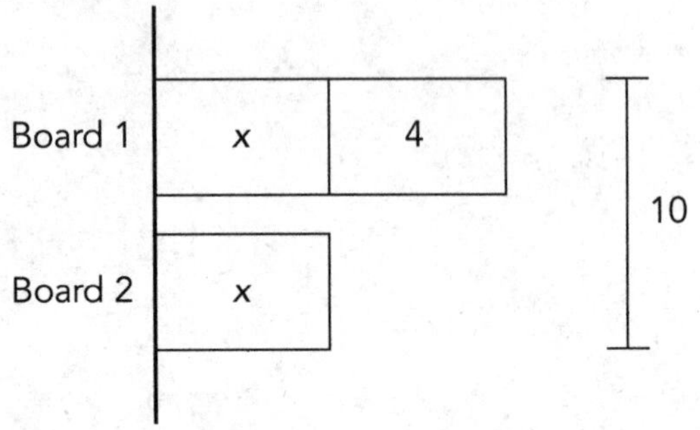

1. Explain what each part of the model represents in terms of this situation.

a. What does the number 4 represent?

b. What does the variable *x* represent?

c. What does the number 10 represent?

2. Use the model to explain what each expression means in terms of this situation.

a. What does the expression $2x$ represent?

b. What does the expression $2x + 4$ represent?

3. How long is each board?

ACTIVITY **1.1**

Creating a Model to Represent Equal Expressions

Fido and Jet are two small dogs. Fido weighs exactly 10 pounds more than Jet. Together, they weigh exactly 46 pounds.

1. Draw a bar model to represent this situation. Let j equal Jet's weight.

2. Use your model to explain what each expression represents in terms of the situation.

a. What does the expression 46 represent?

b. What does the expression $2j$ represent?

c. What does the expression $j + 10$ represent?

d. What does the expression $2j + 10$ represent?

3. How much does each dog weigh? Use the model to help you solve the problem.

ACTIVITY 1.2 Creating a Model to Solve an Equation

You and your friends Jamal and Carla decide to make some money during summer vacation by building and selling dog houses. To get the business started, Jamal contributes $25.55, and Carla contributes $34.45 to buy equipment and materials. You all agree that each person will earn the same amount of money after Jamal and Carla get back what they invested. Your business earns a total of $450.

1. Draw a bar model to represent this situation.

2. Compare your models with your classmates' models.

a. What unknown quantity or quantities are represented in the model?

b. What algebraic expressions can you write to represent different parts of the situation?

You can represent the model you drew as a mathematical sentence using operations and an equals sign. An **equation** is a mathematical sentence created by placing an equals sign (=) between two expressions.

3. **Write an equation to show that the total amount that you, Carla, and Jamal earn, including the amounts Carla and Jamal invested, is equal to $450.**

4. **Describe how the different parts of the equation are represented in the model and in the situation.**

5. **How much money does each person get at the end of the summer? Use your model to solve the problem.**

6. **Explain how the solution is represented in the equation.**

Remember, the solution to an equation is a value for the unknown that makes the equation true.

ACTIVITY
1.3 Solving Addition Equations

In a small town, there are two main sections called the Hill Section and the Lake Section. The town has a population of 3496. The number of people who live in the Hill Section is 295 more than twice the number of people who live in the Lake Section.

1. **Draw a bar model to represent this situation.**

2. **Use your model to write an equation that represents the situation.**

3. **How many people live in each section of town? Use your model to help you solve the problem.**

4. **Explain how the solution is represented in the equation.**

The members of a small town's local arts council are selling raffle tickets. The art council decides that the top three raffle ticket sellers will share a portion of the profits. The second-place seller will receive twice as much as the third-place seller. The first-place seller will receive $20 more than the second-place seller. The profit portion they will share is $200.

5. **Draw a bar model to represent this situation.**

6. **Use your model to write an equation that represents the situation.**

7. **How much will each of the top three sellers receive? Use your model to help you solve the problem.**

8. **Explain how the solution is represented in the equation.**

ACTIVITY 1.4

Solving a Subtraction Equation

Drew is 3 years younger than his brother, Jimmy. The sum of the brothers' ages is 21.

1. **Draw a bar model to represent this situation.**

2. **Use your model to write an equation that represents the situation.**

3. **How old are Jimmy and Drew? Use your model to help you solve the problem.**

4. **Explain how the solution is represented in the equation.**

NOTES

TALK the TALK

Consider the Possibilities!

Think about all the equations you modeled and solved in this lesson.

- $2x + 4 = 10$
- $2j + 10 = 46$
- $3x + 60 = 450$
- $3p + 295 = 3496$
- $5p + 20 = 200$
- $2j - 3 = 21$

1. How are all of these equations similar in structure?

2. What does it mean to solve an equation?

Assignment

Write

Write a definition for *equation* in your own words. Use an example to illustrate your definition.

Remember

The solution to an equation is a value for the unknown that makes the equation true.

Practice

1. The Sharks Aquatic Club recently held a fundraiser to raise money for a local charity. The swimmers received money for each lap that they swam during a one-week period. The three swimmers who raised the most money were Rita, John, and Rodell. Together they swam a total of 2125 laps. John swam three times as many laps as Rita, and Rodell swam 25 more laps than John. How many laps did each swimmer swim?
   a. Draw a picture to represent the situation. Label the unknown parts with variables and the known parts with their values.
   b. Determine the number of laps each person swam using the picture you created. Explain your reasoning.
   c. Write an expression for the number of laps each person swam. Let L represent the number of laps swum by Rita.
   d. Write an equation to represent this situation.
   e. If the swimmers received \$2 for every lap they swam, how much did each swimmer earn for charity?

Stretch

Describe how to solve any equation in the form $ax + b = c$ for the variable x.

Review

1. Simplify each expression by combining like terms.
   a. $3b + 2 + b$
   b. $\frac{1}{2}(h + 4) - \frac{1}{8}(h + 4)$
2. Rewrite each linear expression by factoring out the GCF.
   a. $25x - 5$
   b. $9n + 36$
3. A salesperson receives 12% commission on all the sales that she makes. Calculate the commission on each sale.
   a. A quarter-page ad for \$250.00
   b. A full-page ad for \$800.00

Expressions That Play Together . . .

2

Solving Equations on a Double Number Line

WARM UP

Explain whether or not Expression B is equivalent to Expression A. If the expressions are not equivalent, determine an expression equivalent to Expression A.

1. A: $2(x - 5)$ B: $2x - 5$

2. A: $8 - 2(n + 3)$ B: $6(n + 3)$

3. A: $-(x - 4)$ B: $-x + 4$

LEARNING GOALS

- Identify relationships between expressions.
- Decompose an equation to isolate the unknown.
- Model and solve equations using a double number line.
- Construct equations to solve problems by reasoning about the quantities.

Previously, you have identified expressions that are equivalent. In this lesson, you will model situations as equal expressions on a double number line. How can you maintain equality to determine the unknown quantities in linear equations?

Getting Started

. . . Stay Together

A double number line diagram is a model used to show equivalent relationships.

Consider this double number line. The expressions 12 and 3*x* have the same location, so they have the same value.

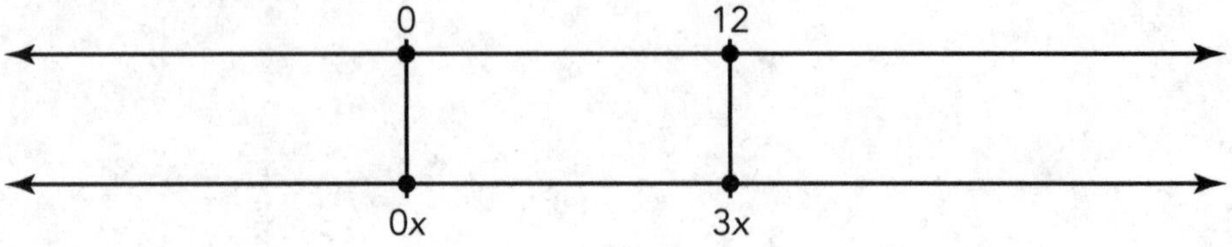

1. Write an equation to show that 3*x* and 12 have the same value.

2. Extend each number line in both directions by identifying and labeling additional equivalent relationships. Explain the reasoning you used to place each relationship.

3. Consider this double number line.

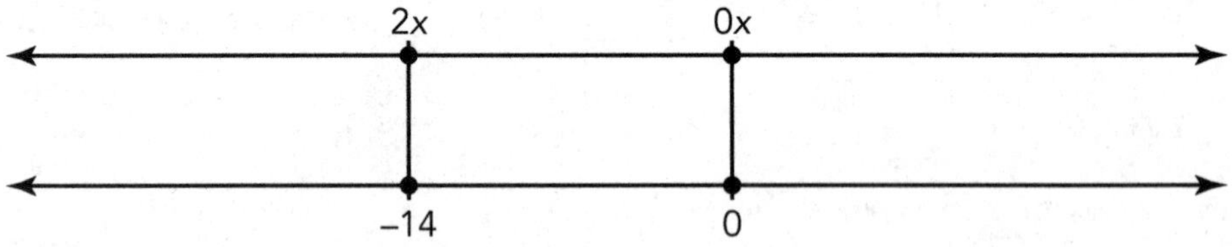

a. Write an equation to show that −14 and 2*x* have the same value.

b. Extend each number line in both directions by identifying and labeling additional equivalent relationships. Explain the reasoning you used to place each relationship.

4. Consider this double number line.

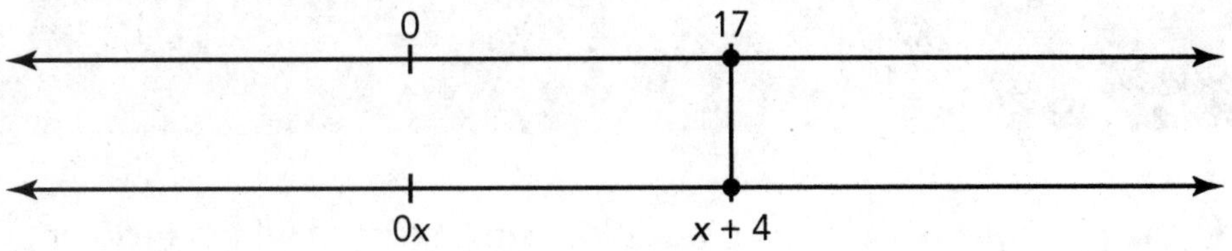

a. Write an equation to show that $x + 4$ and 17 have the same value.

b. Extend each number line in both directions by identifying and labeling additional equivalent relationships. Explain the reasoning you used to place each relationship.

5. Consider this double number line.

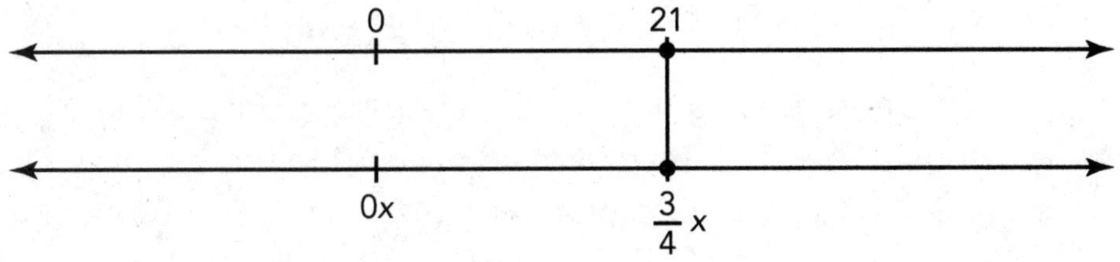

a. Write an equation to show that $\frac{3}{4}x$ and 21 have the same value.

b. Extend each number line in both directions by identifying and labeling additional equivalent relationships. Explain the reasoning you used to place each relationship.

ACTIVITY
2.1

Solving a Two-Step Equation

In the previous lesson, you modeled a problem in which Fido and Jet are two small dogs. Fido weighs exactly 10 pounds more than Jet. Together, they weigh exactly 46 pounds.

This situation can be represented by the equation $2j + 10 = 46$, where j represents Jet's weight. You can also represent this situation and solve the equation using a double number line.

Think about how to transform the equation to isolate the variable.

WORKED EXAMPLE

Solve the equation $2j + 10 = 46$.

First, draw a model to set up the equation.

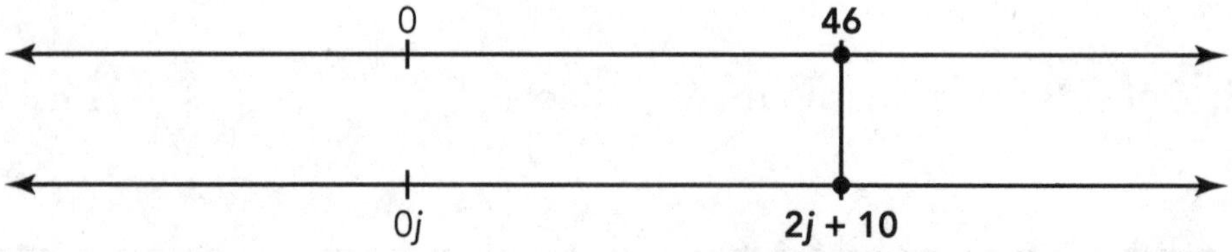

Next, start decomposing the variable expression. Place $2j$ in relationship to $2j + 10$. The expression $2j$ is 10 to the left of $2j + 10$. To maintain equality, place a number that is 10 to the left of 46. So, $2j = 36$.

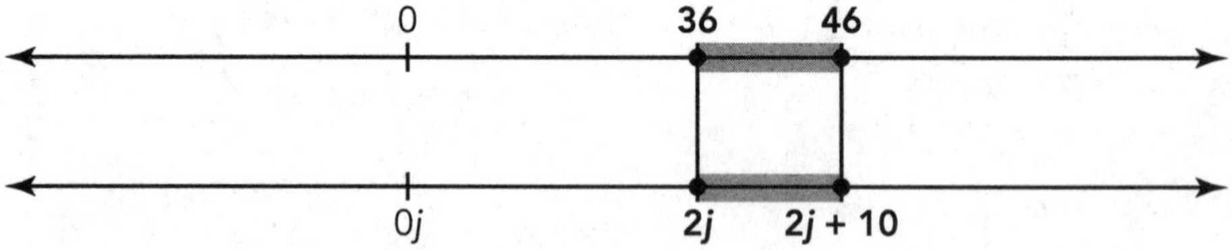

The expression $1j$, or j, is halfway between $0j$ and $2j$. And 18 is halfway between 0 and 36. So, $j = 18$.

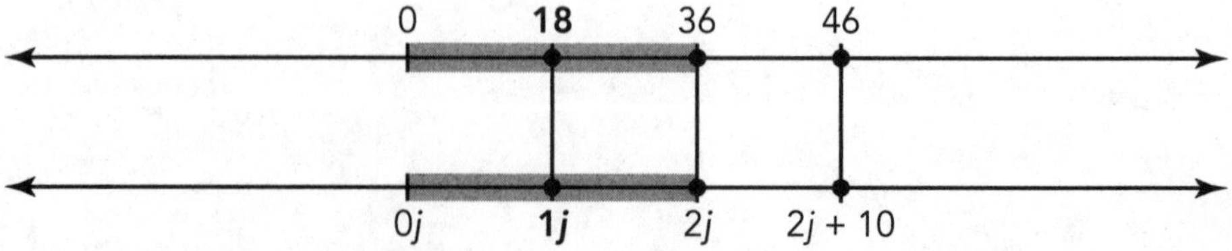

1. How can you check to see if $j = 18$ is the solution to the original equation.

2. What does the solution $j = 18$ represent in terms of this problem situation?

Is there another way to use the double number line to determine the value of j?

3. What operation is used in each step to move toward the solution?

4. Use the double number line shown to solve the equation $21 = 2d + 3$. Describe the steps you use, including the operations represented at each step.

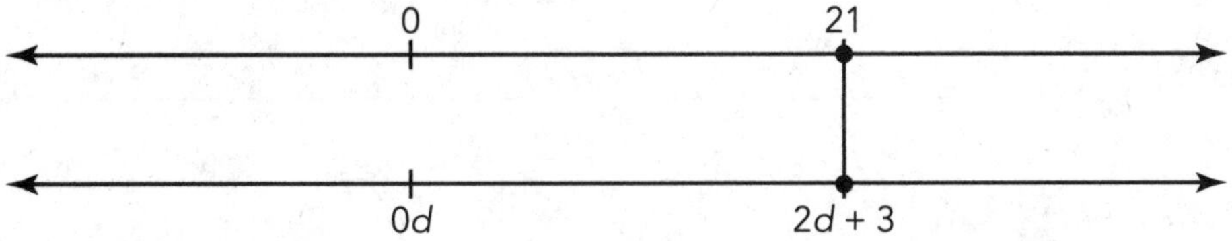
0
21
0d
2d + 3

ACTIVITY 2.2

Practice Solving Two-Step Equations

In this activity, you will use double number lines to solve equations.

1. **Model each equation on the double number line given. Then use the model to solve the equation. Describe the steps and operations you used and explain your reasoning.**

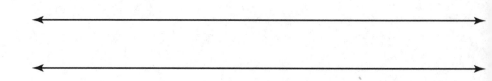

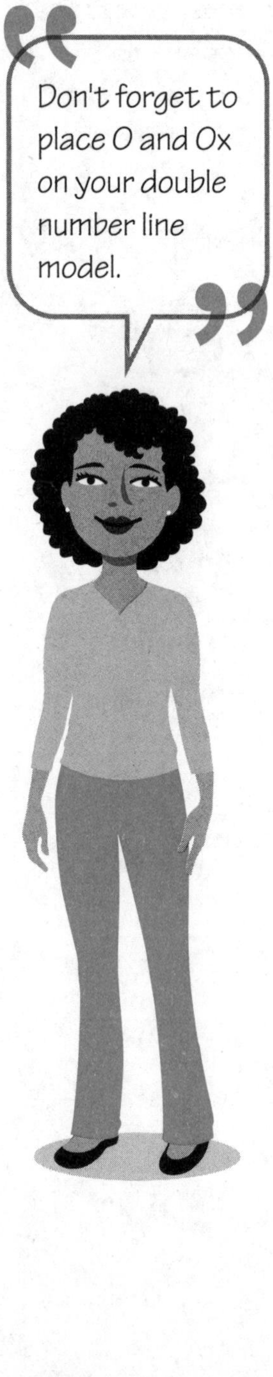

Don't forget to place 0 and 0x on your double number line model.

a. $\frac{1}{2}x + 5 = 15$

b. $52.5 = t - 3.1$

c. $4(b + 1) = 20$

d. $m + 4.5 = -10$

2. **Brent showed how he started to solve the equation $\frac{1}{2}x + 5 = 15$. Describe his method. Then complete his process to solve the equation.**

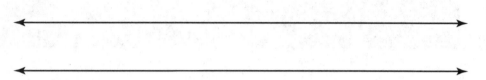

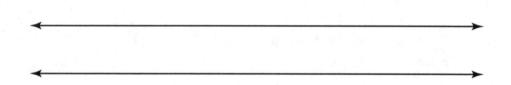

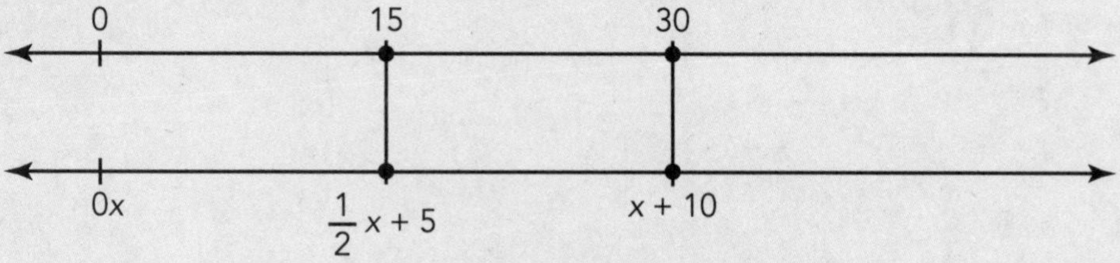

ACTIVITY
2.3 Reasoning with Negatives to Solve Equations

The double number line shows one way to start to solve the equation $-2(3x + 4) = 10$. A through D represent the order in which the steps were completed.

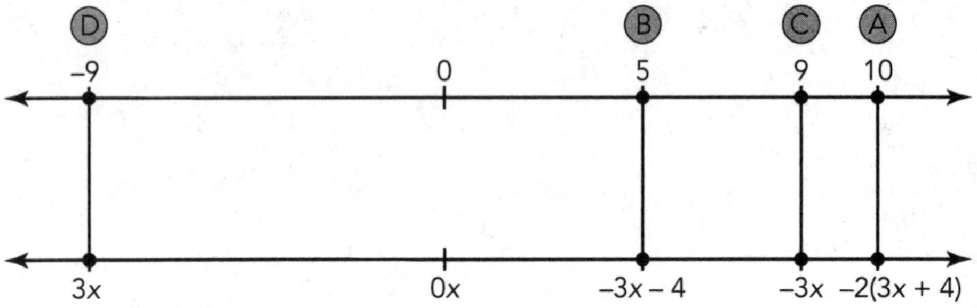

1. Describe each step used to solve the equation. List the operation used at each step.

From Step A to Step B:

From Step B to Step C:

From Step C to Step D:

2. Between which two steps is there a reflection across 0 on the number line? What operation is used to accomplish this reflection?

3. What is the solution to the equation?

4. **Solve each equation using a double number line. Describe your solution steps.**

NOTES

a. $-x + 10 = 40$

b. $-\frac{3}{4}x - 4 = 11$

c. $-3x + 4 = 10$

NOTES

TALK the TALK

Keeping It Together

You have solved a lot of different equations in this lesson and the previous lesson. Now it's your turn.

1. **Start with a solution and create an equation by either multiplying both sides by a constant and then add or subtract a different constant. Describe the process you use to compose your equation. Then give your equation to a classmate to solve.**

2. **Record the steps your partner uses to solve your equation.**

3. **Compare the steps you used to create the equation with the steps your classmate used to solve your equation. What do you notice?**

4. **How do you keep the expressions equal as you solve the equation?**

Assignment

Write

Describe what it means to solve an equation.

Remember

When solving an equation, equality must be maintained. What is done to one expression must be done to the equivalent expression to maintain equality.

Practice

Solve each equation using a double number line.

1. $4x + 12 = 24$
2. $-8x + 25 = -15$
3. $-5x - 12 = 18$
4. $40x + 55 = 695$
5. $-8 = 2x - 14$
6. $11x + 13 = -9$

Stretch

What operation(s) could you use to solve the equation $x^2 + 5 = 86$. What is the solution?

Review

1. During the summer, Matthew and Devan started their own business mowing lawns for people in the Lake Section. Before starting any work, Matthew spends \$15 to fill up the gas tank for the lawnmower. The boys agree that each person will earn the same amount after Matthew is reimbursed the money he spent for gas. After a week of work, the boys earn a total of \$243. Matthew filled up the gas tank just once. How much did each boy earn?
   a. Draw a bar model to represent the situation.
   b. Write an equation to represent the situation.
   c. Use the model to solve the problem.
2. Evaluate each algebraic expression for the variable.
   a. $9g + 5$, for $g = 1.5$
   b. $\frac{2x + 3}{4}$, for $x = 1$
3. Determine each product.
   a. $-6.2(9.1)$
   b. $-0.03(-15)$

3

Formally Yours

Using Inverse Operations to Solve Equations

WARM UP

Solve each equation.

1. $2.3p = -11.73$

2. $\frac{3}{4}r = 10$

3. $y + 5.92 = 1.63$

4. $7\frac{2}{5} + t = 3\frac{1}{4}$

LEARNING GOALS

- Use properties of equality to solve equations.
- Write two-step equations.
- Solve two-step equations of the form $px + q = r$ and $p(x + q) = r$ with efficiency.
- Check solutions to equations algebraically.
- Solve literal equations for specific variables.

KEY TERMS

- two-step equation
- literal equation

You have solved equations using double number lines. How can you use the Properties of Equality and inverse operations to solve equations?

Getting Started

How Does that Work?

Recall that to solve an equation means to determine the value or values for a variable that make the equation true. In the process of solving equations, you must always maintain equality, using the Properties of Equality.

Properties of Equality	For all numbers *a*, *b*, and *c*, . . .
Addition Property of Equality	If $a = b$, then $a + c = b + c$.
Subtraction Property of Equality	If $a = b$, then $a - c = b - c$.
Multiplication Property of Equality	If $a = b$, then $ac = bc$.
Division Property of Equality	If $a = b$ and $c \neq 0$, then $\frac{a}{c} = \frac{b}{c}$.

1. Solve $2x + 6 = 13$ using a double number line model.

2. Explain which Properties of Equality you used in the process of solving the equation.

ACTIVITY 3.1

Strategies for Applying Inverse Operations

Throughout this topic, you have written and solved *two-step equations*. A **two-step equation** requires two inverse operations, or applying two Properties of Equality, to isolate the variable.

Demaryius, Calvin, and Isaac each solved $2x + 6 = 13$ in a different way. Analyze their solution strategies.

> What operation is the inverse of addition? What operation is the inverse of multiplication?

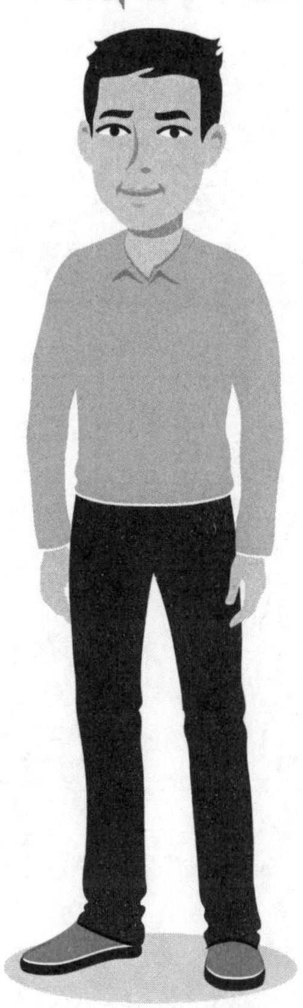

Demaryius

$$2x + 6 = 13$$
$$\frac{2x + 6}{2} = \frac{13}{2}$$
$$\frac{2(x + 3)}{2} = \frac{13}{2}$$
$$x + 3 = 6.5$$
$$-3 = -3$$
$$x = 3.5$$

Calvin

$$2x + 6 = 13$$
$$\frac{2x}{2} + 6 = \frac{13}{2}$$
$$x + 6 = 6.5$$
$$-6 = -6$$
$$x = 0.5$$

Isaac

$$2x + 6 = 13$$
$$-6 = -6$$
$$2x = 7$$
$$\frac{2x}{2} = \frac{7}{2}$$
$$x = 3.5$$

1. **Compare the strategies used by Demaryius and Calvin.**

2. **Compare the strategies used by Demaryius and Isaac.**

3. Solve each equation by first applying either the Addition or Subtraction Property of Equality.

a. $56 = -10 + 2x$

b. $6x + 25 = 79$

To make the addition and subtraction simpler, you can leave fractions in improper form. They already have a common denominator.

c. $38 = 4x - 14$

d. $13 + \frac{x}{3} = 35$

4. Solve each equation by first applying either the Multiplication or Division Property of Equality.

a. $56 = -10 + 2x$

b. $6x + 25 = 79$

c. $38 = 4x - 14$

d. $13 + \frac{x}{3} = 35$

Consider the equations and your solutions in Questions 3 and 4.

5. **Do you prefer one order over the other? If so, why? If your preference changes depending on the equation, explain why.**

ACTIVITY 3.2 Writing and Solving Two-Step Equations

Remember to check each solution and determine if it is reasonable in terms of the scenario.

1. **Shelly is throwing a graduation party. She is sending invitations to her friends and family. She finds a company that charges $6 for a 10-pack of personalized invitations, plus a $5 shipping fee for the entire order, no matter how many 10-packs are ordered. Shelly wants to calculate the cost of an order, based on the number of packs of invitations she orders.**

   a. **Define variables for the two quantities that are changing in this scenario.**

   b. **Write an equation that represents the total cost of any order based on the number of packs of invitations.**

   c. **Use your equation to determine how many packs of invitations are ordered if the total is $53. What about if the total is $29?**

2. Pete's Garage charges $45 per hour for labor when performing auto repairs. The office manager must have the cost of parts and the hours of each job ticket to complete the bills for the customers.

   a. Define variables for the *three* quantities that are changing in this scenario.

   b. Write an equation that represents the total cost of the auto repairs.

   c. Assume that for a given car, the cost of the parts is $101. Use your equation to determine how many hours the mechanic worked on the car if the total bill was $269.75.

3. Felicia's Pet Grooming charges $15 for each dog washed and groomed on the weekend. The cost of the dog shampoo and grooming materials for a weekend's worth of grooming is $23.76. Felicia is interested in her weekend profits.

   a. Define variables for the two quantities that are changing in this scenario.

   b. Write an equation that represents the total profits based on the number of dogs groomed.

   c. Use your equation to determine how many dogs Felicia groomed if her profits were $261.24.

4. Frankie works as a pet sitter all week long but he is more in demand on some days than others. He posts his rates as $12 per visit plus a surcharge, which depends on the day. On his busiest days, Frankie can serve 8 houses for pet sitting. He is interested in his daily profits.

   a. Define variables for the two quantities that are changing in this scenario.

   b. Write an equation that represents the maximum total profits based on the surcharge for that day. Write your equation in the form $a(x + b) = c$.

   c. Beverly and Sean are trying to determine Frankie's Saturday surcharge per house if he makes $142. Beverly thinks the first step in solving the equation is to divide by the coefficient of the parentheses. Sean thinks the first step is to distribute that value through the parentheses. Who's correct?

   d. Determine the Saturday surcharge by solving the equation you wrote in part (b). What is the total fee Frankie charges for pet sitting on a Saturday?

ACTIVITY 3.3 Solving Equations with Efficiency

A savvy mathematician (you!) can look at an equation, see the structure of the equation, and look for the most efficient solution strategy.

As you have seen, there are multiple ways to solve equations. Sometimes an efficient strategy involves changing the numbers in the equation—in mathematically appropriate ways!

1. **Analyze each correct solution strategy to the equation $1.1x + 4.3 = 6.2$.**

Sherry

$$1.1x + 4.3 = 6.2$$
$$1.1x + 4.3 - 4.3 = 6.2 - 4.3$$
$$1.1x = 1.9$$
$$x = \frac{1.9}{1.1}$$
$$x = \frac{19}{11}$$

Maya

$$1.1x + 4.3 = 6.2$$
$$11x + 43 = 62$$
$$11x + 43 - 43 = 62 - 43$$
$$11x = 19$$
$$x = \frac{19}{11}$$

a. **Explain how the two solutions strategies are alike and how they are different.**

b. **What Property of Equality did Maya apply before she started solving the equation?**

Remember, to maintain equality, any operation applied to one side of the equation must be applied to the other side of the equation.

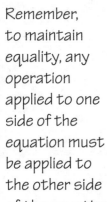

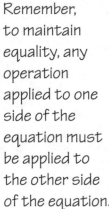

2. **Brian used Maya's strategy to solve the equation $2.6x - 1.4 = 38$. Identify his mistake and then determine the correct solution.**

Brian

$$2.6x - 1.4 = 38$$
$$26x - 14 = 38$$
$$26x = 52$$
$$x = 2$$

3. **Use Maya's strategy to solve each equation. Then check your solution in the original equation.**

a. $-9.6x + 1.8 = -12.3$

b. $2.99x - 1.4 = 13.55$

Now let's consider strategies to solve two different equations that contain fractions.

WORKED EXAMPLE

	$\frac{11}{3}x + 5 = \frac{17}{3}$	$\frac{1}{2}x + \frac{3}{4} = 2$
Step 1:	$3\left(\frac{11}{3}x + 5\right) = 3\left(\frac{17}{3}\right)$	$4\left(\frac{1}{2}x + \frac{3}{4}\right) = 4(2)$
Step 2:	$11x + 15 = 17$	$2x + 3 = 8$
Step 3:	$x = \frac{17 - 15}{11}$	$x = \frac{8 - 3}{2}$
	$= \frac{2}{11}$	$= \frac{5}{2}$

You should be fluent in operating with decimals and fractions, but these strategies can ease the difficulty of the calculations when solving equations.

4. **Answer each question about the strategies used to solve each equation in the worked example.**

a. **Explain Step 1. Why might this strategy improve your efficiency with solving equations?**

b. **What property was applied in Step 2?**

c. **Explain Step 3.**

NOTES

5. **Louise used the strategy from the worked example to solve $3 = \frac{1}{4}x - \frac{1}{4}$. Identify her mistake and determine the correct solution.**

Louise

$3 = \frac{1}{4}x - \frac{1}{4}$

$3 = 4\left(\frac{1}{4}x - \frac{1}{4}\right)$

$3 = x - 1$

$4 = x$

6. **Use the strategy from the worked example to solve $\frac{2}{3}x + \frac{4}{5} = \frac{5}{3}$. Check your solution in the original equation.**

Consider the solution strategies used to solve two more equations.

WORKED EXAMPLE

	$-20x + 80 = 230$	$-38 = -6x - 14$
Step 1:	$10(-2x + 8) = 10(23)$	$-2(19) = -2(3x + 7)$
Step 2:	$-2x + 8 = 23$	$19 = 3x + 7$
Step 3:	$x = \frac{23 - 8}{-2} = -\frac{15}{2}$	$\frac{19 - 7}{3} = x$
		$4 = x$

7. **Answer each question about the strategies used to solve each equation in the worked example.**

   a. **How is the strategy used in this pair of examples different from the strategies used in Questions 1 and 2?**

b. When might you want to use this strategy?

c. Use the strategy from the worked example to solve $44x - 24 = 216$. Check your solution in the original equation.

ACTIVITY 3.4

Solving Literal Equations

You have already learned a lot of important formulas in mathematics. These formulas are also *literal equations*. **Literal equations** are equations in which the variables represent specific measures. Common literal equations occur in measurement and geometry concepts.

1. The formula to convert from degrees Celsius to degrees Fahrenheit is $F = \frac{9}{5}C + 32$.

   a. Calculate the temperature in Celsius, if it is 39°F.

   b. Calculate the temperature in Celsius, if it is 25°F.

   c. Solve the equation for the temperature in Celsius.

To solve for a variable means to isolate that variable on one side of the equation with a coefficient of 1.

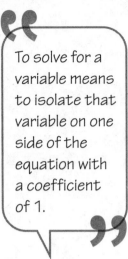

2. The formula for the perimeter of a rectangle can be written as $P = 2l + 2w$, where l and w represent the length and width of the rectangle.

   a. Rewrite the formula by factoring out the coefficient of the variables.

   b. Next, solve the equation for the length.

   c. Solve the equation in part (a) for the width.

   d. How are the equations in parts (b) and (c) alike? Explain why this makes sense.

3. The formula for the area of a trapezoid can be written as $A = \frac{1}{2}(b_1 + b_2)h$, where b_1 and b_2 are the lengths of the bases and h is the length of the height of the trapezoid.

   a. Rewrite the formula as a product of two factors.

   b. Solve the equation for the height of the trapezoid.

   c. Solve the equation in part (a) for one of the bases.

d. When would it be helpful to solve the trapezoid area formula for one of the bases?

4. Solve each equation for the specified variable.

a. $S = 2\pi rh + 2\pi r^2$ for h

b. $V = \pi r^2 h + \frac{2}{3}\pi r^3$ for h.

Throughout this topic, you have solved many linear equations.

5. Analyze each general form.

a. Write a general solution for equations of the form $ax + b = c$ by solving the equation for x.

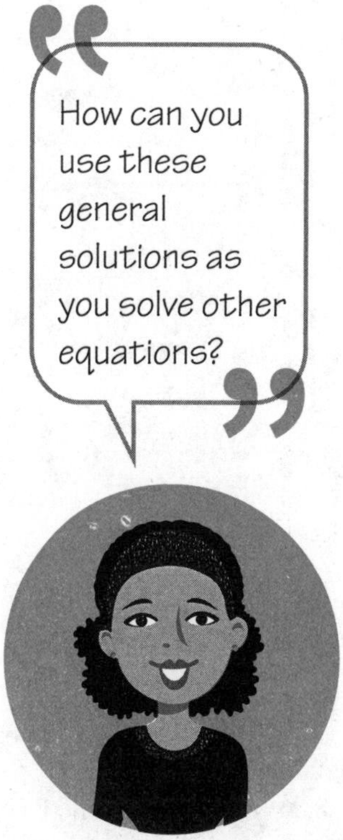

How can you use these general solutions as you solve other equations?

b. Write a general solution of the form $a(x + b) = c$ by solving the equation for x.

ACTIVITY
3.5 Solving More Equations

Number riddles are popular types of problems to solve using two-step equations.

1. Solve each number riddle by writing and solving an equation.

   a. What is a number that when you multiply it by 3 and subtract 5 from the product, you get 28?

   b. What is a number that when you multiply it by 4 and add 15 to the product, you get 79?

   c. Make a number riddle for a partner to solve.

2. Solve each equation. Check your solutions.

   a. $2 + 7x = 16$

   b. $5 + \frac{x}{2} = 16$

   c. $-17 = 2x - 8$

   d. $0.5x - 0.3 = 0.2$

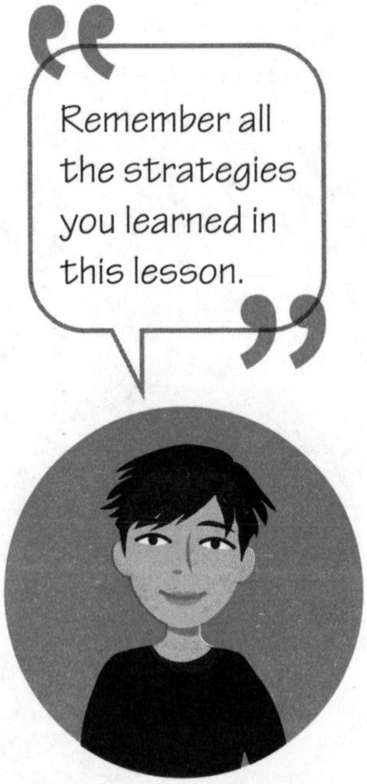

Remember all the strategies you learned in this lesson.

e. $-\frac{1}{4} - \frac{1}{2}x = -\frac{19}{4}$

f. $-\frac{2}{5}x + 4 = 18$

g. $-5 = -3(x + 11)$

h. $8(x + 6) = 18$

i. $\frac{1}{2}(5 - x) = \frac{1}{4}$

j. $6.4 = 1.2(4 + 2x)$

NOTES

TALK the TALK

Get Creative

1. Any equation in the form $ax + b = c$ can be solved in two steps, but do you need to write out both steps to solve the equation?

   a. Isolate the variable x, so that it has a coefficient of 1.

   b. Use your answer from part (a) to solve $4x + 5 = 61$.

NOTES

2. Similarly, any equation in the form $a(x + b) = c$ can be solved without writing out both steps of the two-step solution process.

   a. Isolate the variable x, so that it has a coefficient of 1.

   b. Use your answer to part (a) to solve $4(x - 7) = 20$.

3. Write a real-world situation that can be modeled by each equation.

   a. $3b - 5 = 22$

   b. $19 = 2.5 + 4.5n$

   c. $\frac{1}{2}t + 2 = 16$

Assignment

Write

Explain the process of solving a two-step linear equation.

Remember

You can use the Properties of Equality to rewrite equations and increase your efficiency with solving equations.

- If the equation contains fractions, you can multiply both sides of the equation by the least common denominator.
- If the equation contains decimals, you can multiply both sides of the equation by a multiple of 10.
- If the equation contains large values, you can divide both sides of the equation by a common factor.

Practice

1. Madison Middle School has a Math and Science Club that holds meetings after school. The club has decided to enter a two-day competition that involves different math and science challenges. The first day of competition involves solving multi-step math problems. Teams will receive two points for every problem they get correct in the morning session and three points for every question they get correct in the afternoon session.
   a. Write an equation to represent the situation. Remember to define your variable(s).
   b. The team scores four points in the morning session, but finishes the day with 28 points. Solve the equation and interpret the solution in the context of the problem.
   c. The second day of the competition was the science portion, involving hands-on science problems. Each correct science problem is worth 5 points. If the team started the day with 28 points and ended with 53 points, how many science problems did they get correct? Write and solve an equation to answer the question.
2. Employees at Driscoll's Electronics earn a base salary plus a 20% commission on their total sales for the year. Suppose the base salary is $40,000.
   a. Write an equation to represent the total earnings of an employee. Remember to define your variable(s).
   b. Stewart wants to make $65,000 this year. How much must he make in sales to achieve this salary? Write and solve an equation to answer this question.
   c. Describe the equation $52{,}000 + 0.3s = 82{,}000$ in terms of the problem situation.
3. The manager of a home store is buying lawn chairs to sell at his store. Each pack of chairs contains 10 chairs. The manager will sell each chair at a markup of 20% of the wholesale cost, plus a $2.50 stocking fee.
   a. Write an equation that represents the retail price of a chair, r, in terms of the wholesale price, w.
   b. Use your equation to calculate the retail price of the chair if the wholesale price is $8.40.
   c. Use your equation to calculate the wholesale price if the retail price is $13.30.

4. What is a number that when you multiply it by 0.9 and subtract 6.3 from the product, you get 4.5? Write and solve an equation to solve the riddle.
5. Craig and four of his friends had a car wash to earn some extra money. They split the profits and Craig got an extra \$18 to repay his parents for the car wash supplies. If Craig got \$32, how much total money did they split among themselves? Write and solve an equation to answer the question.
6. Susana bought a laptop for \$500. It was marked \$50 off because it was out of the box and slightly scratched. She also got a 20% student discount, which was taken off the original price. What was the original price of the laptop? Write and solve an equation to answer the question.
7. Solve each equation. Check your solution.
   a. $1 = 3x - 11$
   b. $7x + 2 = -12$
   c. $9 = \frac{y}{4} - 2$
   d. $13 - \frac{a}{7} = 6$
   e. $-5b - 12 = 18$
   f. $-8 = 2h - 14$
   g. $-3(2x + 7) = 18$
   h. $-14 = -2(5 - x)$
   i. $45.99c - 50 = 133.96$
   j. $1.1x + 2.35 = -8.1$
8. Solve each equation for the indicated variable.
   a. $ax + by = c$, for y
   b. $h = \frac{1}{2}gt^2 + 160t$, for g

Stretch

Solve each equation. Check your solution.

1. $1.95(6.2 - 3x) - 4.81 = -18.46$
2. $\frac{2}{3}\left(x - \frac{5}{2}\right) - \frac{7}{6} = -\frac{13}{3}$

Review

Solve each equation using a double number line model.

1. $4x - 5 = 7$
2. $\frac{1}{3}x + 2 = 5$

Evaluate each expression for the indicated value.

3. $-\frac{1}{2}a^2 + \frac{5}{6}a$, for $a = \frac{6}{7}$
4. $-5.3r - 7.6 + 0.4r$, for $r = -2.4$

Determine each quotient.

5. $2\frac{3}{8} \div -2\frac{1}{2}$
6. $-14.8 \div -1.2$

Be Greater Than

4

Solving Inequalities with Inverse Operations

WARM UP

Graph each inequality on a number line.

1. $x > 5$

2. $x \geq 2\frac{1}{2}$

3. $x < 6.2$

4. $x \leq 9$

LEARNING GOALS

- Solve and graph one- and two-step inequalities.
- Solve word problems leading to inequalities of the form $px + q > r$ and $px + q < r$.
- Graph the solution sets of inequalities and interpret the solutions in context.

KEY TERMS

- inequality
- solve an inequality
- solution set
- Properties of Inequalities

You have solved a variety of equations. How is solving inequalities similar to or different from solving equations?

Getting Started

Equations Versus Inequalities

Consider the equation $4x + 9 = 1$. The solution is shown on the number line.

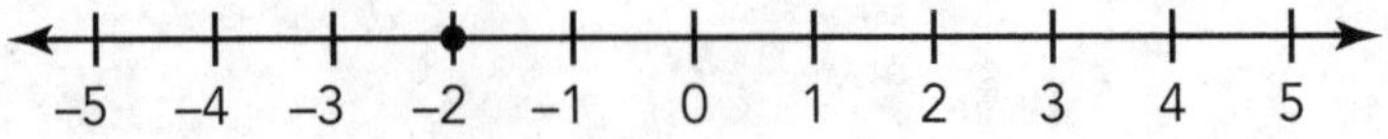

1. Verify the solution is correct. Are there any other solutions to this equation? Explain your reasoning.

An **inequality** is any mathematical sentence that has an inequality symbol. The solution set of an inequality is all values the make the inequality statement true.

Consider the set of numbers {−5, −4, −3, −2, −1, 0, 1}.

2. Use substitution to determine which values are solutions to each inequality. Plot the solutions for each inequality on the given number line.

a. $4x + 9 > 1$

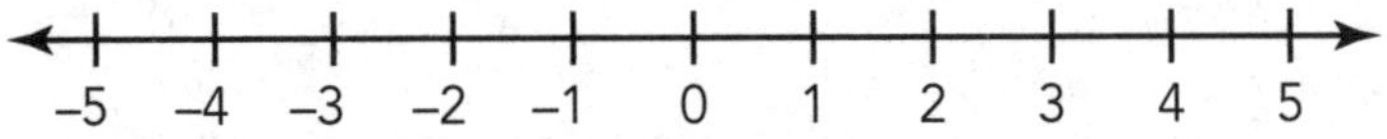

b. $4x + 9 \leq 1$

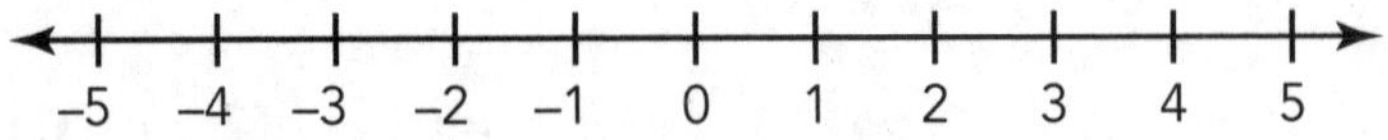

3. Use your number lines to make predictions about other solutions to each inequality. Create a number line to illustrate each of your conjectures.

ACTIVITY 4.1

Adding and Subtracting with Inequalities

In this lesson, you will learn to *solve an inequality*. To **solve an inequality** means to determine the values of the variable that make the inequality true. The objective when solving an inequality is similar to the objective when solving an equation. You want to isolate the variable on one side of the inequality symbol by using the operations of addition, subtraction, multiplication, and division.

The values of the variable that make an inequality true are together called the **solution set** of the inequality.

Let's investigate what happens when each side of an inequality is added or subtracted by the same number.

Consider the relationship between the two numbers 3 and 6. Since 3 is to the left of 6, you know that $3 < 6$.

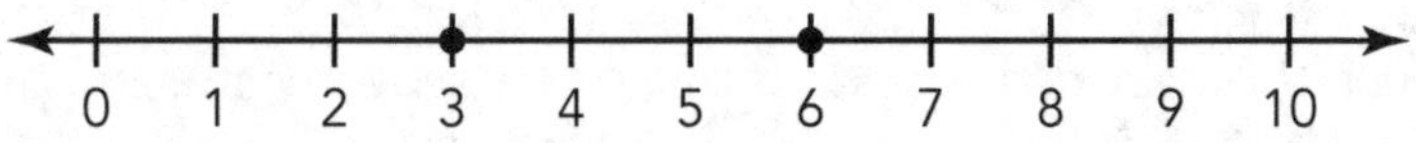

1. **Perform each operation to the numbers 3 and 6. Then, plot the new values on the number line. Finally, write a corresponding inequality statement.**

   a. **Add $\frac{1}{2}$ to each number.**

   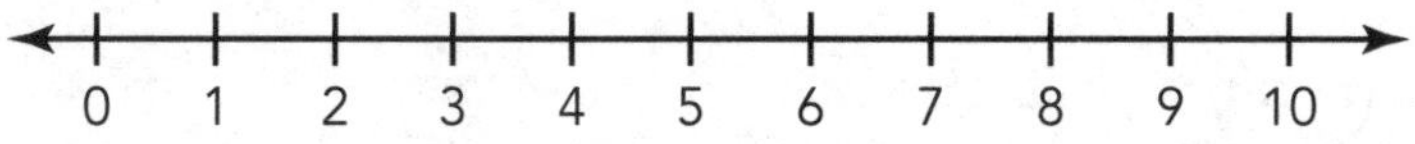

   $3 + \frac{1}{2}$ ___ $6 + \frac{1}{2}$

   b. **Add 2 to each number.**

   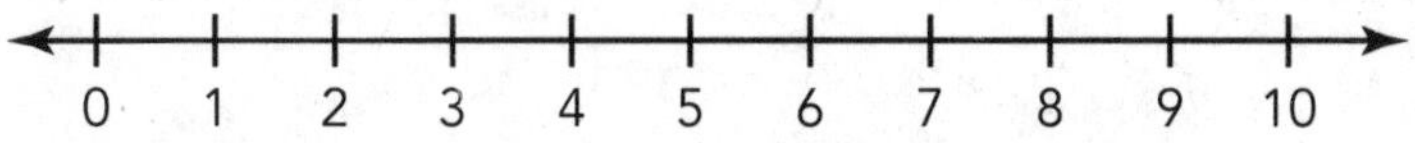

   $3 + 2$ ___ $6 + 2$

   c. **Add 3 to each number.**

   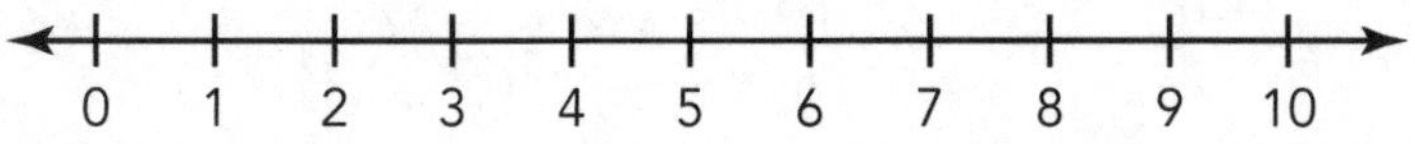

   $3 + 3$ ___ $6 + 3$

NOTES

d. **Subtract $\frac{1}{2}$ from each number.**

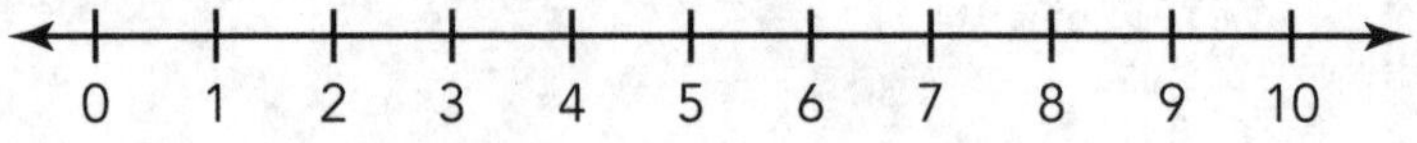

$3 - \frac{1}{2}$ ___ $6 - \frac{1}{2}$

e. **Subtract 2 from each number.**

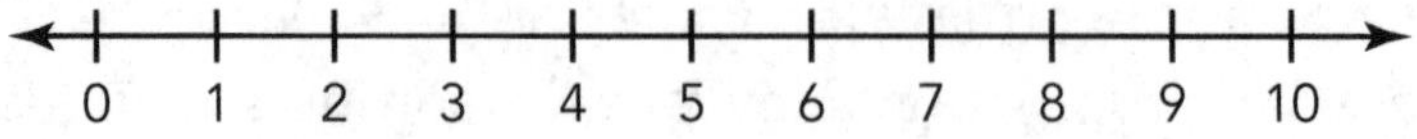

$3 - 2$ ___ $6 - 2$

f. **Subtract 3 from each number.**

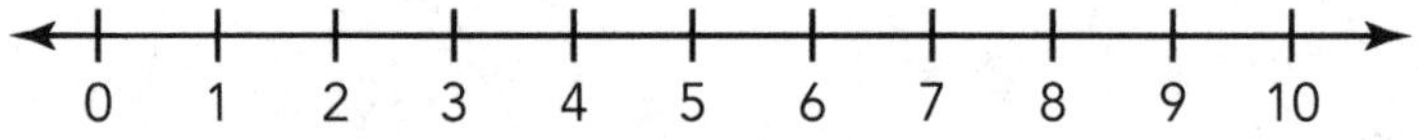

$3 - 3$ ___ $6 - 3$

2. **When you add the same number to each side of the inequality or subtract the same number from each side of the inequality, what do you notice about the resulting inequality symbol?**

3. **Explain why Simone is correct.**

Simone

No matter what number I add to or subtract from both sides of the inequality, the relationship between the two sides of the inequality stays the same:

$$3 < 6$$

$$3 + a < 6 + a$$

$$3 - a < 6 - a$$

4. Consider the inequality $x - 2 > 6 - 2$.

   a. Write an inequality to describe the possible values of x.

   b. What could you do to both sides of the original inequality to determine your answer to part (a)?

5. Suppose you have the inequality $x - 2 > 6$. Determine the possible values of x and sketch the solution set on a number line. Explain your reasoning.

6. Mike is 5 years older than his brother Jim.
   For each question, write and solve an equation or inequality to describe Jim's possible ages. Then, graph the solution set on the number line.

   a. How old will Jim be when Mike is 29 years old?

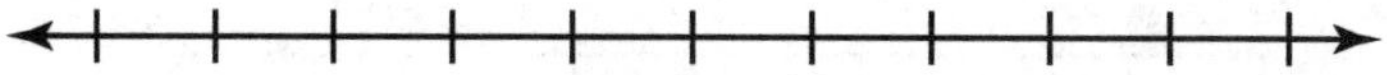

   b. How old will Jim be when Mike is at least 25 years old?

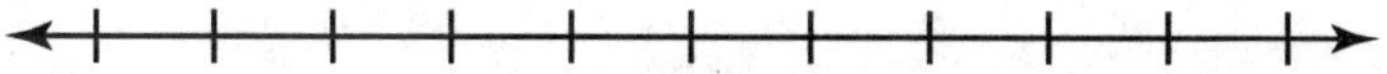

   c. How old will Jim be when Mike is younger than 30 years old?

Recall that the solution to any inequality is shown on a number line by a ray whose starting point is an open or closed circle.
A closed circle means that the starting point is part of the solution set of the inequality.
An open circle means that the starting point is not a part of the solution set of the inequality.

7. Solve each inequality and graph the solution set on the number line. Then choose one value from your solution set and one value outside your solution set to check your work.

a. $13 < x + 11$

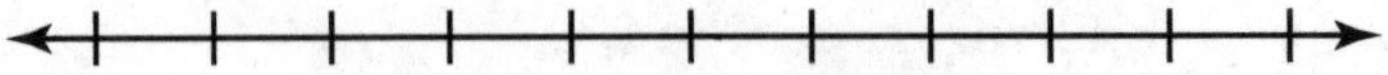

b. $10 + x \geq 45$

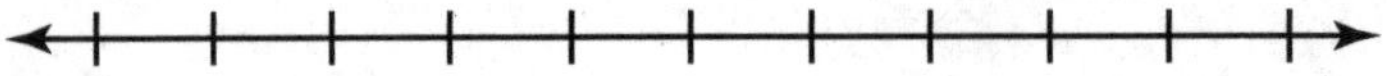

c. $x < 5 + 9$

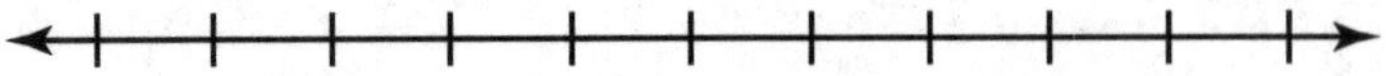

d. $x - 3 \leq 21$

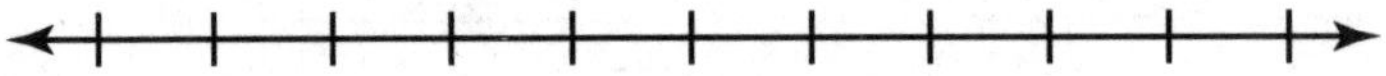

8. Choose one of the inequalities from Question 7 and write a real-world situation that can be modeled by the algebraic statement.

ACTIVITY
4.2

Multiplying and Dividing by Positive Numbers

Next, let's investigate what happens when each side of an inequality is multiplied or divided by the same positive number.

Consider the inequality $3 < 6$.

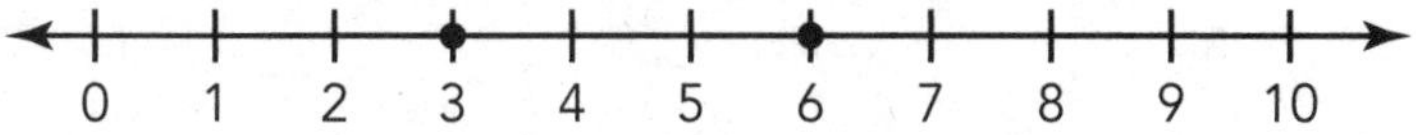

Remember, the representation for division can include fraction notation.

1. Perform each operation to the numbers 3 and 6. Then, plot the new values on the number line. Finally, write a corresponding inequality statement.

a. Multiply each number by $\frac{1}{2}$.

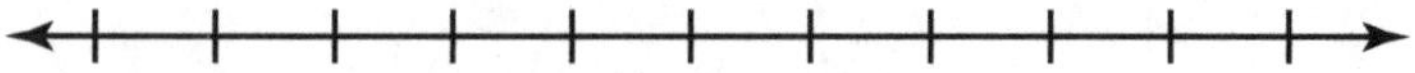

$3\left(\frac{1}{2}\right)$ ___ $6\left(\frac{1}{2}\right)$

b. Multiply each number by 2.

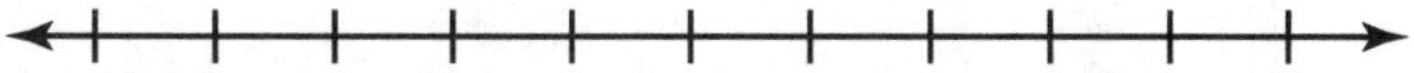

3(2) ___ 6(2)

c. Multiply each number by 3.

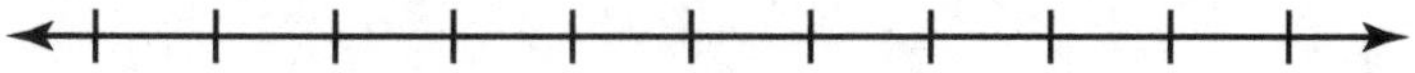

3(3) ___ 6(3)

d. Divide each number by $\frac{1}{2}$.

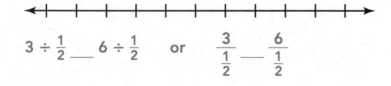

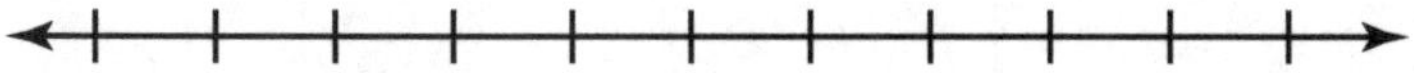

$3 \div \frac{1}{2}$ ___ $6 \div \frac{1}{2}$ or $\frac{3}{\frac{1}{2}}$ ___ $\frac{6}{\frac{1}{2}}$

NOTES

e. Divide each number by 2.

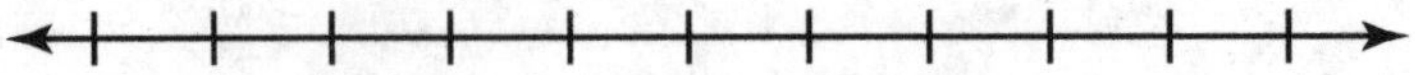

$3 \div 2$ ___ $6 \div 2$ or $\frac{3}{2}$ ___ $\frac{6}{2}$

f. Divide each number by 3.

$3 \div 3$ ___ $6 \div 3$ or $\frac{3}{3}$ ___ $\frac{6}{2}$

2. When you multiply the same positive number to each side of the inequality or divide the same positive number from each side of the inequality, what do you notice about the resulting inequality symbol?

3. Identify the constraints of the value *a* that makes Robin's claim correct.

Robin

No matter what positive number I multiply to or divide from both sides of the inequality, the relationship between the two sides of the inequality stays the same:

$$3 < 6$$

$$3(a) < 6(a)$$

$$\frac{3}{a} < \frac{6}{a}$$

4. Consider the inequality $2x < 6(2)$.

a. Write an inequality to describe the possible values of *x*.

b. What could you do to both sides of the original inequality to determine your answer to part (a)?

5. Suppose you have the inequality $2x < 6$. Determine the possible values of x. Explain your reasoning.

6. Michelle is 3 times as old as her sister Beth.
For each question, write and solve an equation or inequality to describe Beth's possible ages. Then, graph the solution set on the number line.

a. How old will Beth be when Michelle is at least 27 years old?

b. How old will Beth be when Michelle is younger than 30 years old?

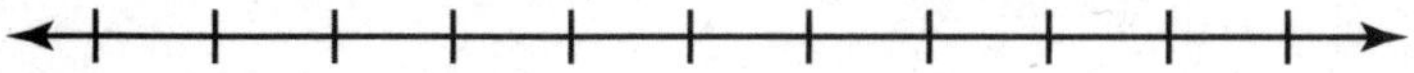

c. How old will Beth be when Michelle is 42 years old?

7. Solve each inequality and graph the solution set on the number line.

a. $10x \geq 45$

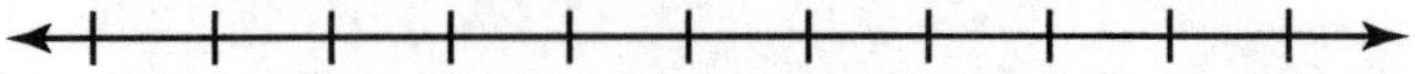

b. $\frac{x}{3} \leq 21$

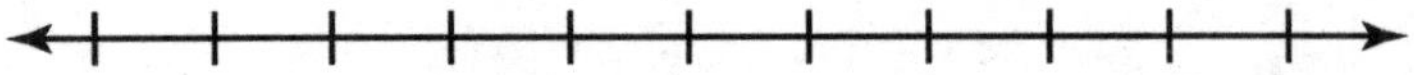

c. $3 < x \div 8$

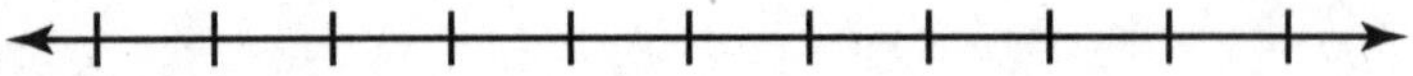

8. Choose one of the inequalities from Question 7 and write a real-world situation that can be modeled by the algebraic statement.

ACTIVITY 4.3

Multiplying and Dividing by Negative Numbers

Finally, let's investigate what happens when each side of an inequality is multiplied or divided by the same negative number.

Consider the inequality $3 < 6$.

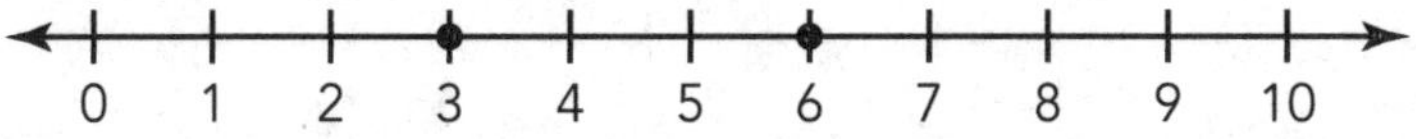

1. **Perform each operation to the numbers 3 and 6. Then, plot the new values on the number line. Finally, write a corresponding inequality statement.**

   a. **Multiply each number by $-\frac{1}{2}$.**

   $3\left(-\frac{1}{2}\right)$ ___ $6\left(-\frac{1}{2}\right)$

   b. **Multiply each number by −2.**

   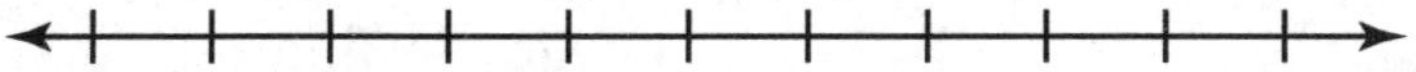

   3(−2) ___ 6(−2)

   c. **Multiply each number by −3.**

   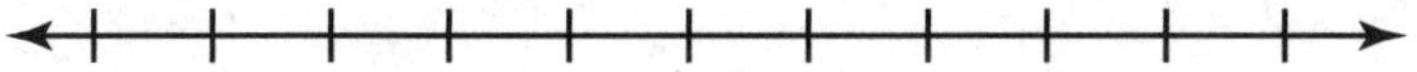

   3(−3) ___ 6(−3)

d. Divide each number by $-\frac{1}{2}$.

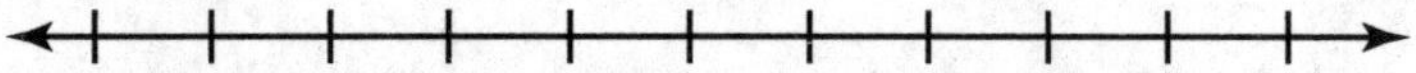

$3 \div \left(-\frac{1}{2}\right)$ ___ $6 \div \left(-\frac{1}{2}\right)$ or $\frac{3}{\left(-\frac{1}{2}\right)}$ ___ $\frac{6}{\left(-\frac{1}{2}\right)}$

e. Divide each number by −2.

$3 \div (-2)$ ___ $6 \div (-2)$ or $\frac{3}{(-2)}$ ___ $\frac{6}{(-2)}$

f. Divide each number by −3.

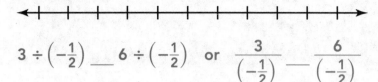

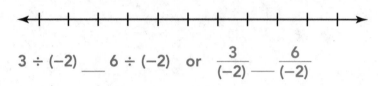

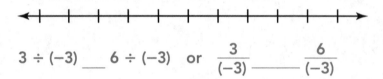

$3 \div (-3)$ ___ $6 \div (-3)$ or $\frac{3}{(-3)}$ ___ $\frac{6}{(-3)}$

2. When you multiply the same negative number to each side of the inequality or divide the same negative number from each side of the inequality, what do you notice about the resulting inequality symbol?

3. Jenna and Brendan are trying to solve $-4x < 20$. Consider their solutions and explanations.

Brendan's Solution

$-4x < 20$

$x < -5$

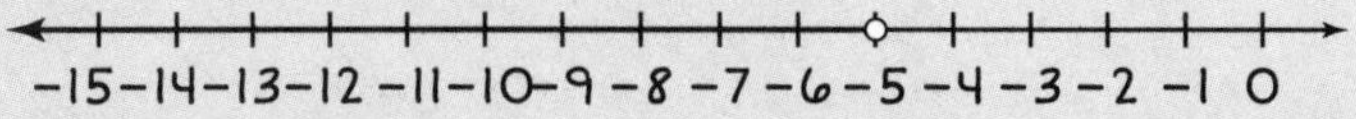

I divided both sides by −4 to solve the inequality.

Jenna's Solution

$-4x < 20$

$x > -5$

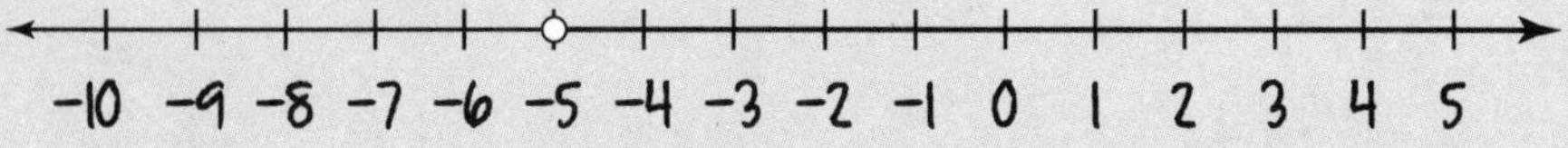

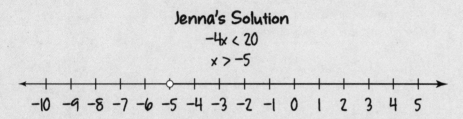

I know that when I multiply or divide any given number by a negative number, I have to pay attention to the sign of my answer. So when I divide both sides of the inequality by − 4, the inequality sign should reverse.

a. Determine who is correct. List three values from each person's solution, and verify that those solutions make the original inequality $-4x < 20$ true. What do you notice? Explain your reasoning.

Check for Brendan's solution. Check for Jenna's solution.

b. Circle the correct solution and explanation, and cross out the incorrect solution and explanation from Brendan's and Jenna's work.

4. Solve each inequality and graph the solution set. Then, list three values from each solution set, and verify that each value makes the original inequality true.

a. $8x > 16$

b. $\frac{x}{3} \leq -4$

c. $-5x < 35$

d. $\frac{x}{-2} \geq 5$

ACTIVITY

4.4 Solving Two-Step Inequalities

Aaron wants to buy new football pads that cost $55.00 at GoodSportsBuys.com. The online store charges $11 for shipping on orders less than $75. He also wants to buy some packages of eyeblack strips for $4 each, but he does not want to pay more than the $11.00 shipping fee.

1. **Write and solve an inequality that describes the possible number of packages of eyeblack strips Aaron can purchase and still remain in the $11.00 shipping fee category. Let *p* represent the number of packages of eyeblack strips. Explain your solution in terms of the problem situation.**

You just solved a problem that involved setting up and solving a two-step inequality. Let's compare and contrast the strategies and solutions of an equation and inequality that are similar in structure.

2. **Describe the steps you would take to solve the equation $3x - 2 = 7$. Then, solve the equation.**

3. A set of possible solutions for each inequality is shown. Circle the solutions that make the inequality true. Then, list three additional solutions to the inequality.

   a. $3x - 2 \geq 7$

   $\{-2, -1, 0, 1, 2, 3, 4, 5, 6, 7\}$

   b. $3x \geq 9$

   $\{-2, -1, 0, 1, 2, 3, 4, 5, 6, 7\}$

   c. $x \geq 3$

   $\{-2, -1, 0, 1, 2, 3, 4, 5, 6, 7\}$

4. What do you notice about the solutions you circled in Question 3, parts (a) through (c)?

5. What do you notice about the three additional solutions you wrote for each inequality?

6. Compare the sequence of the three inequalities to the steps you used to solve the equation in Question 2. What do you notice? Explain your reasoning.

7. **Graph the solution set for $3x - 2 \geq 7$.**

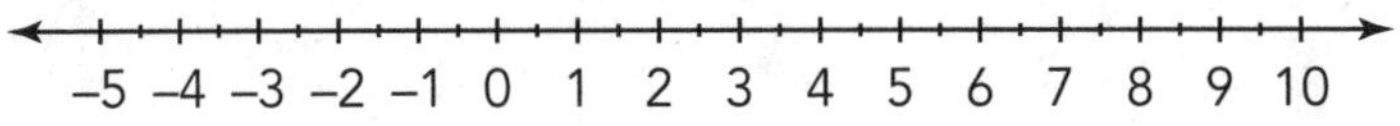

NOTES

You can check your solution to an inequality by choosing a value that is in your solution set and substituting it into the original inequality. If that substituted value makes the inequality true, then you have verified a correct solution.

8. **Choose a value from the solution set of the inequality $3x - 2 \geq 7$, and verify that it is a solution.**

9. **Analyze the solution strategy and solution for each inequality.**

Ella

$$-\frac{1}{2}x + \frac{3}{4} < 2$$

$$-4\left(-\frac{1}{2}x + \frac{3}{4} < 2\right)$$

$$2x - 3 > -8$$

$$2x > -5$$

$$x > \frac{-5}{2}$$

$$x > -2.5$$

Jeff

$$-12x + 20 < 32$$

$$\frac{-12x + 20}{-4} < \frac{32}{-4}$$

$$3x - 5 < -8$$

$$3x < -3$$

$$x < -1$$

Describe the strategy that Ella used correctly.

Identify the error in Jeff's strategy and determine the correct solution.

10. Solve each inequality or equation, and show your work. Then, graph the solution set on a number line.

a. $2x + 5 < -17$

b. $97 \leq -8x + 1$

c. $6.5x - 1.1 > 6.9$

d. $10 < \frac{2x - 3}{5}$

Don't forget about all the solution strategies you have learned.

e. $18 \geq -x + 7$

NOTES

TALK the TALK

Summarizing Inequalities

The **Properties of Inequalities** allow you to solve inequalities involving any numbers.

Properties of Inequalities	For all numbers *a*, *b*, and *c*,...
Addition Property of Inequalities	If $a < b$, then $a + c < b + c$. If $a > b$, then $a + c > b + c$.
Subtraction Property of Inequalities	If $a < b$, then $a - c < b - c$. If $a > b$, then $a - c > b - c$.
Multiplication Property of Inequalities	If $a < b$, then $a \cdot c < b \cdot c$, for $c > 0$. If $a > b$, then $a \cdot c > b \cdot c$, for $c > 0$.
Division Property of Inequalities	If $a < b$, then $\frac{a}{c} < \frac{b}{c}$, for $c > 0$. If $a > b$, then $\frac{a}{c} > \frac{b}{c}$, for $c > 0$.

These properties also hold true for $\leq$ and $\geq$.

1. **Write a paragraph to summarize your understanding of the Properties of Inequalities.**

2. **State the Division Property of Inequalities for $c < 0$.**

3. **Describe how to solve any inequality. How do you check to see if a value is a solution to an inequality?**

NOTES

4. Write a real-world situation that can be modeled by each inequality. Be sure to define your variables.

   a. $20 > 5 + 3.25m$

   b. $65 + 20x \geq 150$

   c. $66 - \frac{1}{2}s > 32$

Assignment

Write

Explain how solving an inequality is similar to and different from solving an equation.

Remember

To solve an inequality means to determine what value or values will replace the variable to make the inequality true.

Practice

1. Match each inequality with the correct solution.

   a. $x < -2$ i. $4x + 12 < 20$

   b. $x < 2$ ii. $55 < 35 + 10x$

   c. $x > -2$ iii. $-\frac{3}{2}x + 12 > 15$

   d. $x > 2$ iv. $-8x < 16$

2. Solve each one-step inequality and graph the solution set on a number line.

   a. $x + 7 \geq 13$ b. $-4 > x - 3$

   c. $\frac{x}{4} \leq \frac{5}{2}$ d. $18.3 > 6.1x$

   e. $3 < \frac{x}{-8}$ f. $-10x \geq 45$

3. Solve each two-step inequality and graph the solution set on a number line.

   a. $-17 < 3 - 5x$ b. $21 - 9x \geq -6$

   c. $-500 \leq 11x - 60$ d. $-x + 38 < 59$

4. Carole has $53.95 and she washes cars for $8 each. Carole wants to attend a musical that costs $145.75.

   a. Write and solve an inequality to determine the minimum number of cars Carole must wash to be able to buy the ticket to the musical.

   b. Is the answer to the question that same as the solution to the inequality? Explain.

5. David has $15 to spend at the gourmet candy store. He wants to buy gummy bears and jelly beans. Gummy bears are $5.25 per pound and jelly beans are $3.90 per pound. If David already has $1\frac{3}{4}$ pounds of jelly beans, how many pounds of gummy bears can he buy? (Weights are measured to the nearest hundredth.) Write and solve an inequality to determine the maximum number of pounds of gummy bears David can buy.

Stretch

Solve each inequality and graph the solution set on a number line.

1. $7(4x + 9) - 13 \geq -87$ 2. $0.25(3 - x) < 0.375$

3. $78 < -9x - 3(-56 + 12x)$ 4. $0.20x - 0.08(x - 10) \leq 24.80$

Review

Solve each two-step equation.

1. $2(3x + 4) = 19$
2. $-3.2x + 9.1 = 4.62$

Rewrite each linear expression by factoring out the coefficient of the variable.

3. $-2x + 7$
4. $3x - 12$

Use properties to rewrite each expression with the fewest possible terms.

5. $\left(\frac{6}{7}x + 4\frac{1}{3}\right) + \left(-1\frac{1}{2}x - 9\right)$
6. $(10.7x - 19.2) - (81.6x - 33.6)$

Two-Step Equations and Inequalities Summary

KEY TERMS

- equation
- two-step equation
- literal equation
- inequality
- solve an inequality
- solution set
- Properties of Inequalities

LESSON 1

Picture Algebra

You can create a model to represent equal expressions.

For example, Jenna is 6 years older than Marco. The sum of their ages is 20.

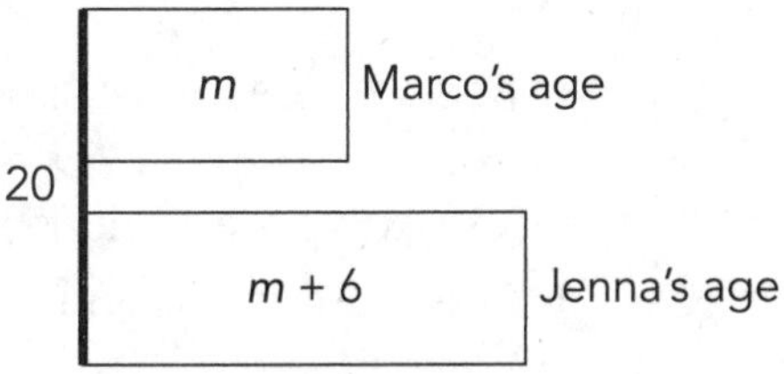

You can represent the model you drew with a mathematical sentence using operations and an equals sign. An **equation** is a mathematical sentence created by placing an equals sign (=) between two expressions.

The equation that represents the model above is $20 = m + (m + 6)$, or $20 = 2m + 6$.

A solution to an equation is a value for the unknown that makes the equation true.

For example, the solution to the equation $20 = 2m + 6$ is $m = 7$.

$$20 = 2(7) + 6$$
$$20 = 14 + 6$$
$$20 = 20$$

Marco is 7 years old, and Jenna is 13 years old.

LESSON
2

Expressions That Play Together

You can use double number lines to help you solve equations. When solving an equation, equality must be maintained. What is done to one expression must be done to the equivalent expression to maintain equality.

For example, solve the equation $2j + 10 = 46$. First, draw a model to set up the equation.

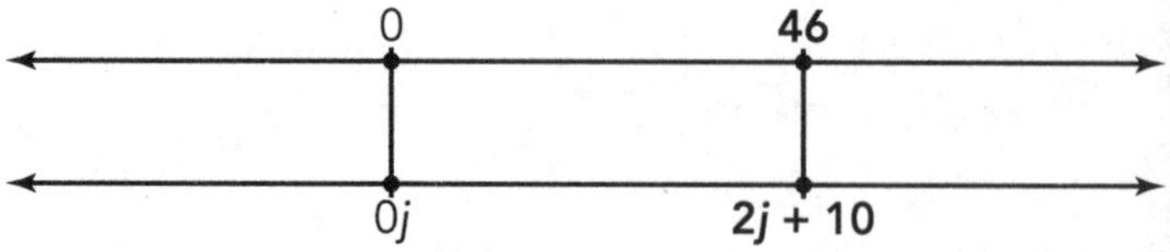

Next, start decomposing the variable expression. Place $2j$ in relationship to $2j + 10$. The expression $2j$ is 10 to the left of $2j + 10$. To maintain equality, place a number 10 to the left of 46. So, $2j = 36$.

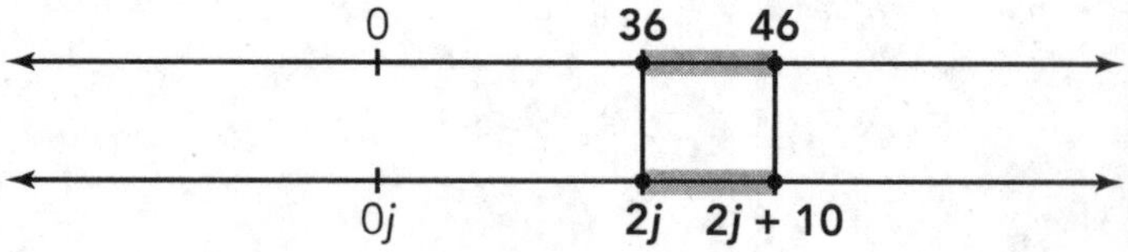

The expression $1j$, or j, is halfway between $0j$ and $2j$, and 18 is halfway between 0 and 36. So, $j = 18$.

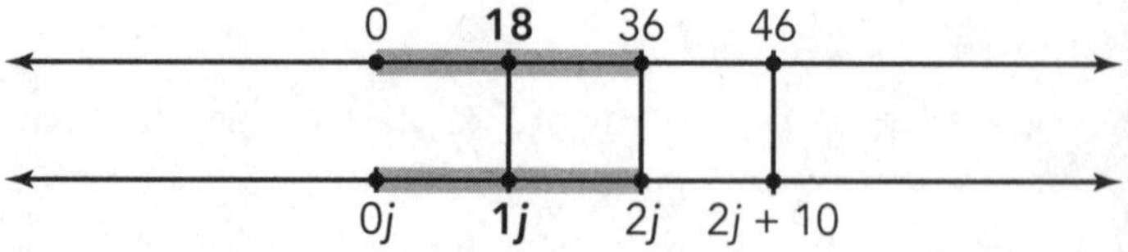

You may need to reason with negatives to solve equations.

For example, the double number line shows one way to solve the equation $-2(3x + 4) = 10$. A through E represent the order in which the steps were completed.

A. Set $-2(3x + 4)$ equal to 10.
B. $-3x - 4$ is halfway between 0 and $-2(3x + 4)$, and 5 is halfway between 0 and 10.
C. $-3x$ is 4 to the right of $-3x - 4$, and 9 is 4 to the right of 5.
D. $3x$ is the reflection of $-3x$ across 0, and -9 is the reflection of 9 across 0.
E. The location of x is one-third the distance from 0 to $3x$, and the location of -3 is one-third the distance from 0 to -9.

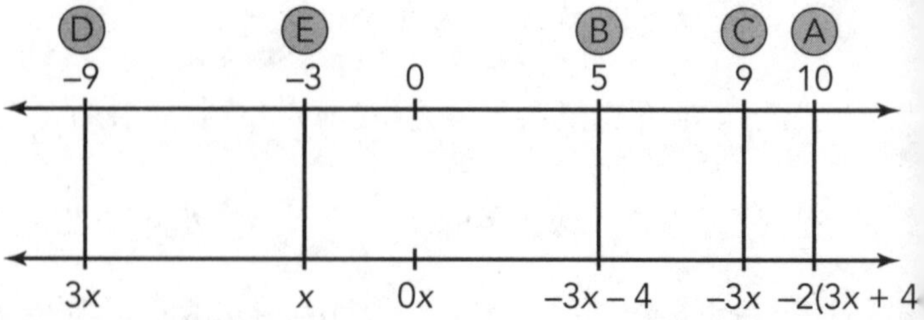

LESSON 3 Formally Yours

A **two-step equation** requires two inverse operations, or applying two Properties of Equality, to isolate the variable.

For example, here is one way to solve the equation $2x + 6 = 13$.

Subtract 6 from each side of the equation.	$2x + 6 - 6 = 13 - 6$
Divide both sides of the equation by 2.	$\frac{2x}{2} = \frac{7}{2}$

The solution is $x = 3\frac{1}{2}$.

You can use the Properties of Equality to rewrite equations and increase your efficiency with solving equations. Analyze the structure of the equation to determine the most efficient solution strategy.

- If the equation contains fractions, you can multiply both sides of the equation by the least common denominator.
- If the equation contains decimals, you can multiply both sides of the equation by a power of 10.
- If the equation contains large values, you can divide both sides of the equation by a common factor.

The formulas you have learned in mathematics are literal equations. **Literal equations** are equations in which the variables represent specific measures. Common literal equations occur in measurement and geometry concepts. An example of a literal equation is $A = \frac{1}{2}bh$, where A represents the area of a triangle, b represents the length of the base of the triangle, and h represents the height of the triangle.

LESSON 4

Be Greater Than

An **inequality** is any mathematical sentence that has an inequality symbol. The solution set of an inequality is all values that make the inequality statement true. To **solve an inequality** means to determine the values of the variable that make the inequality true. Solving two-step inequalities is similar to solving two-step equations. Just be sure to follow the Properties of Inequalities when isolating the variable and finding the solution to the inequality.

The **Properties of Inequalities** allow you to solve inequalities involving any numbers. These properties also hold true for $\le$ and $\ge$.

Properties of Inequalities	For all numbers *a*, *b*, and *c*
Addition Property of Inequalities	If $a < b$, then $a + c < b + c$. If $a > b$, then $a + c > b + c$.
Subtraction Property of Inequalities	If $a < b$, then $a - c < b - c$. If $a > b$, then $a - c > b - c$.
Multiplication Property of Inequalities	If $a < b$, then $a \cdot c < b \cdot c$, for $c > 0$. If $a > b$, then $a \cdot c > b \cdot c$, for $c > 0$.
Division Property of Inequalities	If $a < b$, then $\frac{a}{c} < \frac{b}{c}$, for $c > 0$. If $a > b$, then $\frac{a}{c} > \frac{b}{c}$, for $c > 0$.

For example, solve the inequality $-3x + 7 > 28$.

$$-3x + 7 - 7 > 28 - 7$$
$$-3x > 21$$
$$\frac{-3x}{3} > \frac{21}{3}$$
$$x < 7$$

The solution to any inequality can be represented on a number line by a ray whose starting point is an open or closed circle. For example, the solution $x < 7$ is represented by this number line.

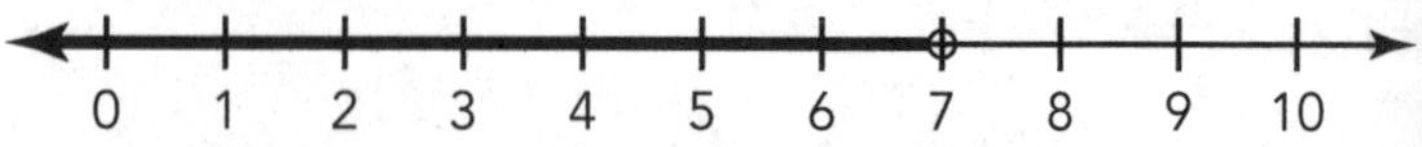

TOPIC 3

Multiple Representations of Equations

H_2O can appear as ice, water, or water vapor (steam or a cloud), but despite its form, the chemical structure is the same. Similarly an equation can be represented in different ways while remaining the same equation.

Module 3: Reasoning Algebraically

TOPIC 3: MULTIPLE REPRESENTATIONS OF EQUATIONS

This topic broadens students' perspective on solving and interpreting linear equations and inequalities through the use of tables and graphs. Students write and solve two-step equations using positive and negative numbers on four-quadrant graphs. Students then compare graphs of linear equations in different forms. Finally, students practice solving problems by writing equations and inequalities for problem situations, analyzing tables and graphs to solve the equations or inequalities, and interpreting the quantities in each problem situation.

Where have we been?

In grade 6, students used multiple representations to model and solve problems, primarily one-step equations. They learned that quantities can vary in relation to each other and are often classified as independent and dependent quantities.

Where are we going?

Students' ability to use symbolic algebra can be supported through the use of visual representations. Using and connecting symbolic and graphical representations of equations and inequalities occurs throughout the study of functions in grade 8 and in high school.

Interpreting Situations in More Than One Quadrant

This graph shows the relationship between the time someone has owned a car, *t*, and the value of the car, *v*. We only have information on the values to the right of the vertical axis, but if we assume that the relationship is linear, we can use an equation to determine car values for negative time values.

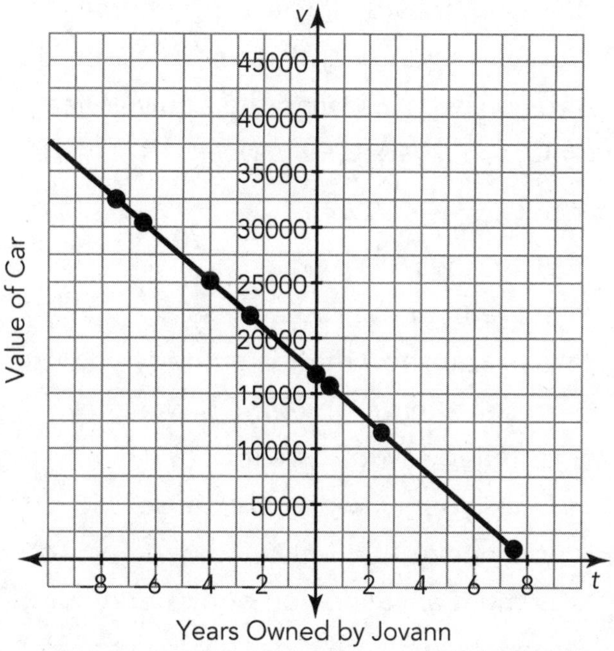

Myth: Memory is like an audio or video recording.

Let's play a game. Memorize the following list of words: strawberry, grape, watermelon, banana, orange, peach, cherry, blueberry, raspberry. Got it? Good. Some believe that the brain stores memories in pristine form. Memories last for a long time and do not change—like a recording. Without looking back at the original list, was apple on it?

If you answered "yes," then go back and look at the list. You'll see that apple does not appear, even though it seems like it should. In other words, memory is an active, reconstructive process that takes additional information, like the category of words (e.g., fruit), and makes assumptions about the stored information.

This simple demonstration suggests memory is not like a recording. Instead, it is influenced by prior knowledge and decays over time. Therefore, students need to see and engage with the same information multiple times to minimize forgetting (and distortions).

#mathmythbusted

Talking Points

You can further support your student's learning by asking questions about the work they do in class or at home. Your student is learning to represent relationships involving the equivalence of values in a variety of ways.

Questions to Ask

- How does this problem look like something you did in class?
- Can you show me the strategy you used to solve this problem? Do you know another way to solve it?
- Does your answer make sense? How do you know?
- Is there anything you don't understand? How can you use today's lesson to help?

Key Term

unit rate of change

The unit rate of change is the amount that the dependent value changes for every one unit that the independent value changes.

Put It on the Plane

1

Representing Equations with Tables and Graphs

WARM UP

Angela charges $35 an hour for tutoring services plus a $5 travel fee if she has to go to the student's house.

1. Name the quantities that are changing in this problem situation.
2. Name the quantities that remain constant.
3. Write an equation for the amount Angela charges, assuming she must travel to the student's house.
4. If Angela made $75, how many hours did she tutor?

LEARNING GOALS

- Write and solve two-step equations to solve real-world problems.
- Use multiple representations to reason about quantities and analyze problem situations.
- Identify independent and dependent variables.
- Interpret negative solutions to problem situations.

You have solved two-step equations algebraically. How can graphs of linear equations be used to solve equations?

Getting Started

It's All Greek to Me

Ms. Jackson translates books for a living. She decides to change her fees to keep up with the cost of living. She will charge an initial fee of $325 to manage each project and $25 per page of translated text. Ms. Jackson does not consider partial pages in her fees.

1. **Name the quantities that change in this problem situation.**

2. **Name the quantities that remain constant.**

3. **Which quantity depends on the other?**

ACTIVITY 1.1

Graphing Linear Equations

You can represent a problem situation in many ways. You used verbal descriptions to represent the relationship between the number of pages Ms. Jackson translates and her total fees. Let's consider how to represent the relationship with tables and graphs.

Number of Pages	Total Fees for the Project (dollars)
1	
2	
	400
	425
10	
	1150
	2100
92	

1. **Complete the table that shows the various projects that Ms. Jackson has managed recently.**

When representing a relationship as a graph, you need to ensure that the bounds of your graph are an appropriate size to surround the data from the table.

2. **What is the least number of pages that Ms. Jackson could translate? What is the greatest number of pages that Ms. Jackson has translated recently?**

3. **What are the least and greatest amounts of money that Ms. Jackson has earned?**

The interval is the number you are counting by on a given axis.

4. **Consider the ranges of values in the table to choose lower and upper bounds for the *x*- and *y*-axes. Write the lower and upper bound values in the table shown for each quantity.**

Variable Quantity	Lower Bound	Upper Bound	Interval
Pages Translated			
Earnings			

Sometimes, you have to adjust your bounds based on the interval you choose. Just make sure that your data remains visible within the bounds that you choose.

5. **Calculate the difference between the upper and lower bounds for each quantity and the number of tick marks that you have on each axis. Then, choose an appropriate interval for each axis and write these in the table.**

Draw a line through the points on your graph to model the relationship.

6. Use the bounds and intervals to label each axis. Then, create a graph of the data from the table.

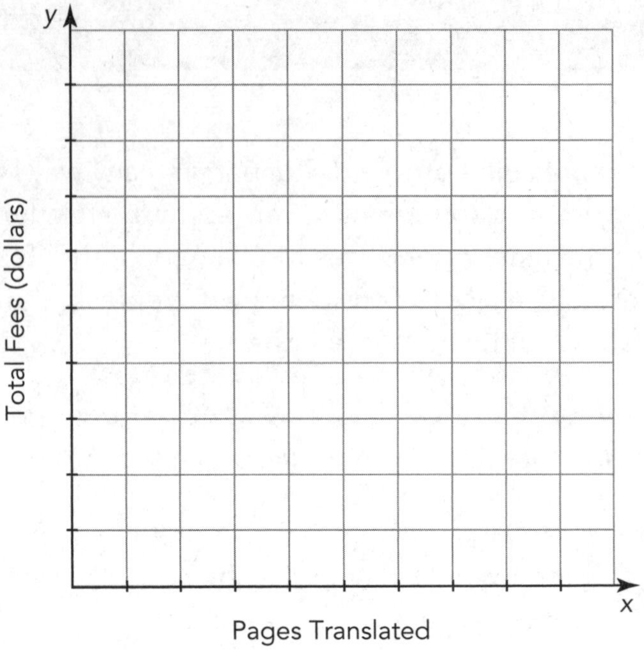

7. Are the data continuous or discrete? Explain your reasoning.

8. Describe the relationship between the two quantities represented in the graph.

9. Write a linear equation to represent this situation. Make sure to define your variables.

When you first analyzed this situation, you listed two quantities that remain constant in this scenario: \$325 and \$25 per page.

10. Refer to your equation and graph to answer each question.

    a. Where is \$325 represented in the graph and in the equation?

    b. Where is \$25 per page represented in the graph and in the equation?

11. Is there a proportional relationship between the number of pages translated and Ms. Jackson's earnings? Justify your answer using the table, equation, and graph.

12. Use the graph to answer each question. Explain your reasoning.

    a. Approximately how much money would Ms. Jackson earn if she translated 57 pages?

    b. Approximately how many pages would Ms. Jackson need to translate to earn $750?

13. For each translating project Ms. Jackson completed this month, determine if her pay was correct. If it is not, state the amount she should have received. Explain each answer in terms of the equation and the graph.

    a. Ms. Jackson translated a 23-page technical manual for Technicians Reference Guide Inc. She received a check for $900.

    b. Ms. Jackson translated a 42-page year-end report for Sanchez and Johnson Law Office. She received a check for $1050.

    c. Ms. Jackson translated a 35-page product specification document for Storage Pros. She received a check for $2075.

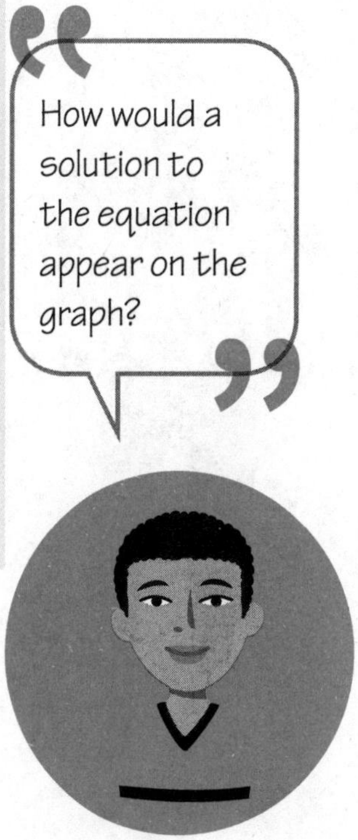

How would a solution to the equation appear on the graph?

You have represented the situation with Ms. Jackson's book translation business multiple ways: as a scenario, in a table, with an equation, and on a graph. These representations are useful for analyzing the situation in different ways.

ACTIVITY 1.2 Interpreting Situations in More Than One Quadrant

El Capitan is a 3000-foot vertical rock formation in Yosemite National Park in California. The granite cliff is one of the most popular challenges for experienced rock climbers. On July 3, 2008, Hans Florine and Yuji Hirayama scaled El Capitan in a record time of 2 hours 43 minutes and 33 seconds.

1. On average, about how fast in feet per minute did the record holders climb?

"What are the two quantities that are changing in this problem situation?"

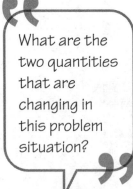

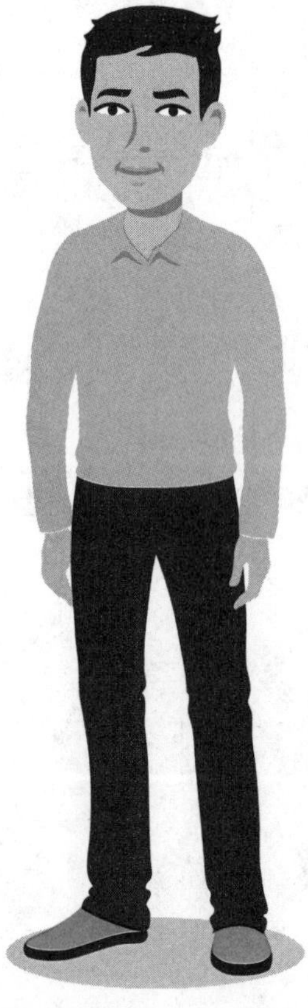

Two new climbers want to attempt to break the record by climbing El Capitan in 2 hours and 30 minutes.

2. If these climbers are to reach their goal, on average, how fast in feet per minute will they have to climb?

You want to watch the climbers attempt to break the record for climbing El Capitan. On the morning of the climb, you arrive late at 11:30 A.M. When you arrive, the climbers are exactly halfway to the top.

3. How many feet high are the climbers?

4. Assuming they are climbing at the average rate needed, how many feet up the cliff will the climbers be:

   a. in two more minutes?

   b. in a quarter of an hour?

   c. in one hour?

Pay attention to the units of measure!

5. Consider the quantities in this scenario.

   a. Which quantity depends on the other?

   b. Identify and define the independent and dependent variables with their units of measure for this situation.

   c. Write an equation for calculating the value of the dependent variable when the value of the independent variable is given.

6. Use your equation to determine how long after 11:30 A.M. it will take the climbers to reach the top at 3000 feet. What time would the climbers reach the top?

7. Use your equation to determine when the climbers are 1400 feet up the cliff. What does this answer mean in terms of the problem situation?

8. Use your equation to determine how high up the cliff the climbers were:

   a. two minutes before 11:30 A.M.

   b. a half hour before 11:30 A.M.

9. Use your equation to determine how many minutes before 11:30 A.M. the climbers started to climb. What time of day was that?

Now that you have represented the situation with an equation, represent it with a table and a graph.

10. Complete the table for this situation.

Quantities	Time	Height
Units of Measure		
Variables		
	0	
	2	
	15	
	60	

11. Plot the points from the table on the coordinate plane shown. Label the axes, and draw the graph of your equation.

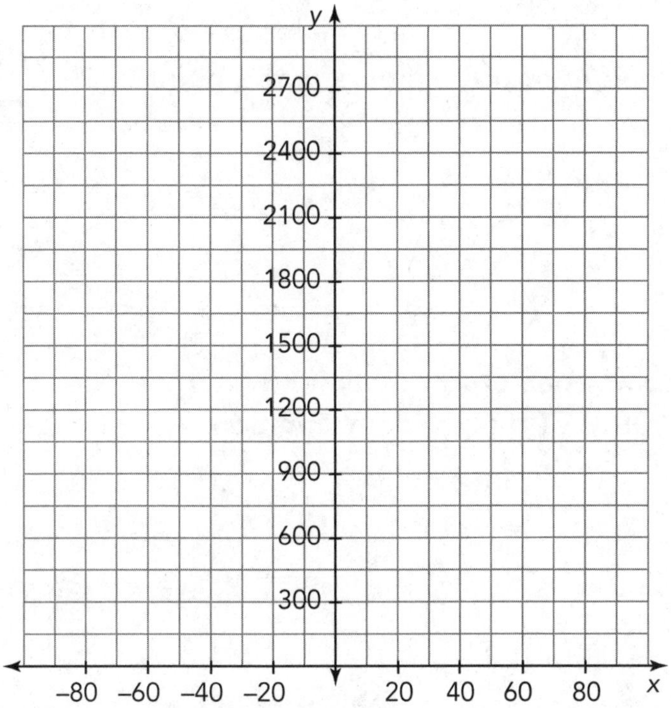

12. What should be the leftmost point on your graph? Explain your reasoning.

This graph displays Quadrants I and II. Why doesn't it include Quadrants III and IV as well?

NOTES

13. What should be the rightmost point on your graph? Explain your reasoning.

14. Locate the point with an *x*-coordinate of −60.

a. What is the height of the climbers at this point?

b. Write this point as an ordered pair and interpret the meaning in terms of the problem situation.

15. This analysis of the climbers' progress assumes that the climbers would climb at a steady rate of 20 feet per minute. In reality, would the climbers be able to do this during the whole climb? If not, how might the graph reflect this?

16. Explain what the negative values of time represent.

NOTES

TALK the TALK

Take Advantage of the Situation

You have represented two situations in four different ways: as a sentence, as a table, as a graph, and as an equation.

1. **Complete the graphic organizer to explain the advantages and disadvantages of each representation.**

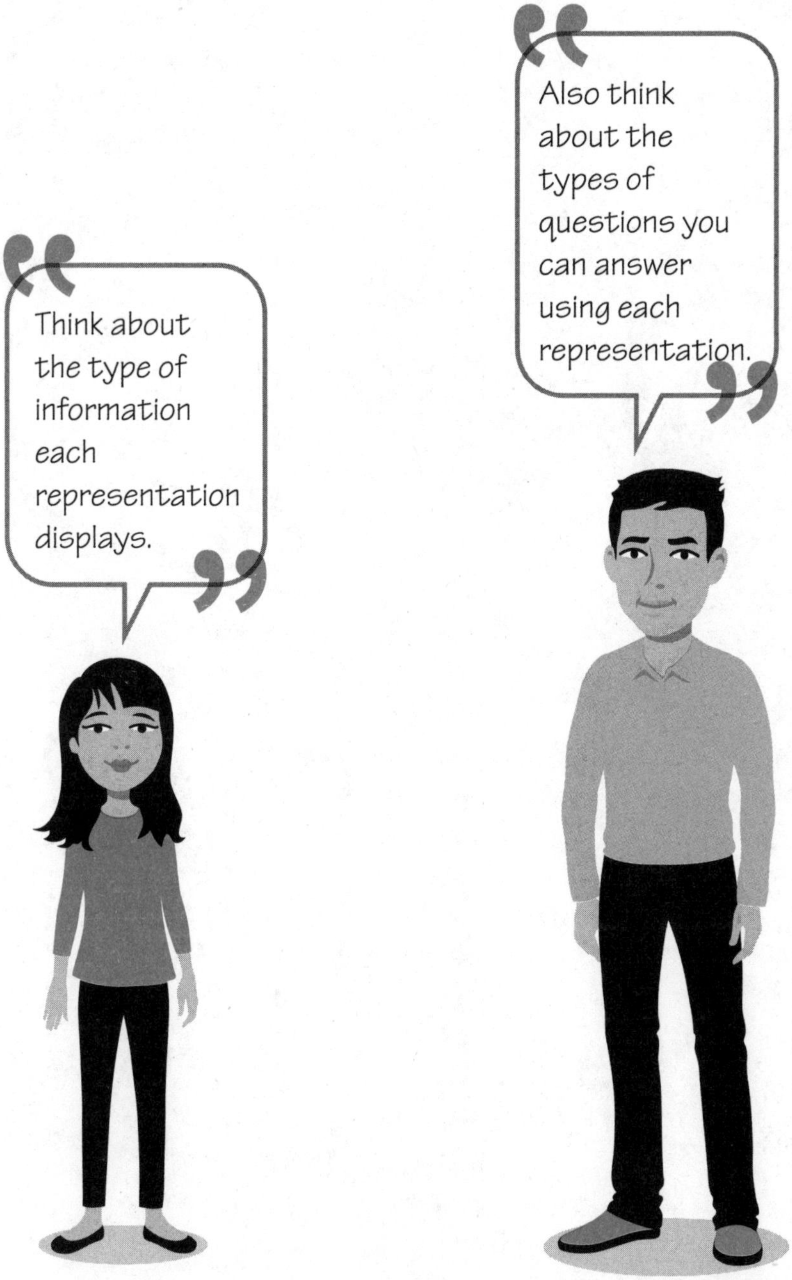

Also think about the types of questions you can answer using each representation.
Think about the type of information each representation displays.

SENTENCE

Advantages

Disadvantages

TABLE

Advantages

Disadvantages

MULTIPLE REPRESENTATIONS

GRAPH

Advantages

Disadvantages

EQUATION

Advantages

Disadvantages

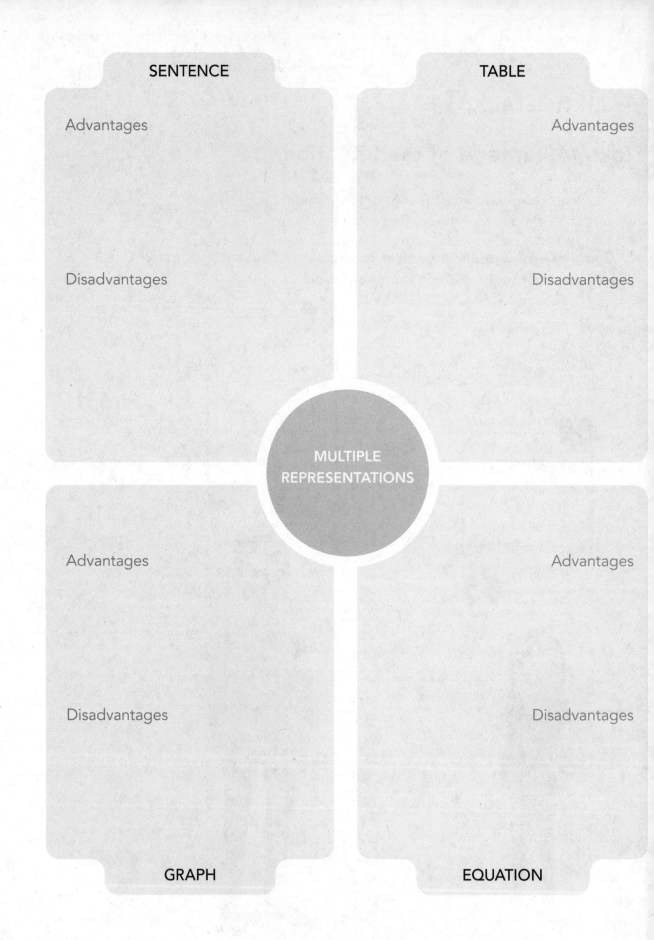

Assignment

Write

Explain how the constant term and the coefficient of the variable of $y = 2x + 5$ would be represented in the graph of the equation.

Remember

A table provides specific values for a given problem situation. A graph is a visual representation of the data related to a problem situation. An equation generalizes a problem situation.

Practice

1. Ben joins a book club. He pays $12 for each book and $5 for shipping and handling charges for each order.
   a. Name the quantities that change in this problem situation and the quantities that remain constant. Determine which quantity is independent and which quantity is dependent.
   b. Create a table of values to represent the total cost if Ben orders 1 or 2 books or spends $41, $65, or $125.
   c. Create a graph of the data from the table. Carefully select the lower bound, upper bound, and intervals. Remember to label the axes and the intervals.
   d. Describe the relationship between the two quantities. Define your variables.
   e. Ben said that he spent exactly $80 on a book order. Use your graph to determine if Ben is correct.
   f. Write an algebraic equation to represent the situation.
   g. Use the equation, table, and graph to explain if this situation represents a proportional relationship.
2. Mr. Hong is a rare coin collector. He recently bought a coin valued at $5400. It has been determined that the coin will increase in value by $30 each month. Mr. Hong plans to sell the coin within 5 years.
   a. Name the quantities that change in this problem situation and the quantities that remain constant. Determine which quantity is independent and which quantity is dependent.
   b. Create a table of values that represents a variety of different number of months for which Mr. Hong could own the coin and the total value of the coin.
   c. Create a graph of the data from the table. Carefully select the lower bound, upper bound, and intervals. Remember to label the axes and the intervals.
   d. Describe the relationship between the two quantities.
   e. Use the graph to determine the approximate worth of the coin if Mr. Hong owns it for 3 years.
   f. Use the graph to determine approximately when will the coin be worth $6600.
   g. Write an algebraic equation to represent the situation. Define your variables.
   h. After owning the coin for 3 years, Mr. Hong wants to sell the coin. He tells a potential buyer it is worth $6480. The buyer disagrees and says it is worth $5490. Who is correct? Explain your reasoning in terms of the equation.

3. Tristan is looking for a new car. He has particular interest in an expensive sports car with a list price of $32,500. Tristan knows that the minute he drives the car off the lot, it will start to lose value, or depreciate. He finds out that the car will depreciate to a scrap value of $1000 in 15 years.
   a. What is the total change in value of the car in 15 years?
   b. What is the average amount of depreciation per year?
   c. When the car is exactly 7.5 years old, Tristan decides to sell it to his friend Jovann. What is the value of the car when Jovann buys it?
   d. What are the two quantities that are changing in part (c)? Define and identify the independent and dependent variables for the quantities you defined with their units of measure.
   e. Write an equation to calculate the value of the car given the number of years Jovann has owned the car.
   f. Create a table of values that includes when Jovann has owned the car 0 years, 6 months, and two and a half years. Also, include when the value of the car was $1000, $22,000, $25,150, $30,400, and $32,500.
   g. Create a graph of the data from the table. Carefully select the lower bound, upper bound, and intervals. Remember to label the axes and the intervals.
   h. Locate the point where the value of the independent quantity is –5. What is the value of the dependent quantity at this point? Write the point as an ordered pair. What does the ordered pair mean in the context of the problem?

Stretch

Write a linear problem situation in which negative values of both the independent and dependent variables are useful in analyzing the situation. Write the related equation and create a graph of the situation.

Review

1. Mr. Hong has coins and old stamps for sale. He decides to advertise the items on an internet site for collectors. It will cost him $84 initially to advertise and $28 for each day he keeps the items on sale. If Mr. Hong does not want to spend more than $700 on advertising, what is the maximum number of days he should advertise? Write and solve an inequality to answer the question.
2. Solve and graph the inequality: $-2x + 3 < 12$
3. Solve each equation. Check your solution.
   a. $16 = 3x - 4$
   b. $1.2x + 5.3 = 5.9$
4. Use long division to convert each fraction to a decimal. Identify each decimal as terminating or non-terminating.
   a. $\frac{5}{9}$
   b. $\frac{11}{20}$

Stretches, Stacks, and Structure

2

Structure of Linear Equations

WARM UP

Use properties to rewrite.

1. $3(x - 1)$
2. $-9(-2 + x)$
3. $\frac{1}{2}(x - 6)$
4. $6 + 3(x + 4)$

LEARNING GOALS

- Write and solve two-step equations.
- Compare two linear problem situations.
- Rewrite expressions in different forms in problem contexts in order to interpret how quantities are related.
- Compare graphs of linear problem situations.
- Compare and interpret forms of linear equations.

All of the linear equations you have written for problem situations have been in the form $y = ax + b$. Are there other common forms of equations used to express linear problem situations?

Getting Started

Learning the Limo Business

Katie is starting her own limousine rental company. She wisely decides to check her competitors' pricing plans before setting her own plan. The table shows the fees from two rival limousine rental companies.

Examine the fee schedule for the two limousine companies provided in the table.

Number of Hours Rented	Limousines by Lilly Fees (in dollars)	Transportation with Class Fees (in dollars)
1	99.99	89.99
2	123.74	126.54
3	147.49	163.09
4	171.24	199.64
5	194.99	236.19

1. Which company would you choose if you were renting a limousine? Support your answer with information from the table.

ACTIVITY 2.1

Different Forms, Same Equation

Katie starts by analyzing the cost structure of Limousines by Lilly.

1. **Consider the cost of renting a limousine from Limousines by Lilly.**

   a. **What does the first hour of a rental from Limousines by Lilly cost?**

   b. **What does each additional rental hour cost from Limousines by Lilly after the first hour?**

   c. **What would it cost to rent a limo from Limousines by Lilly for 10 hours? Explain your reasoning.**

Do you have an estimate for the cost to rent from Lilly for 10 hours?

   d. **What would it cost to rent a limo from Limousines by Lilly for 13 hours? Explain your reasoning.**

   e. **Explain how you calculated each cost.**

2. Write an equation for the total cost, t, of renting from Limousines by Lilly for any given number of rental hours, h.

You can rewrite your equation for Limousines by Lilly before using it to solve problems. Previously, you have learned to simplify algebraic expressions using a variety of strategies.

3. Rewrite your equation in the form $ax + b = c$.

   a. Name the strategies necessary to rewrite the equation you wrote.

   b. Rewrite the equation you wrote for Limousines by Lilly. Explain why the resulting equation is a two-step equation.

   c. Compare the two equations you wrote for this company. What is the same? What is different?

   d. Write a possible fee scenario for Limousines by Lilly to match the rewritten equation.

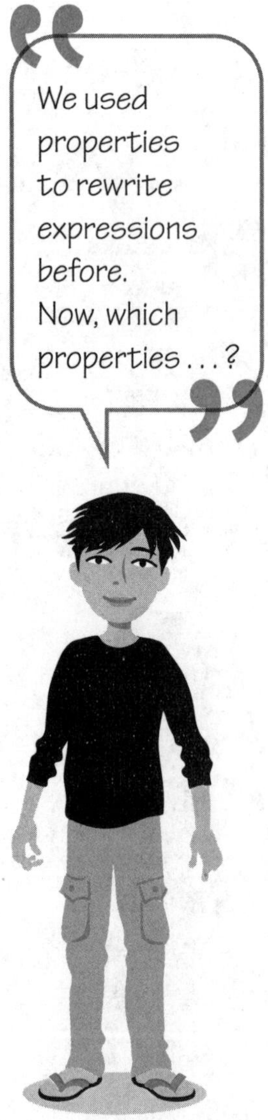

We used properties to rewrite expressions before. Now, which properties . . . ?

4. Use your equation to calculate how many hours you rented from Limousines by Lilly if the total cost is \$266.24.

5. Consider the cost of renting a limousine from Transportation with Class.

   a. What does the first hour of a rental from Transportation with Class cost?

   b. What does each additional rental hour cost from Transportation with Class after the first hour?

   c. Write an equation for the total cost, t, of renting from Transportation with Class for any given number of rental hours, h.

   d. Rewrite your equation in the form $ax + b = c$.

   e. Write a possible fee scenario for Transportation with Class to match the rewritten equation.

   f. Use your equation to determine the number of hours that cost $309.29 from Transportation with Class.

6. What suggestions would you provide to Katie on the fees she should charge for her limo rental business? Explain your reasoning.

ACTIVITY
2.2

Comparing Graphs of Linear Equations

Your job at Storage Pros is to create new boxes to ship the company's plastic containers. Storage Pros makes all different shapes and sizes of plastic containers. To ship the containers, the lids are removed, allowing the containers to be stacked. Storage Pros wants to design its shipping boxes so that they will hold two dozen stacks of the plastic containers without lids in stacks of two dozen, regardless of the size or shape of the container.

The table shows the data gathered from measuring the heights of different-sized stacks of the various plastic containers.

Number of Containers	Stack Height (centimeters)	
	Round	Square
1	9	15
2	9.8	15.4
3	10.6	15.8
4	11.4	16.2
5	12.2	16.6
6		
7		
13		

1. What are the variable quantities in this problem situation?

2. What quantity depends on the other?

3. Create a graph for each container shape's stack height in terms of the number of containers used. Determine the bounds and intervals, complete the table, and label your graph clearly. Use the symbols in the legend shown when graphing.

Variable Quantity	Lower Bound	Upper Bound	Interval
Number of Containers			
Stack Height			

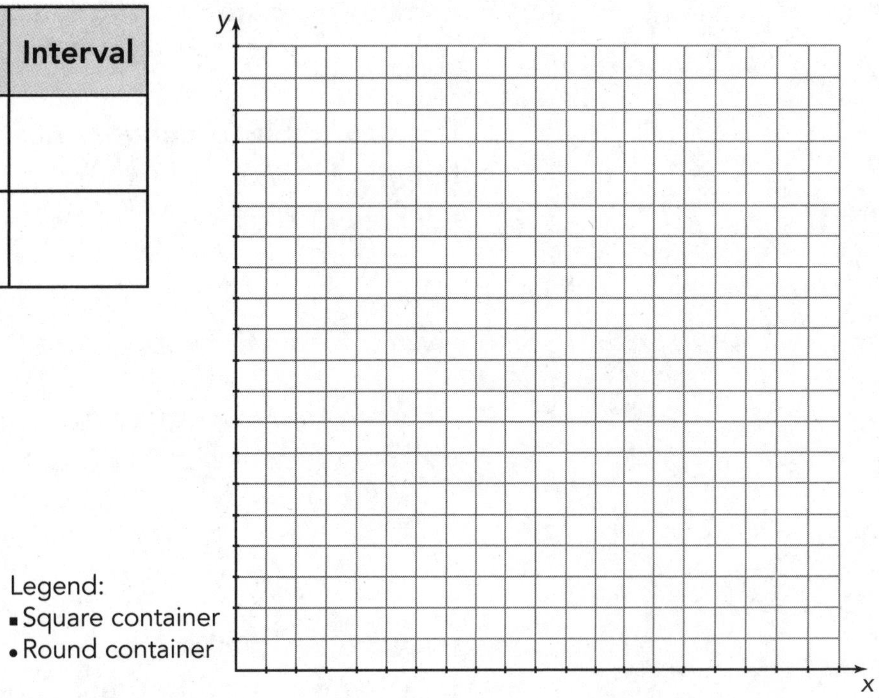

4. Consider the stack of round containers.

   a. What is the height of the first round container?

   b. How does the height change when one round container is added to a stack of round containers?

   c. Let *h* represent the stack height. Write an equation that represents the stack height of the round containers in terms of the number of round containers, c, in the stack.

   d. Use your table, graph, or equation to determine the stack height of 6, 7, and 13 round containers. Add these values to your table and graph.

Draw a line to model the relationship. Do all points on the line make sense?

5. Consider the stack of square containers.

   a. Let c represent the number of containers in a stack of square containers, and let h represent the stack height. Write an equation that gives the stack height in terms of the number of containers in the stack.

   b. Use your table, graph, or equation to determine the stack height of 6, 7, and 13 square containers. Add these values to your table and graph.

6. Analyze the equations you wrote for round and square containers.

   a. How are the two equations you wrote similar? Why are these equations similar? Explain your reasoning.

   b. How are the two equations you wrote different? Why are these equations different? Explain your reasoning.

7. The equations you wrote for the heights of the containers can be rewritten in equivalent forms.

   a. Rewrite each equation in the form $y = ax + b$.

   b. Explain what the numbers in the equations mean in terms of the problem context.

   c. Refer back to the graph. Explain how the numbers in these equations and your graphs are related.

NOTES

8. Use your equations of the form $y = ax + b$ to calculate the stack height of:

   a. two dozen round containers.

   b. two dozen square containers.

9. What height should Storage Pros make its boxes to accommodate the height of a stack of two dozen of either type of container?

10. Storage Pros had extra boxes that were 45 centimeters tall.

    a. How many round containers can be in each stack inside the box?

    b. How many square containers can be in each stack inside the box?

ACTIVITY

2.3

Interpreting Forms of Equations

In the limousine and container scenarios, you represented the situations with two different equations.

1. Complete the table to summarize the different forms of the equations. Use the variables *x* and *y* for the independent and dependent variables.

	$y = ax + b$	$y = c + d(x - 1)$
Limousines by Lilly		$y = 99.99 + 23.75(x - 1)$
Transportation with Class		
Round Containers	$y = 0.8x + 8.2$	
Square Containers		

2. Use your equations to explain the meaning of the *c* and *d* terms in $y = c + d(x - 1)$.

3. Use your equations to explain the meaning of the *a* and *b* terms in $y = ax + b$.

Any letter can be used as a variable. It is common to use *a* and *b* in forms of equations, but the different variables were used to reduce the possibility of confusing the equations.

4. Refer back to the graphs of the plastic containers and the related equations. Explain if and how the two equations of the form $y = ax + b$ can be visualized on the graph.

5. Which form of the linear equations do you prefer? Explain your reasoning.

How can you check that your equations are correct?

NOTES

TALK the TALK

Back to the Limos!

At the beginning of the lesson, you wrote equations for the fee schedule of Limousines by Lilly and Transportation with Class.

1. **Determine which graph represents each equation. Use your equations to explain your reasoning.**

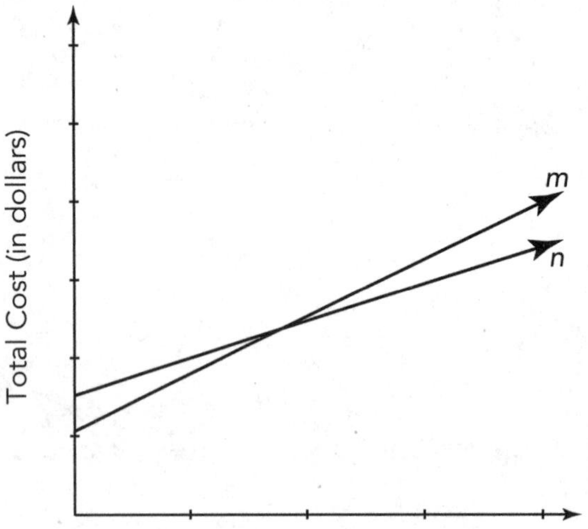

2. **Suppose Katie decides to charge $124.99 for the first *three* hours and then $49.99 for each additional hour. Write an equation to represent Katie's fee schedule.**

Assignment

Write

Write a problem situation that could be modeled by a linear equation in x and y that includes the expression $x - c$, where c is a positive integer.

Remember

Different forms of an equation reveal different information about a problem situation and about other representations of the problem situation.

Practice

Write an equation to represent each situation. Define your variables and solve the equation.

1. At the Namaste Yoga Studio, the first two yoga classes are free with a registration fee of $15. Each class after that is $45. How many classes can you take for $1185?
2. Clara has a coupon for $10 off at her favorite clothing store. The coupon is applied before any discounts are taken. The store is having a sale, and offering 15% off everything. If Clara has $50 to spend, how much can her purchases total before applying the discount and her coupon? Round to the nearest cent.
3. A dog kennel charges $40 to board a dog for one night and $35 per night each night after that. Henry paid a total of $215 for dog boarding. For how many nights did Henry board his dog?
4. Drake's Drugstore is getting ready for the upcoming summer season. The manager of the store wants to add lawn chairs to the stock. He asks the buyer to determine the two lowest priced wholesalers of lawn chairs. The table shows the data that the buyer collects from two wholesalers.

Packs of Chairs	Price from Wholesaler A (dollars)	Price from Wholesaler B (dollars)
1	$90.99	$98.99
2	$173.98	$179.98
3	$256.97	$260.97
4	$339.96	$341.96

   a. Let p represent the total number of packs of chairs bought from Wholesaler A and let c represent the total cost. Write an equation to calculate the total cost of any number of packs of chairs.
   b. Let p represent the total number of packs of chairs bought from Wholesaler B and let c represent the total cost. Write an equation to calculate the total cost of any number of packs of chairs.
   c. Write the equations from parts (a) and (b) in the form $y = ax + b$.
   d. Calculate the cost of eight packs of chairs from each wholesaler.
   e. The manager wants to buy at least seven packs of chairs. Which wholesaler should the drugstore use this year? Explain your reasoning.

5. Geoffrey owns the Super Backyard Shed Company. He makes custom built sheds for residential homeowners, and he buys the majority of his building materials from two large home stores in the area. Both stores, Build It and All Things Home, offer reward cards for the purchase of lumber. The more boards that Geoffrey buys at one time, the more points he will earn. The points can then be used for future purchases. The table shows the number of reward points that he will earn.

Number of Boards Purchased	Store	
	Build It	All Things Home
1	10	5
2	12.5	8
3	15	11
4	17.5	14
5	20	17
6		
7		

a. Complete the table to show the number of reward points earned for the purchase of 6 and 7 boards. Use the table and scenario to answer each question.

b. What are the variable quantities in this problem situation? State which quantity depends on the other.

c. Create graphs for each store's reward points in terms of the number of boards purchased. Identify the bounds and intervals. Be sure to label your graph clearly.

d. How does the number of reward points change when the number of boards bought at Build It is increased by 1? Explain your reasoning.

e. How does the number of reward points change when the number of boards bought at All Things Home is increased by 1? Explain your reasoning.

f. Let p represent the number of reward points and b represent the number of boards purchased at one time. Write equations to represent the number of reward points that Geoffrey will earn in terms of the number of boards purchased from each store.

g. Rewrite each equation in the form $y = ax + b$.

h. Determine the number of points that would be earned if Geoffrey buys 12 boards at a time from each store.

i. If Geoffrey earned 65 reward points, how many boards could he have bought at each store?

Stretch

Greg needs to hire someone to clear his driveway of snow this winter season. A neighbor has a plow attached to his truck and charges $30 for each time he plows the driveway. Mel's Landscaping runs a snow-clearing business and charges $50 for the first time they plow and $25 for each additional time they plow. Write and solve an equation to determine when the costs of each option are the same. Under what conditions would Greg choose his neighbor? Mel's Landscaping?

Review

1. The winner of the 95th annual hotdog eating contest consumed 207 hotdogs (and buns!) in 10 minutes. You are determined to break this record!
   a. What would you have to do to break this record?
   b. How many hotdogs would you have to eat every minute?
2. The 96th annual contest begins at noon. Your best friend got caught in traffic and arrives halfway through the event.
   a. How many hotdogs have you consumed?
   b. Assuming you eat at the average rate needed, after the arrival of your best friend, how many total hotdogs will you consume in one minute? two minutes? three minutes?
   c. Identify and define the independent and dependent variables with their units of measure for this situation.
   d. Create a table of values for the in minutes after 12:05 PM and the number of hotdogs consumed.
   e. Write an equation for calculating the value of the dependent variable when the value of the independent variable is given.
   f. Use your equation to determine how long after 12:05 PM it will take you to consume 187 hotdogs.
   g. Use your equation to determine when you would have consumed a total of 83 hotdogs.
   h. What does the answer to part (g.) mean in this problem situation?

3. Solve each equation and check your solution.
   a. $42 = \frac{3}{5}x + 12$
   b. $\frac{-7}{3}x - 11 = -25$

Deep Flight I

3

Building Inequalities and Equations to Solve Problems

WARM UP

Determine the parts of the solution set that make each inequality true.

Solution set: {1, 2, 3, 4, 5, 6, 7, 8, 9, 10, 11, 12, 13, 14, 15}

1. $x > 6$
2. $x + 2 > 6$
3. $2x + 2 > 6$
4. $6 < 2(x + 2) - 4$

LEARNING GOALS

- Solve word problems by building and interpreting inequalities of the form $px + q < r$ and $px + q > r$.
- Graph the solution sets of inequalities in order to solve problems.
- Calculate and interpret the unit rate of change in a problem situation.

KEY TERM

- unit rate of change

You have graphed equations to solve problems. How can you use the graphs of inequalities to help you solve problems?

Getting Started

Lemonade at the Pool

The concession stand at a local swimming pool sells small and large glasses of freshly squeezed lemonade. This weekend, they made more than $250 selling glasses of lemonade. A large glass of lemonade sells for $4.00, and the total sales generated from selling small glasses of lemonade was $65.

1. **Write an inequality to represent the relationship between the amount they made and the number of large glasses they sold.**

2. **Solve the inequality. Interpret the solution in terms of the problem situation.**

3. **Graph the solution set on the number line.**

ACTIVITY 3.1

Unit Rate of Change

To explore one of the last unknown regions on our planet, companies are starting to produce single-person, submersible deep-sea submarines like the Deep Flight I. Suppose the submarine Deep Flight I is going to do a dive starting at sea level, descending 480 feet every minute.

1. **Identify the independent and dependent quantities and their units of measure, and define variables for these quantities. Then, write an equation to represent Deep Flight I's depth.**

2. **Use your equation to complete the table shown for this problem situation. Do not forget to define the quantities, units of measures, and variables for this situation.**

	Independent Quantity	Dependent Quantity
Quantities		
Units of Measure		
Variables		
	0	
	1	
	2	
	3	
	4	
	5	
	6	

Depths in feet below sea level can be represented by negative numbers.

NOTES

3. Consider the possible values for time and depth.

   a. What do you think are all the possible values for time in terms of this situation? Write an inequality to express your answer.

   b. What do you think are all the possible values for depth in terms of this situation? Write an inequality to express your answer.

4. Examine your table. What do you notice about each depth value in relation to the one before and the one after?

The **unit rate of change** describes the amount that the dependent variable changes for every one unit that the independent variable changes.

5. In this problem, what is the unit rate of change?

6. How deep would the submarine be after:

   a. 2.5 minutes?

   b. 90 seconds?

   c. 45 seconds?

7. How many minutes would it take Deep Flight I to be:

   a. 1400 feet below sea level?

   b. 2100 feet below sea level?

8. Construct a graph of this problem situation. Label the units on each axis. Then, plot all the points from the table and from Questions 6 and 7. Finally, draw the graph to represent the problem situation.

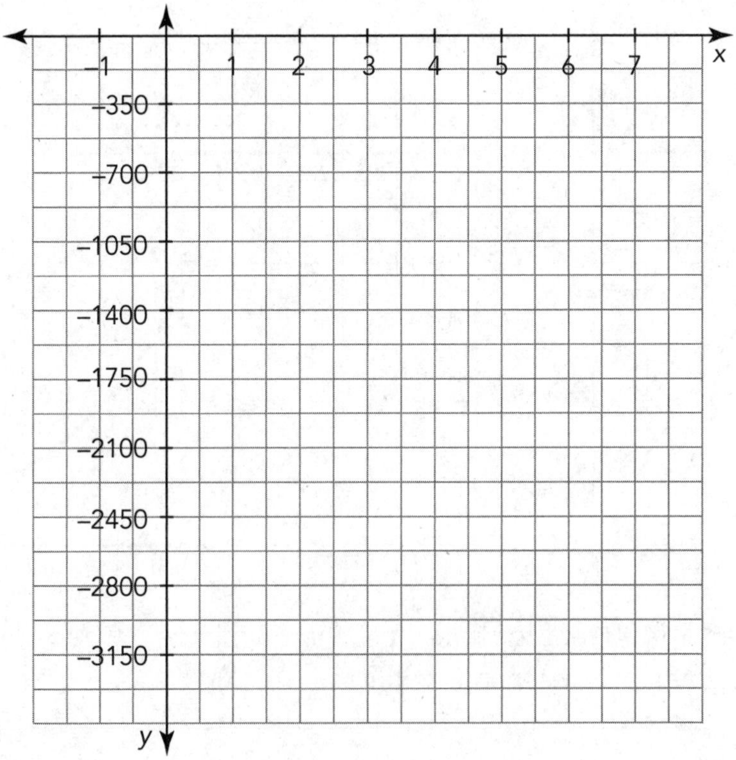

ACTIVITY
3.2 Representing Inequalities on Graphs

You can use your graph to estimate solutions to inequality problems. Use the graph to estimate the times Deep Flight I will be more than 1400 feet below sea level and the times Deep Flight I will be less than 1400 feet below sea level.

WORKED EXAMPLE

Each of these graphs shows the relationship between the time in minutes and the depth of Deep Flight I.

The rectangle on the left graph shows the set of all depths for Deep Flight I less than 1400 feet below sea level. The oval on the right graph shows the set of all depths for Deep Flight I more than 1400 feet below sea level.

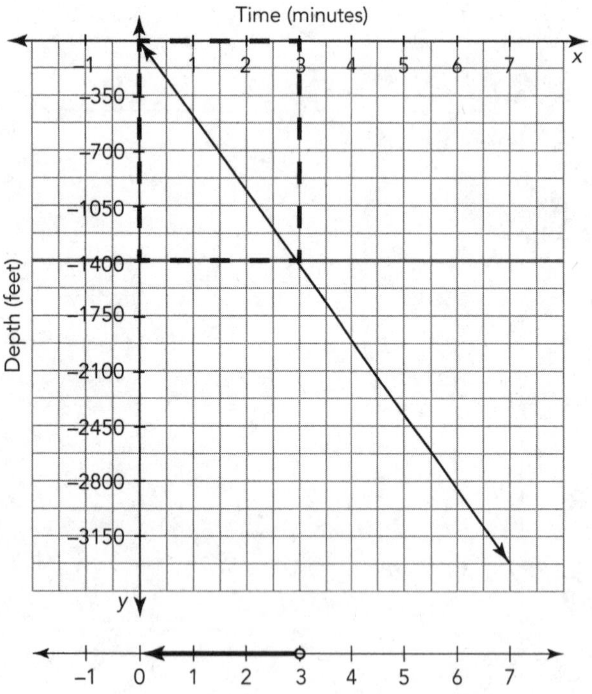

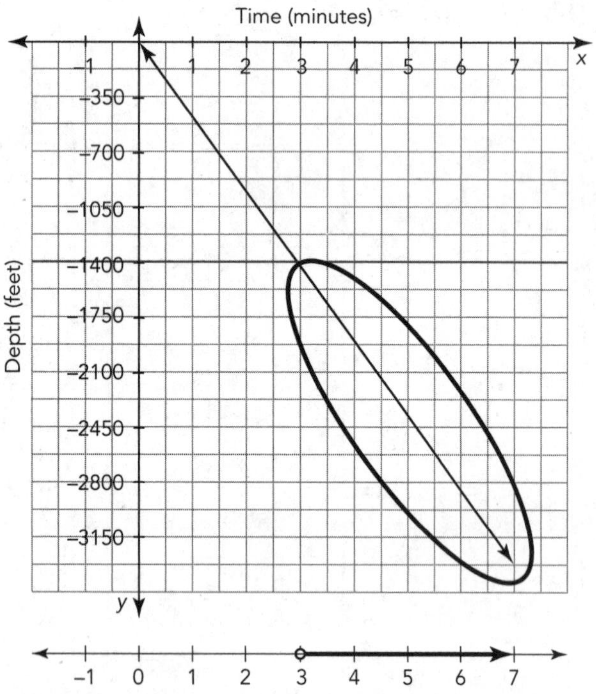

Deep Flight I will be greater than −1400 feet for times less than 3 minutes. Deep Flight I will be less than −1400 feet for times greater than 3 minutes.

1. Use the graph to estimate the times Deep Flight I will be:

   a. less than 2100 feet below sea level.

   b. more than 2100 feet below sea level.

2. Write an inequality and solve it to determine the time Deep Flight I is:

   a. less than 2100 feet below sea level.

   b. more than 2100 feet below sea level.

How do the graph and the inequality model the starting depth?

3. How do your answers using the graph compare to those when you wrote and solved inequalities?

ACTIVITY 3.3

Graphing Equations and Inequalities

Deep Flight I can dive to a depth of 3300 feet below sea level and can ascend to the surface at a rate of 650 feet per minute.

1. **Suppose Deep Flight I is going to ascend to sea level starting at its maximum depth of 3300 feet below sea level. Identify the independent and dependent quantities, define variables for these quantities, and write an equation to represent Deep Flight I's depth.**

2. **Use your equation to complete the table shown for this problem situation.**

	Independent Quantity	Dependent Quantity
Quantities		
Units of Measure		
Variables		
	0	
	1	
	2	
	3	
	4	
	5	

3. **Why does the table end at 5 minutes for this problem situation?**

4. **Consider the possible values for time and depth.**

   a. **What do you think are all the possible values for time in terms of this situation? Write inequalities to express your answer.**

b. What do you think are all the possible values for depth in terms of this situation? Write inequalities to express your answer.

5. Examine your table. What do you notice about each depth value in relation to the one before and the one after?

6. In this problem, what is the unit rate of change?

7. How deep would the submarine be after ascending for:

a. 2.5 minutes?

b. 90 seconds?

c. 45 seconds?

How do I represent "sea level" as a number?

8. How many minutes would it take Deep Flight I to ascend to:

a. 1000 feet below sea level?

b. 2100 feet below sea level?

c. sea level?

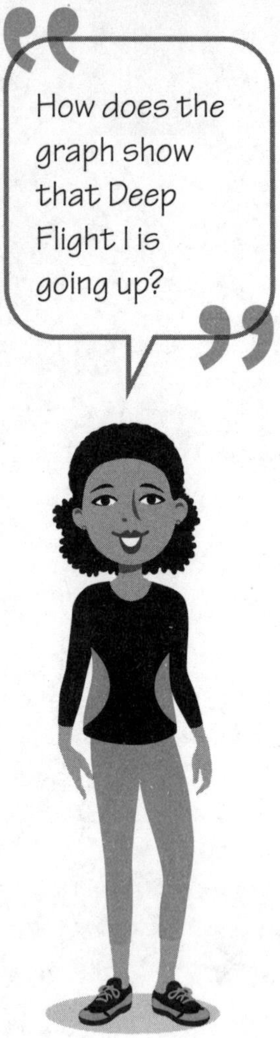

How does the graph show that Deep Flight I is going up?

9. Use your information to construct a graph of this problem situation. First, label the units of measure on each axis. Then, plot all the points from the table and from Questions 7 and 8. Finally, draw the graph to represent the problem situation.

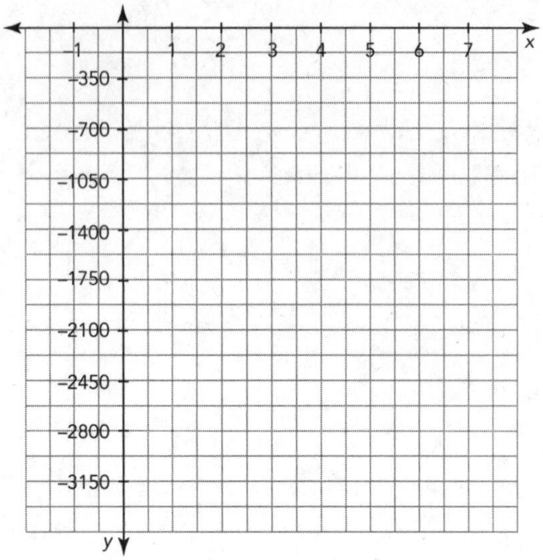

10. Draw a box or oval on the graph to estimate each.

    a. the time Deep Flight I is above 1000 feet below sea level

    b. the time Deep Flight I is below 2000 feet below sea level

11. Write an inequality and solve it to determine the time Deep Flight I is above 1000 feet below sea level.

12. Write an inequality and solve it to determine the time Deep Flight I is below 2000 feet below sea level.

NOTES

TALK the TALK

Digging to China

Did you ever hear the saying, "If you dig deep enough, you will dig to China?" You would have to live in South America, possibly Argentina, for this to happen. If you live in the United States, chances are you would pop out on the other side of the Earth in the Indian Ocean!

Technically speaking it would be impossible to dig a hole to the other side of the Earth, but let's pretend.

Suppose you were digging at a rate of 10 feet a day. Assume you are at sea level when you begin digging.

1. **Identify the independent and dependent quantities and their units of measure, and define variables for these quantities.**

2. **Write an equation to represent the depth of the hole, where *d* represents depth in feet, and *t* represents the time in days.**

NOTES

3. If there are 365 days in a year, write an equation to represent the depth of the hole, where *d* represents depth in feet and *t* represents the time in years.

4. Use your equation to complete the table for this problem situation.

Time (Years)	Depth (Feet)
t	*d*
0	
1	
2	
3	
4	
5	

5. Write an inequality and solve it to determine the number of years the hole is more than one mile deep. There are 5280 feet in a mile.

6. Write an inequality and solve it to determine the number of years the hole has not reached to the other side of the Earth yet.

Assignment

Write

In your own words, describe how to estimate an inequality using the graph of an equation. Include an example in your description.

Remember

The unit rate of change is the amount that the dependent value changes for every one unit that the independent value changes.

Practice

The Transverse Tire Company produces all types of tires at its factory. Due to fixed costs associated with running the factory, the company starts with a loss of $200,000, or a profit of −$200,000, at the beginning of each month. The first major hurdle the company faces each month is to break even, or reach the point at which the profit is zero. The tires are sold in batches of 1000. The company earns $40,000 for each batch of tires they manufacture and sell.

1. Identify the two quantities that are changing in this situation, identify the independent and dependent quantities, and define the variables for these quantities. Then write an equation to represent the profit the company will make when they manufacture and sell batches of tires.
2. Use your equation to complete a table for this problem situation.
3. What is the unit rate of change in this problem?
4. How much profit would the company make if they manufactured and sold 3 and one-half batches (3500 tires)?
5. How many batches of tires does the company have to manufacture and sell to have a profit of –$190,000?
6. Construct a graph for the problem situation.

Stretch

Timothy and his manager have discussed the use of an herbicide to help decrease the growth of plants that will grow near the trees, because they will take nutrients away from the tree and thus the trees will grow at a slower rate. They decide to do some research on the subject to decide. They find a study that indicates that the growth of the seedlings without using herbicides was $8(2h + 2) - 4(2h + 9)$ and the growth of the seedlings with herbicides was $7h + 1\frac{3}{4}(4h - 2\frac{1}{8})$. Graph each expression. Sketch the portion of the graphs that make sense to this problem. Are the two growth rates the same? Explain your reasoning.

Review

1. One grocery basket is 12 inches in height. When two baskets are stacked inside of each other, the total height of the two baskets is 13.5 inches.
   a. Determine the stack height for 1 basket, 2 baskets, 3 baskets, 4 baskets, and 5 baskets.
   b. Write an equation to represent the stack height, s, of a given number of baskets, b.
   c. Solve the equation if there are 250 baskets.
   d. Solve the equation if the stack height is 125.875 feet tall.

2. Rewrite each expression with the fewest terms possible.
   a. $(-2y + 3) + (-7y - 14)$
   b. $(9x - 4) - 5(2x - 7)$

Texas Tea and Temperature

4

Using Multiple Representations to Solve Problems

WARM UP

1. How many minutes are in a quarter of an hour?

2. How many minutes are in an hour and a half?

3. How is five and a half minutes written as a decimal?

LEARNING GOALS

- Use multiple representations to analyze and interpret problem situations.
- Use tables, graphs, and equations to represent and solve word problems by reasoning about quantities.

Different representations of a problem can give you different insights into possible solutions. How can you use a variety of representations to help you solve problems?

Getting Started

Matching Game

Four equations are given. Match each equation to a graph or table and explain your reasoning. Then, complete the table and graph for the unmatched equation.

Equations

1. $y = 6$
2. $y = \frac{1}{6}x$
3. $y = -x + 6$
4. $2x + y = 6$

Tables and Graphs

A.

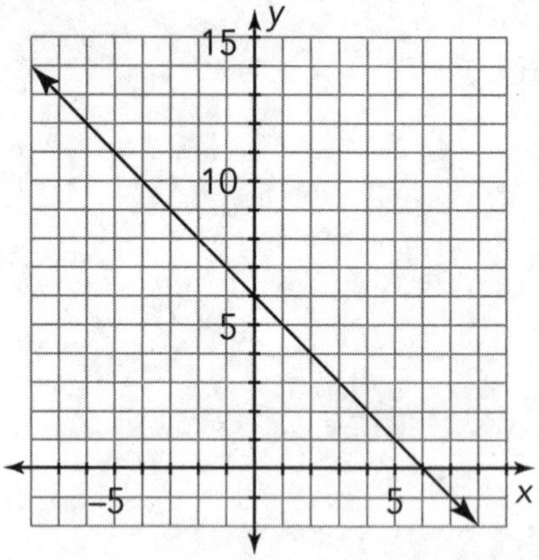

x	y

B.

x	y
$\frac{1}{6}$	6
0	6
1	6

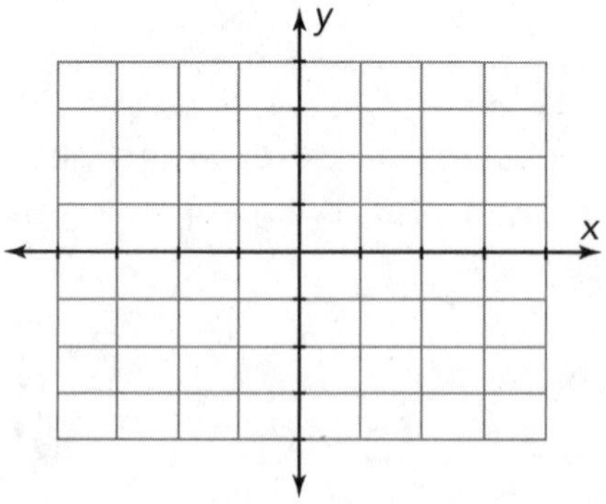

C.

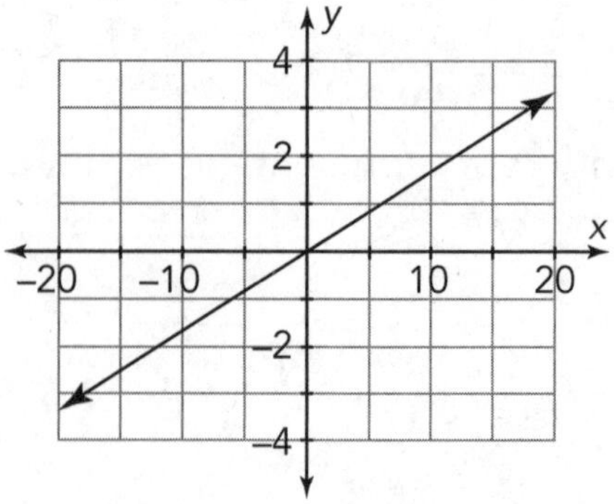

ACTIVITY **4.1**

Starting with a Verbal Description to Solve a Problem

A tank that currently contains 2500 gallons of oil is being emptied at a rate of 25 gallons per minute. The capacity of this tank is 3000 gallons.

1. **How many gallons are currently in the tank?**

2. **How fast is the tank being emptied?**

3. **What are the two quantities that are changing? Define variables for these quantities and identify which is the independent variable and which is the dependent variable.**

4. **What is the unit rate of change in this situation? Explain your reasoning.**

5. **Write an equation that relates the two quantities.**

6. How many gallons will be in the tank after:

   a. a quarter of an hour?

   b. five and a half minutes?

   c. an hour and a half?

7. When will the tank be:

   a. half full?

   b. empty?

8. How long ago did the tank contain 2600 gallons?

9. How long ago was the tank full?

10. Complete the table for this problem situation.

	Independent Quantity	Dependent Quantity
Quantities		
Units of Measure		
Variables		

11. Label the units of measure on each axis and plot all the points from the table. Then, graph the equation for this situation. Make sure to label the units on the axes.

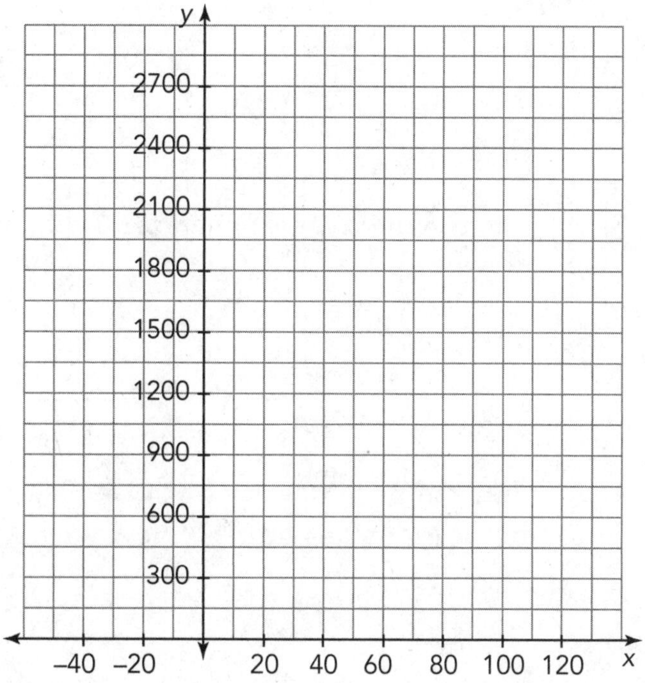

How does your graph show that the tank is being emptied?

ACTIVITY
4.2

Starting with an Equation to Solve a Problem

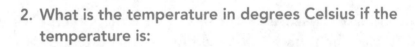

You can also write this formula as F = 1.8C + 32.

The equation that converts a temperature in degrees Celsius to a temperature in degrees Fahrenheit is $F = \frac{9}{5}C + 32$, where F is the temperature in degrees Fahrenheit, and C is the temperature in degrees Celsius.

1. What is the temperature in degrees Fahrenheit if the temperature is:

a. 36°C ?

b. −20°C ?

2. What is the temperature in degrees Celsius if the temperature is:

a. 32°F ?

b. 212°F ?

3. What is the unit rate of change? Explain your reasoning.

4. At what temperature are both the Fahrenheit and Celsius temperature values equal? Show your work.

5. Complete the table with the information you calculated in Question 1 through Question 4.

	Independent Quantity	Dependent Quantity
Quantities		
Units of Measure		
Variables		

6. Label the units of measure on each axis and plot all the points from the table. Then, graph the equation for this situation.

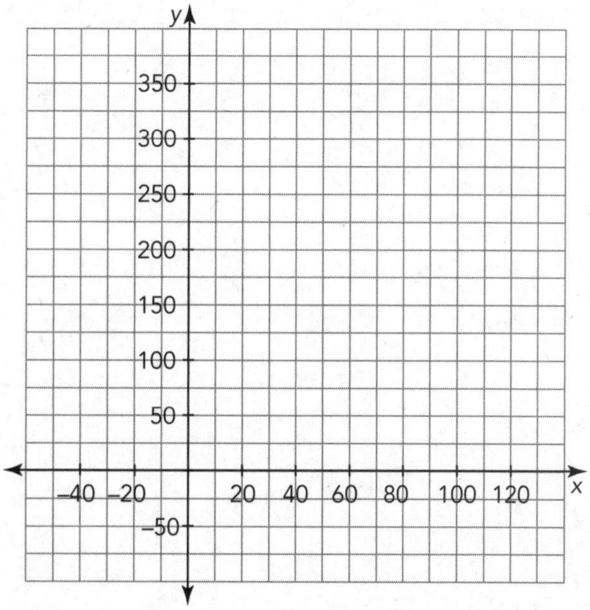

ACTIVITY 4.3 Starting with a Table to Solve a Problem

Herman and Melville found this table. The bottom three entries in the second column were smudged, and the boys couldn't read them.

Time (minutes)	Total Cost (dollars)
0	20
1	23
2	26
3	29
5	35
10	
20	
50	

Let's see if you can calculate the unknown values.

1. **What is the unit rate of change shown in the table? Explain your reasoning.**

2. **Define variables for the quantities in the table, and write an equation that relates the two quantities.**

3. **Use your equation to complete the table. Show your work.**

4. **Use your completed table to construct a graph.**

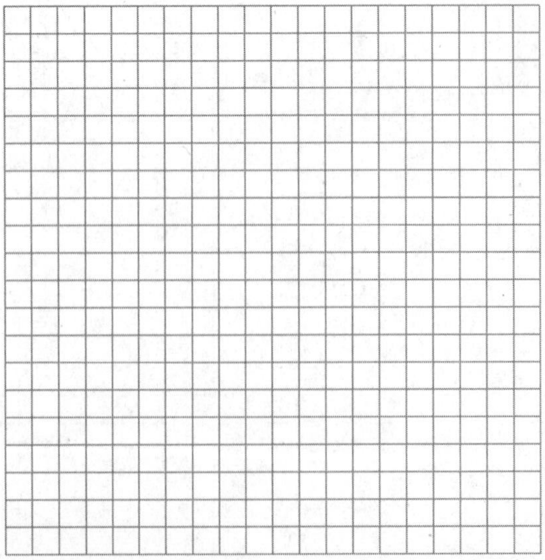

ACTIVITY
4.4

Starting with a Graph to Solve a Problem

This graph shows the relationship between two quantities.

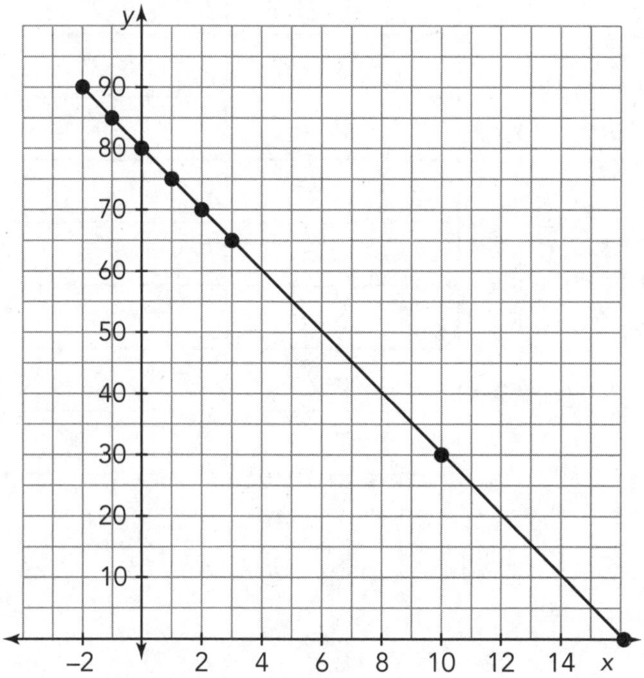

Independent Variable	Dependent Variable
0	80

1. Complete the table using the information in the graph.

2. Write an equation for this relationship.

3. Write a problem situation that can be represented by this graph, table, and equation. Explain what the unit rate means in context.

NOTES

TALK the TALK

Equivalent Representations

Ms. Marston wrote the table shown on the board.

She asked her students to complete the table, write the unit rate of change, and finally, write an equation for this relationship.

x	y
0	−5
1	−3
2	−1
3	1
4	
5	
6	
7	

1. **Complete the table of values and identify the unit rate of change.**

2. **Three of Ms. Marston's students wrote equations to represent this relationship.**

   Molly: $y = 2x - 5$

   Carson: $y = 2(x - 2.5)$

   David: $y = \frac{1}{2}(4x - 10)$

   Who is correct? Explain your reasoning.

3. **Create a problem situation that might fit this equation.**

Assignment

Write

Which representation of equal expressions—tables, graphs, equations, or verbal descriptions—do you prefer? Explain why you prefer this representation and provide an example.

Remember

Multiple representations such as a table, an equation, and a graph can be used to represent a problem situation.

Practice

The Department of Transportation in each state is responsible for the improvements and repairs of that state's roads. One important job is to repaint the road lines that have worn away or faded. A painting crew is painting a 24-mile stretch of road. They have already completed a total of 9.5 miles of the road. The crew has been painting at a rate of 0.25 mile per hour and continues to paint at the same rate.

1. Identify the two quantities that are changing in this situation, identify the independent and dependent quantities, and define the variables for these quantities. Then write an equation that relates the two quantities.
2. What is the unit rate of change in this situation? Explain.
3. How many total miles of the road will be completed if the crew works for another 2 hours?
4. How many more hours does the crew need to work to complete half of the job?
5. Complete the table and then construct a graph.

	Independent Quantity	Dependent Quantity
Quantities		
Units of Measure		
Variables		
	0	
	2	
	5	
	6.5	
		12
		24
		8
		0

Stretch

How could you graph the solutions of an inequality on a coordinate plane? Create a situation that can be modeled with an equation on the coordinate plane. Then show how to model inequalities and their solutions on the coordinate plane.

Review

1. Fernando is using a garden hose to fill his backyard pool at a rate of 10 gallons per minute. The pool already contains 9000 gallons of water. The capacity of the pool is 12,000 gallons.
   a. Define the independent and dependent variables.
   b. Define the unit rate of change.

2. Use double number lines to solve each equation.
   a. $2(x + 1) = 10$
   b. $-(x - 5) = 0$

3. Solve for each unknown.
   a. $\frac{1.6}{2.8} = \frac{x}{7}$
   b. $\frac{2}{d} = \frac{0.4}{5}$

Multiple Representations of Equations Summary

KEY TERM

- unit rate of change

LESSON 1 Put It on the Plane

You can represent a problem situation in many ways.

For example, Ms. Jackson translates books for a living. Her earnings can be represented by a verbal description, table, graph, and equation.

Verbal description: Ms. Jackson charges an initial fee of $275 to manage a project and $25 per page of translated text.

Table:

Number of Pages	Total Earnings for the Project (dollars)
1	300
3	350
10	525
25	900

Graph:

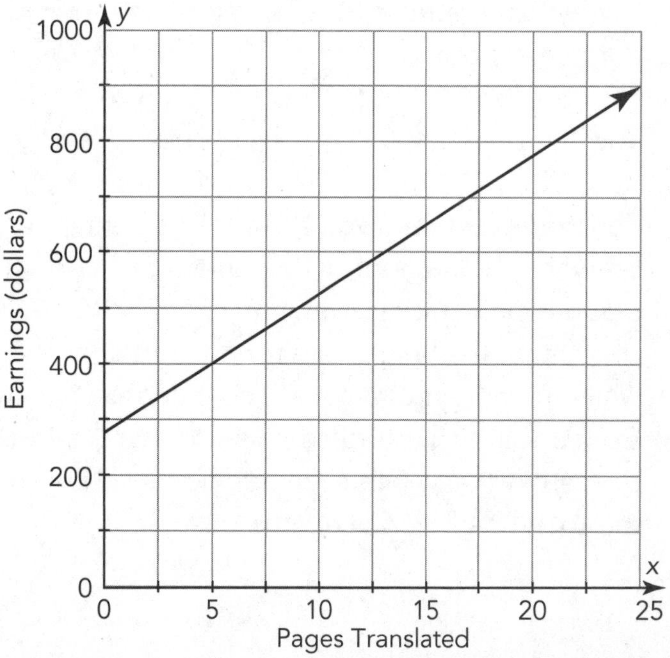

Equation: $y = 275 + 25x$

To solve a linear equation from a graph, locate the value of the given variable, independent or dependent, and determine the exact, if possible, or estimated point corresponding to that variable.

For example, you can use the graph to determine that Ms. Jackson will earn $400 if she translates 5 pages for a customers. She will earn approximately $775 for translating 20 pages.

LESSON 2 Stretches, Stacks, and Structure

Different forms of an equation reveal different information about a problem situation and about other representations of the problem situation. An equation can have different forms, but it is still the same equation.

An equation in the form $y = c + d(x - 1)$ can be rewritten in the form $y = dx + (c - d)$. Consider this example. A limousine rental company charges $250 for the first two hours the limousine is rented and $30 per hour after that. The equation that represents this scenario can be written as $y = 250 + 30(x - 2)$. The equation can be simplified and rewritten as $y = 190 + 30x$. The structure of each equation reveals different aspects of the scenario. Although the two equations are equivalent, the first one reveals that the customer is going to pay $250 upfront for the first two hours and then $30 for any additional hours.

You can compare the graphs of linear equations.

For example, the graph shown represents the relationship between the number of containers of a certain shape to their height when stacked within each other. You can tell from the graph that the height of a round container is 8 centimeters, while the height of a square container is 12 centimeters. Each additional round container raises the total height by 0.5 centimeter, while each additional square container raises the total height by 1 centimeter.

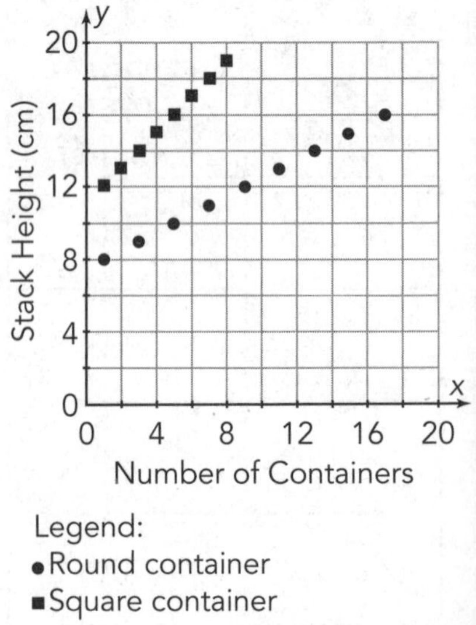

LESSON 3

Deep Flight I

The **unit rate of change** is the amount that the dependent value changes for every one unit that the independent value changes.

For example, suppose the submarine Deep Flight I is going to do a dive starting at sea level, descending 480 feet every minute. The unit rate of change is −480 feet per minute. You can use a graph to estimate solutions to inequality problems.

Estimate the times Deep Flight I will be more than 1400 feet below sea level and the times Deep Flight I will be less than 1400 feet below sea level.

Each of these graphs shows the relationship between the time in minutes and the depth of Deep Flight I. The rectangle on the left graph shows the set of all depths for Deep Flight I less than 1400 feet below sea level. The oval on the right graph shows the set of all depths for Deep Flight I more than 1400 feet below sea level.

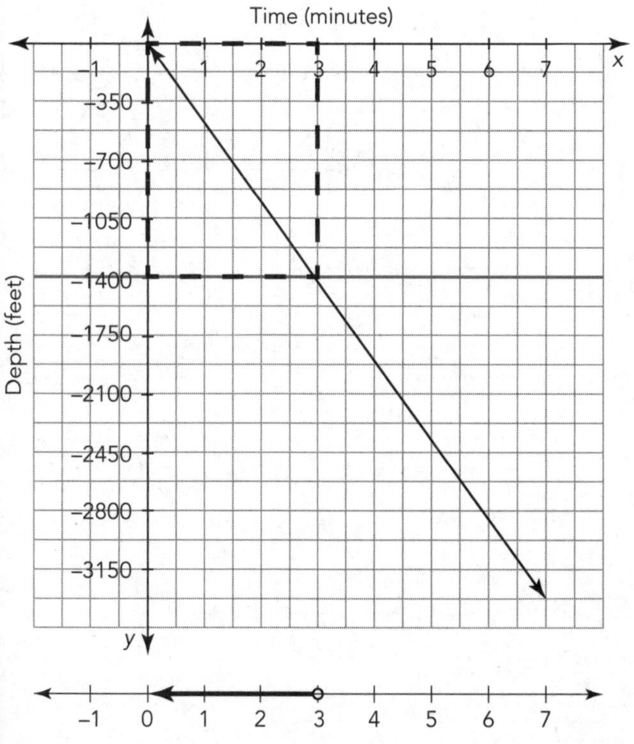

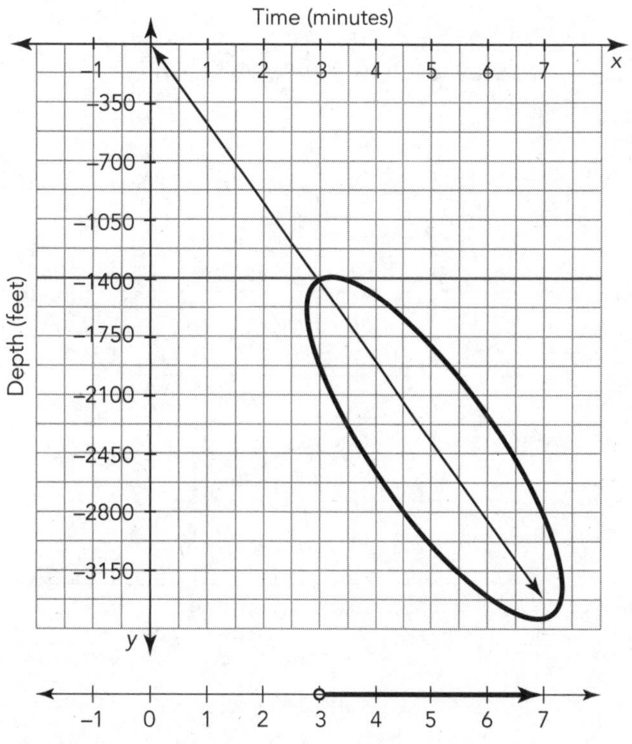

Deep Flight I will be less than 1400 feet below sea level for times less than 3 minutes. The submarine will be more than 1400 feet below sea level for times greater than 3 minutes.

LESSON 4

Texas Tea and Temperature

Multiple representations such as a table, an equation, and a graph can be used to represent a problem situation. You may start with any of these representations to solve a problem and move from one to another by studying their forms and determining unit rates of change.

For example, suppose you are given this table of values.

Time	Height of the Water in the Beaker
days	inches
0	6
1	5.5
4	4
8	2

You can use the values in the table to represent the problem situation with a graph, equation, and verbal description.

Equation:
$y = 6 - 0.5x$

Verbal description:
The height of the water in the beaker begins at 6 inches. The height of the water decreases by 0.5 inches each day.

Graph:

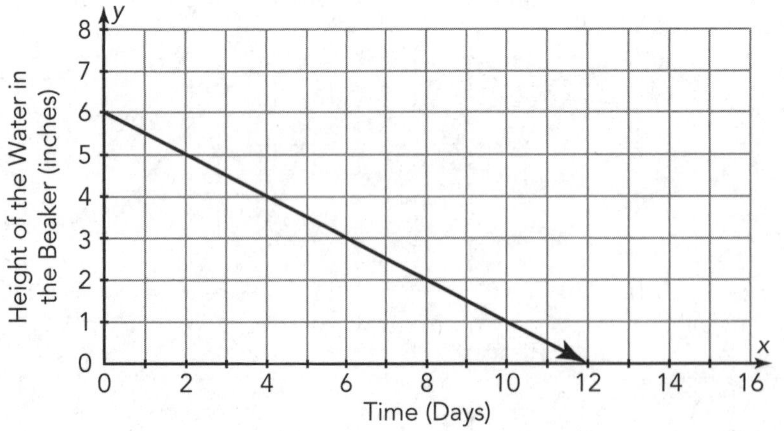

MODULE 4

ANALYZING POPULATIONS AND PROBABILITIES

In this module, you will learn the basics of probability and use the theoretical and experimental probability of simple and compound events to make predictions. You will use models and simulations to determine probabilities. You will build on your experiences with measures of center, the five-number summary, plots of numerical data, and proportional reasoning to draw comparative inferences between two populations.

TOPIC 1

Introduction to Probability

Behind two of the doors are delicious cakes. Behind one is a hungry tiger. If you can only pick a door once, what are your chances of snacking vs. being snacked on?

Module 4: Analyzing Populations and Probabilities

TOPIC 1: INTRODUCTION TO PROBABILITY

In this topic, students use familiar objects, such as number cubes and spinners, to learn the terminology of probability, including outcome, experiment, sample space, event, simple event, probability, complementary events, and equally likely. Students calculate probabilities rolling number cubes, using spinners, and drawing marbles from a bag. For real-world situations or probabilistic situations that require a large number of trials, students use simulation techniques, including random number tables, to simulate the results of experiments.

Where have we been?

This topic is students' formal introduction to probability, but they have encountered probabilistic situations throughout their lives and in previous school years. The topic opens with asking students to interpret the meaning of a meteorologist's forecast. They use their intuition of the meaning of "chance of rain" and rewrite the percent as a fraction.

Where are we going?

In later lessons, students will use probability and ideas about randomness to explore sampling and drawing inferences about data, which is the start of the formal study of statistical inference. The basic ideas developed in this topic will be used in the next topic on compound probability.

Using a Number Line to Interpret Probabilities

The probability of an event is a value from 0 to 1, with 0 meaning that the event is impossible, and 1 meaning that the event is certain.

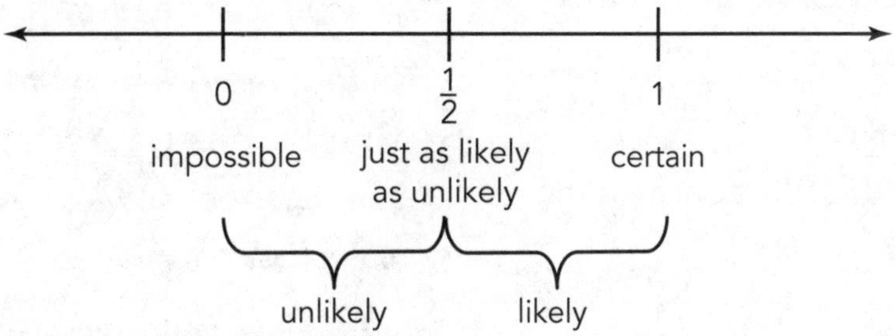

Myth: Cramming for an exam is just as good as spaced practice for long-term retention.

Everyone has been there. You have a big test tomorrow, but you've been so busy that you haven't had time to study. So you had to learn it all in one night. You may have gotten a decent grade on the test. However, did you to remember the material a week, month, or year later?

The honest answer is, "probably not." That's because long-term memory is designed to retain useful information. How does your brain know if a memory is "useful" or not? One way is the frequency in which you encounter a piece of information. If you only see something once (like during cramming), then your brain doesn't deem those memories as important. However, if you sporadically come across the same information over time, then it's probably important. To optimize retention, encourage your student to periodically study the same information over expanding intervals of time.

#mathmythbusted

Talking Points

You can further support your student's learning by resisting the urge, as long as possible, to get to the answer in a problem that your student is working on. Probability is a tricky concept. Students will need time and space to struggle with all the implications of thinking about events in terms of their probabilities. Practice asking good questions when your student is stuck.

Questions to Ask

- Let's think about this. What are all the things you know?
- What do you need to find out?
- How can you model this problem?

Key Terms

sample space

A list of all possible outcomes of an experiment is called a sample space. A sample space is typically enclosed in brackets, { }, with commas between the outcomes.

event

An event is one or a group of possible outcomes for a given situation.

complementary event

Given an event *A*, a complementary event to *A* is the event *not A*, which contains all of the outcomes not in event *A*.

experimental probability

Experimental probability is the ratio of the number of times an event occurs to the total number of trials performed.

Rolling, Rolling, Rolling . . .

1

Defining and Representing Probability

WARM UP

Convert each fraction to a decimal and a percent.

1. $\frac{4}{5}$

2. $\frac{7}{100}$

3. $\frac{5}{12}$

4. $\frac{24}{25}$

5. $\frac{21}{40}$

LEARNING GOALS

- Differentiate between an outcome and an event for an experiment.
- List the sample space for an experiment.
- Determine the probability for an event and the complement of an event.
- Identify the probability of an event as a number between 0 and 1 which can be expressed as a fraction, decimal, or percent.
- Determine that the sum of the probabilities of the outcomes of an experiment is always 1.

KEY TERMS

- outcome
- experiment
- sample space
- event
- simple event
- probability
- complementary events
- equally likely

You have used ratios to represent relationships between two quantities. How can you use ratios to represent the likelihood of an event?

Getting Started

What Are the Chances?

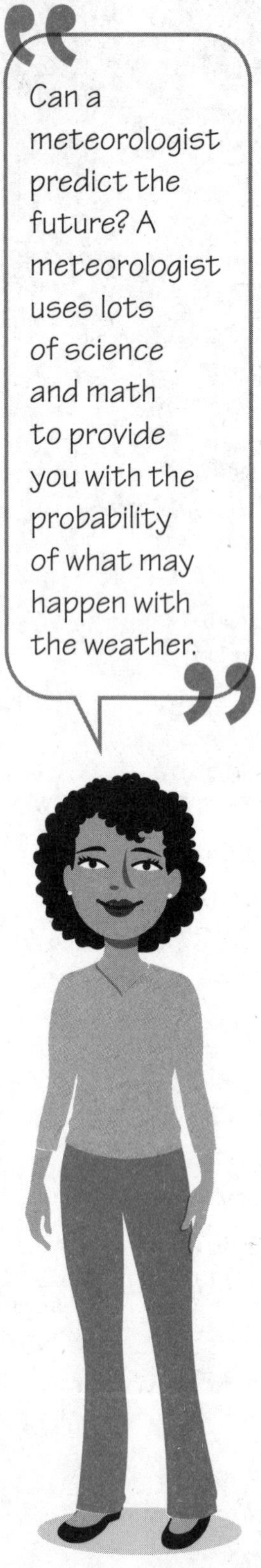

Can a meteorologist predict the future? A meteorologist uses lots of science and math to provide you with the probability of what may happen with the weather.

Consider each statement.

1. **The local weatherman broadcasted that there is a 40% chance of rain today.**

   a. **In your own words, explain what the statement means.**

   b. **Rewrite Question 1 using an equivalent fraction in place of the percent. Explain what it means.**

2. **For a multiple-choice question with four answer choices, the likelihood of guessing the correct answer is $\frac{1}{4}$.**

   a. **In your own words, explain what the statement means.**

   b. **Rewrite Question 2 using an equivalent percent in place of the fraction. Explain what it means.**

ACTIVITY 1.1

Calculating Simple Probabilities

A six-sided number cube has one number, from 1 through 6, on each face. Number cubes are often used when playing board games.

1. **Create a list of all the possible numbers that can appear on the top face if you roll a six-sided number cube.**

The numbers on the faces of a six-sided number cube are the *outcomes* that can occur when rolling a six-sided number cube. An **outcome** is the result of a single trial of a probability *experiment*. An **experiment** is a situation involving chance that leads to results, or outcomes. A list of all possible outcomes of an experiment is called a **sample space**.

A sample space is typically enclosed in braces, { }, with commas between the outcomes.

2. **List the sample space for the experiment of rolling a six-sided number cube.**

An **event** is one possible outcome or a group of possible outcomes for a given situation. A **simple event** is an event consisting of one outcome. For example, in the number cube experiment, an event could be rolling an even number. However, rolling a 5 is a simple event.

An event is a subset of the sample space.

Probability is a measure of the likelihood that an event will occur. It is a way of assigning a numerical value to the chance that an event will occur. The probability of an event is often written as *P*(event). For example, in the number cube experiment, the probability of rolling a 5 could be written as *P*(5). The probability of rolling an even number could be written as *P*(even).

There is a formula to determine the probability of an event.

$$\text{probability} = \frac{\text{number of times an event can occur}}{\text{number of possible outcomes}}$$

WORKED EXAMPLE

To determine the probability of rolling an odd number, or $P(\text{odd})$, follow these steps.

Step 1: First, list all the possible outcomes in the event.
The possible odd numbers that can be rolled are 1, 3, and 5.

Step 2: Add the number of outcomes.
There are 3 possible outcomes of rolling an odd number.

Step 3: Use the equation to determine the probability of rolling an odd number.

$$P(\text{odd}) = \frac{\text{number of times an odd can occur}}{\text{number of possible outcomes}} = \frac{\text{3 possible odd numbers}}{\text{6 possible numbers}}$$

The probability of rolling an odd number is $\frac{3}{6}$ or $\frac{1}{2}$.

So, to determine P(4) consider how many times a 4 can occur when you roll a six-sided number cube.

3. What is the probability of rolling a 4, or $P(4)$? Explain your reasoning.

4. What is the probability of rolling a 6, or $P(6)$? Explain your reasoning.

5. Determine the probability of rolling an even number.

a. Which outcome or outcomes make up the event of rolling an even number?

b. Calculate the probability of rolling an even number.

6. Determine the probability of rolling a number that is *not* even.

   a. Which outcome or outcomes make up the event of rolling a number that is *not* even?

   b. Calculate the probability of rolling a number that is *not* even.

7. Determine the probability of rolling a number greater than 4.

   a. Which outcome or outcomes make up the event of rolling a number greater than 4?

   b. Calculate the probability of rolling a number greater than 4.

8. Determine the probability of rolling a number that is *not* greater than 4.

   a. Which outcome or outcomes make up the event of rolling a number that is *not* greater than 4?

   b. Calculate the probability of rolling a number that is *not* greater than 4.

ACTIVITY
1.2 Complementary Events

In the previous activity, you calculated the probability of *complementary events*. **Complementary events** are events that together contain all of the outcomes in the sample space.

One way to notate the complement of an event A is *not A*. For instance, suppose that *P*(even) represents the probability of rolling an even number on a number cube. Then, *P*(not even) represents the probability of rolling a number that is *not* even on a number cube.

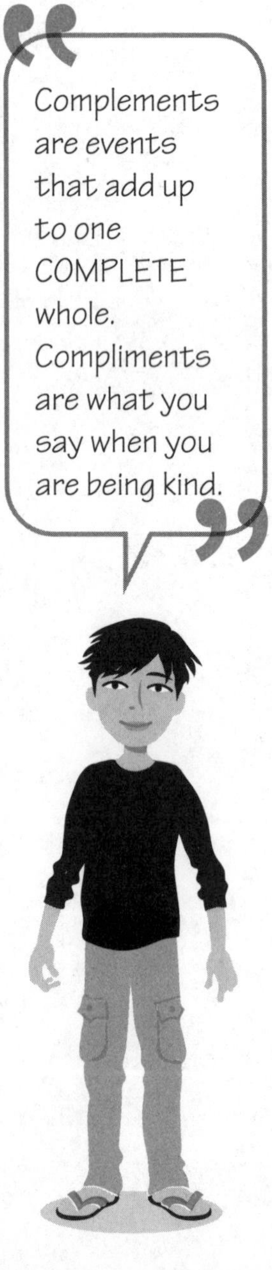

Complements are events that add up to one COMPLETE whole. Compliments are what you say when you are being kind.

1. **Consider the events from Activity 1.1, Questions 5 and 6—"rolling an even number" and "rolling a number that is not even." What do you notice about the sum of the probabilities of these two complementary events?**

2. **Consider the events from Activity 1.1, Questions 7 and 8—"rolling a number greater than 4" and "rolling a number that is not greater than 4." What do you notice about the sum of the probabilities of these two complementary events?**

NOTES

3. What is the sum of the probabilities of *any* two complementary events? Explain why your answer makes sense.

4. The probability of rolling a 5 or less on a number cube is $P(5 \text{ or less}) = \frac{5}{6}$. Leah and Jasmine calculated $P(\text{not 5 or less})$. Their work is shown.

Leah

$$P(\text{not 5 or less}) = \frac{\text{number of possible outcomes}}{\text{total number of outcomes}} = \frac{1}{6}$$

Jasmine

$$P(\text{not 5 or less}) = 1 - P(5 \text{ or less}) = 1 - \frac{5}{6} = \frac{1}{6}$$

Explain the difference between Leah's strategy and Jasmine's strategy.

ACTIVITY 1.3

Simple Probability and Spinners

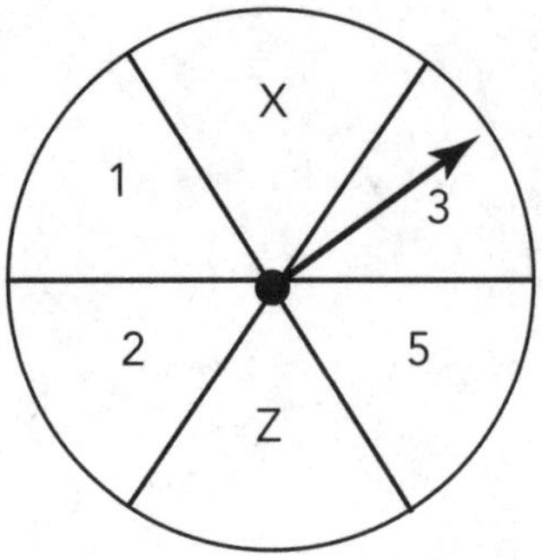

Consider the spinner shown. All sections of the spinner are the same size. An experiment consists of spinning the spinner one time.

1. **How many possible outcomes are there in the experiment? How did you determine your answer?**

2. **List the sample space for the experiment.**

3. **Determine the probability that the spinner lands on a letter.**

   a. **Describe the event and the possible outcomes of the event.**

   b. **Calculate *P*(letter).**

   c. **Describe the complement of this event and the possible outcomes of the complement.**

   d. **Calculate *P*(not a letter).**

NOTES

4. Determine the probability that the spinner lands on an odd number.

   a. Describe the event and the possible outcomes of the event.

   b. Calculate *P*(odd number).

   c. Describe the complement of this event and the possible outcomes of the complement.

   d. Calculate *P*(not an odd number).

5. Determine the probability that the spinner lands on a vowel.

   a. Describe the event and the possible outcomes of the event.

   b. Calculate *P*(vowel).

   c. Describe the complement of this event and the possible outcomes of the complement.

   d. Calculate *P*(not a vowel).

The Spinning Square Game is a game at the Kid Zone. The game consists of spinning the square spinner. If a player takes a spin and the spinner lands on *B*, the player wins a prize. If the spinner lands on *A*, the player does not receive a prize.

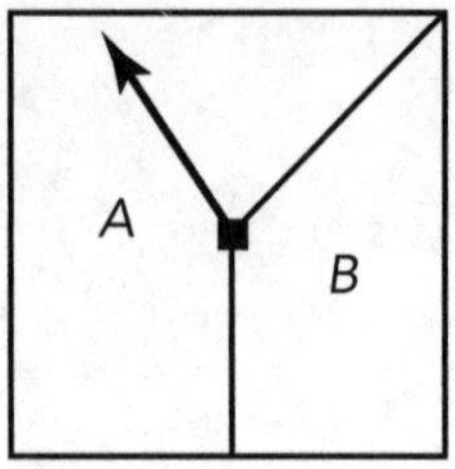

6. Predict each probability.

a. $P(A) =$

b. $P(B) =$

7. Britney predicts the probability that the spinner will land on *A* to be 5. Is Britney correct? Explain your reasoning.

ACTIVITY
1.4 Probabilities from 0 to 1

1. What is the greatest possible probability in any experiment? Explain your reasoning.

2. What is the least possible probability in any experiment? Explain your reasoning.

3. What is the probability of an event that is just as likely to occur as not occur? Explain your reasoning.

The probability of an event occurring is a number between 0 and 1. If the event is certain to happen, then the probability is 1. If an event is impossible to happen, then the probability is 0. If an event is just as likely to happen as not happen, then the probability is 0.5, or $\frac{1}{2}$.

Probabilities can be expressed as fractions, decimals, or percents.

NOTES

Complete the chart representing the different probabilities.

4.

	Fraction	Decimal	Percent
P(certain event)			
P(event that is just as likely as unlikely to occur)			
P(impossible event)			

The number line shown represents the probabilities, from 0 to 1, of any event occurring.

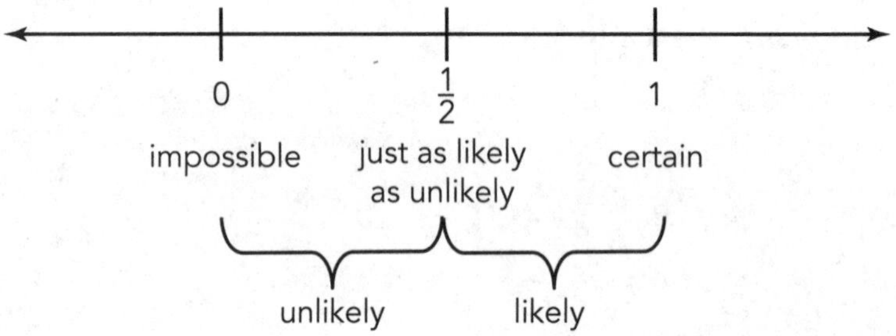

5. Estimate the probability of each event occurring. Then, place the letter corresponding to the estimated probability of the event on the number line.

	Fraction	Decimal	Percent
a. The next baby born at your local hospital will be a boy.	______	______	______
b. Your neighbors will get a pet dinosaur.	______	______	______
c. You will have a test in one of your classes this month.	______	______	______
d. A seventh grader is more than 6 feet tall.	______	______	______

ACTIVITY 1.5

A Simple Probability Experiment

Suppose there are 2 blue, 3 green, and 5 yellow marbles in a bag. One marble will be drawn from the bag.

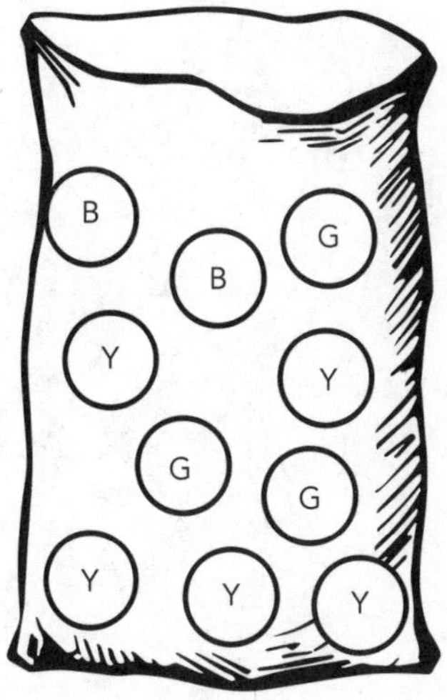

1. List the sample space for the experiment.

2. Calculate each probability.

a. $P(B) =$

b. $P(G) =$

c. $P(Y) =$

When the probabilities of all the outcomes of an experiment are equal, then the outcomes are called **equally likely**.

3. Are the outcomes in the marble experiment equally likely? Explain your reasoning.

4. Determine the sum of all the probabilities.

$P(B) + P(G) + P(Y) =$

5. Determine the sum of the probabilities for all the outcomes of the first spinner in Activity 1.3.

$P(1) + P(2) + P(3) + P(5) + P(X) + P(Z) =$

6. Do you think the sum of the probabilities for all outcomes of any experiment will always be 1? Explain your reasoning.

NOTES

TALK the TALK

Absolutely/Never

1. Can the sum of the probabilities for all outcomes of some experiment ever be greater than 1? Explain your reasoning.

2. Write an event that has a probability of 1.

3. Write an event that has a probability of 0.

4. If $P(\text{not event } X) = 1$, what is $P(\text{event } X)$?

5. If $P(\text{not event } Y) = 0$, what is $P(\text{event } Y)$?

Assignment

Write

Complete each statement using a term from the word box.

experiment	probability	event	equally likely
outcome	sample space	simple event	complementary events

1. A(n) ________________ is one or a group of possible outcomes for a given situation.
2. A list of all possible outcomes of an experiment is called a(n) ________________ .
3. A(n) ________________ is a situation involving chance that leads to results.
4. The measure of the likelihood that an event will occur is its ________________.
5. The result of an experiment is a(n) ________________.
6. An event consisting of one outcome is a(n) ________________.
7. When the probability of all the outcomes of an experiment are equal, then the probabilities are called ________________.
8. ________________ are two events that together contain all of the outcomes in the sample space.

Remember

Probability is a measure of the likelihood that an event will occur. To calculate the probability of an event, or *P*(event), determine the ratio of the number of times the event occurs to the total number of outcomes.

Practice

1. Rasheed is getting dressed in the dark. He reaches into his sock drawer to get a pair of socks. He knows that his sock drawer contains six pairs of socks, and each pair is a different color. Each pair of socks is folded together. The pairs of socks in the drawer are red, brown, green, white, black, and blue.
   a. How many possible outcomes are there in the experiment?
   b. What are the possible outcomes of the experiment?
   c. List the sample space for the experiment.
   d. Calculate *P*(blue).
   e. Calculate *P*(green).
   f. Calculate *P*(not red).
   g. Calculate *P*(not purple)

2. Consider the square spinner shown and assume all sections are the same size. An experiment consists of spinning the spinner one time.

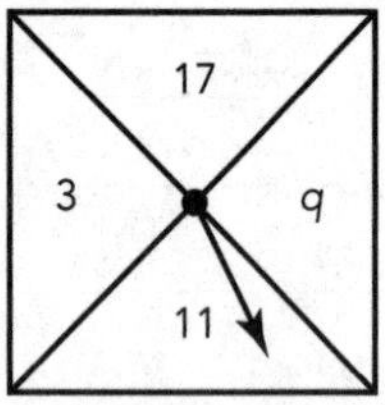

   a. How many possible outcomes are there in the experiment?
   b. What are the possible outcomes of the experiment?
   c. List the sample space for the experiment.
   d. Calculate $P(q)$.
   e. Calculate P(number).
   f. Calculate P(not a number greater than 10).
   g. Calculate P(number less than 2).

3. Determine whether each event is certain to occur, just as likely to occur as not to occur, or impossible to occur. Then write the probability.
   a. A coin is flipped and the coin lands heads up. Express the probability as a fraction.
   b. Tuesday follows Monday in the week. Express the probability as a percent.
   c. You have only white shirts in your closet. Express the probability of reaching into your closet and choosing a red shirt as a fraction.
   d. A box contains 2 green balls and 2 yellow balls. You reach into the box and grab a yellow ball. Express the probability as a decimal.

Stretch

Create a spinner with 4 sections, *A* through *D*, so that each section has the given probability.

Section A: 10%
Section B: 20%
Section C: 30%
Section D: 40%

Review

1. Cho is driving east from San Francisco along Route 80. The graph represents the relationship between the time that Cho has driven and the distance that she has driven.

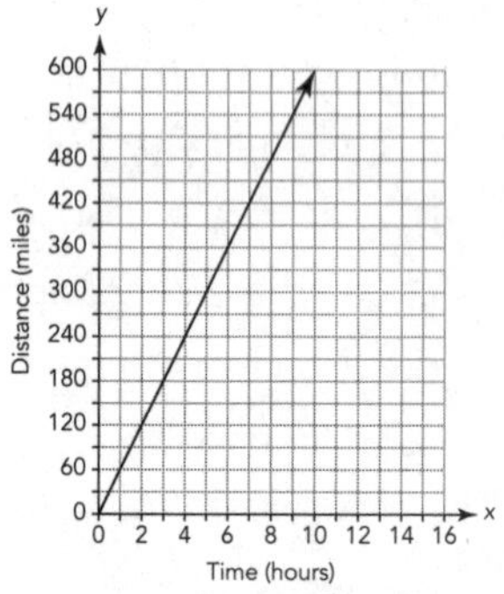

   a. How far does Cho drive in 5 hours?
   b. How fast is Cho driving?
   c. Write an equation to determine the number of hours that Cho drives for any number of hours. Be sure to define your variables.
2. Louis is researching a type of fish called carp. He discovers that one variety of carp can grow 5 pounds during each year of its life. He decides to purchase a very young carp of this variety that weighs 2 pounds. Define variables and write an equation that represents the relationship between the amount of time in years that Louis has the carp and the weight of the carp.
3. Solve each equation using any method.
   a. $\frac{x}{3} + 2 = 14$
   b. $6n - 13 = 27$

Give the Models a Chance

2

Probability Models

WARM UP

Determine each ratio.

1. number of heads to number of sides of coin

2. number of 6s to number of faces on a six-sided number cube.

3. number of day names ending in "day" to total number of day names

LEARNING GOALS

- Develop a probability model for an experiment and use it to determine probabilities of events.
- Develop and interpret a uniform probability model assigning equal probability to all outcomes.
- Construct and interpret a non-uniform probability model.

KEY TERMS

- probability model
- uniform probability model
- non-uniform probability model

You now know about simple probabilities and how to write them. How can you use models to represent probabilities and solve problems?

Getting Started

Pocket Probabilities

Molly has 3 pennies, 4 nickels, 3 dimes, and 2 quarters in her pocket. She takes one coin out of her pocket and hides it in the palm of her hand. She wants her best friend to guess which coin she is holding.

1. **Complete the table. Use a fraction to represent each probability.**

Outcome	Penny	Nickel	Dime	Quarter
Probability				

2. **Determine the sum of the probabilities.**

3. **What coin would you advise Molly's best friend to guess? Explain your reasoning.**

ACTIVITY **2.1**

Using Probability Models

Jorge and Tristan are training to be magicians and are working on a card trick. They have 5 cards of different colors—red, blue, yellow, green, and purple. They are discussing the likelihood of an audience member picking each color, assuming that they can't see the card's color.

1. List the sample space for choosing a card.

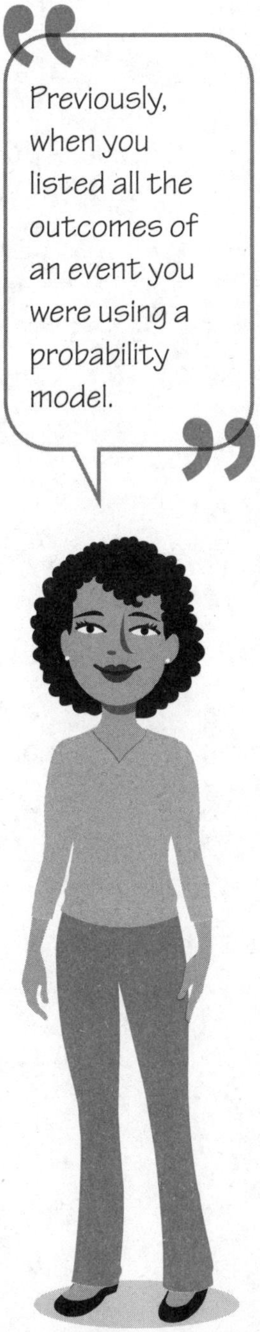

Previously, when you listed all the outcomes of an event you were using a probability model.

2. What is the probability of selecting each card? Write the probability for each in the table.

Outcome	R	B	Y	G	P
Probability					

When solving a probability problem, it is helpful to construct a *probability model*. A **probability model** is a list of each possible outcome along with its probability. Probability models are often shown in a table. The probability model for choosing a card is shown.

A probability model will list all the outcomes which will be greater than 0, but less than 1. The sum of all the probabilities for the outcomes will always be 1.

3. Why is the sum of the probabilities in a probability model always 1?

4. **Tristan claims, "The model is correct because the probabilities for all outcomes are equal to each other." Jorge disagrees and says, "The sum of all the probabilities is 1, but that does not mean the probabilities of all the outcomes are equal." Who is correct? Explain your reasoning.**

A **uniform probability model** occurs when all the probabilities in a probability model are equally likely to occur. Each color card in the magicians' trick had the same probability of being chosen.

When all probabilities in a probability model are not equal to each other, it is called a **non-uniform probability model**. An example would be a weather forecast that states there is a 30 percent chance of rain. That means there is a 70 percent chance of *not* raining. The sum of these two probabilities is 1, but the outcomes do not have the same probability.

ACTIVITY 2.2

Constructing and Interpreting Probability Models

An eight-sided polyhedron is like a six-sided number cube, but instead it has 8 sides.

1. Construct a probability model for each situation. Explain how you constructed the model. Then, determine whether or not the probability model is a uniform probability model.

   a. Rolling an 8-sided polyhedron with the numbers 1–8

Outcome								
Probability								

   b. Choosing a marble from a bag of marbles containing 1 green marble, 2 red marbles, and 7 blue marbles

Outcome			
Probability			

   c. Selecting a member of the Chess Club whose members are Samuel, Martha, Carol, Jon, Sally, Ronaldo, and Simon:

Outcome							
Probability							

d. Selecting a male member of the Chess Club whose members are Samuel, Martha, Carol, Joanne, Sally, Ronaldo, and Simon:

Outcome		
Probability		

2. Use the probability model to calculate each probability.

Outcome	2	3	4	5	6	7
Probability	$\frac{1}{12}$	$\frac{3}{12}$	$\frac{1}{12}$	$\frac{5}{12}$	$\frac{1}{12}$	$\frac{1}{12}$

a. $P(3) =$

b. $P(8) =$

c. $P(\text{number less than 8}) =$

d. $P(\text{prime number}) =$

e. $P(\text{even number}) =$

ACTIVITY
2.3

More with Probability Models

When Mr. York receives his homeroom list for this year, he cannot believe it—all of the last names in his homeroom start with one of 5 letters! The table shows how many students in Mr. York's homeroom have last names beginning with the letters listed.

Letter	Number of Students
A	7
B	4
M	5
S	12
O	2

1. How many students are in Mr. York's homeroom?

2. Create a probability model for selecting a student from Mr. York's homeroom.

3. Use the probability model to determine each probability.

a. Randomly choosing a student with a last name that begins with a vowel.

b. Randomly choosing a student with a last name that does not begin with S.

c. Randomly choosing a student with a last name that begins with C.

NOTES

TALK the TALK

Compare and Contrast

Your best friend is not in school today and misses this lesson. Help your friend understand what you have learned. Write 1–2 paragraphs that explain the answers to these two questions.

1. **What is the difference between a uniform probability model and a non-uniform probability model?**

2. **Will the sum of all the probabilities of the outcomes of an event be equal to 1 for both uniform and non-uniform probability models?**

Assignment

Write

Complete each sentence.

1. When all probabilities in a probability model are the same, it is called a ______________________.
2. When all probabilities in a probability model are not the same, it is called a ______________________.
3. A ______________________ is a list of each possible outcome along with its probability.

Remember

When the probabilities of all the outcomes in a situation are represented in a probability model, the sum of the probabilities is 1.

Practice

1. Use the probability model to determine each probability.

Outcome	1	2	3	4	5	6	7	8
Probability	$\frac{2}{25}$	$\frac{4}{25}$	$\frac{1}{25}$	$\frac{5}{25}$	$\frac{2}{25}$	$\frac{4}{25}$	$\frac{3}{25}$	$\frac{4}{25}$

a. *P*(4)
b. *P*(7)
c. *P*(less than 7)
d. *P*(greater than 8)
e. *P*(odd number)
f. *P*(less than 10)
g. Is this a uniform probability model? Explain your answer.

2. Use the probability model to determine each probability.

Outcome	A	B	C	D	E	F
Probability	$\frac{2}{20}$	$\frac{5}{20}$	$\frac{2}{20}$	$\frac{7}{20}$	$\frac{1}{20}$	$\frac{3}{20}$

a. *P*(B)
b. *P*(F)
c. *P*(not C)
d. *P*(consonant)
e. *P*(not A)
f. *P*(vowel)
g. Is this a uniform probability model? Explain your answer.

Stretch

Mark flipped a coin 10 times and got 70% heads and 30% tails. What will happen to these percents as Mark continues flipping the coin? Try it out to test your prediction.

Review

1. A drawer contains 15 T-shirts. There are 4 blue, 9 green, and 2 black T-shirts. A T-shirt is grabbed at random from the drawer. Which statement(s) correctly describe the likelihood of an event? Select True or False and explain your reasoning.

a. It is unlikely that a black T-shirt will be selected.	True	False
b. It is certain that a green T-shirt will be selected.	True	False
c. It is impossible that a red T-shirt will be selected.	True	False
d. It is likely that a blue T-shirt will be selected.	True	False

2. A local park rents cabins for people who want to vacation by the forest. The fee for the rental is $27 per night. There is also a $55 cleaning and maintenance charge that is added to the total bill.
   a. Define variables for the number of days that a cabin is rented and the cost of the rental. Use the variables to write an equation that represents the cost to rent the cabin, given the number of days that the cabin is rented.
   b. Use the equation to determine how many days the cabin can be rented for $190. Show all of your work.
3. Use the Distributive Property to rewrite each expression.
   a. $-7(-5g + 12) - 27$
   b. $\frac{-6.4y + 14.4}{-0.16}$

Toss the Cup 3

Determining Experimental Probability of Simple Events

WARM UP

Write each fraction as a percent.

1. $\frac{3}{10}$
2. $\frac{1}{4}$
3. $\frac{9}{20}$
4. $\frac{2}{5}$

LEARNING GOALS

- Predict the experimental probability of a chance event by collecting data in a probability experiment.
- Develop a probability model using frequencies in data generated from a probability experiment.
- Use proportional reasoning to determine the theoretical probability of random events.
- Calculate the difference between a theoretical prediction and the experimental results as a percent error ratio.

KEY TERMS

- theoretical probability
- experimental probability
- percent error

You can create probability models of simple events. Do these models always reflect what actually happens when you toss a coin, roll a number cube, or spin a spinner? How are the probability models related to these actions in the real-world?

Getting Started

Flip It!

1. With a partner, flip a coin 30 times, record the results, and then calculate the probability of each event.

Outcome	Tally	Total	Probability
Heads			
Tails			

For this probability experiment, the probability is the number of times the outcome occurred over the total number of flips.

2. Combine the results of your experiment with those of your classmates. Then calculate the probability of each event.

3. What is the actual probability of flipping heads?

4. How does the actual probability compare to the calculated probability in Question 2?

ACTIVITY 3.1

Determining Experimental Probability

Two friends are designing a game called Toss the Cup.

The game is played between two players. To play the game, a paper or plastic cup is needed. To start the game, the paper cup is tossed in the air.

- If the cup lands on its bottom, Player 1 wins a point.

- If the cup lands on its top, Player 2 wins a point.

- If the cup lands on its side, neither player receives a point.

1. Predict the probability for each position in which the cup can land.

2. List the sample space for the game.

3. Can you use the sample space to determine the probability that the cup lands on its top, bottom, or side? Explain why or why not.

4. Do you think all the outcomes are equally likely? Explain your reasoning.

5. Play the game 25 times with a partner. Decide who will be Player 1 and who will be Player 2.

Result	Tally Marks	Total
Bottom Player 1		
Top Player 2		
Side		

a. Record your results in the table using tally marks. Then, write your and your opponent's total score, and write the number of times the cup landed on its side.

b. Summarize your results.

The **theoretical probability** of an event is the ratio of the number of desired outcomes to the total number of possible outcomes. This is the kind of probability you have been working with in previous lessons.

Experimental probability is the ratio of the number of times an event occurs to the total number of trials performed.

$$\text{Experimental Probability} = \frac{\text{number of times the event occurs}}{\text{total number of trials performed}}$$

6. What is the experimental probability of the cup landing:

a. on its bottom?

b. on its top?

c. on its side?

7. Do you think this is a fair game to play? Why or why not?

8. Is it possible to determine the exact probability of the cup landing on its top, bottom, or side? Explain your reasoning.

ACTIVITY
3.2 Predicting Theoretical Probability Using Experimental Probability

Examine the spinner shown.

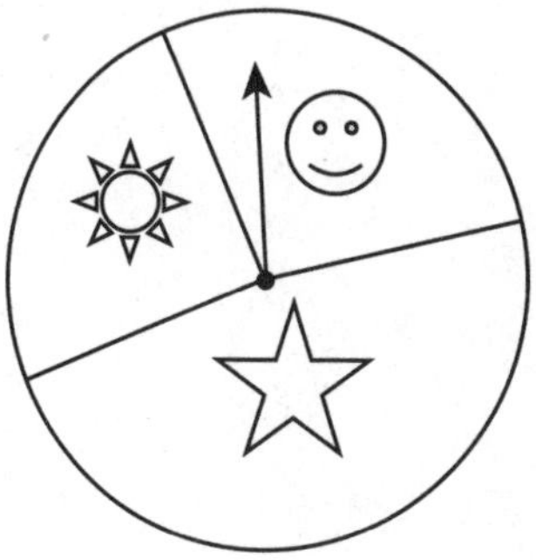

1. List the sample space.

2. Can you use the sample space to determine the probabilities of the spinner landing on each symbol? Explain why or why not.

3. On which symbol(s) does the spinner have the best chance of landing? On which symbol(s) does the spinner have the worst chance of landing?

4. Predict the probability of the spinner landing on each symbol.

a. *P*() =

b. *P*() =

c. *P*() =

5. Jonah and Melanie make the following predictions for the spinner landing on each symbol. Explain why each student is incorrect.

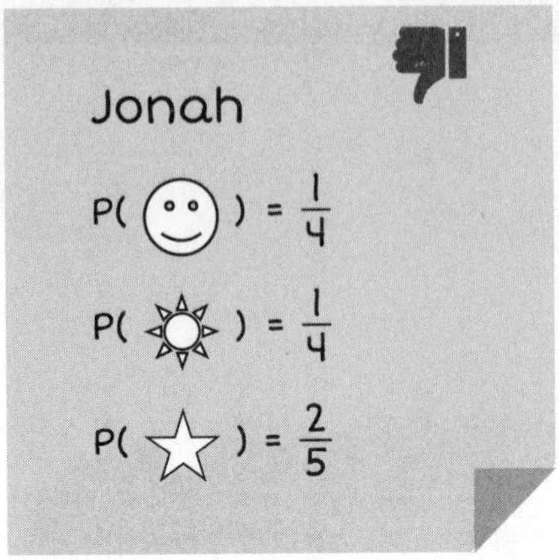

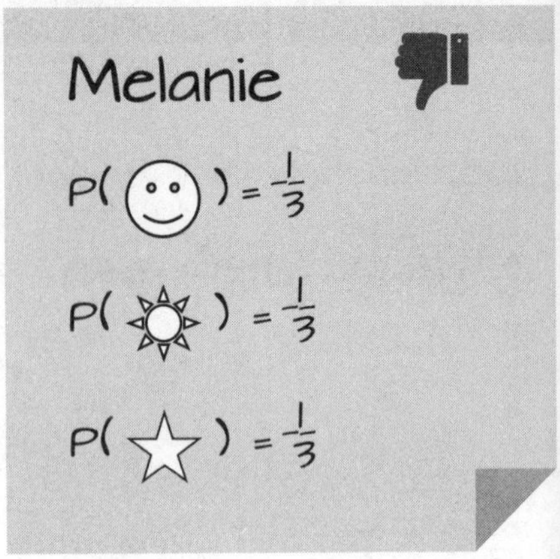

6. Is there a way to determine the exact probabilities of landing on each of the shapes? Explain your reasoning.

NOTES

Let's determine the experimental probability of the spinner landing on each of the symbols. Use a paper clip as the arrow part of the spinner. Place a pencil point through the paper clip, and then on the center of the circle. Working with a partner, one person will spin the spinner and the other person will record the result of each spin.

7. Spin the spinner 50 times and record the data using tally marks. Then, complete the table.

Shape	Tally	Total	Probability
☺			
☼			
☆			

8. Calculate the experimental probabilities using your data.

a. $P($☺$) =$

b. $P($☼$) =$

c. $P($☆$) =$

9. Compare the experimental probabilities with your predictions from Question 4. What do you notice? Why did this happen?

NOTES

ACTIVITY 3.3 Comparing Probabilities Using Proportional Reasoning

If you know the probability of an event, then you can use proportional reasoning to predict the number of times that event will occur throughout an experiment.

WORKED EXAMPLE

The probability that a spinner will land on  is $\frac{7}{20}$.

If you spin the spinner 60 times, you can predict the number of times the spinner will land on the  section.

Step 1: Set up a proportion.

$$\frac{\text{number of times an event will occur}}{\text{number of possible outcomes}} \qquad \frac{7}{20} = \frac{x}{60}$$

Step 2: Solve the proportion.

$$\frac{7}{20} = \frac{x}{60}$$

$$7(60) = 20x$$

$$\frac{420}{20} = \frac{20x}{20}$$

$$21 = x$$

If you spin the spinner 60 times, you can expect it to land on the  21 times.

1. Suppose these are the probabilities for the symbols on the spinner.

$P(☺) = \frac{7}{20}$ $P(☼) = \frac{2}{5}$ $P(☆) = \frac{1}{4}$

a. If you spin the spinner 40 times, predict the number of times the spinner would land on each symbol.

☺ ☼ ☆

b. If you spin the spinner 100 times, predict the number of times you would land on each symbol.

☺ ☼ ☆

c. How did you predict the number of times the spinner would land on each symbol for the given number of times the spinner would be spun?

d. Do you think you would land on the symbol exactly the number of times you calculated in parts (a) and (b) if you spin the spinner? Why or why not?

NOTES

To compare the theoretical and experimental probabilities, you can use a measure called *percent error*. In probability, the **percent error** describes how far off the experimental probability is from the theoretical probability as a percent ratio.

WORKED EXAMPLE

Suppose you spun the ☺ 20 times out of 50 trials. The experimental probability, P_E (☺), is $\frac{20}{50}$ or $\frac{2}{5}$. The theoretical probability, P_T (☺), is $\frac{7}{20}$.

The percent error can be calculated using this formula:

$$\frac{P_E - P_T}{P_T} \cdot 100 = \frac{\frac{2}{5} - \frac{7}{20}}{\frac{7}{20}} \cdot 100$$

$$= \frac{\frac{8}{20} - \frac{7}{20}}{\frac{7}{20}} \cdot 100$$

$$= \frac{\frac{1}{20}}{\frac{7}{20}} \cdot 100 \approx 14.3\%$$

2. Write a sentence to interpret the result in the worked example.

3. What would it mean to have a 0% error? Use an example with the formula to explain your reasoning.

4. Use the spinner results from the previous activity to calculate the percent errors for P(☼) and P(☆) and describe their meaning.

ACTIVITY 3.4

Practice with Probability and Percent Error

As the number of trials increases, the experimental probability tends to get closer and closer to the theoretical probability. What do you think will happen to the percent error as the number of trials increases?

1. Flip a coin 10 times. Record each measure.

Outcome	Tally
Heads	
Tails	

a. experimental probability of flipping heads

b. theoretical probability of flipping heads

c. percent error for *P*(heads)

2. Combine your results with a partner. Describe how the experimental probability, theoretical probability, and percent error changed.

3. Combine your results with the class. Describe how the experimental probability, theoretical probability, and percent error changed.

4. What seems to happen to the percent error as the number of trials increases? Why do you think this happens?

NOTES

A four-sided polyhedron is like a six-sided number cube. It's just that it has four sides instead of six! What do you think a four-sided polyhedron looks like?

TALK the TALK

Theoretical or Experimental?

1. Explain the difference between experimental and theoretical probability.

2. Determine if each probability of the scenario can be calculated experimentally, theoretically, or both. Explain your reasoning.

   a. The probability of the spinner landing on red.

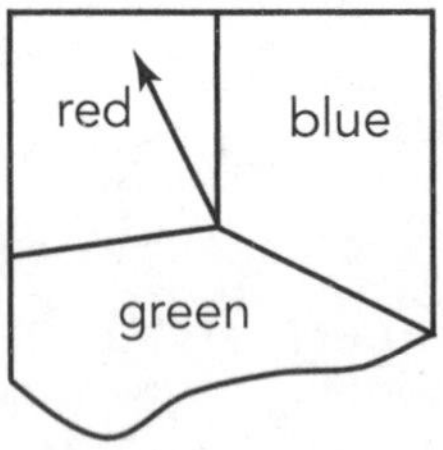

   b. *P*(sum of 4) when a four-sided number polyhedron with numbers 1 through 4 is rolled twice.

   c. Probability a particular medicine will cure a disease.

   d. Probability a bridge will collapse given the bridge's dimensions and appropriate mathematical formulas.

Assignment

Write

Define each term in your own words.

1. experimental probability
2. theoretical probability

Remember

The percent error describes how far off the experimental probability is from the theoretical probability.

The percent error is the ratio $\frac{P_E - P_T}{P_T} \cdot 100$.

Practice

1. Suppose the probabilities for the letters on a spinner are known to be:

   $P(A) = \frac{1}{4}$ $P(B) = \frac{1}{3}$ $P(C) = \frac{5}{12}$

   Predict the number of times you would land on each letter if you were to spin the spinner the number of times given.

   a. You spin the spinner 12 times.

   $P(A)$: $P(B)$: $P(C)$:

   b. You spin the spinner 96 times.

   $P(A)$: $P(B)$: $P(C)$:

   c. You spin the spinner 6000 times.

   $P(A)$: $P(B)$: $P(C)$:

2. A six-sided number cube was rolled 30 times. Use the results listed in the table to answer each question.

   a. What is the theoretical probability of rolling a number less than 4?

   b. What is the experimental probability of rolling a number less than 4?

   c. What is the percent error for P(less than 4)?

   d. What is the theoretical probability of rolling a 2?

   e. What is the experimental probability of rolling a 2?

   f. What is the percent error for $P(2)$?

   g. How might you adjust the experiment to decrease the percent error?

Outcome	Tally
1	卌 |||
2			
3	卌 |||
4					
5				
6	卌

Stretch

Consider the Toss the Cup game. Suppose that the area of a base of the cup is 3.14 square inches, and the area of the other base is 7.065 square inches. From base to base the height of the cup is 5.5 inches. Determine the surface area of the side of the cup and use the three areas to determine the probability of landing on the side or one of the bases, assuming the shape of the cup doesn't matter.

Review

1. Charlie got a new board game that came with the spinner shown.

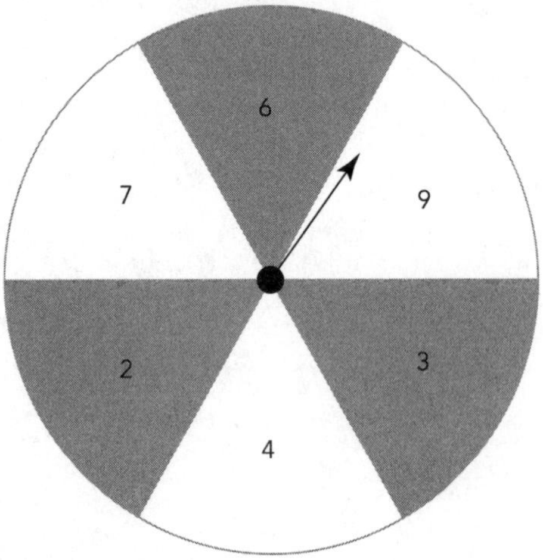

   a. Complete the probability model for using this spinner.

Outcome	2	3	4	6	7	9
Probability						

   b. What is the sum of the probabilities in the probability model?
   c. What is the probability that Charlie spins the spinner and gets an even number?
2. Zoey is researching her smartphone data plan. She currently gets 2 gigabytes of data per month. She looks at her past usage and notices that she uses an average of 0.04 gigabytes of data per day.
   a. Write an equation to represent the relationship between the number of days and the amount of data Zoey has left for the month.
   b. Does she have enough data in her monthly plan for her average usage? Should she change plans?
3. Use long division to convert each fraction to a decimal. Show all your work. Label each decimal as *terminating* or *non-terminating*.
   a. $\frac{5}{6}$ b. $\frac{15}{16}$

A Simulating Conversation

4

Simulating Simple Experiments

WARM UP

Solve each proportion.

1. $\frac{3}{x} = \frac{1}{24}$
2. $\frac{4}{9} = \frac{10}{y}$
3. $\frac{3}{5} = \frac{p}{212}$

LEARNING GOALS

- Conduct trials using a simulation to determine probability.
- Conduct a large number of trials and observe the long-run relative frequency of outcomes to demonstrate that experimental probability approaches theoretical probability.

KEY TERMS

- simulation
- random number table

Conducting probability experiments are helpful when you are rolling a number cube, flipping a coin, spinning a spinner, etc. What about more complicated experiments? How can you use models to run simulations of experiments when it's not possible to do the experiments in real life?

Getting Started

Designing Sims

1. Design a spinner that could be used to generate the experimental probability of guessing the correct answer on a true or false test question. Explain your design.

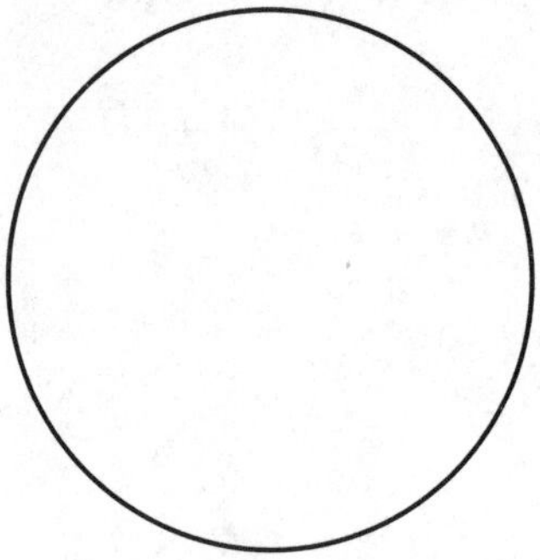

2. Design a spinner that could be used to generate the experimental probability of guessing the correct answer on a multiple-choice test where each question has three possible answers. Explain your design.

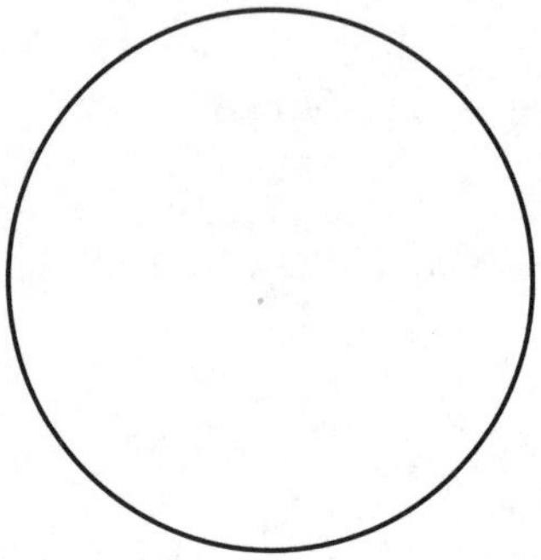

3. Design a spinner that could be used to generate the experimental probability of guessing the correct answer on a multiple-choice test where each question has four possible answers. Explain your design.

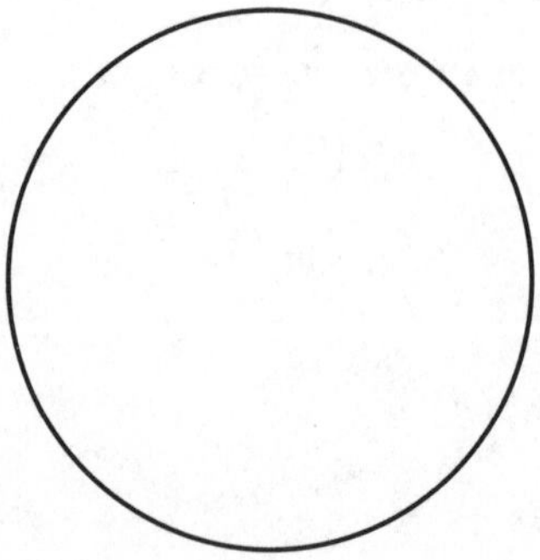

ACTIVITY
4.1 Simulating Baby Births

NOTES

What percent of babies born at a certain hospital are girls? One way to answer the question is to perform a *simulation*. A **simulation** is an experiment that models a real-life situation. When conducting a simulation, you must choose a model that has the same probability of the event.

1. **What model might be appropriate for creating a simulation of this event?**

2. **Describe the sample space for this situation.**

3. **What is the event you are trying to determine?**

4. **Suppose the probability of a family having a girl is $\frac{1}{2}$. What percent of babies born at a hospital would you expect to be girls?**

Let's use the toss of a coin as the model. Heads will represent the birth of a girl, and tails will represent the birth of a boy.

5. **If you toss a coin twice, list all the possible outcomes from this simulation.**

6. Toss your coin 2 times.
   a. How many of the coin tosses resulted in heads?

   b. According to your simulation, what is the experimental probability of a baby girl being born?

   c. Share your results with your classmates. Then, create a dot plot of all the experimental probabilities. Did everyone end up with the same results as the theoretical probability of a girl being born?

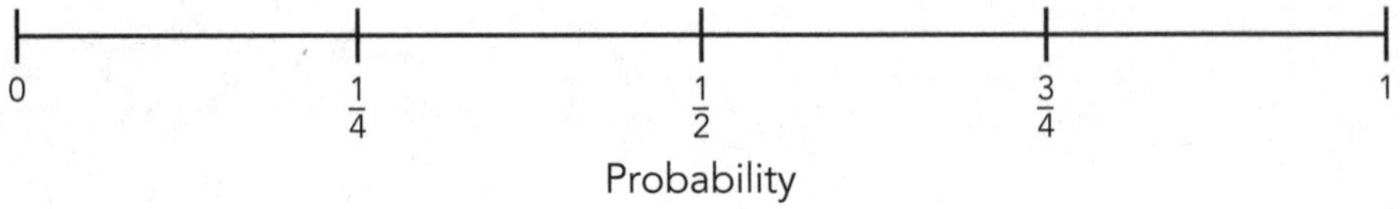

7. Toss your coin 8 times.
   a. How many of the coin tosses resulted in heads?

   b. According to your simulation, what is the experimental probability of a baby girl being born?

   c. Share your results with your classmates. Then, create a dot plot of all the experimental probabilities. How do these results compare to the results from Question 6?

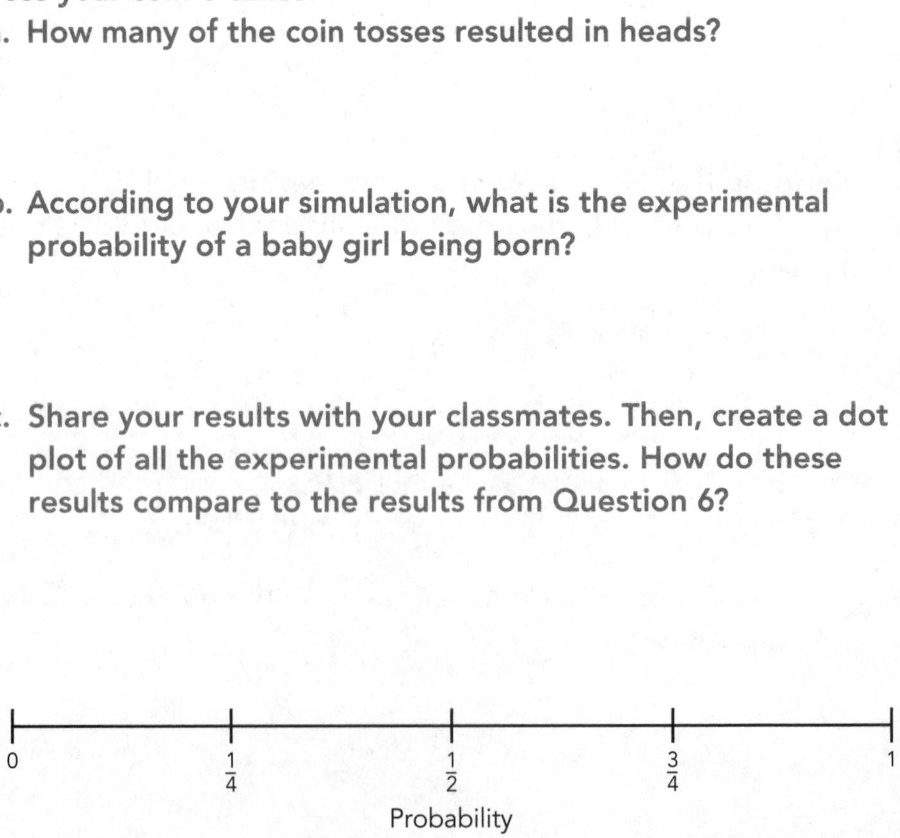

8. Conduct 50 trials of the simulation. Record the results in the table using tally marks.

Result	Tally	Total	Percent
Heads			
Tails			

9. Share your results with your classmates. Then, create a dot plot of all the probabilities. What do you notice?

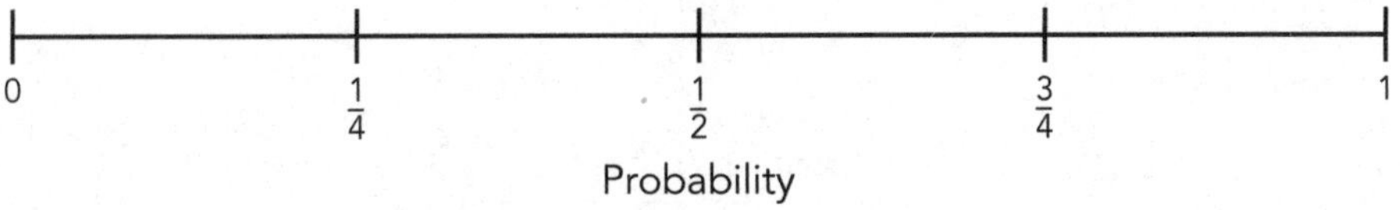

10. What can you conclude about the experimental probability of an event and its theoretical probability as the number of trials of the simulation increases?

Using simulations to generate experimental probabilities is very useful in estimating the probability of an event for which the theoretical probability is difficult, or impossible, to calculate. As you have investigated, the experimental probability of an event approaches the theoretical probability when the number of trials increases.

ACTIVITY 4.2 Guessing on Tests

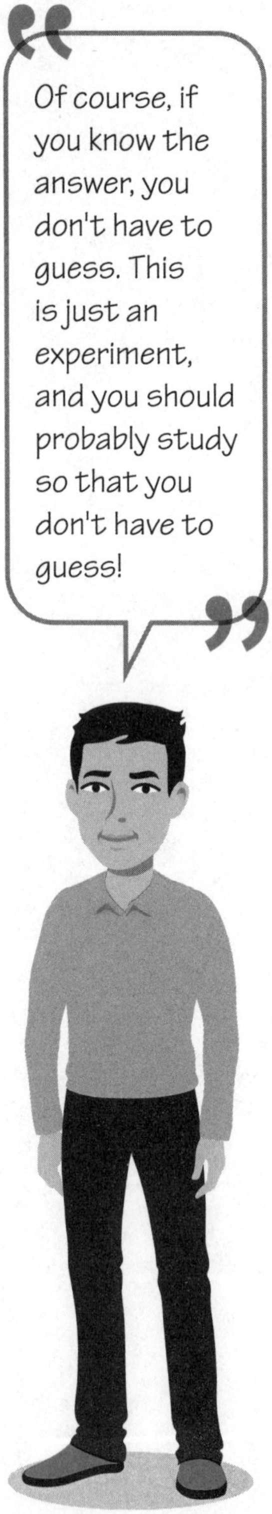

Of course, if you know the answer, you don't have to guess. This is just an experiment, and you should probably study so that you don't have to guess!

Mr. Garcia, your history teacher, is giving a five-question multiple-choice test. Each question has 4 possible answers. How many questions can you expect to get correct simply by guessing?

1. **Estimate the number of questions you expect to get correct by guessing.**

One model that you could use to simulate this problem situation is a spinner divided into 4 sections that are the same size.

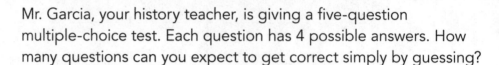

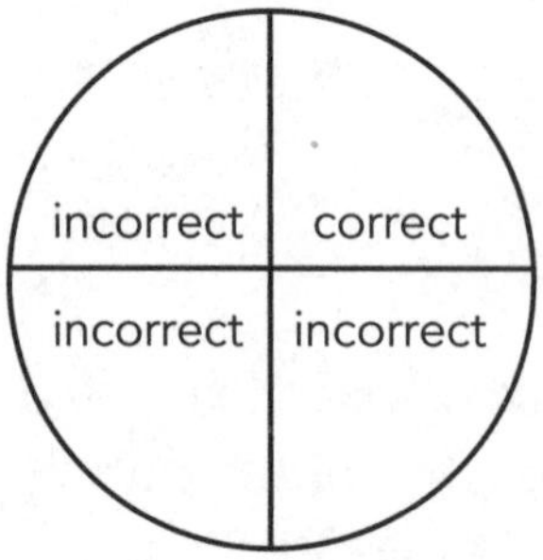

2. **According to the spinner shown, what is the probability of correctly guessing the answer to one question?**

3. **Describe one trial of the experiment if you want to simulate guessing on every question of the test.**

4. **Will one trial provide a good estimate of how many questions you should expect to get correct? Explain your reasoning.**

5. Conduct 50 trials of the simulation. Record your results.

Trial Number	Number Correct
1	
2	
3	
4	
5	
6	
7	
8	
9	
10	
11	
12	
13	
14	
15	
16	
17	

Trial Number	Number Correct
18	
19	
20	
21	
22	
23	
24	
25	
26	
27	
28	
29	
30	
31	
32	
33	
34	

Trial Number	Number Correct
35	
36	
37	
38	
39	
40	
41	
42	
43	
44	
45	
46	
47	
48	
49	
50	

NOTES

6. Graph your results on the dot plot.

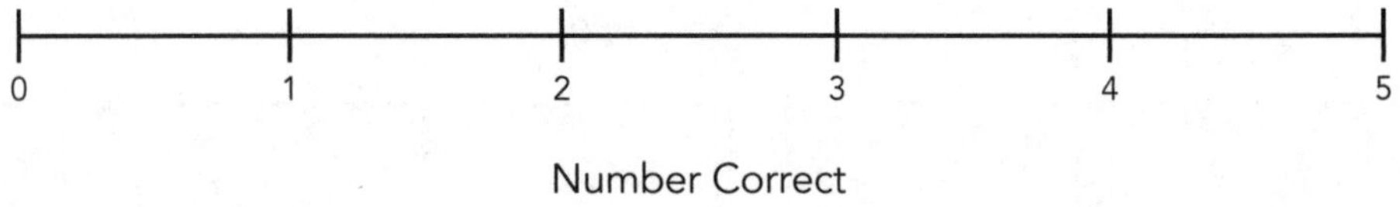

7. According to your simulation, about how many questions would you expect to get correct on the test by only guessing?

8. Do you think that guessing on a five question multiple-choice test will result in a good grade on the test?

ACTIVITY 4.3

Simulation Using Random Numbers

What if each multiple choice question had 5 answer choices instead of 4? How does this change the probability of guessing correct answers?

Instead of creating a new spinner for this simulation, you can design and carry out a simulation for the five-question test guessing experiment using a *random number table*. A **random number table** is a table that displays random digits.

Choose any line in the random number table and let the numbers 00–19 represent a correct guess and 20–99 represent incorrect guesses, since each answer choice in a question has a 20% probability of being selected.

The digits of a random number table are often displayed with a space after every five digits so that the digits are easier to read. Some random number tables also place a space after every five lines for the same reason.

WORKED EXAMPLE

This line of a random number table shows 1 trial of the simulation. The numbers 12, 64, 56, 20, and 00 are chosen. This corresponds to correct, incorrect, incorrect, incorrect, correct.

Line 4	12645	62000	61555	76404	86210	11808	12841	45147	97438	60022

In this trial, the correct answer was guessed 2 times.

Use the random number table at the end of the lesson to select random two-digit numbers as a simulation.

1. **Conduct 1 trial of the experiment. List and interpret the results of your first trial.**

You do not have to start your first trial at the beginning of a line of the random number table. You can randomly start at any number on the line.

2. **Conduct a total of 25 trials. Record your results.**

Trial Number	Number Correct
1	
2	
3	
4	
5	
6	
7	
8	
9	
10	
11	
12	
13	

Trial Number	Number Correct
14	
15	
16	
17	
18	
19	
20	
21	
22	
23	
24	
25	

3. Represent the results from your table on the dot plot shown.

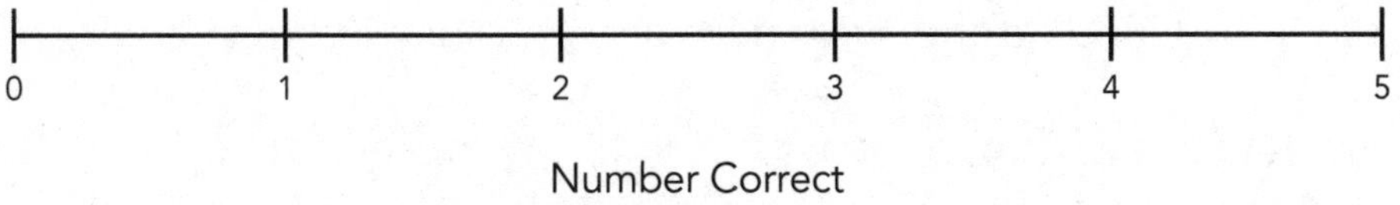

4. What is the experimental probability of guessing:

a. 0 questions correctly?

b. 1 question correctly?

c. 2 questions correctly?

d. 3 questions correctly?

e. 4 questions correctly?

f. all 5 questions correctly?

5. How do the results from this experiment with 5 answer choices for each question compare to the results from the experiment with 4 answer choices for each question?

NOTES

TALK the TALK

Mind Readers

Describe a simulation to model each situation, and then describe one trial. Conduct the simulation and answer the question.

1. **How many questions would you get correct on a 10-question true/false test simply by guessing?**

   Simulation:

   Trial:

   Conduct the simulation one time:

2. **A board game requires you to roll a 6 on a number cube before you can begin playing. How many times would you expect to roll the cube before you can begin the game?**

   Simulation:

   Trial:

   Conduct the simulation 10 times and calculate the mean of your answers:

NOTES

3. Stefan claims he can read your mind. He gives you four cards: a red 1, a blue 2, a blue 3, and a red 4. You draw one of the cards and look at it without showing Stefan.

   a. If you ask Stefan to guess the color, what percent of the time could he guess correctly?

      Simulation:

      Trial:

      Conduct the simulation 10 times and count the number of times your card is selected:

NOTES

b. If you ask Stefan to guess the number, what percent of the time should he guess correctly?

Simulation:

Trial:

Conduct the simulation 10 times and count the number of times your card is selected:

Random Number Table										
Line 1	65285	97198	12138	53010	94601	15838	16805	61404	43516	17020
Line 2	17264	57327	38224	29301	18164	38109	34976	65692	98566	29550
Line 3	95639	99754	31199	92558	68368	04985	51092	37780	40261	14479
Line 4	61555	76404	86214	11808	12840	55147	97438	60222	12645	62090
Line 5	78137	98768	04689	87130	79225	08153	84967	64539	79493	74917

Line 6	62490	99215	84987	28759	19107	14733	24550	28067	68894	38490
Line 7	24216	63444	21283	07044	92729	37284	13211	37485	11415	36457
Line 8	18975	95428	33226	55901	31605	43816	22259	00317	46999	98571
Line 9	59138	39542	71168	57609	91510	27904	74244	50940	31553	62562
Line 10	29478	59652	50414	31966	87912	87154	12944	49862	96566	48825

Line 11	96155	95009	27429	72918	08457	78134	48407	26061	58754	05326
Line 12	29621	66583	62966	12468	20245	14015	04014	35713	03980	03024
Line 13	12639	75291	71020	17265	41598	64074	64629	63293	53307	48766
Line 14	14544	37134	54714	02401	63228	26831	19386	15457	17999	18306
Line 15	83403	88827	09834	11333	68431	31706	26652	04711	34593	22561

Line 16	67642	05204	30697	44806	96989	68403	85621	45556	35434	09532
Line 17	64041	99011	14610	40273	09482	62864	01573	82274	81446	32477
Line 18	17048	94523	97444	59904	16936	39384	97551	09620	63932	03091
Line 19	93039	89416	52795	10631	09728	68202	20963	02477	55494	39563
Line 20	82244	34392	96607	17220	51984	10753	76272	50985	97593	34320

Assignment

Write

1. Each time you repeat an experiment, it is called a(n) ____.
2. A(n) ________________ is an experiment that models a real-life situation.

Remember

As the number of trials increases, the experimental probability gets closer and closer to the theoretical probability.

Practice

Conduct each experiment as described and record your results in the table. Use your results to determine the experimental probability.

1. At the first intersection of a corn maze, a person can go left, right, or straight. Use the spinner to model the person choosing the direction they will go. Use a paper clip as the arrow part of the spinner. Place a pencil point through the paper clip and then on the center of the circle. Perform 30 trials of the experiment. Record the results in a table using tally marks.

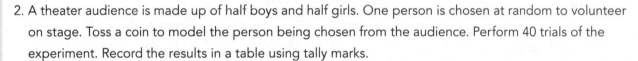

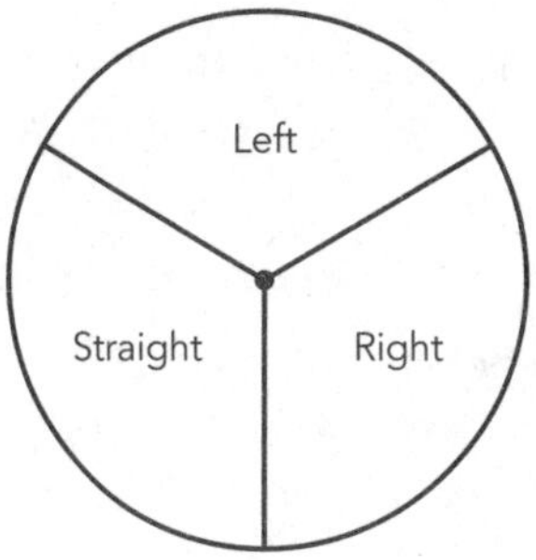

   What is your experimental probability that the person turns right?

2. A theater audience is made up of half boys and half girls. One person is chosen at random to volunteer on stage. Toss a coin to model the person being chosen from the audience. Perform 40 trials of the experiment. Record the results in a table using tally marks.

   What is your experimental probability that the volunteer is a girl?

3. Two thirds of the fish in a lake are trout. A fisherman catches 1 fish. Roll a number cube to model the fisherman catching the fish. Perform 25 trials of the experiment. Record the results in a table using tally marks.

   What is your experimental probability that the fisherman catches a fish that is not a trout?

4. A drawer contains 10 white socks and 10 brown socks. The socks are mixed up. Joy chooses 1 sock without looking. Use a number cube to model Joy choosing the sock. Perform 30 trials of the experiment. Record the results in a table using tally marks.

   What is your experimental probability that Joy chooses a brown sock?

5. A multiple-choice quiz has 4 questions. Each question has 3 possible answers. You guess the answer to each question. Use 3 slips of paper, one labeled *correct*, one labeled *incorrect*, and another labeled *incorrect*, to model guessing the answer to one question. Perform 10 trials of the experiment, where each trial consists of pulling a slip of paper from a bag without looking 4 times. Be sure to return the paper you chose back into the bag before choosing again. Record the results in a table.

   What is your experimental probability that you get at least 2 questions correct?

6. A basketball player makes a foul shot 75% of the time. He is given the chance to make 2 foul shots. Use the spinner to model the player attempting a foul shot. Perform 20 trials of the experiment, where each trial consists of spinning the spinner 2 times. Record the results in a table.

   What is your experimental probability that the player makes both foul shots?

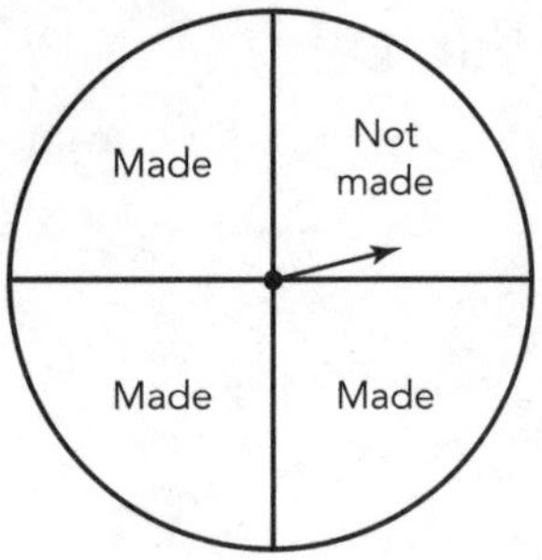

Stretch

You will learn about compound probability in the next topic. However, you can always use experimental probability to help you make a better guess about a theoretical probability that you don't know about.

Determine the experimental probability of rolling two ones in a row on a number cube. Use your results to reason about determining the theoretical probability for this compound event.

Review

1. Determine if each probability can be determined experimentally, theoretically, or both. Explain your reasoning.
   a. Humans will land on Mars in the next 10 years.
   b. A number cube is rolled two times and the product of the two numbers is recorded.
   c. A box contains red, white, and blue marbles and you are not allowed to look inside the box. You reach in and grab a blue marble.
   d. A coin is tossed ten times and the results are recorded.
   e. The next car to pass you will be silver in color.
2. Write an equation to represent each situation. Define your variables and solve the equation.
   a. Jade has to earn $230 for her dance team fundraiser selling candy bars. If she has already earned $165, how many more candy bars does she have to sell at $1.50 each to meet her goal?
   b. Zola is making a 60-minute playlist of her favorite songs. If each song is approximately 4 minutes and 30 seconds long, how many songs will be in the playlist?
3. Determine each sum. Show your work.
   a. $-44.3 + 94.2$
   b. $6\frac{4}{5} + \left(-10\frac{2}{3}\right)$

Introduction to Probability Summary

KEY TERMS

- outcome
- experiment
- sample space
- event
- simple event
- probability
- complementary events
- equally likely
- probability model
- uniform probability model
- non-uniform probability model
- theoretical probability
- experimental probability
- percent error
- simulation
- random number table

LESSON 1 Rolling, Rolling, Rolling . . .

A six-sided number cube that has one number, from 1 through 6, on each face is rolled.

The numbers on the faces of the cube are the outcomes that can occur. An **outcome** is the result of a single trial of a probability experiment. An **experiment** is a situation involving chance that leads to results, or outcomes. The experiment is rolling the number cube. A list of all possible outcomes of an experiment is called a **sample space**. For example, the sample space for rolling the six-sided number cube is {1, 2, 3, 4, 5, 6}. An **event** is one possible outcome or a group of possible outcomes for a given situation. It is a subset of the sample space. A **simple event** is an event consisting of one outcome. In the number cube experiment, an event could be rolling an even number, while rolling a 5 is a simple event.

Probability is a measure of the likelihood that an event will occur. The probability of an event is often written as *P*(event). In the number cube experiment, the probability of rolling a 5 could be written as *P*(5), and the probability of rolling an even number could be written as *P*(even).

The probability of an event occurring is a number between 0 and 1. If the event is certain to happen, then the probability is 1. If an event is impossible, then the probability is 0. If an event is just as likely to happen as not happen, then the probability is 0.5, or $\frac{1}{2}$.

The number line shown represents the probabilities, from 0 to 1, of any event occurring.

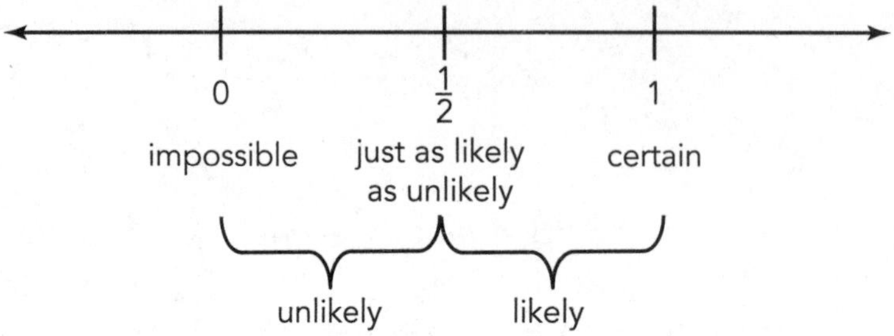

Probability is the ratio of the number of times an event can occur to the number of possible outcomes.

$$\text{Probability} = \frac{\text{number of times an event can occur}}{\text{number of possible outcomes}}$$

To determine the probability of rolling an odd number on a six-sided number cube, or *P*(odd), follow these steps:

- First, list all the possible outcomes. The possible odd numbers that can be rolled are 1, 3, and 5.
- Next, add the number of outcomes. There are 3 possible outcomes of rolling an odd number.
- Then, use the equation to determine the probability of rolling an odd number.

$$P(\text{odd}) = \frac{\text{3 possible odd numbers}}{\text{6 possible numbers}}$$

The probability of rolling an odd number is $\frac{3}{6}$ or $\frac{1}{2}$.

Complementary events are events that together contain all of the outcomes in the sample space. If *P*(even) represents the probability of rolling an even number, then *P*(not even) is the complementary event.

LESSON 2 Give the Models a Chance

When solving a probability problem, it is helpful to construct a probability model. A **probability model** is a list of each possible outcome along with its probability. Probability models are often shown in a table.

For example, the probability model for rolling a six-sided number cube is shown.

Outcome	1	2	3	4	5	6
Probability	$\frac{1}{6}$	$\frac{1}{6}$	$\frac{1}{6}$	$\frac{1}{6}$	$\frac{1}{6}$	$\frac{1}{6}$

A probability model lists all the outcomes. The probability of each outcome will be greater than 0, but less than 1. The sum of all the probabilities for the outcomes will always be 1.

A **uniform probability model** occurs when all the probabilities in a probability model are equally likely to occur. When all the probabilities in a probability model are not equal to each other, it is called a **non-uniform probability model**.

LESSON 3 Toss the Cup

The **theoretical probability** of an event is the ratio of the number of desired outcomes to the total possible outcomes. **Experimental probability** is the ratio of the number of times an event occurs to the total number of trials performed.

$$\text{Experimental Probability} = \frac{\text{number of times event occurs}}{\text{total number of trials performed}}$$

If you know the probability of an event, then you can use proportional reasoning to predict the number of times the event will occur throughout an experiment.

For example, the probability that a spinner will land on blue is $\frac{2}{3}$. If you spin the spinner 60 times, you can set up and solve a proportion to predict the number of times the spinner will land on the blue section.

$$\frac{2}{3} = \frac{x}{60}$$
$$2(60) = 3x$$
$$\frac{120}{3} = \frac{3x}{3}$$
$$40 = x$$

If you spin the spinner 60 times, you can expect it to land on blue 40 times.

To compare theoretical and experimental probabilities, you can use a measure called percent error. In probability, the **percent error** describes how far off the experimental probability is from the theoretical probability as a percent ratio.

For example, suppose you spin blue 30 times out of 40 trials. The experimental probability, P_E(blue), is $\frac{30}{40}$ or $\frac{3}{4}$. The theoretical probability, P_T(blue), is $\frac{2}{3}$.

The percent error can be calculated using this formula:

$$\frac{P_E - P_T}{P_T} \cdot 100 = \frac{\frac{3}{4} - \frac{2}{3}}{\frac{2}{3}}$$

$$= \frac{\frac{9}{12} - \frac{8}{12}}{\frac{8}{12}} \cdot 100$$

$$= \frac{\frac{1}{12}}{\frac{8}{12}} \cdot 100 = 12.5\%$$

LESSON 4

A Simulating Conversation

A **simulation** is an experiment that models a real-life situation. When conducting a simulation, you must choose a model that has the same probability of the event. Using simulations to generate experimental probabilities is very useful in estimating the probability of an event for which the theoretical probability is difficult, or impossible, to calculate.

You can design and carry out a simulation for an experiment using a random number table. A **random number table** is a table that displays random digits. You assign a range of numbers to each outcome that models the same probability of an event and then choose any line from the table to perform a trial.

For example, in a five-question multiple-choice test each question has five possible answer choices. How many questions can you expect to get correct simply by guessing?

Each answer choice has a 20% chance of being selected, but only $\frac{1}{5}$ of the guesses are correct, while the others are incorrect. Let the numbers 00–19 represent a correct guess and 20–99 represent incorrect guesses.

This line of a random number table shows one trial of the simulation.

Line 4	12645	62000	61555	76404	86210	11808	12841	45147	97438	60022

The numbers 12, 64, 56, 20, and 00 are chosen. This corresponds to correct, incorrect, incorrect, incorrect, correct. In this trial, the correct answer was guessed 2 times out of 5.

You need to run multiple trials of this simulation to predict the number of questions you can expect to get correct simply by guessing.

TOPIC 2

Compound Probability

The genetics of feline coat color are complicated. The gene for the base color – black vs. orange – is on the X chromosome, so male cats with both colors are rare. There are two separate genes for white patches, and a gene for whether a cat is solid white. All cats have the tabby gene, though sometimes it's masked.

Module 4: Analyzing Populations and Probabilities

TOPIC 2: COMPOUND PROBABILITY

In this topic, students build on their understanding of the probability concepts from the previous topic. They use arrays and lists to organize the possible outcomes of an experiment that includes two simple events. Students list outcomes that are contained in an event, distinguishing between "and" and "or" situations. Students then design and conduct simulations for compound probability problems. They are provided opportunities to reinforce their new knowledge of compound probabilities.

Where have we been?

In previous lessons, students explored simple events. At the start of this topic, students use two simple events—tossing two coins—and create an array of outcomes. Throughout this topic, probability concepts that students learned in the prior topic (e.g., experimental versus theoretical probability, predictions, and simulation) are reinforced and deepened.

Where are we going?

This topic is the culmination of students' learning about probability until they reach high school. In high school, students will engage with probability from a more formal and formula-driven perspective. This topic provides students with the opportunity to build intuition about compound events before formalizing language around independent and dependent events and learning formulas and rules for mutually exclusive events and conditional probability.

Using an Array to Organize Outcomes

This array shows all the possible sums of rolls when rolling two number cubes. There are 6 × 6, or 36, possible outcomes.

	Number Cube 1	1	2	3	4	5	6
Number Cube 2	1	2	3	4	5	6	7
	2	3	4	5	6	7	8
	3	4	5	6	7	8	9
	4	5	6	7	8	9	10
	5	6	7	8	9	10	11
	6	7	8	9	10	11	12

Myth: "I'm not smart."

The word "smart" is tricky because it means different things to different people. For example, would you say a baby is "smart"? On the one hand, a baby is helpless and doesn't know anything. But on the other hand, a baby is exceptionally smart because they are constantly learning new things every day.

This example is meant to demonstrate that "smart" can have two meanings. It can mean "the knowledge that you have," or it can mean "the capacity to learn from experience." When someone says they are "not smart," are they saying they do not have lots of knowledge, or are they saying they lack the capacity to learn? If it's the first definition, then none of us are smart until we acquire that information. If it's the second definition, then we know that is completely untrue, because everyone has the capacity to grow as a result of new experiences.

So, if your student doesn't think that they are smart, encourage them to be patient. They have the capacity to learn new facts and skills. It might not be easy, and it will take some time and effort. But the brain is automatically wired to learn. Smart should not refer only to how much knowledge you currently have.

#mathmythbusted

Talking Points

You can further support your student's learning by asking questions about the work they do in class or at home. Your student is learning about probability, compound probability, and drawing inferences from random samples.

Questions to Ask

- How does this problem look like something you did in class?
- Can you show me the strategy you used to solve this problem? Do you know another way to solve it?
- Does your answer make sense? How do you know?

Key Terms

tree diagram

A tree diagram is a tree-shaped diagram that illustrates the possible outcomes of a given situation.

compound event

A compound event combines two or more events, using the word *and* or the word *or*.

Evens or Odds?

1

Using Arrays to Organize Outcomes

WARM UP

Solve each proportion for the unknown value.

1. $\frac{x}{150} = \frac{1}{12}$
2. $\frac{12}{x} = \frac{1}{36}$
3. $\frac{1}{8} = \frac{x}{100}$
4. $\frac{x}{16} = \frac{1}{4}$

LEARNING GOALS

- Conduct trials of an experiment.
- Predict the theoretical probability of an event using the results from the trials of an experiment.
- Represent and organize sample spaces for compound events using arrays, lists, and tables.
- Identify the outcomes in the sample space which compose a compound event.
- Calculate the experimental and theoretical probabilities of an experiment.
- Calculate probabilities of multiple outcomes using theoretical probabilities.
- Use proportional reasoning to predict the probability of random events.

You have calculated experimental and theoretical probabilities of simple events. How do you determine the sample space and theoretical probabilities of more complex events?

Getting Started

Tossing Coins

Suppose you and a partner each flip a coin at the same time. What are the different outcomes that could occur?

1. **Use an array to list the possible outcomes of tossing two coins into the air at the same time.**

		Student 1	
		Heads	**Tails**
Student 2	**Heads**		
	Tails		

2. **Use your array to write the sample space for tossing two coins at the same time.**

3. **Conduct this experiment for 30 trials and record the results.**

   a. **Calculate the experimental probability of each outcome in the table.**

Outcome Student 1	Outcome Student 2	Tally	Total	Probability	Class Probability
Heads	Heads				
Heads	Tails				
Tails	Heads				
Tails	Tails				

b. Combine the results of your experiment with those of your classmates. Then calculate the experimental probability of each outcome and record the class probabilities in the table.

4. Which probability is more accurate: the probabilities from the experiment with your partner or the class probabilities? Explain your reasoning.

5. Use your table to predict the actual probabilities of each outcome. Create a probability model table to display your predictions.

ACTIVITY 1.1

Experimental Probability of Sums

How can you organize your list to make sure you account for all the possibilities?

Joel and Hiram are playing a game using 2 six-sided number cubes. The number cubes are rolled, and the sum of the 2 numbers shown is calculated. If the sum is even, Joel wins a point. If the sum is odd, Hiram wins a point.

1. **Make a list of all possible outcomes when rolling 2 six-sided number cubes.**

2. **Use your list to create the sample space for the possible sums in the game.**

3. **Do you think each of the outcomes in the sample space is equally likely? Explain your reasoning.**

4. **Predict who has a better chance of winning this game. Explain your reasoning.**

5. Play the game 25 times with a partner.

   a. List each possible outcome in the first column. Tally your results in the second column.

   b. Calculate the experimental probability for each outcome. Express your probability as a fraction and as a percent. Record your probabilities in the third column of the table.

Outcome	Tally	Probability

6. According to your experiment, who would win the game between Joel and Hiram? Explain your reasoning.

7. Does the outcome of the game match your prediction of the winner? Explain your reasoning.

8. Suppose you wanted to calculate the theoretical probability of each sum. Explain how you might proceed.

Make a plan, but do not carry it out. You will calculate the theoretical probabilities of this experiment in the next activity.

ACTIVITY 1.2 Theoretical Probability of Sums

Recall the game Joel and Hiram are playing with 2 six-sided number cubes. Now, you will calculate the theoretical probability of each sum.

As you experienced, making a list can sometimes take a lot of time.

By playing the game in the experiment, you can see that this game has a non-uniform probability model. However, calculating the theoretical probabilities of each outcome is difficult without knowing them all. One method to determine the probabilities of the outcomes is to make a list of all the possible outcomes.

1. How many different possibilities are there when rolling 2 six-sided number cubes?

When there are a large number of possible outcomes, an array like the one you used before is useful in organizing the outcomes. The entries in the array should be related to the experiment.

2. The array shown has two numbers filled in: 2 and 7.

		Number Cube 1					
		1	**2**	**3**	**4**	**5**	**6**
Number Cube 2	1	2					
	2						
	3						
	4			7			
	5						
	6						

a. What does the 2 represent in the array?

b. What does the 7 represent in the array?

3. Complete the array.

4. How many different possibilities are in the number array?

5. Does it appear that the list of all the possibilities when rolling 2 number cubes has the same number of possibilities as the number array?

6. Using the array, determine the number of times each sum appears and the theoretical probability, in fraction form, of each sum. Record your answers in the table.

7. Is there an equally likely chance for each outcome to occur from rolling 2 number cubes according to the theoretical probabilities?

8. According to the theoretical probabilities, who should win the game? Explain your reasoning.

Outcome	Number of Times	Probability

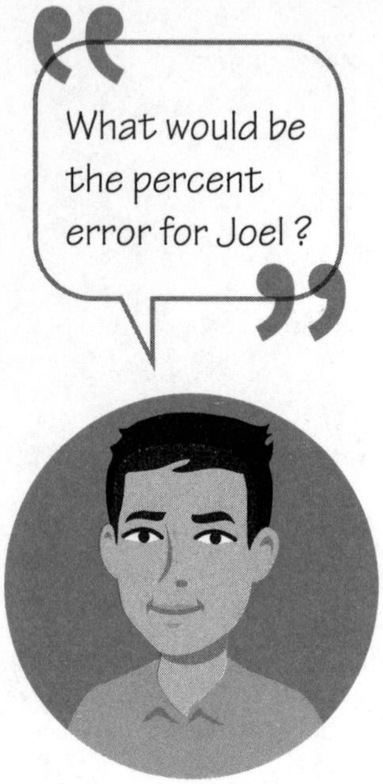

What would be the percent error for Joel?

9. Did the experimental probability of your experiment in the previous activity match the theoretical probability of the game? If not, why do you think the results of the experimental and theoretical probabilities were different?

10. Calculate the percent error between the experimental and theoretical probabilities of Hiram winning the game.

Remember, when you know an event's probability of occurring, use proportional reasoning to predict how often the event may occur for any number of trials.

11. Calculate each probability when rolling 2 number cubes and summing the resulting numbers. Explain your calculations.

a. P(prime number)

b. P(greater than 7)

c. P(1)

12. If the number cubes are tossed 180 times, how many times do you predict the following sums would occur?

a. 1

b. 4

c. 9

d. 10

e. 12

f. prime number

13. Kelsey claims that the probability of getting a sum of 4 when rolling two number cubes should be 1 out of 11 since there are 11 possible outcomes. Is Kelsey correct? If not, how could you convince Kelsey that her thinking is incorrect?

ACTIVITY
1.3 Probabilities of Products

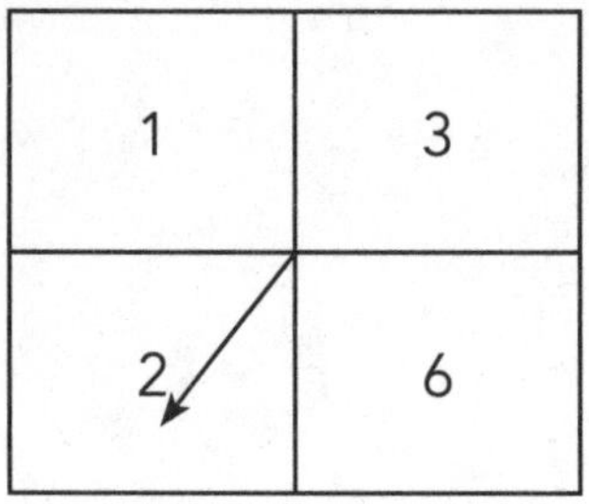

The square spinner shown is spun twice, and the results of the two spins are multiplied together to produce a product that is recorded.

1. Determine all the possibilities for obtaining the products using a list.

2. Complete the array to determine the possible products.

		Spin 1			
Spin 2					

3. List the sample space.

4. Are all outcomes equally likely? Explain your calculations.

5. Calculate the probability of each product. Record your answers in the table.

Outcome	Probability

6. Did you calculate the experimental or theoretical probability? Explain how you know.

7. Calculate each probability shown for the experiment with the square spinner.
   a. *P*(even product)
   b. *P*(odd product)
   c. *P*(spin results in a multiple of 3)
   d. *P*(perfect square)
   e. *P*(less than 50)

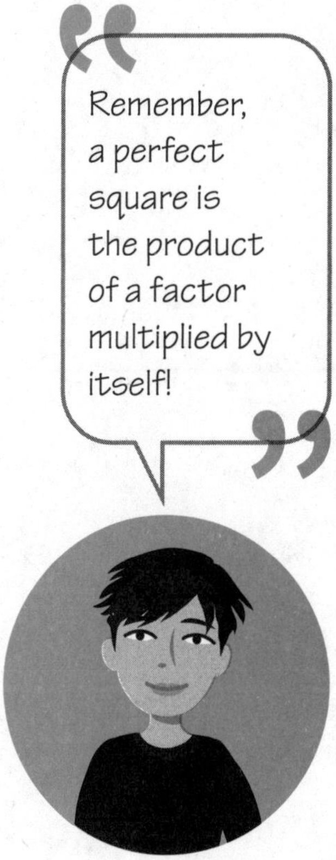

Remember, a perfect square is the product of a factor multiplied by itself!

NOTES

8. If this experiment is conducted 200 times, how many times do you predict you would get each product?

   a. 2

   b. 3

   c. 6

   d. 36

   e. an even product

   f. an odd product

NOTES

TALK the TALK

Tossing More Coins

Think back to the experiment you conducted in the *Tossing Coins* activity. You listed the sample space and made an array of possibilities for tossing two coins.

Suppose you are now interested in the number of heads when you toss two coins.

1. Create an array to display the sample space.

		First Coin	
		Heads	**Tails**
Second Coin	**Heads**		
	Tails		

2. List the sample space for the number of heads when you toss two coins.

3. Using the array, determine the theoretical probability of each outcome. Record your answers in the table.

Outcome	Probability

NOTES

4. Determine the probability of tossing at least 1 head.

5. If you were to conduct 100 trials of the experiment, how many times would you expect to toss 2 heads?

Assignment

Write

Describe the advantages of using an array to determine the sample space for an experiment.

Remember

To organize the outcomes in a number array, list the outcomes for one trial along one side and the outcomes for the other trial along the other side of an array. Combine the results in the intersections of each row and column.

Practice

1. Brett received a dart board for his birthday. The rule book says that two darts are to be thrown and that an individual's score is the sum of the two numbers.

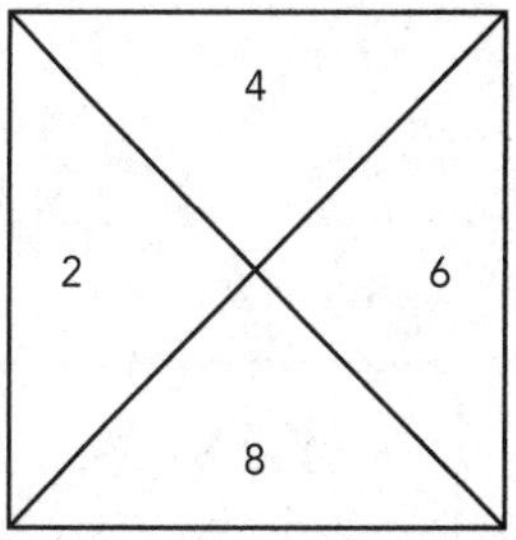

   a. Complete an array to determine all the possibilities for obtaining the sums.
   b. List the sample space for the sum of the numbers.
   c. Are all outcomes equally likely? Explain your reasoning.
   d. How many possibilities are in the array?
   e. Use the array to help create a probability model listing the theoretical probabilities for each sum.
   f. Calculate each probability of an even sum, a sum greater than 8, and an odd sum.
   g. If two darts are thrown 80 times, how many times do you predict each of the following sums would occur? 8? 10? 14?

2. Kyle writes the numbers 1, 2, and 3 on papers and puts them in a bag. He chooses one paper, writes the number down, returns it to the bag, and chooses another number. He calculates the difference between the two numbers.
   a. Complete an array to determine all the possibilities for obtaining the differences.
   b. List the sample space for the difference of the numbers.
   c. Are all outcomes equally likely? Explain your reasoning.
   d. How many possibilities are in the array?
   e. Use the array to help create a probability model listing the theoretical probabilities for each difference.
   f. If Kyle repeats this experiment 100 times, how many times do you predict he would get a difference of 2?

Stretch

There is a famous probability problem known as the Monty Hall problem—named after the original host of the game show *Let's Make a Deal*. In this problem, there are three doors. Behind one of the doors is a prize. Behind the other two doors are donkeys. You choose one door. The game show host opens one of the doors that you did not choose to reveal a donkey. Then, the host asks you if you would like to stay on the door you chose or switch to the other unopened door. Should you stay or switch? Or does it matter?

Review

1. Since 1903, the National League has played the American League in the World Series. The World Series is usually won by the team winning the best out of 7 games. The table shows the number of games that were played to win each series during the first 100 World Series.

Number of Games	Number of Series Won in Given Number of Games
4 games	17 series
5 games	24 series
6 games	21 series
7 games	33 series
8 games	5 series

   a. What is the probability that the next World Series will take 7 games to determine a winner?
   b. What is the probability that the next World Series will take 4 games?
   c. Is this theoretical or experimental probability? Use a complete sentence to explain.

2. Javon's music collection is 40% hip-hop and 60% rock. If his music player randomly selects songs to play, what is the probability of it selecting 3 hip-hop songs in a row? Describe a simulation that could be used to estimate this probability.

3. Rewrite each expression with the fewest number of terms.
   a. $\frac{3}{5}a + 7\frac{2}{3} - 11 - \frac{9}{10}a$
   b. $9 - 0.4(1.1s - 9)$

Three Girls and No Boys?

2

Using Tree Diagrams

WARM UP

Nora's treat bag has 5 chocolate bars, 7 peanut butter cups, and 8 sour gummies. If she selects 1 piece of candy at random, determine each probability.

1. *P*(chocolate bar)

2. *P*(peanut butter cups)

3. *P*(sour gummy)

4. *P*(not sour gummy)

LEARNING GOALS

- Develop a probability model and use it to determine probabilities.
- Construct a tree diagram to determine the theoretical probability of an event.
- Construct and interpret a non-uniform probability model.

KEY TERM

- tree diagram

Organized lists and arrays are two strategies for analyzing experiments that have a number of different outcomes. How can you use tree diagrams to display outcomes and display their probability of occuring?

Getting Started

Three Children, Three Girls

What is the probability that if a family has 3 children, those 3 children are girls? Let's say that the theoretical probability of a girl being born is equal to the theoretical probability of a boy being born, $\frac{1}{2}$.

Let's simulate the event of a family with 3 children having 3 girls.

1. **Choose an appropriate model to simulate the probability of a family having three girls. Explain how you will represent girls and boys in your model.**

2. **Conduct 25 trials of the simulation. Record the results in the table shown.**

Trial	Results
1	
2	
3	
4	
5	
6	
7	
8	
9	

Trial	Results
10	
11	
12	
13	
14	
15	
16	
17	
18	

Trial	Results
19	
20	
21	
22	
23	
24	
25	

3. **List all possible outcomes for the number of girls among 3 children.**

4. **Use the results from your simulation to construct a probability model.**

Outcome	0 girls	1 girl	2 girls	3 girls
Probability				

5. **What is the experimental probability that a family with 3 children has 3 girls according to your probability model?**

ACTIVITY
2.1

Introduction to Tree Diagrams

In the previous simulation, your probability model is based on experimental probabilities. In some cases, this is the only method of constructing a probability model. For example, in an earlier lesson you determined the experimental probabilities of a cup landing on its top, bottom, or side when it was tossed. It would be difficult or impossible to determine the theoretical probabilities for the cup toss. However, it is possible to determine the theoretical probability for a family with 3 children having 3 girls.

One method to calculate the theoretical probability for a family having 3 girls is to list all of the possible outcomes for a family having 3 children, and then determine how many of those outcomes include 3 girls.

1. Karl says, "I think that the probability of a family having 3 girls is 1 out of 3 because there is only one outcome that has all three children being girls. There are only two other outcomes."

Germaine says, "I don't think that's correct. I think the probability is much lower since there are many combinations of boys and girls in a family of three."

Who's correct? Explain your reasoning.

NOTES

2. List all of the possible outcomes for having 3 children, using G to represent girls and B to represent boys.

3. What does the outcome BGG represent?

4. Complete the probability model using all possible outcomes.

Outcome	0 girls	1 girl	2 girls	3 girls
Probability				

5. What is the theoretical probability that a family having 3 children has 3 girls?

A tree diagram has two main parts: the branches and the ends. An outcome of each event is written at the end of each branch.

Another method of determining the theoretical probability of an event is to construct a *tree diagram*. A **tree diagram** illustrates the possible outcomes of a given situation. Tree diagrams can be constructed vertically or horizontally.

You can construct a tree diagram to show all the possible outcomes for a family having 3 children.

WORKED EXAMPLE

What are the possible outcomes for a family having 3 children?

List the possible outcomes of the 1st child.

List the possible outcomes of the 2nd child.

List the possible outcomes of the 3rd child.

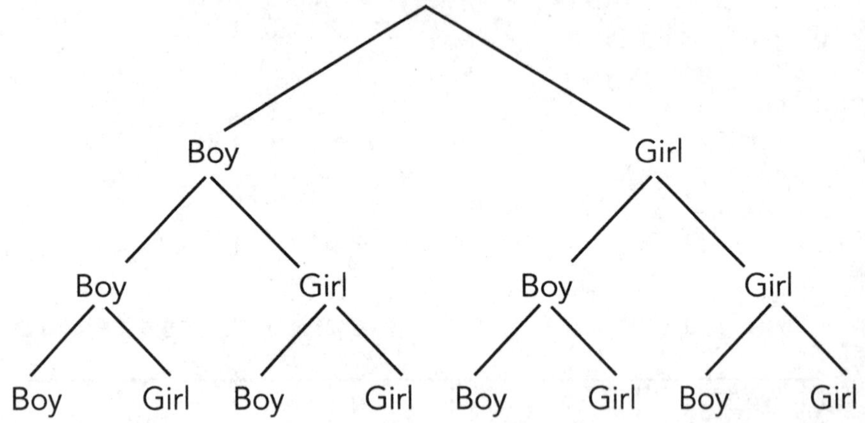

6. **How would this tree diagram change if you were trying to determine the possible outcomes for a family having 4 children?**

7. **How does the tree diagram in the worked example compare to the list you made in Question 2?**

8. **Circle the outcome(s) of a family having three children that are all girls on the tree diagrams shown.**

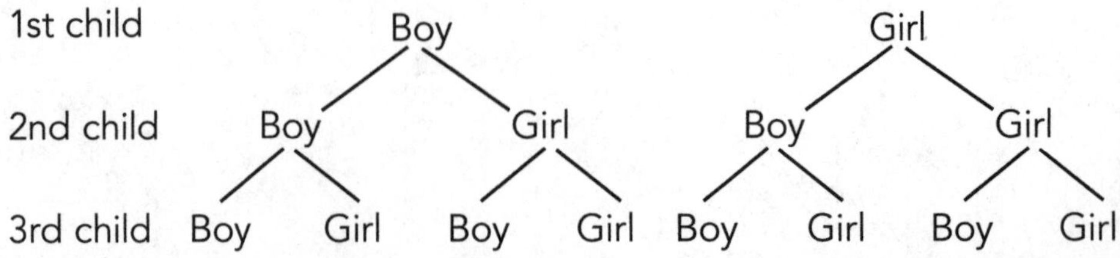

9. **Circle the outcome(s) of a family having three children in which two of the children are girls in the tree diagrams shown.**

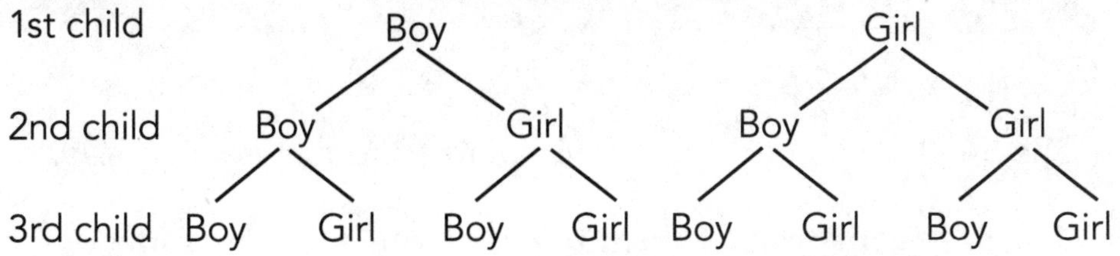

10. **Circle the outcome BBG in the tree diagrams shown.**

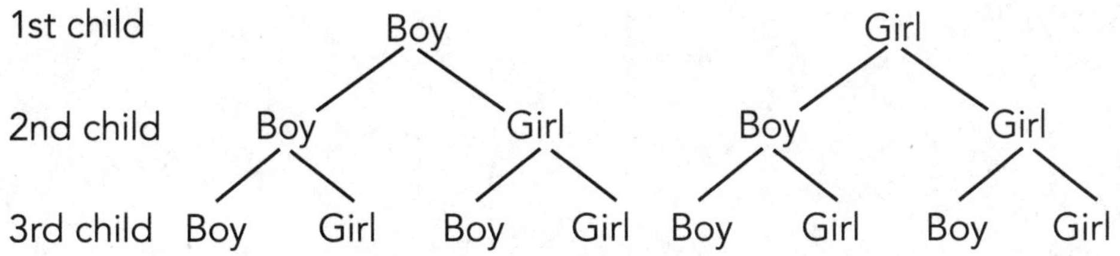

11. **Complete the probability model shown with the information from the tree diagrams.**

Outcome	0 girls	1 girl	2 girls	3 girls
Probability				

12. **Is there a difference in the theoretical probability of each outcome between the list of outcomes you wrote and the tree diagrams you analyzed?**

ACTIVITY

2.2 Using Tree Diagrams to Determine Probabilities

The 5-sided spinner is spun twice and a product is calculated.

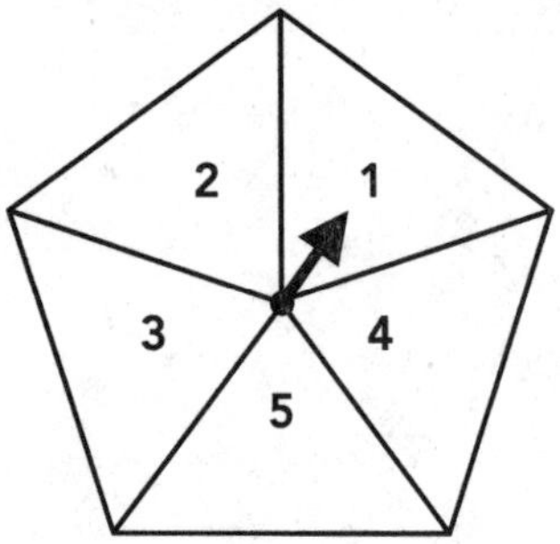

1. Construct a tree diagram to determine all the possible outcomes. Then, list the product at the end of each branch of the tree.

2. Construct a probability model for spinning the spinner twice and recording the product.

Product	Probability
1	
2	
3	
4	
5	
6	
8	
9	
10	
12	
15	
16	
20	
25	

3. Use the probability models you created to calculate the probability for each event shown.

a. *P*(10)

b. *P*(less than 10)

c. *P*(multiple of 5)

d. *P*(not a multiple of 5)

4. Which events from Question 3 represent complementary events? Explain your reasoning.

5. Betina says that the product being less than 10 and the product being more than 10 are complementary events. Davika disagrees. Who is correct? Explain your reasoning.

6. What event would be complementary to the event that the product is an even number? Determine the probability of both events.

7. What is the sum of the probabilities of two complementary events? Explain why your answer makes sense.

NOTES

TALK the TALK

True-False Trees

1. Construct a tree diagram to determine all the possible outcomes for correctly guessing the answers to a 3-question true-false quiz.

2. Construct a probability model for the tree diagram you completed in Question 1.

3. Calculate the probabilities:

   a. *P*(3 questions correct) =

   b. *P*(1 or 2 questions correct) =

   c. *P*(0 questions correct) =

Assignment

Write

How are tree diagrams useful when constructing probability models?

Remember

A **tree diagram** illustrates the possible outcomes of a given situation.

Practice

1. Dinah's family has 4 children. The birth order of the children is G, G, B, G. Create a tree diagram to list all the possible birth orders of a family of 4 children. Then determine the probability of Dinah's family birth order.
2. Kimberly is learning probability in middle school while her little brother, Rodney, is learning arithmetic in first grade. Kimberly uses a six-sided number cube to help Rodney learn how to add one-digit numbers. She rolls two cubes, numbered 1 through 6, and Rodney adds up the two numbers on the faces.
   a. Construct a tree diagram to determine all the possible outcomes. List the sum at the end of each branch of the tree.
   b. Construct a probability model for rolling 2 six-sided number cubes and determining the sum of the faces.
   c. What is the probability that the sum is 7?
   d. What is the probability that the sum is 11?
   e. Calculate the probability that the sum is an even number.
   f. Calculate the probability that the sum is greater than 5.
   g. What event would be complementary to the event that the sum is greater than 5? Explain your reasoning.
3. When Kimberly and Rodney finish their math homework, they go outside to shoot some hoops. On average, Kimberly makes half of all of the shots she takes.
   a. She shoots the basketball 4 times. Construct a tree diagram for all possible outcomes of the 4 shots.
   b. Construct the probability model.
   c. What is the probability she makes all 4 shots?
   d. Calculate the probability she makes 3 or more shots.
   e. Calculate the probability she makes 2 or more shots.

Stretch

Different colored beads are placed in two tin cups. The first cup contains 1 bead of each color: blue, purple, and green. The second cup contains 1 bead of each color: yellow, garnet, blue, and green.

1. What is the probability of choosing the same color from each cup?
2. What is the probability of choosing blue from the first cup or blue from the second cup?

Review

1. The spinner shown has 5 equal sections. Use the spinner to determine each probability.

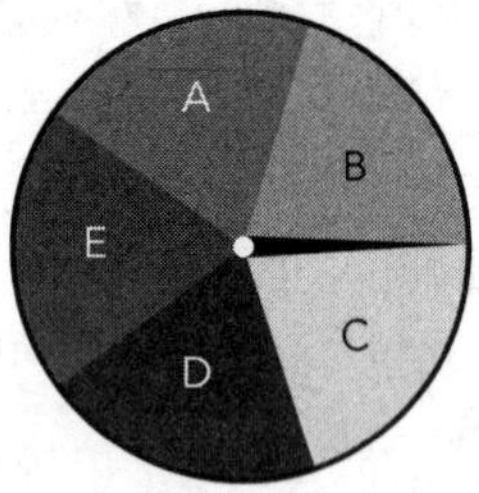

   a. $P(C) =$
   b. $P(\text{vowel}) =$
   c. Suppose you spin twice.
      i. What is the probability of spinning two As?
      ii. What is the probability of spinning an A and a B?
2. In each table, x varies directly with y. Determine the constant of proportionality and express your answer as $y = kx$.

a.

x	3	6	11	15
y	57	114	209	285

b.

x	5	9	13	15
y	13	23.4	33.8	39

3 Pet Shop Probability

Determining Compound Probability

WARM UP

Sam has six crayons. The crayons are blue, red, green, purple, brown, and yellow. He chooses one crayon at random.

1. What is the probability that the crayon Sam chooses will be red or purple?

2. What is the complementary event?

3. What is the probability of the complementary event?

LEARNING GOALS

- Calculate probabilities of compound events using tables.
- Represent the sample space for compound events and calculate probabilities of compound events using tree diagrams.

KEY TERM

- compound event

You know how to calculate the probabilities of simple events. You have used organized lists, arrays, and tree diagrams to calculate the probabilities of more complicated events. How do you define a probability event that combines multiple simple events? How can you calculate the probability of these events?

Getting Started

And Or What?!

What's the difference between the words *and* and *or*? You've been using them your whole life, so you can imagine that you are pretty sure of the difference. However, these words have a very specific meaning in mathematics, and it is important to understand the difference.

For each situation, identify how many of your classmates are in each category.

1. **Cat owners vs. dog owners**
   a. **Cat owners**
   b. **Dog owners**
   c. **Cat or dog owners**
   d. **Cat and dog owners**

2. **Even birth dates vs. odd birth dates**
   a. **Even birthdays**
   b. **Odd birthdays**
   c. **Even or odd birthdays**
   d. **Even and odd birthdays**

3. **Athletes vs. musicians**
   a. **Athletes**
   b. **Musicians**
   c. **Athletes or musicians**
   d. **Athletes and musicians**

What is the difference between *and* and *or*?

The word *or* is used to identify a union—the set of items that are in either set or both.

The word *and* is used to identify an intersection—the set of items that are in both sets.

4. **If you know the answers to parts (a) and (b) from Questions 1–3, can you determine the answers to the other two situations? Explain why or why not.**
   a. **part (c)?**
   b. **part (d)?**

You can calculate the probability of multiple events, say events *A* and *B*. Sometimes, you will want to know the probability of *A* or *B* occurring. Other times, you will want to know the probability of *A* and *B* occurring.

ACTIVITY
3.1

Compound Events

Garden Plain Pet Shelter has the following animals available for adoption. You will complete a probability model and use it to determine the probability that the next pet chosen at random is a dog or a cat.

Pets	Number Available
cat	4
dog	7
snake	1
rabbit	3
bird	5

1. How many pets are available for adoption?

2. Complete the probability model for adopting a pet from Garden Plain Pet Shelter.

Outcome	Cat	Dog	Snake	Rabbit	Bird
Probability					

3. Is the model a uniform or a non-uniform probability model? Explain your reasoning.

4. What is the probability the next pet adopted is:

a. a dog? **b. a snake?** **c. a cat?**

5. Determine the probability that the next pet adopted is a dog or a cat.

a. How many of the pets are dogs or cats?

b. How many total pets are there?

c. What is the probability the next pet adopted is a dog or a cat?

Examples of students' methods to solve Question 5 are shown.

Tenisha

I added the number of cats and dogs and got a total of 11. 4 + 7 = 11

That's 11 pets out of 20.

$\frac{\text{desired}}{\text{total}} = \frac{11}{20}$

Jermaine

Don't want 9 out of 20.

So what's left is 11 out of 20.

DRew

CATS $\frac{4}{20}$

DOGS $+\frac{7}{20}$

$\frac{11}{20}$

Daryl

$\frac{2}{3}$

Cats and dogs

That's 2 animals listed out of 5

Mark

Probability of a cat $\frac{4}{20}$ or $\frac{1}{5}$

Probability of a dog $\frac{7}{20}$

$\frac{1}{5} + \frac{7}{20} = \frac{8}{25}$

6. Analyze each student's responses to the question.

a. Describe the strategy Jermaine used.

NOTES

b. Describe the strategy Drew used.

c. What is the difference between Tenisha's work and Drew's work?

d. Explain to both Daryl and Mark why their methods are incorrect for determining the probability that the next pet adopted will be a cat or dog.

A **compound event** combines two or more events, using the word "and" or the word "or."

Determining the probability of a compound event with the word "and" is different from a compound event with "or."

The difference is that a compound event with the word "and" means that you are determining the probability that both events occur.

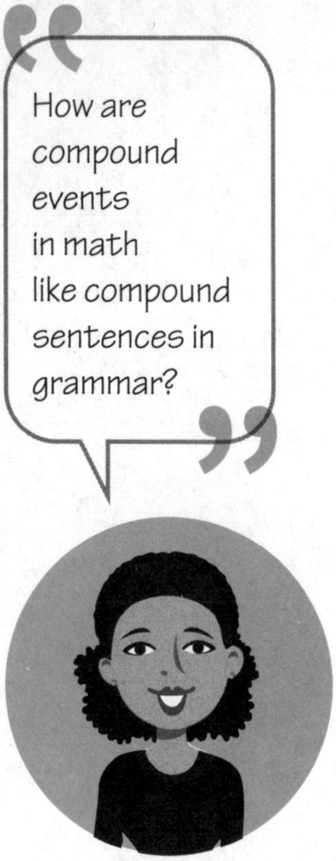

When determining a compound event with "or," you are determining the probability that one, or the other, or both outcomes occur.

7. **What is the probability that the next pet adopted is a 4-legged animal?**

   a. **What events make up "the next pet adopted being a 4-legged animal"?**

   b. **For how many events are you determining the probability? How do you know?**

   c. **Rewrite Question 7 using the events you wrote in part (a).**

   d. **Determine the probability that the next pet adopted is a 4-legged animal. Show how you determined your answer.**

ACTIVITY 3.2

Tree Diagrams and Compound Events

The cards shown were placed face down in two piles so that they could be randomly chosen.

1. **If one card is randomly chosen from each pile, determine the probability of randomly choosing a matching pair.**

   a. **What are the possible outcomes for randomly choosing one card from each pile? Make sure you show your work by either creating an organized list or constructing a tree diagram.**

   b. **How many possible outcomes are there?**

   c. **What events make up randomly choosing a matching pair?**

   d. **Rewrite Question 1 using the events you wrote in part (c).**

   e. **Determine the probability of randomly choosing a pair.**

2. **Determine the probability of randomly choosing two cards that sum to 5. Show your work.**

3. The class is asked to determine the probability of randomly choosing 2 odd cards. Lucy says,"The probability of drawing 2 odd cards is 4 out of 7 because there are 7 cards and 4 of them are odd." Do you agree with Lucy's statement? If not, explain to Lucy why her reasoning is not correct.

4. Write a problem using the number cards for which Lucy's answer would be correct.

5. What outcomes make up the event of "choosing 2 odd cards" given one card is chosen from each pile?

6. Determine the probability of randomly choosing 2 odd cards.

7. Determine the probability of selecting one card from each pile where the first card is a 2 and the second card is odd.

   a. List the event(s) for determining the probability.

   b. List the outcome(s) for the event(s).

   c. Determine the probability of selecting one card from each pile where the first card is a 2 and the second card is odd.

8. Determine the probability that the first card is a 2 or the second card is odd.

   a. List the event(s) for determining the probability.

   b. Determine the outcome(s) for the event(s).

   c. How many outcomes are listed? Are any of the outcomes listed in both events?

   d. How many unique outcomes are there for the two events?

   e. Determine the probability that the first card is a 2 or the second card is odd.

   f. Why would you not count all of the outcomes when calculating the probability?

9. Explain the difference between the events in Questions 7 and 8.

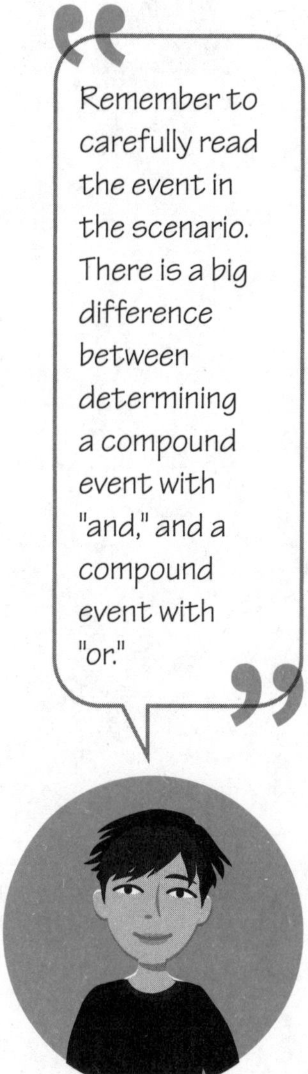

When there are two or more events for which you are determining the probability, an outcome might occur for both events. When this occurs and you are determining the number of outcomes, count the repeated outcome only once.

NOTES

TALK the TALK

Evens and Odds

You and a friend are playing a game in which you take turns rolling a 6-sided number cube, and spinning a spinner with 4 congruent sections numbered 1–4.

You and your friend take turns.

- If your friend rolls an odd number and spins an even number, he or she wins.
- If you roll an even number and spin an odd number, you win.

1. List the possible outcomes for playing the game.

2. Explain why the events of your friend winning or of you winning are compound events.

3. List the outcomes for the event of your friend winning the game and for the event of you winning the game. Then calculate each probability and record in the table.

	Outcomes of the Event	Probability
Your Friend Wins		
You Win		

4. Do you and your friend have equally likely chances of winning the game? Explain your reasoning.

5. List the outcomes for and determine the probability for each statement.

a. *P*(even number on the number cube and even number on the spinner)

b. *P*(even number on the number cube or even number on the spinner)

Assignment

Write

Explain how to determine the probability of a compound event. Be sure to include both types of compound events.

Remember

A compound event combines two or more events using the word "and" or the word "or."

Practice

Color	Number of Tiles
Blue	10
Yellow	12
Pink	6
Green	3
Purple	9

1. Porter is pulling colored tiles out of a bag to use for an art project. The table shows the number of tiles of each color that are in the bag. Porter selects tiles from her bag.
   a. How many tiles are in her bag?
   b. Complete the probability model for pulling tiles from the bag.

Outcome	Blue	Yellow	Pink	Green	Purple
Probability					

   c. What is the probability that Porter pulls a green or purple tile?
   d. What is the probability that Porter pulls a pink, green, or purple tile?
   e. What is the probability that Porter pulls a pink and purple tile in one draw?

2. Once Porter finishes placing the tiles in her art project, she needs to determine the color of the grout that goes in between the tiles and the color of the frame around the project. She flips a coin to decide if she is going to use blue or yellow grout. She assigns heads to blue grout and tails to yellow grout. She puts a yellow, green, blue, and purple tile in a bag and pulls one out to determine the frame color.
   a. Determine the possible outcomes for flipping a coin and picking a tile out of the bag.
   b. How many possible outcomes are there?
   c. What events make up choosing the same color for grout and the frame?
   d. Determine the probability of choosing the same color for grout and the frame.
   e. What events make up choosing blue for the grout or the frame?
   f. Determine the probability of choosing blue for the grout or the frame.

Stretch

In a popular board game, if you roll doubles on two six-sided number cubes, you roll again. However, if you roll doubles three times in a row, you lose your turn and are further penalized. Determine the probability of rolling three doubles in a row.

Review

1. Everleigh has 3 shirts and 2 pairs of pants in her drawer. She has 2 red shirts and a blue shirt. The pants are a pair of jeans and a pair of khakis.
   a. What is the probability that she picks a red shirt with khakis?
   b. What is the probability that she picks the blue shirt and jeans?
2. Construct a probability model for rolling a 5-sided polyhedron.
   Is the probability model a uniform probability model? Explain your reasoning.
3. Determine each difference. Show your work.
   a. $-9\frac{3}{4} - 10\frac{7}{10}$
   b. $-34.9 - (-71.2)$

On a Hot Streak

4

Simulating Probability of Compound Events

WARM UP

1. Explain how to use a six-sided number cube to simulate whether someone prefers gymnastics, soccer, or baseball, given that these outcomes are equally likely.

2. Explain how to use a random number table to simulate whether an evenly divided spinner lands on red, blue, green, or yellow.

LEARNING GOALS

- Use simulations to estimate compound probabilities.
- Design and use a simulation to generate frequencies for compound events.
- Determine probabilities of compound events using simulation.

Calculating the theoretical probability of many compound events requires advanced rules and formulas. How can you simulate real-world compound events using tools you already have?

Getting Started

Shoot Out

John is the star player on his basketball team. So far this season, he has made 5 out of 6 free throws.

Use your knowledge of probability to answer each question.

1. **Out of the next 6 free throws, how many would you expect him to make?**

2. **Out of the next 10 free throws, how many would you expect him to make?**

3. **Predict the likelihood that John will make his next free throw.**

4. **Predict the likelihood that he will make his next 5 free throws.**

5. **Suppose John made 5 free throws in a row. Predict what will happen on his next free throw.**

ACTIVITY
4.1

Simulating Free Throws

John is also the team's top 3-point shooter. Suppose John is fouled while attempting a 3-point shot; he then attempts 3 free throws.

1. **What might be a good simulation tool for John attempting the free throws?**

2. **Explain what constitutes a success, or John making a free throw, and what constitutes a failure, or John missing a free throw, using your tool.**

3. **John's coach wants to know the probability that John will make all 3 shots. Use a simulation to determine the probability.**

   a. **Describe one trial of the simulation.**

   b. **Conduct 10 trials of the simulation and record your results in the table.**

   c. **Count the number of times that your simulation resulted in John making all 3 free throws.**

Trial Number	Number of Free Throws Made
1	
2	
3	
4	
5	
6	
7	
8	
9	
10	

"How is calculating the mean of the probabilities similar to compiling all of the class data and then computing the probability?"

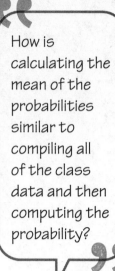

d. According to your simulation, what is the probability that John makes all 3 free throws?

e. Calculate the mean of the probabilities from the simulations conducted by your classmates. What does this tell you?

John has been on a "hot streak" lately!

4. Design and conduct a simulation to model the number of times John would shoot before missing a shot. That is, on what shot number would you expect John to miss?

   a. Describe one trial of the simulation.

   b. Conduct 10 trials of the simulation and record the results in the table.

Trial Number	Number of Shots For First Miss
1	
2	
3	
4	
5	
6	
7	
8	
9	
10	

   c. Calculate the mean number of shots it takes for John to miss a shot.

   d. Compile your data with your classmates' data. Calculate the mean number of shots John takes before he misses one.

   e. How was this simulation different from the first simulation?

ACTIVITY
4.2

Using Random Numbers to Simulate Compound Probability

Overall, the percent of people in the U.S. having each blood group is given in the table. The percents have been rounded to the nearest whole number percent.

Blood Groups	A	B	O	AB
Percent of Population	42%	10%	44%	4%

Suppose the Red Cross is having a blood drive at the community center.

1. **What is the probability that the next person who enters the community center to donate blood has Group A blood?**

2. **What is the probability that the next person who enters the community center to donate blood has Group A or Group O blood?**

3. **Determine the probability that out of the next 5 people to donate blood, at least 1 person has Group AB blood.**

   a. **Describe different strategies you could use to simulate the blood groups of people who give blood.**

   b. **Because of the values of the percents, use a random number table for this simulation. How could you assign numbers to people to account for the different blood groups?**

A random number table is provided at the end of the lesson.

   c. **Describe one trial of the simulation.**

   d. **Conduct 20 trials of the simulation and record your results in the table.**

   e. **Out of the 20 trials, how many had at least 1 number that represented an AB blood donor?**

   f. **According to your simulation, what is the probability that out of the next 5 people to donate blood, at least one of them has Group AB blood?**

Trial Number	Number of AB blood donors
1	
2	
3	
4	
5	
6	
7	
8	
9	
10	
11	
12	
13	
14	
15	
16	
17	
18	
19	
20	

4. How many people would be expected to donate blood before a person with Group B blood would donate blood?

   a. Describe one trial of the simulation.

   b. Conduct 20 trials of the simulation and record your results in the table.

   c. Calculate the average for your 20 trials.

   d. About how many people would be expected to donate blood before a person with Group B blood enters?

Trial Number	Number of Donors Until a Group B
1	
2	
3	
4	
5	
6	
7	
8	
9	
10	
11	
12	
13	
14	
15	
16	
17	
18	
19	
20	

How could you get a more accurate estimate to answer this question?

NOTES

TALK the TALK

It's Good!

The kicker of the high school football team makes 7 out of every 10 extra point attempts.

1. **Design and conduct a simulation for each situation. Conduct 20 trials of your simulation and prepare to present your results to your classmates.**

   a. **Determine the probability that the kicker will successfully make 3 out of the next 4 extra points he attempts.**

   b. **Determine the number of extra point attempts it takes for his first miss.**

Random Number Table										
Line 1	65285	97198	12138	53010	94601	15838	16805	61404	43516	17020
Line 2	17264	57327	38224	29301	18164	38109	34976	65692	98566	29550
Line 3	95639	99754	31199	92558	68368	04985	51092	37780	40261	14479
Line 4	61555	76404	86214	11808	12840	55147	97438	60222	12645	62090
Line 5	78137	98768	04689	87130	79225	08153	84967	64539	79493	74917
Line 6	62490	99215	84987	28759	19107	14733	24550	28067	68894	38490
Line 7	24216	63444	21283	07044	92729	37284	13211	37485	11415	36457
Line 8	18975	95428	33226	55901	31605	43816	22259	00317	46999	98571
Line 9	59138	39542	71168	57609	91510	27904	74244	50940	31553	62562
Line 10	29478	59652	50414	31966	87912	87154	12944	49862	96566	48825
Line 11	96155	95009	27429	72918	08457	78134	48407	26061	58754	05326
Line 12	29621	66583	62966	12468	20245	14015	04014	35713	03980	03024
Line 13	12639	75291	71020	17265	41598	64074	64629	63293	53307	48766
Line 14	14544	37134	54714	02401	63228	26831	19386	15457	17999	18306
Line 15	83403	88827	09834	11333	68431	31706	26652	04711	34593	22561
Line 16	67642	05204	30697	44806	96989	68403	85621	45556	35434	09532
Line 17	64041	99011	14610	40273	09482	62864	01573	82274	81446	32477
Line 18	17048	94523	97444	59904	16936	39384	97551	09620	63932	03091
Line 19	93039	89416	52795	10631	09728	68202	20963	02477	55494	39563
Line 20	82244	34392	96607	17220	51984	10753	76272	50985	97593	34320

Assignment

Write

Explain the difference between designing and conducting a simulation that asks for the probability of a specific number of successes in a given number of observations and a simulation that asks for the number of observations until the first success.

Remember

Many events involve very advanced rules for probability. In most cases, a simulation can be used to model the event.

Practice

1. In 1900, half of the babies born in America were born with blue eyes. What is the probability that 3 out of 4 babies born had blue eyes?
   a. What might be a good model for simulating the probability of a baby being born with blue eyes in 1900?
   b. Describe how you would assign outcomes and then describe one trial of the simulation.
   c. Conduct 20 trials of the simulation and record your results in a table.
   d. According to your simulation, what is the probability that 3 out of 4 babies born have blue eyes?

2. By the start of the 21st century, only 1 in 6 babies in America was born with blue eyes. What is the probability that at least 1 out of 2 babies has blue eyes?
   a. What might be a good model for simulating the probability of a baby being born with blue eyes in 2001?
   b. Describe how you would assign outcomes and then describe one trial of the simulation.
   c. Conduct 20 trials of the simulation and record your results in a table.
   d. According to your simulation, what is the probability that at least 1 out of 2 babies born in 2001 has blue eyes?

3. The preferences of customers who rent movies online are given in the table. Design and conduct a simulation for each question. Be sure to describe how you would assign outcomes and what makes up one trial. Conduct 10 trials for each.

Movie Type	Comedy	Drama	Science Fiction	Documentary
Percent of Customers	31%	42%	22%	5%

   a. Determine the probability that out of the next 5 customers to rent a movie, at least 1 rents a science fiction movie.
   b. Determine the number of customers you would expect to rent movies until someone rents a science fiction movie.

Stretch

In this lesson, you have simulated the probabilities from binomial distributions and from geometric distributions. Research each type of probability distribution. Explain the information contained in each problem from the lesson in terms of the parameters of binomial and geometric distributions. Select one of the Activities from the lesson and calculate the theoretical results of each of your simulations.

Review

1. Alison has a set of alphabet tiles. She puts the tiles representing the six letters of her name into a bag. Suppose Alison draws a tile, puts it back, and then draws a second tile.
   a. What is the probability that she draws an A and an N?
   b. What is the probability that she draws an A or an N?
2. A local eatery noticed that there were anywhere from zero to four double yolk eggs in each carton. Today the eatery opened and used 12 cartons of eggs.
   - 8 cartons contained no double yolk eggs
   - 1 carton contained one double yolk egg
   - 1 carton contained two double yolk eggs
   - 1 carton contained three double yolk eggs
   - 1 carton contained four double yolk eggs

   Determine the probability that the next carton of eggs the eatery opens will contain four double yolk eggs.
   a. Design a probability model by creating a table.
   b. What could be a good model for simulating experimental data?
   c. Describe 1 trial of the simulation.
   d. How many trials do you think you would need to conduct for the experimental probability to approach the theoretical probability?
3. Determine each quotient.
   a. $-4\frac{5}{8} \div 5\frac{1}{2}$
   b. $-102.9 \div -3.3$

Compound Probability Summary

KEY TERMS

- tree diagram
- compound event

LESSON 1

Evens or Odds?

To organize the outcomes for two events in a number array, list the outcomes for one event along one side and the outcomes for the other event along the other side. Combine the results in the intersections of each row and column.

For example, this array shows the sample space—all the possible outcomes—for rolling two six-sided number cubes and calculating the product of the numbers shown.

		Number Cube 1					
		1	**2**	**3**	**4**	**5**	**6**
Number Cube 2	**1**	1	2	3	4	5	6
	2	2	4	6	8	10	12
	3	3	6	9	12	15	18
	4	4	8	12	16	20	24
	5	5	10	15	20	25	30
	6	6	12	18	24	30	36

The probability of the product being a 6 is $\frac{4}{36}$ or $\frac{1}{9}$.

LESSON 2

Three Girls and No Boys?

One method of determining the theoretical probability of an event is to construct a tree diagram. A **tree diagram** illustrates the possible outcomes of a given situation. Tree diagrams can be constructed vertically or horizontally. A tree diagram has two main parts: the branches and the ends. An outcome of each event is written at the end of each branch.

For example, you can construct a tree diagram to show all the possible outcomes for a family having three children.

List the possible outcomes of the 1st child.

List the possible outcomes of the 2nd child.

List the possible outcomes of the 3rd child.

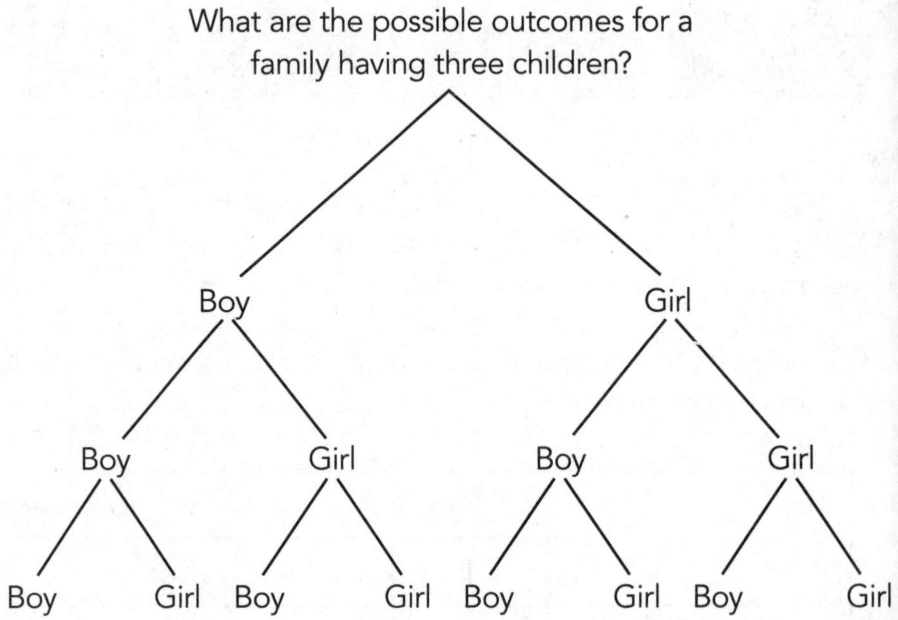

You can use a tree diagram to determine the probability of an event. In the tree diagram shown, there are 8 possible outcomes for a family having three children. The probability for a family having three girls is $\frac{1}{8}$.

LESSON 3

Pet Shop Probability

A **compound event** combines two or more events using the word *and* or the word *or*. Determining the probability of a compound event with the word *and* is different from determining the probability of a compound event with the word *or*.

The difference is that a compound event with the word *and* means that you are determining the probability that both events occur.

For example, the cards shown were placed face down in two piles so that they could be randomly chosen.

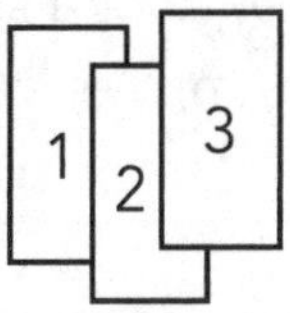

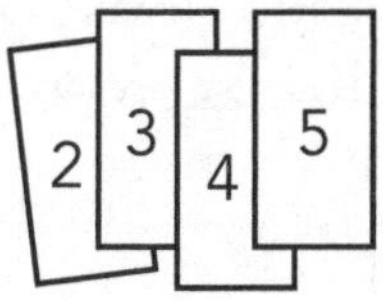

The possible outcomes for randomly choosing one card from each pile are {1, 2; 1, 3; 1, 4; 1, 5; 2, 2; 2, 3; 2, 4; 2, 5; 3, 2; 3, 3; 3, 4; 3, 5}.

Determine the probability that the first card is a 1 and the second card is even.

The possible desired outcomes are {1, 2; 1, 4}. The probability that the first card is a 1 and the second card is even is $\frac{2}{12}$, or $\frac{1}{6}$.

When determining the probability of a compound event with the word *or*, you are determining the probability that one or the other or both outcomes occur.

For example, using the same experiment above, determine the probability that the first card is a 1 or the second card is even.

The possible desired outcomes are (1, 2; 1, 3; 1, 4; 1, 5; 2, 2; 2, 4; 3, 2; 3, 4}.

The probability that the first card is a 1 or the second card is even is $\frac{8}{12}$, or $\frac{2}{3}$.

LESSON 4

On a Hot Streak

Many events involve very advanced rules for probability. In most cases, a simulation can be used to model the event. A random number table can be used to simulate compound probability in many of these events.

For example, the preferences of customers who rent movies online are provided in the table. You can design and conduct a simulation to predict the probability that out of the next 10 customers to rent a movie, at least 3 rent a comedy.

Movie Type	Comedy	Drama	Science Fiction	Documentary
Percent of Customers	31%	42%	22%	5%

You could use a random number table for this simulation. First, assign each movie type a range of two-digit numbers that correspond to the percent of customers who prefer that type.

- Comedy: 00–30
- Drama: 31–72
- Science Fiction: 73–94
- Documentary: 95–99

Then, run trials of the experiment. Each trial consists of selecting 10 two-digit numbers from the random number table. The experimental probability of at least 3 of the next 10 customers renting a comedy is the number of trials that contained at least 3 the numbers from 00 to 30 divided by the total number of trials.

TOPIC 3

Drawing Inferences

Choosing a sample randomly from a population is a good way to select items that are representative of the entire population.

Module 4: Analyzing Populations and Probabilities

TOPIC 3: DRAWING INFERENCES

In this topic, students continue developing their understanding of the statistical process by focusing on the second component of the process: data collection. They learn about samples, populations, censuses, parameters, and statistics. Students display data and compare the difference of the measures of center for two populations to their measures of variation. Then students draw conclusions about two populations using random samples.

Where have we been?

In grade 6, students learned about and used aspects of the statistical problem-solving process: formulating questions, collecting data, analyzing data, and interpreting the results. They also used numerical data displays, including both measures of center (mean, median, mode) and measures of variation (mean absolute deviation, range, and interquartile range).

Where are we going?

In high school, students will learn about specific types of random sampling and the inherent bias in sampling techniques. They will continue analyzing and comparing random samples from populations and comparing their measures of center and variation.

Using a Random Number Table to Select Random Samples

When selecting samples for an experiment, a random number table can be used to assign individuals to groups. The first three lines of a sample random number table are shown.

Random Number Table										
Line 1	65285	97198	12138	53010	94601	15838	16805	61404	43516	17020
Line 2	17264	57327	38224	29301	18164	38109	34976	65692	98566	29550
Line 3	95639	99754	31199	92558	68368	04985	51092	37780	40261	14479

Myth: Faster = smarter.

In most cases, speed has nothing to do with how smart you are. Why is that? Because it largely depends on how familiar you are with a topic. For example, a bike mechanic can look at a bike for about 8 seconds and tell you details about the bike that you probably didn't even notice (e.g., the front tire is on backwards). Is that person smart? Sure! Suppose, instead, you show the same bike mechanic a car. Will s/he be able to recall the same amount of detail as for the bike? No!

It's easy to confuse speed with understanding. Speed is associated with the memorization of facts. Understanding, on the other hand, is a methodical, time-consuming process. Understanding is the result of asking lots of questions and seeing connections between different ideas. Many mathematicians who won the Fields Medal (i.e., the Nobel prize for mathematics) describe themselves as extremely slow thinkers. That's because mathematical thinking requires understanding over memorization.

#mathmythbusted

Talking Points

You can support your student's learning by approaching problems slowly. Students may observe a classmate learning things very quickly, and they can easily come to believe that mathematics is about getting the right answer as quickly as possible. When this doesn't happen for them, future encounters with math can raise anxiety, making problem solving more difficult, and reinforcing a student's view of himself or herself as "not good at math." Slowing down is not the ultimate cure for math difficulties. But it's a good first step for children who are struggling. You can reinforce the view that learning with understanding takes time, and that slow, deliberate work is the rule, not the exception.

Key Terms

parameter

When data are gathered from a population, the characteristic used to describe the population is called a parameter.

statistic

When data are gathered from a sample, the characteristic used to describe the sample is called a statistic.

random sample

A random sample is a sample that is selected from the population in such a way that every member of the population has the same chance of being selected.

1

We Want to Hear From You!

Collecting Random Samples

WARM UP

Light It Up Light Bulb Company tests 24 of the bulbs they just produced and found that 3 of them were defective. Use proportions to predict how many light bulbs would be defective in shipments of each size.

1. 100 light bulbs

2. 400 light bulbs

3. 750 light bulbs

LEARNING GOALS

- Differentiate between a population and a sample.
- Differentiate between a parameter and a statistic.
- Differentiate between a random sample and a non-random sample.
- Identify the benefits of random sampling of a population, including supporting valid statistical inferences and generalizations.
- Use several methods to select a random sample.

KEY TERMS

- survey
- data
- population
- census
- sample
- parameter
- statistic
- random sample

The statistical process is a structure for answering questions about real-world phenomena. How can you make sure that the data you collect accurately answer your statistical questions?

Getting Started

Reviewing the Statistical Process

There are four components of the statistical process:

- Formulating a statistical question.
- Collecting appropriate data.
- Analyzing the data graphically and numerically.
- Interpreting the results of the analysis.

In this lesson, you will explore the second component of the statistical process, data collection. You will learn strategies for generating samples.

1. **Summarize each of the four components. You may want to use examples to support your answers.**

How could you describe the students in your classroom? How do the students in your classroom compare to other groups of students in your school, or to other seventh graders in the United States?

2. **Formulate a statistical question about your classmates. How might you collect the information to answer your question?**

One data collection strategy you can use is a *survey*. A **survey** is a method of collecting information about a certain group of people. It involves asking a question or a set of questions to those people. When information is collected, the facts or numbers gathered are called **data**.

3. **Answer each question in the survey shown. You will use the results in the next activity.**

   a. **What is your approximate height?** ____________________

   b. **Do you have a cell phone?** **Yes** ______ **No** ______

   c. **About how many text messages do you send each day?** _____

ACTIVITY
1.1 Representative Samples

The **population** is the entire set of items from which data can be selected. When you decide what you want to study, the population is the set of all elements in which you are interested. The elements of that population can be people or objects.

A **census** is the data collected from every member of a population.

Some examples of populations include:

- every person in the United States
- every person in your math class
- every person in your school
- all the apples in your supermarket
- all the apples in the world

1. Use your survey to answer each question.

a. Besides you, who else took the math class survey?

b. What is the population in your class survey?

c. Are the data collected in the class survey a census? Explain your reasoning.

Ever since 1790, the United States has taken a census every 10 years to collect data about population and state resources. The original purposes of the census were to decide the number of representatives a state could send to the U.S. House of Representatives and to determine the federal tax burden.

According to the 2016 census, approximately 323,000,000 people live in the United States!

2. Describe the population for the United States census.

3. Why do you think this collection of data is called "the census"?

In most cases, it is not possible or logical to collect data from every member of the population. When data are collected from a part of the population, the data are called a **sample**. A sample should be representative of the population. In other words, it should have characteristics that are similar to the entire population.

At Bower Valley Middle School, 29% of students had perfect attendance last year. This is a parameter because you can count every single student at the school.
Nationally, 16% of all teachers miss 3 or fewer days per year. This characteristic is a statistic because the population is too big to survey every single teacher.

When data are gathered from a population, the characteristic used to describe the population is called a **parameter**.

When data are gathered from a sample, the characteristic used to describe the sample is called a **statistic**. A statistic is used to make an estimate about the parameter.

4. After the 2000 census, the United States Census Bureau reported that 7.4% of Georgia residents were between the ages of 10 and 14. Was a parameter or a statistic reported? Explain your reasoning.

5. A recent survey of 1000 teenagers from across the United States shows that 4 out of 5 carry a cell phone with them.

   a. What is the population in the survey?

   b. Were the data collected in the survey a census? Why or why not?

   c. Does the given statement represent a parameter or a statistic? Explain how you determined your answer.

   d. Of those 1000 teenagers surveyed, how many carry a cell phone? How many do not carry a cell phone?

NOTES

6. Use your math class survey, or the data from a sample class survey provided at the end of this lesson, to answer each question. Use a complete sentence to justify each answer.

   a. How many students in the class have a cell phone?

   b. What percent of the students in the class have a cell phone?

   c. Does the percent of students in the class that have a cell phone represent a parameter or a statistic? Explain how you determined your answer.

7. Suppose you only want to survey a sample of the class about whether they have a cell phone. Discuss whether or not these samples would provide an accurate representation of all students in a class. Use complete sentences to justify your answers.

   a. the selection of all of the girls for the sample

   b. the selection of the students in the first seat of every row

c. the selection of every fourth student alphabetically

d. the selection of the first 10 students to enter the classroom

Oh, I see! To get accurate characteristics of a population, I must carefully select a sample that represents, or has similar characteristics as, the population.

8. Suppose you wanted to determine the number of students who have a cell phone across the entire seventh grade.

   a. What is the population?

   b. Suggest and justify a method of surveying students in the seventh grade to obtain a representative sample.

When information is collected from a sample in order to describe a characteristic about the population, it is important that such a sample be as representative of the population as possible. A **random sample** is a sample that is selected from the population in such a way that every member of the population has the same chance of being selected.

ACTIVITY
1.2 Selecting a Random Sample

Ms. Levi is purchasing standing desks for her classroom. She wants to set up the desks to minimize the amount of desk height adjusting by the students and decides to use the mean height of students in her math class as a guide. Rather than using the heights of all students in her class, she decides to collect a random sample of students in her class.

What is Ms. Levi's statistical question?

1. What is the population for this problem?

2. Ms. Levi received two suggestions to randomly sample her class. Decide if each strategy represents a random sample. If not, explain why not.

   a. Ms. Levi chooses the girls in the class.

   b. Ms. Levi chooses all of the students wearing white sneakers.

3. Ms. Levi decides to select a random sample of five students in her class, and then calculate the mean height. She assigns each student in her class a different number. Then, she randomly selects 5 numbers.

a. Explain why Ms. Levi's method of taking a sample is a random sample.

b. Do you think randomly selecting 5 students will accurately represent the population of her class? If not, do you think she should pick more or fewer students?

c. Damien hopes Ms. Levi will assign him the number 7 because it will have a better chance of being selected for the sample. Do you agree or disagree with Damien? Explain your reasoning.

d. Julie claims Ms. Levi must begin with the number 1 when assigning numbers to students. Jorge says she can start with any number as long as she assigns every student a different number. Who is correct? Explain your reasoning.

NOTES

One way to select the students is to write the numbers (or student names) on equal-sized pieces of paper, put the papers in a bag, draw out a piece of paper, and record the result. To create a true random sample, the papers should be returned to the bag after each draw.

Help Ms. Levi randomly select five students from her class.

4. With your partner, create a bag with 30 numbers from which to select your sample.

a. Draw 5 numbers and record your results.

b. Compare your sample with the samples of your classmates. What do you notice?

5. Suppose Ms. Levi starts with the number 15 when she assigns each of the 30 students in her class a number. How can you change your selection process to accommodate the list beginning at 15?

6. Suppose that the 5 numbers selected from your bag resulted in 5 girls.

a. Is the sample still a random sample? Explain your reasoning.

b. How is this outcome different from choosing all girls to represent the sample in Question 2?

ACTIVITY
1.3

Using Random Number Tables to Select a Sample

The standing desks improved student motivation, attendance, and achievement so much in Ms. Levi's class that the principal, Ms. Garrett, has decided to order standing work desks for every seventh grade class in the school.

The school has 450 seventh grade students, and Ms. Garrett would like to take a random sample of 20 seventh graders, determine their heights, and use their mean height for the initial set-up of the standing desks. However, Ms. Garrett does not want to write the 450 names on slips of paper.

Technology, such as spreadsheets, graphing calculators, and random number generator applications, can be used to generate random numbers.

There are other ways to select a random sample. One way to select a random sample is to use a random number table like you used previously to simulate events.

You can use a random number table to choose a number that has any number of digits in it. For example, if you are choosing 6 three-digit random numbers and begin with Line 7, the first 6 three-digit random numbers would be: 242, 166, 344, 421, 283, and 070.

Random Number Table										
Line 6	62490	99215	84987	28759	19177	14733	24550	28067	68894	38490
Line 7	24216	63444	21283	07044	92729	37284	13211	37485	10415	36457
Line 8	16975	95428	33226	55903	31605	43817	22250	03918	46999	98501
Line 9	59138	39542	71168	57609	91510	77904	74244	50940	31553	62562
Line 10	29478	59652	50414	31966	87912	87154	12944	49862	96566	48825

1. What number does "070" represent when choosing a three-digit random number? Why are the zeros in the number included? Explain your reasoning.

Do you think Ms. Levi's class was a representative sample of all seventh graders?

2. If selecting a three-digit random number, how would the number 5 be displayed in the table?

3. Begin on Line 10 and select 5 three-digit random numbers.

4. Explain how to assign numbers to the 450 seventh grade students so that Ms. Garrett can take a random sample.

5. Use Line 6 as a starting place to generate a random sample of 20 students.

   a. What is the first number that appears?

b. What do you think Ms. Garrett should do with that number?

c. Continuing on Line 6, what are the 20 three-digit numbers to be used to select Ms. Garrett's sample?

d. What should you do if a three-digit number appears twice in the random number table?

e. Will choosing a line number affect whether Ms. Garrett's sample is random?

f. Will choosing a line number affect who will be chosen for the sample?

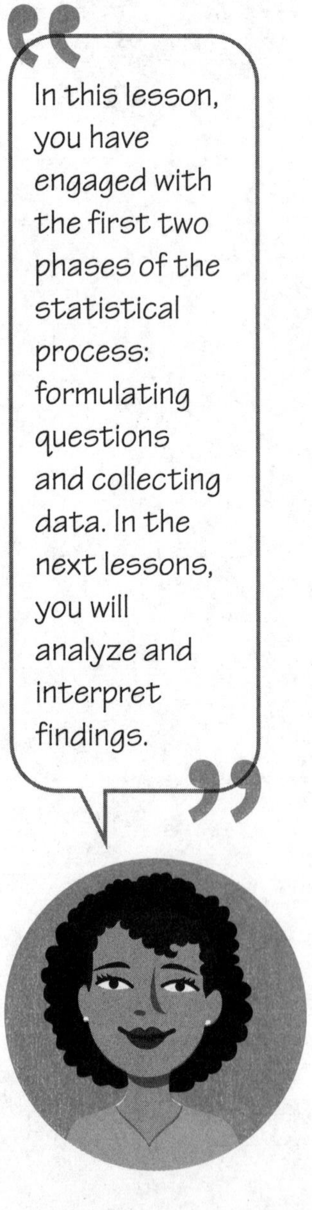

In this lesson, you have engaged with the first two phases of the statistical process: formulating questions and collecting data. In the next lessons, you will analyze and interpret findings.

NOTES

TALK the TALK

Lunching with Ms. Garrett

Ms. Garrett wishes to randomly select 10 students for a lunch meeting to discuss ways to improve school spirit. There are 1500 students in the school.

1. **What is the population for this problem?**

2. **What is the sample for this problem?**

3. **Ms. Garrett selects three to four student council members from each grade to participate. Does this sample represent all of the students in the school? Explain your answer.**

4. **Ms. Levi recommended that Ms. Garrett use a random number table to select her sample of 10 students. How would you recommend Ms. Garrett assign numbers and select her random sample?**

Results from a Sample Class Survey			
Student	**1. What is your approximate height?**	**2. Do you carry a cell phone with you?**	**3. About how many text messages do you send in one day?**
1-Sue (F)	60 in.	Yes	75
2-Jorge (M)	68 in.	Yes	5
3-Alex (M)	63 in.	No	0
4-Maria (F)	65 in.	Yes	20
5-Tamika (F)	62 in.	Yes	50
6-Sarah (F)	68 in.	Yes	100
7-Beth (F)	56 in.	Yes	60
8-Sam (M)	70 in.	No	0
9-Eric (M)	69 in.	Yes	50
10-Marcus (M)	66 in.	Yes	100
11-Carla (F)	61 in.	Yes	0
12-Ben (M)	68 in.	Yes	60
13-Will (M)	64 in.	Yes	50
14-Yasmin (F)	66 in.	Yes	40
15-Paulos (M)	60 in.	Yes	90
16-Jon (M)	67 in.	Yes	10
17-Rose (F)	64 in.	Yes	0
18-Donna (F)	65 in.	Yes	25
19-Suzi (F)	63 in.	Yes	30
20-Kayla (F)	58 in.	Yes	80

Assignment

Write

Match each definition to the corresponding term.

1. the facts or numbers gathered by a survey
2. the characteristic used to describe a sample
3. the collection of data from every member of a population
4. a method of collecting information about a certain group of people by asking a question or set of questions
5. a sample that is selected from the population in a such a way that every member of the population has the same chance of being selected
6. the characteristic used to describe a population
7. the entire set of items from which data can be selected
8. the data collected from part of a population

a. census
b. data
c. parameter
d. population
e. sample
f. statistic
g. survey
h. random sample

Remember

Statistics obtained from data collected through a random sample are more likely to be representative of the population than those statistics obtained from data collected through non-random samples.

Practice

1. Explain which sampling method is more representative of the population.
   a. Katie and Cole live in Springfield, RI, and are interested in the average number of skateboarders who use their town's Smooth Skate Park in one week. Katie recorded the number of skateboarders who used the park in June. Cole recorded the number of skateboarders who used the park in January.
   b. Fiona and Rachel want to determine the most popular lunch choice in the school cafeteria among seventh graders. They decide to collect data from a sample of seventh graders at school. Fiona surveys twenty seventh graders that are in line at the cafeteria. Rachel surveys twenty seventh graders whose student ID numbers end in 9.
2. The coach of the soccer team is asked to select 5 students to represent the team in the Homecoming Parade. The coach decides to randomly select the 5 students out of the 38 members of the team.
   a. What is the population for this problem?
   b. What is the sample for this problem?
   c. Suggest a method for selecting the random sample of 5 students.

3. Consider the population of integers from 8 to 48.
   a. Select a sample of 6 numbers. Is this a random sample? Explain your reasoning.
   b. How can you assign random numbers to select a sample using a random number table?
   c. Use the random number table to choose 6 numbers from this population.
   d. Use a different line of the random number table to choose 6 numbers from this population.
   e. Compare the results from each sample. Do the results surprise you? Explain.
4. The manager of the Millcreek Mall wants to know the mean age of the people who shop at the mall and the stores in which they typically shop. Dennis has been put in charge of collecting data for the Millcreek Mall. He decides to interview 100 people one Saturday because it is the mall's busiest shopping day.
   a. What is the population for this situation?
   b. What is the sample?
   c. When Dennis calculates the mean age of the people who shop at the mall, will he be calculating a parameter or a statistic? Explain your reasoning.
   d. Describe three different ways Dennis can take a sample. Describe how any of these three possible samples may cause the results of Dennis's survey to inaccurately reflect the average age of shoppers at the mall.
   e. Dennis decides to use a random number table to choose the next 10 people to interview. Explain how to choose 10 two-digit numbers between 1 and 80 from a random number table.
   f. Record the numbers of the people who would be interviewed. Be sure to specify which line you used to generate your list.
   g. Suppose Dennis uses a random number table to generate his sample, resulting in Dennis interviewing 10 people who all go into the gaming store. Does this mean the sample is not random? Explain.

Stretch

Variations of random samples are often preferred to truly random samples. Two variations are called **stratified random samples** and **systematic random samples.** Research each type of random sampling. Define each type of sample and give an example, perhaps from the lesson, of when each might provide a more representative sample than a truly random sample.

Review

1. A soccer player makes 4 out of every 5 penalty shots she attempts.
   a. What might be a good model for simulating the number of shots the soccer player makes in when attempting 4 penalty shots?
   b. Describe how you would assign outcomes and then describe one trial of the simulation.
   c. Conduct 20 trials of the simulation and record your results in a table.
   d. According to your simulation, what is the probability that the soccer player makes exactly 3 out of the next 4 penalty shots?
2. Mike spins two spinners. The first spinner is divided into 4 equal sections and each is labeled with a perfect square (4, 9, 16, 25). The second spinner is divided into 5 equal sections and each is labeled with an even number (2, 4, 6, 8, 10).
   a. Create an array to illustrate the possible products of the result of spinning both spinners.
   b. What is the probability that the product is a perfect square?
   c. What is the probability that the product is a perfect cube?
   d. What is the probability that the product is a multiple of 10?
3. Solve each equation for the unknown.
   a. $7 - 2(3t + 9) = -47$
   b. $-2.5 = \frac{(5.5h - 7)}{1.5 + 4}$

Tiles, Gumballs, and Pumpkins

2

Using Random Samples to Draw Inferences

WARM UP

Mr. Mario has three bulletin boards in his classroom. What is the average amount of space per bulletin board?

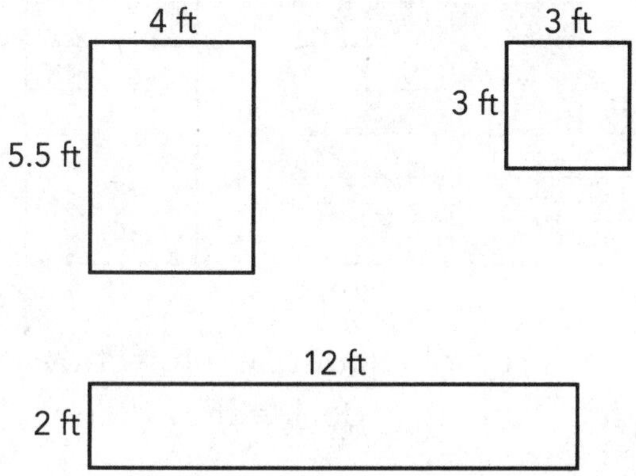

LEARNING GOALS

- Investigate how results from a random sample are more reliable in representing the population than results from a sample that is not random.
- Use data from a random sample and proportional reasoning to draw inferences about a population parameter.
- Calculate the percent error between population parameters and sample statistics.

Now that you know how to generate random samples, how can you use random samples to make inferences about population parameters?

Getting Started

Selecting Squares

The Art Club created a design on the floor of the art room. Each of the 40 numbered squares on the floor will have colored tiles. The club needs to calculate how many colored tiles they must buy. Each small grid square represents a square that is one foot long and one foot wide.

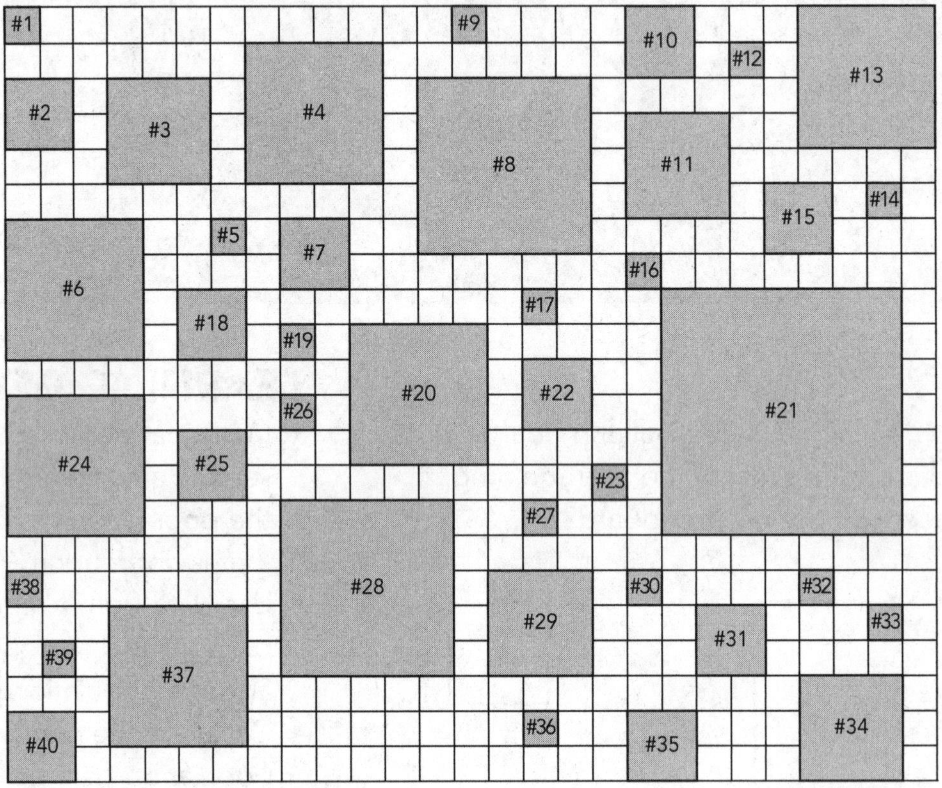

The Art Club needs to complete the art room floor plan project by tomorrow! Because they are short of time, they decide they do not have enough time to measure all 40 squares.

1. **Suggest a method for the Art Club to use to sample the 40 squares. What would they do once they collect their sample?**

ACTIVITY 2.1

Using Multiple Samples to Make Predictions

Samantha says, "Since we don't have a lot of time, why don't we just select 5 squares and calculate their total area? That should be good enough for us to estimate the total area of all the squares that will need colored tiles."

I wonder why Samantha picked those squares.

1. **Do you think Samantha's idea could work to estimate the total area for all the squares that need colored tiles? Explain your reasoning.**

2. **What is the population for this problem?**

WORKED EXAMPLE

As you learned, you can select a sample to estimate parameters of a population. In this problem situation, the Art Club is going to set up a ratio using the sample of squares they select to the total area of those sample squares.

They will use the ratio:

number of squares in the sample : total area of the sample squares.

Samantha decides to select the following squares: 1, 15, 21, 37, and 40.

Total area

#1: $1 \times 1 = 1$ square foot

#15: $2 \times 2 = 4$ square feet

#21: $7 \times 7 = 49$ square feet

#37: $4 \times 4 = 16$ square feet

#40: $2 \times 2 = 4$ square feet

Ratio

number of squares in the sample	:	total area of the sample squares
5 squares	:	74 square feet

So, the total area of these 5 squares is 74 square feet.

3. **Select 5 numbered squares that you think best represent the 40 squares that need colored tiles. Record the numbers of the squares you selected.**

4. **Calculate the total area of the 5 numbered squares you selected.**

You will use these descriptions throughout this lesson.

Now that you have collected your data, you need to analyze the data. Remember, there are three common distributions of data: skewed left, skewed right, and symmetric. The distribution of data can help you determine whether the mean or median is a better measure of center. Examine the diagrams shown.

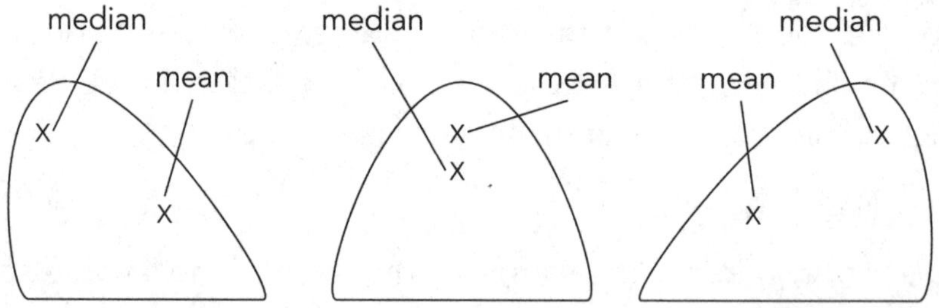

skewed right

The mean of a data set is greater than the median when the data are skewed to the right.

The median is the best measure of center because the median is not affected by very large data values.

symmetric

The mean and median are equal when the data are symmetric.

skewed left

The mean of a data set is less than the median when the data are skewed to the left.

The median is the best measure of center because the median is not affected by very small data values.

The median is not affected by very large or very small data values, but the mean is affected by these large and small values.

5. **Compare the total area of your sample to the total areas of your classmates' samples.**

   a. **Record the total area you calculated for your sample on the dot plot shown. Then, record the total areas your classmates calculated on the same dot plot.**

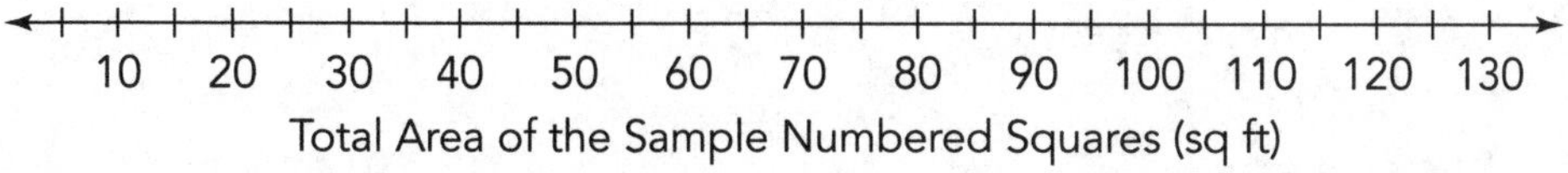

   b. **Describe the distribution of the dot plot.**

   c. **Estimate the total area for a sample of 5 squares using the data values in the dot plot.**

You can set up a ratio of the sample of 5 squares to the total area of those 5 sample squares, as Samantha did, and then you can set up a proportion to estimate the total area of those 40 squares in the Art Club's floor plan design. In doing so, you are scaling up from your sample to the population of the squares.

6. **Write a ratio of the number of squares in your sample to the total area of the squares.**

7. **Estimate the total area of all 40 squares on the floor plan using proportional reasoning.**

8. Compare the estimated total area of the 40 squares on the floor plan with your classmates' estimated total areas.

   a. Record the estimated total area of the 40 squares on the floor plan on the dot plot shown. Then, record your classmates' estimates of the total area of the 40 squares.

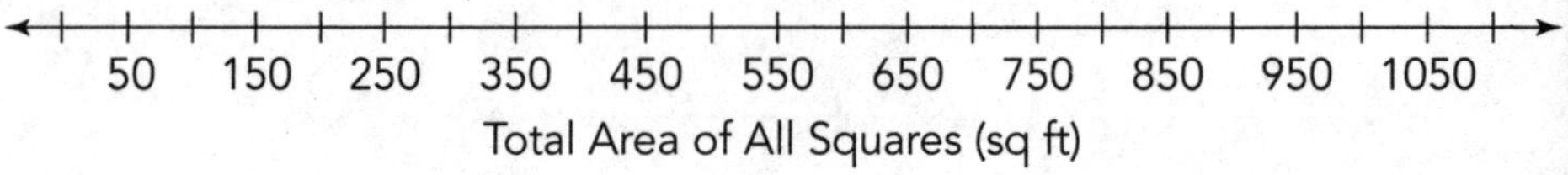

   b. Describe the shape of the distribution. Compare with the distribution in Question 5.

   c. Estimate the total area of the squares in the floor plan using data values in the dot plot.

ACTIVITY 2.2

Using Random Samples to Make Predictions

Samples chosen by looking at the squares and trying to pick certain squares will probably contain many more of the larger squares in the floor plan. Most of the squares actually have small areas (17 of the 40 squares have an area of 1 square foot, and 10 of the 40 squares have an area of 4 square feet); therefore, you need to use another method to randomly choose squares.

1. **How might you randomly choose 5 squares for your sample?**

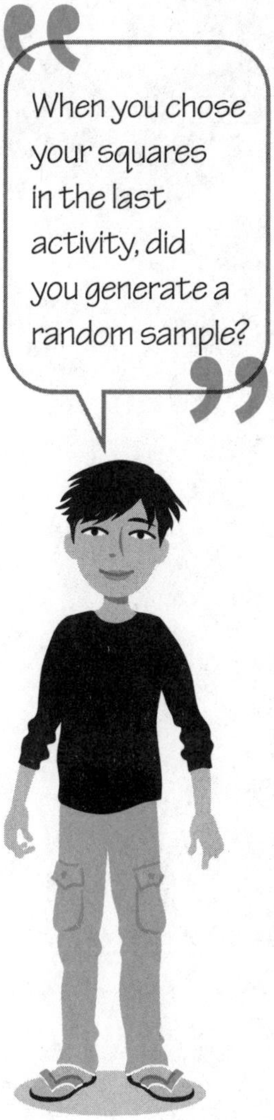

When you chose your squares in the last activity, did you generate a random sample?

2. **Soo Jin has a suggestion on how to randomly select the numbered squares. She says, "I can cut out the squares from the floor plan, and then I can put these squares in a bag. That will help me randomly select squares." Will Soo Jin's method result in a random sample? Explain your reasoning or suggest a way to modify her strategy.**

3. **How can you use the random number table to choose 5 numbered squares for your sample?**

4. Use a random number table to choose 5 numbered squares using two-digit numbers ranging between 01 and 40. Record the square numbers.

5. Calculate the total area of the 5 numbered squares you selected.

6. Compare the total area of your sample to the total areas your classmates calculated from their random samples.

   a. Record the total areas your classmates calculated and the total area you calculated on the dot plot shown.

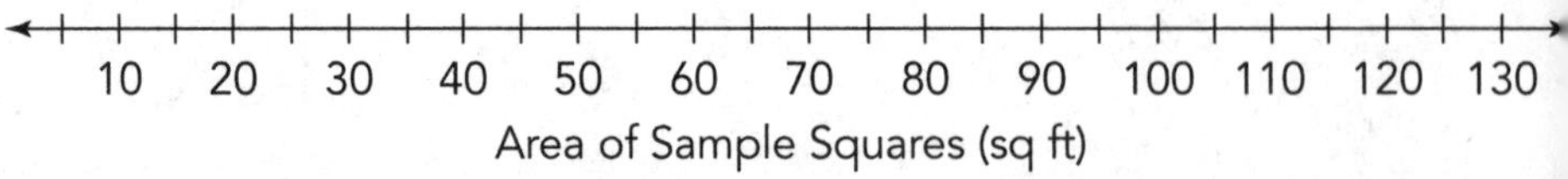

   b. How do the values plotted on this dot plot compare to the values plotted in the previous activity? Compare the shapes and the centers of the data values for both dot plots.

7. Using proportional reasoning, estimate the total area of all 40 squares on the floor plan using the area you calculated from the random sample.

8. Compare your estimated total area from the random sample for all 40 squares with your classmates' total area estimates.

   a. Record your estimated total area of the 40 squares on the dot plot shown. Then, record your classmates' estimates of the total area of the 40 squares on the dot plot.

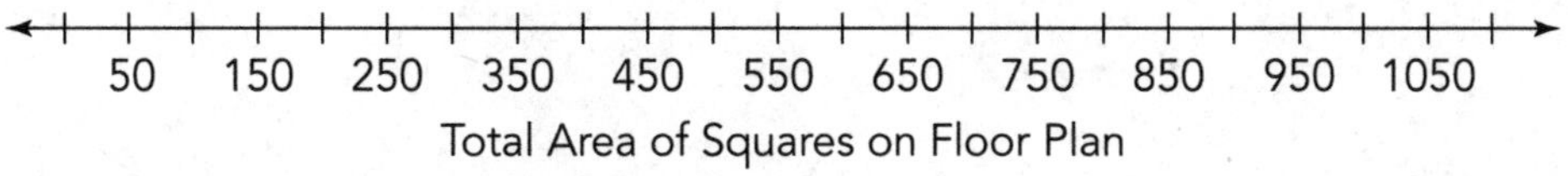

   b. Estimate the total area of the squares in the floor plan using data values in the dot plot.

   c. How do the values plotted on this dot plot compare to the values plotted in Activity 2.1, Question 8? Compare the distributions and the centers of the data values for both dot plots.

9. The actual total area of the 40 numbered squares is 288 square feet.

   a. Is 288 a parameter or a statistic? Explain your reasoning.

   b. Locate 288 on each dot plot you created in the previous activity and this activity. What do you notice?

   c. Calculate the percent error for the parameter and your statistics from this activity and the previous activity for the total sum of the areas of the squares.

   d. Based on your percent error, which sample is more accurate? Is this what you expected? Explain your reasoning.

Percent error is the absolute value of the ratio of the difference between the statistic and parameter to the parameter.

ACTIVITY
2.3

Using Samples to Justify Predictions

The student council holds regular fundraisers to raise money for community service projects. To raise money for Back-to-School Backpacks for the local homeless shelter, they hold a Gumball Guessing Competition. They place differently colored gumballs in a large, clear gumball machine. Students pay $1.00 to predict the percent of blue gumballs in the machine. Any students who predict within 5% of the actual percent win a $5.00 credit at the school store and a share of the gumballs.

To make their predictions, students take a sample of 25 gumballs (and then return the gumballs to the machine) and use the percent of blue gumballs in the sample to make their guess. The results from the first 100 students' samples are provided in the table.

Percent of Blue Gumballs in the Sample	Number of Samples
12%	5
16%	8
20%	13
24%	13
28%	16
32%	18
36%	13
40%	10
44%	3
48%	1

1. **Create a dot plot of the results. Be sure to label your dot plot.**

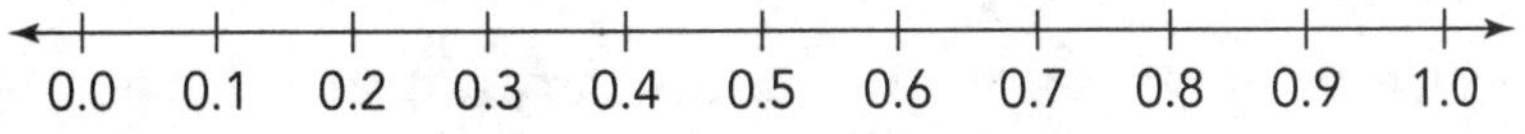

2. **Use the results to predict the likely percent of gumballs that are blue. Explain your reasoning.**

3. **How many of the students obtained a sample that was less than 25% blue gumballs?**

4. The gumball machine holds 10,000 gumballs and there are 2936 blue gumballs in the machine.

   a. How many students will split the gumballs? How many gumballs will each student receive?

   b. Is it reasonable that none of the estimates were equal to the actual percent of blue gumballs? Explain your reasoning.

   c. Suppose a disgruntled student argued that there must be at least 40% blue gumballs. Use the analysis to explain why this is unlikely.

   d. The principal did not take a random sample to create his estimate. Instead, he based his estimate on a visual inspection of the gumball machine. His guess was 35%. Calculate the percent error of the principal's guess from the true percent of blue gumballs.

NOTES

TALK the TALK

Pumpkin Patch

Right before pumpkin picking season, you are hired by Paula's Pumpkin Patch. Your first task is to determine the number of pumpkins available for picking. In addition to growing pumpkins in the pick-your-own field, Paula also grows gourds.

The diagram on the next page shows the field that contains the pumpkins and the gourds. The stars represent the gourds. Notice that there are also gaps in the field.

You and Paula agree that it would take too long to count all the pumpkins in the field.

1. **Design and carry out a method to estimate the total number of pumpkins in the field without counting all the shapes. Then prepare a presentation for your classmates that includes an explanation of your method, your results, and justification of your estimate.**

Pumpkins and Gourds

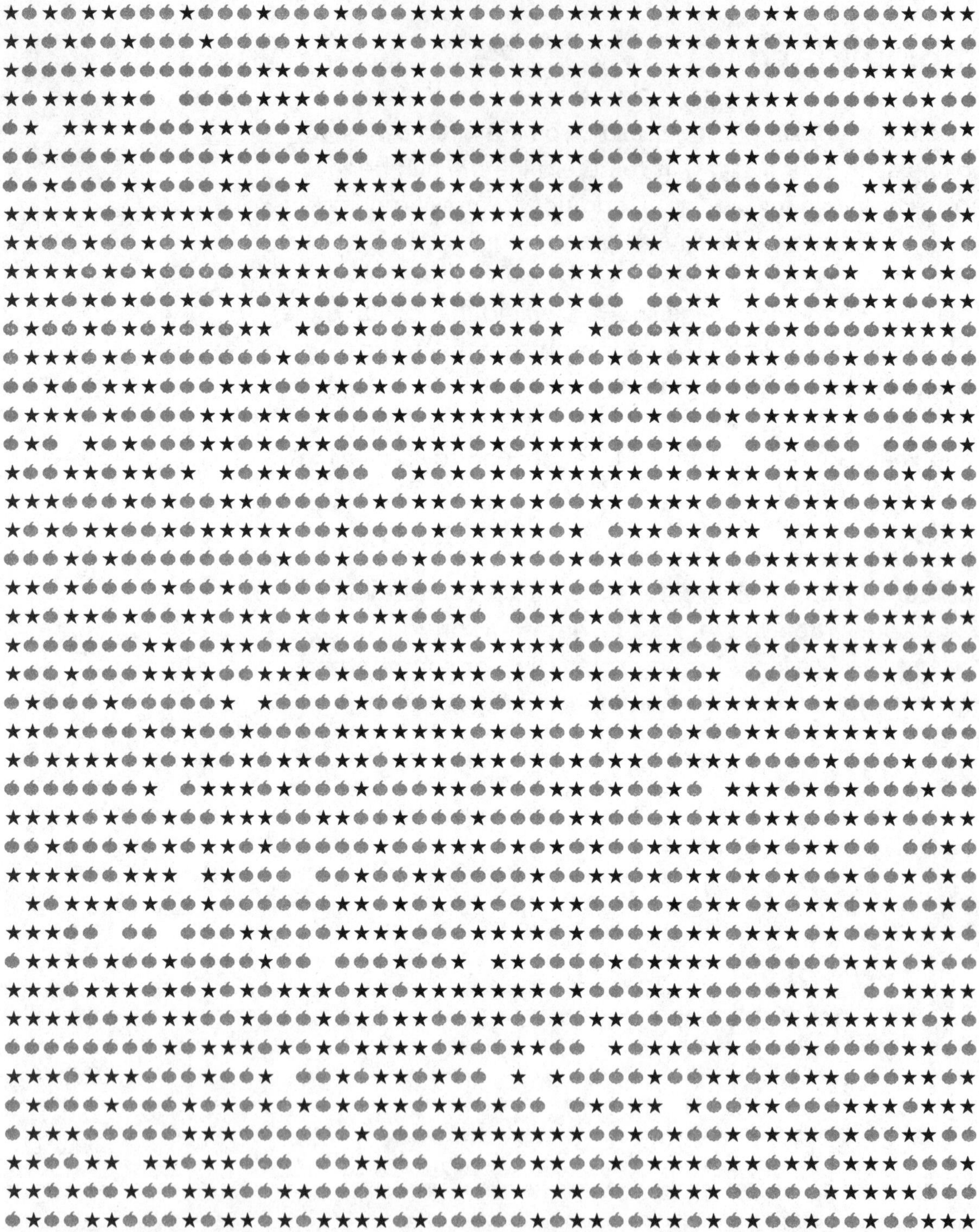

Assignment

Write

Explain the purpose and process of taking a sample when you are interested in a characteristic of the population.

Remember

If you are estimating a parameter that is a count, rather than a percentage, you can use proportional reasoning to scale up from the ratio of the number of observations in your sample to the statistic.

Practice

The table at the end of this assignment shows the names and ages at inauguration of 45 presidents of the United States.

1. You want to determine the mean age of the U.S. presidents at their inaugurations. Instead of calculating the mean using all 45 presidents' ages, you will take a sample.
   a. What is the population for this situation?
   b. Select 10 presidents whose ages best represent the mean age of a U.S. president at inauguration.
   c. Record the ages of these presidents.
   d. Explain why you chose these presidents.
   e. Is this a random sample? Explain your reasoning.
   f. Calculate the mean age of the presidents you selected. Round to the nearest year.
   g. Record the mean age you calculated and the mean age your classmates calculated on a dot plot.
   h. Describe the distribution of the dot plot in part (g).
2. You decide to use another method to choose presidents.
   a. Randomly select 10 presidents. Record the ages of these presidents.
   b. Is this a random sample? Explain your reasoning.
   c. Calculate the mean age of the presidents you selected. Round to the nearest year.
   d. Is the mean age of the 10 presidents you selected a statistic or parameter? Explain your reasoning.
   e. Record the mean age you calculated and the mean age your classmates calculated on a dot plot.
   f. Describe the distribution of the line plot in part (e).
   g. Calculate the actual mean age at inauguration of all 45 presidents. Round to the nearest year. Plot this age with an A on the dot plot in part (e).
   h. Calculate the percent error between the statistic from your random sample and the true mean age.
3. Why is a random sample more desirable than a sample that is not chosen randomly?

Stretch

Design a simulation that takes 100 samples of size 25 from a population in which 42% of the members of the population have a particular characteristic (e.g., blood group). Formulate a question and collect the data. For each sample, compute the percentage of observations with the given characteristic. Then analyze your results: summarize your sample percentages in a table and on a dot plot. Interpret the results: What are some predictions or generalizations about the population parameter based on your sample?

Review

1. Ms. Patel, the sponsor of the spirit team, wants to survey the team about upcoming events. Which sampling methods would result in representative samples? Explain your reasoning.
   a. Surveying the first 5 members who arrive at the volleyball game.
   b. Drawing 5 names from a box that contains the names of all the members and surveying those 5 members.
   c. Surveying the 5 members who have been members the longest.
2. Mike spins each spinner one time. He determines the product of the two numbers.
   a. Create an array to illustrate the possible products.
   b. What is the sample space?
   c. Determine P(multiple of 10).
   d. Determine $P(0)$.

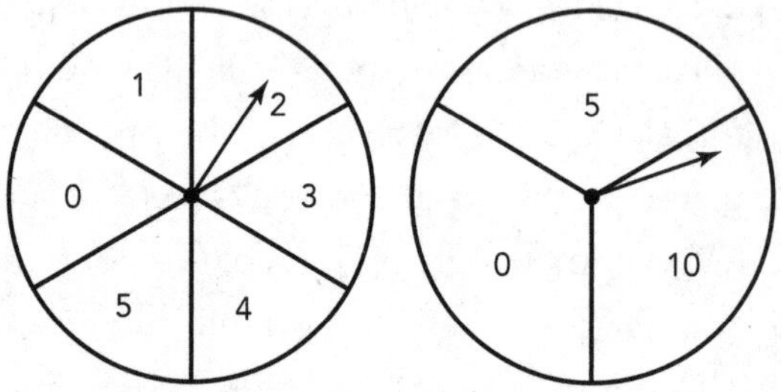

3. A game requires spinning a spinner numbered 1 through 5 and rolling a six-sided number cube.
   a. Determine the possible outcomes for playing the game.
   b. What is the probability of spinning an even number and rolling an even number?
   c. What is the probability of spinning a 5 or rolling a 5?

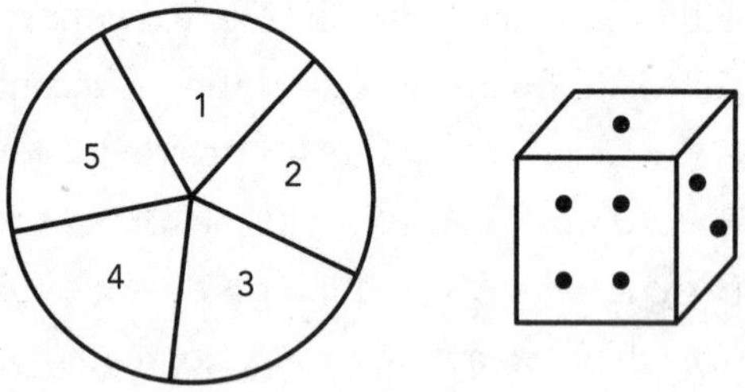

4. Evaluate the expression $1.2(x + 0.9) - 10.8$ for each unknown.
   a. $x = -5.5$ b. $x = 8.9$

Presidents of the United States			
President	Age at Inauguration	President	Age at Inauguration
George Washington	57	Franklin Pierce	48
John Adams	61	James Buchanan	65
Thomas Jefferson	57	Abraham Lincoln	52
James Madison	57	Andrew Johnson	56
James Monroe	58	Ulysses S. Grant	46
John Quincy Adams	57	Rutherford B. Hayes	54
Andrew Jackson	61	James A. Garfield	49
Martin Van Buren	54	Chester A. Arthur	51
William Henry Harrison	68	Grover Cleveland	47
John Tyler	51	Benjamin Harrison	55
James K. Polk	49	Grover Cleveland	55
Zachary Taylor	64	John F. Kennedy	43
William McKinley	54	Lyndon B. Johnson	55
Theodore Roosevelt	42	Richard Nixon	56
William Howard Taft	51	Gerald Ford	61
Woodrow Wilson	56	Jimmy Carter	52
Warren G. Harding	55	Ronald Reagan	69
Calvin Coolidge	51	George H.W. Bush	64
Herbert Hoover	54	Bill Clinton	46
Franklin D. Roosevelt	51	George W. Bush	54
Harry S. Truman	60	Barack Obama	47
Dwight D. Eisenhower	62	Donald Trump	70
Millard Fillmore	50		

Spicy or Dark?

Comparing Two Populations

3

WARM UP

The dot plot shows the number of football games boys and girls attended. The "o" represents boys' responses, and the "x" represents girls' responses.

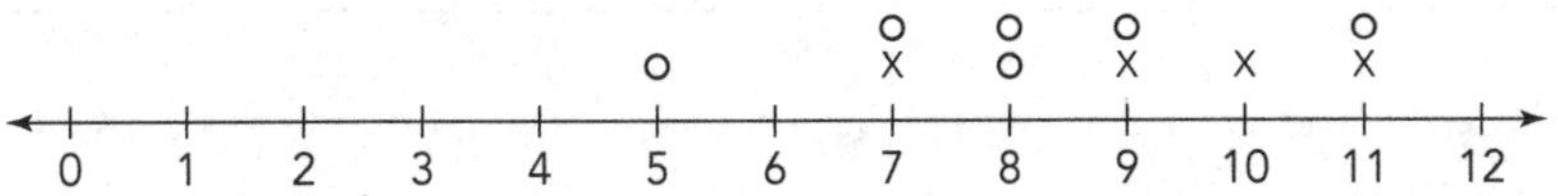

1. Estimate the mean number of games the boys attended.

2. Estimate the mean number of games the girls attended.

3. What observations can you make from your estimations of the data?

LEARNING GOALS

- Calculate the measures of center and measures of variability for two populations.
- Compare the measures of center to the measures of variability for two populations.
- Informally assess the degree of overlap of two numerical data distributions.

You have used measures of center and measures of variation to analyze single data sets. How can you use statistics to compare two different data sets in terms of their measures of center and variation?

Getting Started

Couch Potatoes

Several teenagers were surveyed to determine the number of hours they spend watching TV during a typical weekend. Another group was surveyed about the number of hours they spend playing outside. Eight surveys were randomly chosen from each group.

Survey Number	Hours Spent Watching TV (Per Weekend)
1	5
2	3
3	10
4	6
5	15
6	9
7	8
8	3

Survey Number	Hours Spent Playing Outside (Per Weekend)
1	1
2	2
3	0
4	3
5	8
6	2
7	3
8	3

1. Create a dot plot for each data set.

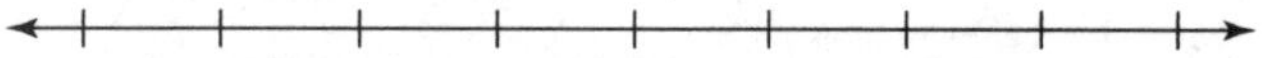

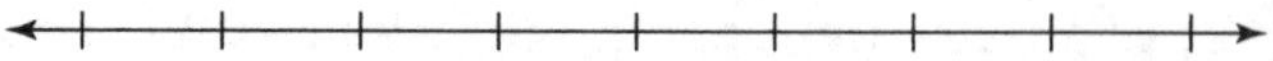

2. Calculate the mean, median, interquartile range (IQR), and mean absolute deviation (MAD) for each data set.

The IQR is the difference between the third quartile and the first quartile. The MAD is the mean of the absolute values of the deviations of each data point from the mean.

3. What do these measures of center and variation tell you about the data from the surveys?

ACTIVITY
3.1

Comparing Measures of Center and Variation

Jessica has just opened a new restaurant, Choco-Latta, which serves nothing but chocolate milk. She is experimenting with two new flavors—a spicy chocolate milk and a dark chocolate milk.

Jessica has asked you to provide a report analyzing customer feedback about the new flavors. You have conducted a survey of 20 random customers, asking each customer to rate a flavor on a scale of zero to one hundred.

Flavor	Rating	Flavor	Rating
Spicy	50	Spicy	70
Dark	20	Dark	30
Dark	30	Dark	40
Spicy	100	Spicy	70
Spicy	60	Dark	20
Spicy	80	Dark	60
Spicy	60	Spicy	80
Dark	10	Dark	20
Dark	30	Spicy	60
Dark	40	Spicy	70

"The 4 steps of the statistical process are
1. Formulate a statistical question.
2. Collect data.
3. Analyze the data.
4. Interpret the data."

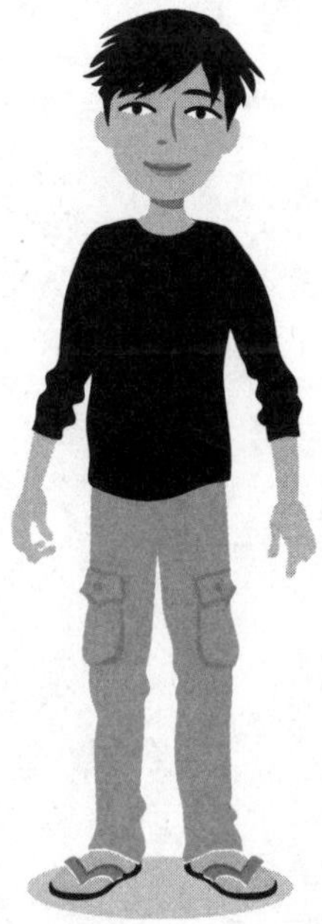

1. Display the results on a dot plot. Use an "x" to represent the Spicy flavor responses, and an "o" to represent the Dark flavor responses.

Flavor Ratings

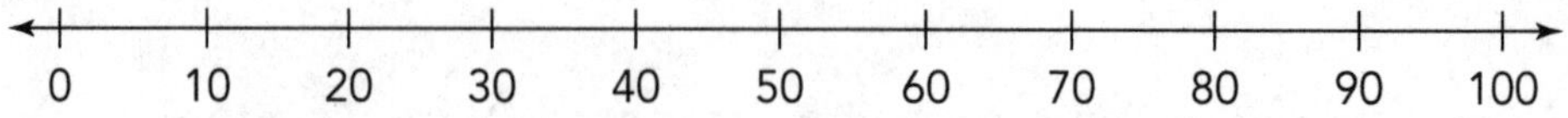

2. What observations can you make from your dot plot?

3. Describe the distribution of data values for Spicy flavor and for Dark flavor.

Remember, you can describe distributions as skewed right, symmetric, or skewed left.

4. Analyze the data values on your dot plot for Spicy and Dark.

   a. Estimate the mean rating for the Spicy flavor. Mark the mean on your dot plot with an "S." Explain how you determined your estimate.

   b. Estimate the mean rating for the Dark flavor. Mark the mean on your dot plot with a "D." Explain how you determined your estimate.

5. Calculate the actual mean rating for the Spicy flavor.

6. Calculate the actual mean rating for the Dark flavor.

7. What observations can you make about the spread of the two data sets?

8. Calculate the mean absolute deviation for the ratings of the Spicy flavor and the Dark flavor.

9. Interpret and compare the mean absolute deviations for the Spicy flavor and the Dark flavor.

10. How can you tell by looking at your dot plot that the mean absolute deviations would be equal for the Spicy flavor and the Dark flavor?

NOTES

11. **Can you report on which flavor has a more consistent rating? Explain your reasoning.**

WORKED EXAMPLE

Comparing the difference of means with the variation in each data set can be an important way of determining just how different two data sets are.

Consider these data sets.

5, 3, 4, 5, 10	5, 3, 100, 5, 10
Mean = 5.4	Mean = 24.6

The difference in their means is 19.2. Depending on what you are measuring, that can be a big difference.

But this difference of 19.2 is actually less than the mean absolute deviation of the right data set (30.16). This indicates that the data sets may overlap. The right data set is the same as the left one except for one number.

12. **For the Spicy flavor and Dark flavor data, compare the difference in the means with each mean absolute deviation. What observations can you make?**

13. **What recommendation will you give to Jessica about the two new flavors?**

ACTIVITY
3.2 Comparing Distributions

NOTES

In 2009, the Los Alamos Middle School's football team won only 2 games. The school decided to give the coach another chance at improving the team the next year. In 2010, the team won 7 games. Did scoring points have something to do with Los Alamos improving their record? The stem-and-leaf plot shows the number of points scored in each game by Los Alamos Middle School's football team in 2009 and 2010.

Los Alamos Middle School Football Team

Points scored 2009						Points scored 2010			
		7	3	0	0				
7	4	4	2	0	1	4	7	7	
			9	8	2	4	7	8	8
				5	3	5	8		
					4	2	5		

Key = 0|1|4 means 10 and 14

1. In which year did the Los Alamos Middle School football team score more points?

2. Describe the distribution of the stem-and-leaf plots for each year.

3. Create a combined dot plot to represent the data. Use "x"s and "o"s to represent data from the different years.

Points Scored by Los Alamos Middle School Football Team, 2009 and 2010

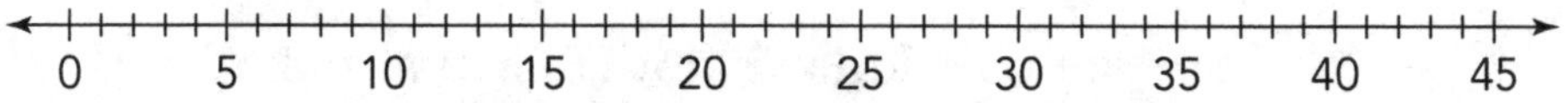

a. How does the shape of the stem-and-leaf plot distribution compare with the shape of the dot plot distributions?

4. Determine the five number summary and IQR for each data set. Then, complete the table shown.

	2009	2010
Minimum		
Q1		
Median		
Q3		
Maximum		
IQR		

5. In order to calculate the five number summary and IQR, did you use the data from the stem-and-leaf plot or the dot plots? Explain.

6. Compare the median and the IQR for the two data sets.

7. How does the difference in the medians compare to the IQR?

8. Do you think that scoring more points may have been one reason the Los Alamos Middle School football team improved its record?

The final step in the statistical process is to interpret the data.

NOTES

TALK the TALK

Summarize

Write 1–2 paragraphs to summarize this lesson. Answer each question in your response.

1. **How can you compare the mean and the spread of data for two populations from a dot plot?**

2. **If the measures of center for two populations are equivalent, how can the mean absolute variation show the differences in variation for two populations?**

Assignment

Write

Explain how to compare the difference of means with the variation of two populations in order to interpret the differences between the two populations.

Remember

Data for two populations may overlap. Comparing the measures of center and variation for the two populations can help you interpret the differences between the two populations.

Practice

The head librarian at the Branford Public Library is investigating the current trends in technology and the effects of computers and electronic books on the loaning of books. She thinks that the users at the library on the computers are generally younger than the people who actually check out books. She asks the ages of a sample of both computer users and book borrowers. The results are shown in the table.

Patron		Age
Computer user	Book borrower	
C		27
C		16
	B	57
C		20
	B	55
	B	60
C		22
	B	59
	B	63
C		20
C		24
	B	63
	B	60
C		22
C		20
C		17
	B	66
	B	60
	B	55
C		25

1. Display the results on a dot plot. Use an "o" to represent the computer users' ages, and an "x" to represent the book borrowers' ages from the information in the table.
2. Display the results using a stem-and-leaf plot. Be sure to include a key.
3. Describe the distribution of data values for the computer users and the book borrowers.
4. Calculate the mean age of the computer users and the mean age of the book borrowers.
5. Calculate, interpret, and compare the mean absolute deviations for both the computer users and the book borrowers.
6. Determine the five-number summary for the computer uses and the book borrowers.
7. Calculate, interpret, and compare the IQR for both the computer users and the book borrowers.
8. What can you say about these two populations?

Stretch

Let the difference in means between two data sets be *k*. Let the mean absolute deviation for the first data set be *m* and the mean absolute deviation for the second data set be *n*. Is it possible for the data sets to overlap if both $\frac{k}{m}$ and $\frac{k}{n}$ are greater than 1? If so, provide an example.

Review

1. Louie is using a computer program to randomly generate a digit from 1 to 6. Which statement most accurately describes how many times Louie's program will generate a 3 if he runs it 300 times? Explain your choice.
   a. exactly 50 times
   b. approximately 50 times
   c. exactly 100 times
   d. approximately 100 times
2. The school cafeteria has a hot food line and a cold food line for both breakfast and lunch. The cafeteria manager wants to estimate the percentage of students who select their meals from the hot food line. The manager collected data from the first 50 students who arrive for lunch and determined that 42% of students select their meals from the hot food line. Which statement is true about the cafeteria manager's sample? Explain your choice.
   a. The sample is the percent of students who select foods from the hot food line.
   b. The sample shows that exactly 42% of the student body select food from the hot food line.
   c. The sample might not be representative of the population because it only included the first group of lunch students.
   d. The sample size is too small to make any generalizations.
3. The spinner is divided into 8 equal sections. Determine each probability.
   a. *P*(greater than 3)
   b. *P*(not greater than 3)

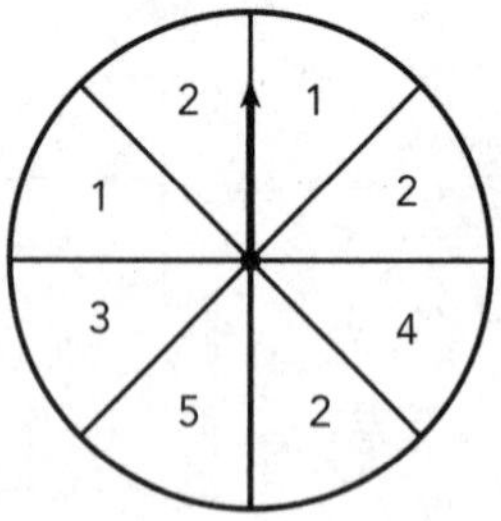

4. Determine each difference.
   a. $-7.7 - (-77.7)$
   b. $4\frac{1}{5} - 10\frac{3}{4}$

Finding Your Spot to Live

4

Using Random Samples from Two Populations to Draw Conclusions

Warm Up

Determine the mean absolute deviation of each data set. Round to the nearest hundredth.

1. 10, 5, 1, 3, 4

2. 100, 50, 10, 30, 40

LEARNING GOALS

- Compare the measures of variation for random samples from two populations.
- Express the difference between the centers of two data distributions as a multiple of a measure of variability.
- Use measures of variation to draw conclusions about two populations.

You have learned about measures of variation and have calculated the variations of different data sets. How can you compare data sets in terms of their variation to solve problems?

Getting Started

Downloading Podcasts

Square Roots is a radio show that airs 10 times a week on local radio station WMTH.

WMTH is trying to raise its commercial airtime rates during *Square Roots*. The station claims that while this music show is listened to by hundreds of middle school students via the radio, there are actually a greater number of middle school students who listen to the show by regularly downloading the podcast. Advertisers disagree with WMTH's claim. Advertisers want the station to verify its claim that there are more students listening by downloaded podcasts than actual listeners. To do so, WMTH and the advertisers choose Bryce Middle School to collect data. They send out a survey and ask the following two questions:

- Do you listen to *Square Roots* on the radio or download the podcast?
- How often do you listen to *Square Roots* per week?

All 389 students at Bryce Middle School who listen to *Square Roots* responded to the survey.

1. **What are the two populations for the *Square Roots* survey WMTH is conducting?**

WMTH decides to select a random sample for each population.

2. **There are 180 regular radio listeners and 209 podcast listeners at Bryce Middle School. Describe how WMTH and the advertisers can randomly select students for their sample.**

ACTIVITY
4.1 Simulating Random Samples

Let's use a random number table to simulate random samples from the data. The random number table and data are at the end of the lesson.

1. **Use the random number table and the list of radio and podcast listeners in Bryce Middle School at the end of the lesson to help WMTH randomly select a sample.**

   a. **Randomly select 10 radio listeners. Record each student's last name. Then, use the list to record the number of times each student listened to *Square Roots* during the week.**

   b. **Randomly select 10 podcast listeners. Record each student's last name. Then, use the list to record the number of podcasts each student downloaded in one week.**

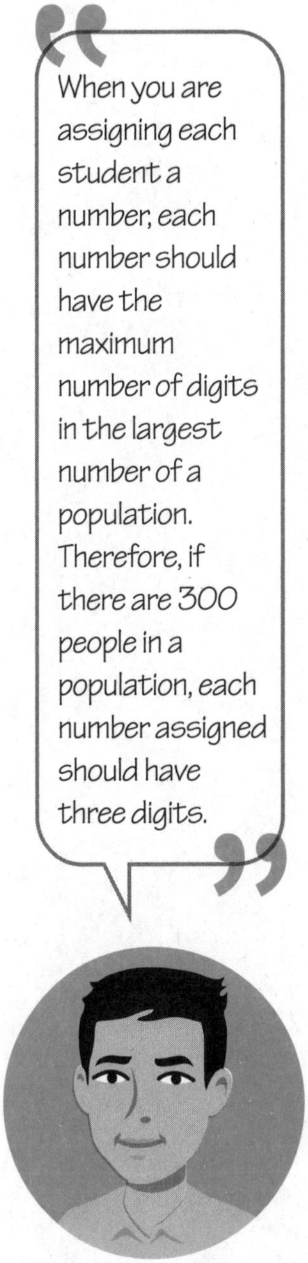

When you are assigning each student a number, each number should have the maximum number of digits in the largest number of a population. Therefore, if there are 300 people in a population, each number assigned should have three digits.

2. Construct a combined dot plot for the two groups. What conclusions can you draw?

Radio Shows and Podcasts
(per week)

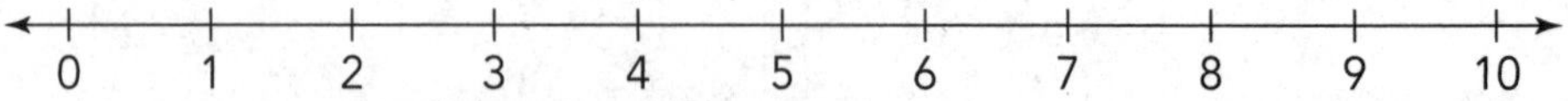

3. Describe the distribution for each graph. Describe any clusters or gaps in the data values in each graph.

4. Estimate the mean for each dot plot. Explain how you determined your estimate.

5. Calculate the mean number of radio shows listened to in a week, and the mean number of podcasts downloaded in a week.

6. Compare the two samples. Are more shows listened to on the radio, or are more podcasts downloaded?

7. Calculate the mean absolute deviation for each group. Compare the measures of center and variation.

8 Richard says,"If we had started on a different line number in the random number table, our results would have been the same." Is Richard correct? Explain your reasoning.

9. Combine your data with the data from other classmates. Calculate measures of center and variation for the two combined random samples, and interpret your results.

The third step in the statistical process is to interpret the data.

10. Determine the difference of means for the two samples and describe this difference as a multiple of the measure of variation.

ACTIVITY
4.2 Comparing Random Samples

Dominique graduated from college and now has a choice of two jobs. One of the jobs is in Ashland, and the other job is in Belsano. Since Dominique enjoys mild weather and average temperatures in the 60s (°F), she decides to compare the monthly average temperatures of the two cities. She gathered the following sample of average monthly temperatures for a previous year for the two cities as shown in the table.

Month	Ashland Average Monthly Temperatures (°F)	Belsano Average Monthly Temperatures (°F)
January	56	48
February	58	55
March	60	59
April	61	62
May	65	66
June	70	69
July	75	78
August	82	88
September	73	82
October	68	69
November	60	59
December	56	49

1. What are some ways Dominique could analyze the data to determine which city is warmer?

2. Dominique decides to calculate the mean and median temperature for each city to determine which city is warmer overall. Calculate the mean and median temperature for both cities. What do you notice?

3. Jacqui says that since Ashland and Belsano have very similar mean and median temperatures, Dominique could choose either city to live in because they both have mild temperatures. Do you agree or disagree? Explain your reasoning.

Don't forget to add a key to the plot.

4. Construct a back-to-back stem-and-leaf plot for the average monthly temperature for each city.

Ashland		Belsano

5. What conclusions can you draw from the plot?

6. Determine and interpret the five number summary and IQR for each data set. Then, describe some observations from the data of each five number summary.

	Ashland	**Belsano**
Minimum:		
Q1:		
Median:		
Q3:		
Maximum:		
IQR:		

NOTES

7. Construct and label box-and-whisker plots for each data set using the same number line for both. What conclusions can you make?

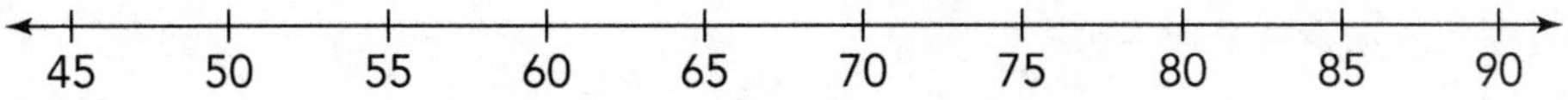

8. Compare the mean and variation of the samples. If you were Dominique, which city would you choose to live in? Explain your reasoning.

ACTIVITY 4.3

Analyzing Displays of Data from Random Samples

Web sites often analyze customer visits to see if there are patterns or trends. Gaining information about patterns helps companies display the information users want.

A sample of customer visits to Horizon, a news and opinion website, are shown in the histograms. The histograms display the number of visits customers made to the Articles and Photo Gallery sections of the website, along with how long each customer spent viewing content in each section.

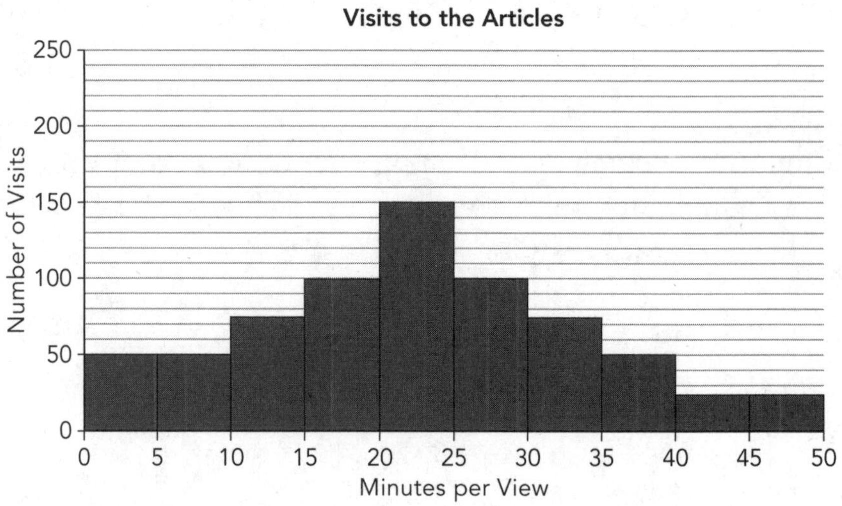

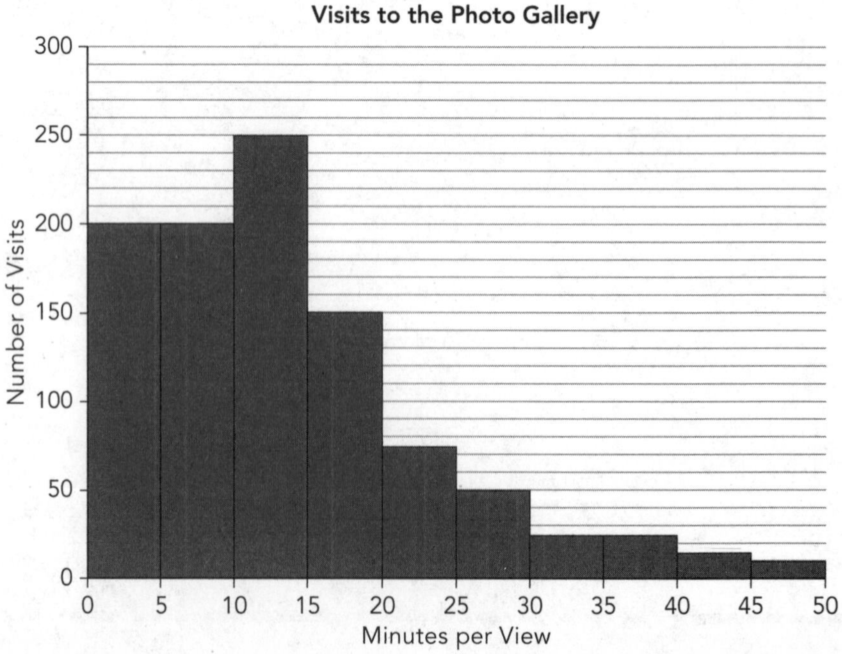

1. Describe the populations and samples for this problem.

2. What do the intervals along the *x*-axis and *y*-axis represent for each histogram?

3. About how many visits were made to the Articles sample? the Photo Gallery sample? Explain how you determined your answer.

4. Desmond claims that the variation in the length of views of each section in terms of the range is about the same for both sections. Do you agree or disagree?

5. Describe the shape of each histogram and explain what this means in terms of the number of minutes per view.

6. Determine whether the mean or the median is greater for each section. Then, explain why that measure of center is greater in value for each section.

7. If you calculate the mean absolute deviation for the length of the views, which section would have more variation in the length of views? Why?

8. The box-and-whisker plots shown represent the view durations for the Photo Gallery and Articles sections. Using the information you know from the histograms for each section, which box plot do you think represents the view durations for Articles, and which represents the view durations for Photo Gallery? Explain your choice.

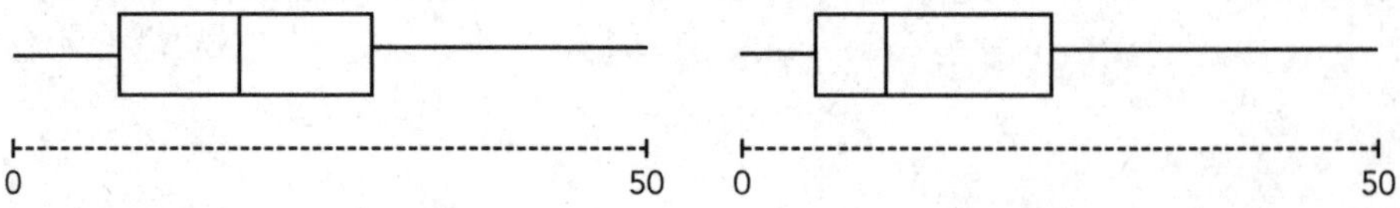

9. In terms of the box-and-whisker plots, which section has more variation in the duration of views? Explain your reasoning.

NOTES

TALK the TALK

Into Each Life Some Rain Must Fall

Sam lives in Seattle, Washington, and says it seems like it rains all the time. Richard lives in Washington, D.C., and says it seems like it doesn't rain very much.

The table contains the average monthly rainfall for both cities over the past 30 years.

1. **Use any method you want to determine the validity of Sam's and Richard's statements.**

Month	Seattle, Washington Average Monthly Rainfall (inches)	Washington, D.C. Average Monthly Rainfall (inches)
January	5.24	3.21
February	4.09	2.63
March	3.92	3.60
April	2.75	2.77
May	2.03	3.82
June	1.55	3.13
July	0.93	3.66
August	1.16	3.44
September	1.61	3.79
October	3.24	3.22
November	5.67	3.03
December	6.06	3.05

Square Roots Fans Who Listen on the Radio

Student Number	Student Name	Radio Shows Listened (per week)
1	Abunto	1
2	Adler	3
3	Aizawa	3
4	Alescio	4
5	Almasy	8
6	Ansari	6
7	Aro	7
8	Aung	2
9	Baehr	7
10	Bellmer	1
11	Bilski	4
12	Blinn	6
13	Bonetto	3
14	Breznai	1
15	Cabot	3
16	Chacalos	0
17	Cioc	0
18	Cole	3
19	Creighan	4
20	Cuthbert	6

Student Number	Student Name	Radio Shows Listened (per week)
21	D'Ambrosio	0
22	Datz	4
23	Delecroix	2
24	Difiore	6
25	Dobrich	7
26	Donoghy	1
27	Donaldson	5
28	Dreher	2
29	Dubinsky	1
30	Dytko	8
31	Fabry	7
32	Fetcher	1
33	Fontes	5
34	Frick	3
35	Furmanek	5
36	Gadgil	4
37	Gavlak	4
38	Gibbs	0
39	Gloninger	2
40	Goff	1

Student Number	Student Name	Radio Shows Listened (per week)
41	Granger	0
42	Guca	2
43	Haag	8
44	Heese	5
45	Hilson	1
46	Holihan	1
47	Hudack	1
48	Ianuzzi	3
49	Islamov	4
50	Jacobsen	5
51	Jessell	4
52	Ji	1
53	Johnson	2
54	Jomisko	1
55	Jones	6
56	Joy	5
57	Jumba	1
58	Juth	7
59	Jyoti	6
60	Kachur	2

Square Roots Fans Who Listen on the Radio

Student Number	Student Name	Radio Shows Listened (per week)
61	Kanai	0
62	Keller	2
63	Khaing	7
64	Kindler	5
65	Kneiss	5
66	Kolc	1
67	Kuisis	2
68	Labas	1
69	Lasek	8
70	Leeds	5
71	Lin	0
72	Litsko	2
73	Lodi	3
74	Lookman	2
75	Lucini	1
76	Lykos	0
77	MacAllister	1
78	Magliocca	6
79	Marchick	5
80	McGuire	1

Student Number	Student Name	Radio Shows Listened (per week)
81	McNary	7
82	Meadows	0
83	Merks	8
84	Mickler	5
85	Minniti	4
86	Mohr	3
87	Mordecki	5
88	Mueser	3
89	Musati	3
90	Myron	2
91	Nadzam	4
92	Nazif	7
93	Newby	0
94	Ng	1
95	Nino	2
96	Northcutt	4
97	Novi	3
98	Null	8
99	New	5
100	Nyiri	1

Student Number	Student Name	Radio Shows Listened (per week)
101	Nzuyen	2
102	O'Bryon	0
103	Obitz	3
104	Oglesby	8
105	Ono	1
106	Paclawski	0
107	Pappis	6
108	Peery	3
109	Phillips	5
110	Potter	3
111	Pribanic	7
112	Pwono	5
113	Quinn	2
114	Rabel	5
115	Rayl	2
116	Rea	4
117	Reynolds	5
118	Rhor	8
119	Rielly	8
120	Risa	7

Square Roots Fans Who Listen on the Radio

Student Number	Student Name	Radio Shows Listened (per week)
121	Robinson	8
122	Roethlein	1
123	Romanski	7
124	Rouce	7
125	Rubio	7
126	Rutland	3
127	Rychcik	1
128	Sabhnani	6
129	Sandroni	2
130	Saxon	3
131	Scalo	4
132	Schessler	1
133	Seeley	0
134	Shanahan	3
135	Siejk	1
136	Skaro	3
137	Slonaker	8
138	Sobr	2
139	Spatz	4
140	Sramac	2

Student Number	Student Name	Radio Shows Listened (per week)
141	Stevens	4
142	Tabor	0
143	Tevis	5
144	Thomas	0
145	Thompson	1
146	Thorne	1
147	Tiani	0
148	Tokay	6
149	Toomey	6
150	Trax	1
151	Truong	8
152	Tunstall	1
153	Twiss	6
154	Tyler	0
155	Ueki	0
156	Uriah	6
157	Vagnelli	6
158	Van Dine	5
159	Vella	1
160	Vidnic	0

Student Number	Student Name	Radio Shows Listened (per week)
161	Volk	5
162	Vyra	4
163	Wadhwani	5
164	Warnaby	0
165	Weasley	2
166	Weidt	8
167	Whitelow	0
168	Wilson	4
169	Woller	1
170	Woo	0
171	Wunderlich	6
172	Wycoff	4
173	Xander	8
174	Yahya	0
175	Yezovich	4
176	Youse	0
177	Yuzon	8
178	Za Khai	3
179	Ziff	2
180	Zuk	5

Square Roots Fans Who Download Show Podcasts

Student Number	Student Name	Podcasts Downloaded (per week)
1	Aaronson	2
2	Abati	0
3	Ackerman	4
4	Aderholt	2
5	Akat	7
6	Aleck	9
7	Alessandro	5
8	Allen	3
9	Ansil	1
10	Archer	5
11	Badgett	9
12	Bartle	2
13	Bibby	9
14	Bilich	5
15	Bloom	3
16	Boccio	5
17	Bracht	3
18	Bujak	7
19	Caliari	9
20	Cerminara	8
21	Chang	4
22	Clarke	9
23	Crnkovich	0
24	Dahl	0
25	Dax	7
26	Defoe	1
27	Dengler	4
28	Di Minno	4
29	Dilla	5
30	Draus	5
31	Duffy	0
32	Ecoff	3
33	Esparra	7
34	Fakiro	7
35	Ferlan	4
36	Fetherman	2
37	Fillipelli	6
38	Fisher	2
39	Folino	9
40	Forrester	9
41	Frena	1
42	Galdi	8
43	Gansberger	3
44	Gianni	1
45	Glencer	1
46	Godec	7
47	Goldstein	0
48	Graef	6
49	Gula	1
50	Hagen	2
51	Haupt	8
52	Herc	4
53	Hnat	9
54	Hodak	3
55	Hoyt	2
56	Huang	3
57	Iannotta	4
58	Irwin	5
59	Jackson	7
60	Jamil	1

Square Roots Fans Who Download Show Podcasts

Student Number	Student Name	Podcasts Downloaded (per week)
61	Jessop	1
62	Johnson	9
63	Joos	9
64	Joseph	5
65	Jubic	3
66	Juhl	7
67	Jung	9
68	Jurgensen	4
69	Jyoti	0
70	Kaib	5
71	Kapoor	6
72	Kennedy	2
73	Kimel	5
74	Klaas	4
75	Ko	9
76	Krabb	1
77	Ladley	9
78	Lawson	1
79	Lemieux	7
80	Lewan	6

Student Number	Student Name	Podcasts Downloaded (per week)
81	Ling	6
82	Loch	4
83	Lorenzo	4
84	Lovejoy	5
85	Luba	8
86	Lukitsch	4
87	Luzzi	8
88	Lyman	5
89	MacIntyre	8
90	Maddex	5
91	Marai	2
92	Mato	9
93	McCaffrey	0
94	McElroy	5
95	McMillan	3
96	Meng	9
97	Michelini	5
98	Misra	0
99	Miller	8
100	Modecki	7

Student Number	Student Name	Podcasts Downloaded (per week)
101	Moorey	6
102	Mox	7
103	Mrkali	7
104	Mu	0
105	Muller	3
106	Murphy	2
107	Mwambazi	6
108	Myers	4
109	Nangle	3
110	Neilan	7
111	Nicolay	5
112	Niehl	6
113	Nix	2
114	Noga	3
115	Nowatzki	7
116	Nuescheler	5
117	Nye	6
118	Nytra	6
119	O'Carrol	6
120	Obedi	7

Square Roots Fans Who Download Show Podcasts

Student Number	Student Name	Podcasts Downloaded (per week)	Student Number	Student Name	Podcasts Downloaded (per week)	Student Number	Student Name	Podcasts Downloaded (per week)
121	Oehrle	8	141	Rea	5	161	Scopaz	4
122	Olds	5	142	Renard	7	162	Sebula	4
123	Oleary	0	143	Rex	7	163	Shah	1
124	Ondrey	1	144	Richards	7	164	Sidor	6
125	Owusu	9	145	Ridout	7	165	Skraly	6
126	Palamides	9	146	Rivera	6	166	Sokolowski	5
127	Pappas	0	147	Roberts	4	167	Speer	6
128	Pecori	3	148	Rodwich	0	168	T'Ung	9
129	Pennix	4	149	Roney	7	169	Tamar	9
130	Pendleton	1	150	Ross	6	170	Tebelius	1
131	Phillippi	2	151	Rothering	0	171	Tesla	4
132	Pieton	6	152	Rua	4	172	Thuma	0
133	Ploeger	2	153	Russo	8	173	Tibi	2
134	Pressman	4	154	Ryer	8	174	Tobkes	9
135	Puzzini	1	155	Sagi	8	175	Torelli	8
136	Qu	4	156	Sallinger	6	176	Tozzi	0
137	Qutyan	8	157	Sau	7	177	Traut	6
138	Raab	5	158	Sbragia	7	178	Trax	0
139	Raeff	0	159	Schaier	5	179	Tu	8
140	Rav	1	160	Schmit	2	180	Tumicki	2

Square Roots Fans Who Download Show Podcasts

Student Number	Student Name	Podcasts Downloaded (per week)
181	Tyson	1
182	Uansa	0
183	Ulan	4
184	Urbano	7
185	Uzonyi	7
186	Vaezi	8
187	Vinay	6
188	Vu	8
189	Wallee	0
190	Waldock	4

Student Number	Student Name	Podcasts Downloaded (per week)
191	Wallace	2
192	Webb	9
193	Weisenfeld	0
194	Whalen	7
195	Wiley	9
196	Williams	5
197	Williamson	6
198	Witek	9
199	Wojcik	3
200	Woollett	6

Student Number	Student Name	Podcasts Downloaded (per week)
201	Wulandana	8
202	Wysor	9
203	Xiao	4
204	Yee	6
205	Yost	1
206	Young	7
207	Yuros	6
208	Zaki	0
209	Zimmerman	1

Random Number Table										
Line 1	65285	97198	12138	53010	94601	15838	16805	61004	43516	17020
Line 2	17264	57327	38224	29301	31381	38109	34976	65692	98566	29550
Line 3	95639	99754	31199	92558	68368	04985	51092	37780	40261	14479
Line 4	61555	76404	86210	11808	12841	45147	97438	60022	12645	62000
Line 5	78137	98768	04689	87130	79225	08153	84967	64539	79493	74917
Line 6	62490	99215	84987	28759	19177	14733	24550	28067	68894	38490
Line 7	24216	63444	21283	07044	92729	37284	13211	37485	10415	36457
Line 8	16975	95428	33226	55903	31605	43817	22250	03918	46999	98501
Line 9	59138	39542	71168	57609	91510	77904	74244	50940	31553	62562
Line 10	29478	59652	50414	31966	87912	87154	12944	49862	96566	48825
Line 11	96155	95009	27429	72918	08457	78134	48407	26061	58754	05326
Line 12	29621	66583	62966	12468	20245	14015	04014	35713	03980	03024
Line 13	12639	75291	71020	17265	41598	64074	64629	63293	53307	48766
Line 14	14544	37134	54714	02401	63228	26831	19386	15457	17999	18306
Line 15	83403	88827	09834	11333	68431	31706	26652	04711	34593	22561
Line 16	67642	05204	30697	44806	96989	68403	85621	45556	35434	09532
Line 17	64041	99011	14610	40273	09482	62864	01573	82274	81446	32477
Line 18	17048	94523	97444	59904	16936	39384	97551	09620	63932	03091
Line 19	93039	89416	52795	10631	09728	68202	20963	02477	55494	39563
Line 20	82244	34392	96607	17220	51984	10753	76272	50985	97593	34320

Assignment

Write

Explain how to use measures of center and variation to compare two populations.

Remember

You can use the means and mean absolute deviations to compare two populations with approximately symmetric data sets. You can use the medians and the interquartile range to compare two populations with skewed data sets.

Practice

1. Repeat the sampling procedure you used with the data in Activity 4.1. Choose a different line number in the random number table.
   a. Record the results for 20 students.
   b. Construct a combined dot plot for the two groups, using the same scale.
   c. Describe the distribution of the data for each group.
   d. Estimate and then calculate the mean for the data in each group.
   e. Compare your new results with your results from Activity 4.1.
2. Ratings are not limited to television shows alone. Ratings can also be used to show people's opinions of hotels and restaurants. One of the things that can help a restaurant get good ratings is the time it takes to be seated (the wait time) at a restaurant without reservations.
3. Big Al's Steak House and Trail's End both claim to have the shortest wait times in town. To check out the claims, Ramon, a restaurant reviewer, records the time it takes to be seated without reservations. The results of wait times for 8 visits to each restaurant are shown in the table.

Big Al's Steak House Wait Times (minutes)	Trail's End Wait Times (minutes)
5	11
13	19
22	14
7	14
20	15
21	20
20	10
12	17

   a. Describe the populations and samples for this problem.
   b. Calculate the mean wait times between the two restaurants. Which restaurant seems to have faster service?

c. Complete the dot plot of the times. What do you notice?

Wait Times

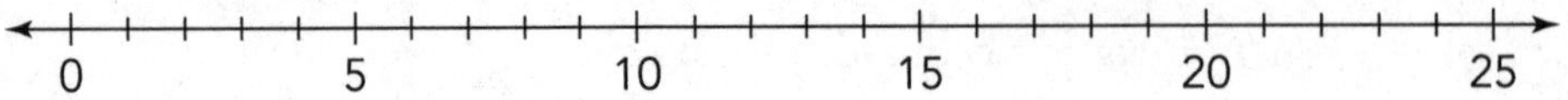

o = Big Al's Steak House

x = Trail's End

d. Determine the median wait time for each restaurant.

e. Explain the difference in median times for the two restaurants.

f. Which measure of center would you use if:

  a. you are Big Al's Steak House and want to claim you have the shortest wait time?

  b. you are Trail's End and want to claim you have the shortest wait time?

  c. you are a customer and want the shortest wait time?

g. Suppose another restaurant reviewer records wait times at each restaurant several times. Do you think it is possible that the wait times might be different from Ramon's wait times? Explain your reasoning.

h. How could we be more certain which restaurant has the shortest wait time?

Stretch

Conduct your own experiment! Collect data from samples drawn from two populations. Then, analyze the data and report on your findings.

Review

Describe the difference in means between each data set as a multiple of the mean absolute deviation of each data set.

1. {1, 2, 3, 4, 5} {5, 5, 5, 5, 5}
2. {62, 41, 11, 60, 55} {50, 112, 149, 131, 60}

A spinner has 6 equal sections, labeled 1 through 6. Determine each compound probability.

3. What is the probability that the next spin is a 2 or a 5?
4. What is the probability that the next spin is a 1, 2, or 3?

Evaluate each expression for $x = -0.5$.

5. $x^4 + x^3$
6. $-x^4 - x^3$

Drawing Inferences Summary

KEY TERMS

- survey
- data
- population
- census
- sample
- parameter
- statistic
- random sample

LESSON 1 We Want to Hear From You!

There are four components of the statistical process:

- Formulating a statistical question.
- Collecting appropriate data.
- Analyzing the data graphically and numerically.
- Interpreting the results of the analysis.

One data collection strategy you can use is a survey. A **survey** is a method of collecting information about a certain group of people. It involves asking a question or a set of questions to those people. When information is collected, the facts or numbers gathered are called **data**.

The **population** is the entire set of items from which data can be selected. When you decide what you want to study, the population is the set of all elements in which you are interested. The elements of that population can be people or objects. A **census** is the data collected from every member of a population.

In most cases, it is not possible or logical to collect data from every member of the population. When data are collected from a part of the population, the data are called a **sample**.

When data are gathered from a population, the characteristic used to describe the population is called a **parameter**. When data are gathered from a sample, the characteristic used to describe the sample is called a **statistic**. A statistic is used to make an estimate about the parameter.

When information is collected from a sample in order to describe a characteristic about the population, it is important that such a sample be as representative of the population as possible. A **random sample** is a sample that is selected from the population in such a way that every member of the population has the same chance of being selected.

LESSON 2 Tiles, Gumballs, and Pumpkins

If you are estimating a parameter that is a count, rather than a percentage, you can use proportional reasoning to scale up from the ratio of the number of observations in your sample to the statistic.

There are three common distributions of data: skewed left, skewed right, and symmetric. The distribution of data can help you determine whether the mean or median is a better measure of center.

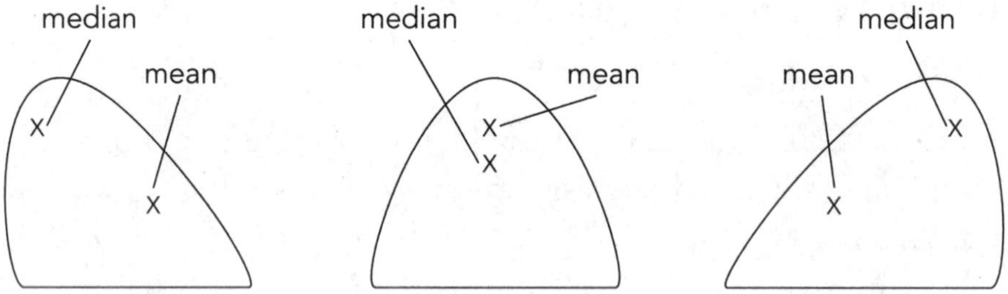

skewed right

The mean of a data set is greater than the median when the data are skewed to the right.

The median is the best measure of center because the median is not affected by very large data values.

symmetric

The mean and median are equal when the data are symmetric.

skewed left

The mean of a data set is less than the median when the data are skewed to the left.

The median is the best measure of center because the median is not affected by very small data values.

LESSON 3

Spicy or Dark?

Data for two populations may overlap. Comparing the measures of center and variation for the two populations can help you interpret the differences between the two populations.

Comparing the difference of means with the variation in each data set can be an important way of determining just how different two data sets are.

For example, consider these data sets.

5, 3, 4, 5, 10	5, 3, 100, 5, 10
Mean = 5.4	Mean = 24.6

The difference in their means is 19.2. Depending on what you are measuring, that can be a big difference. However, this difference of 19.2 is actually less than the mean absolute deviation of the right data set (30.16). This indicates that the data sets may overlap. The right data set is the same as the left one except for one number.

LESSON 4

Finding Your Spot to Live

You can use the means and mean absolute deviations to compare two populations with approximately symmetric data sets. You can use the medians and the interquartile range to compare two populations with skewed data sets.

For example, suppose Forrest wanted to compare the number of text messages sent each day by middle school students to the number of text messages sent each day by high school students. He randomly selected and surveyed 10 students from each grade. The data sets provided represent the number of text messages each student said they send each day.

Grade 7: 44, 40, 43, 73, 74, 76, 56, 59, 66, 54

Grade 8: 77, 86, 69, 52, 76, 79, 60, 61, 57, 85

Forrest created a back-to-back stem-and-leaf plot to display the data.

Grade 7 Leaf	Stem	Grade 8 Leaf
4 3 0	4	
9 6 4	5	2 7
6	6	0 1 9
6 4 3	7	6 7 9
	8	5 6

For grade 7, the mean number of texts sent per day is 58.5 and the mean absolute deviation is 11.1. The median is 57.5 and the interquartile range is 29. For grade 8, the mean number of texts sent per day is 70.2 and the mean absolute deviation is 10.4. The median is 69 and the interquartile range is 22.

MODULE 5

CONSTRUCTING AND MEASURING

The lessons in this module build on your experiences with angles and triangles and introduce the construction of familiar geometric objects. You will construct basic geometric objects with a compass and straightedge and later use these techniques to construct triangles. You will use patty paper to investigate special types of angle relationships and then use those relationships to write and solve equations to determine unknown values in a figure. You will use your knowledge of polygons and polyhedra to create and describe cross-sections of right rectangular prisms and pyramids. Finally, you will extend your knowledge of volume and surface area to solve problems involving a variety of three-dimensional solids.

TOPIC 1

Angles and Triangles

A jib is a triangular sail that sits ahead of the foremast of a sailing ship. Its most crucial function is as an airfoil, increasing performance and overall stability by reducing turbulence on the leeward side of the mainsail.

Module 5: Constructing and Measuring

TOPIC 1: ANGLES AND TRIANGLES

This topic begins by establishing the building blocks of geometry, using appropriate drawings, vocabulary, and notation. Students learn about formal constructions and use construction tools to duplicate segments and angles and to make additional constructions. Students then explore different pairs of angles. Finally, students use both patty paper and formal construction tools to determine if given information defines a unique triangle, multiple triangles, or no triangles.

Where have we been?

In the very first topic in this course, students were introduced to a compass to construct congruent circles. Geometric terms students have used in the past—point, line, and plane—are formally defined, and students learn the notation for each.

Where are we going?

This topic provides the building blocks for the remaining geometry topics in middle school, as well as those in high school. In grade 8, students will build from analyzing what happens when two lines intersect to analyzing what happens when more than two lines intersect. In grade 8 and in high school geometry, students will use transformations to establish conditions for similarity and congruence.

Using Constructions to Reason About Geometry

Students learn about the ancient method of constructions to create representations of geometric objects. With constructions, one is allowed only a compass and straightedge (not a ruler) to create geometric figures. The construction shown involves duplicating a line segment. This construction demonstrates that congruent line segments are line segments that have the same length.

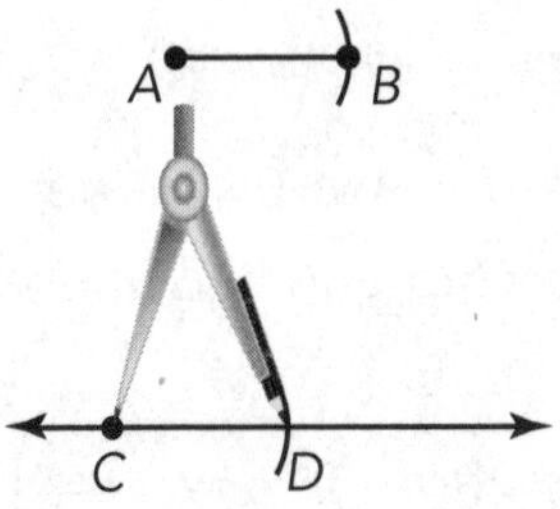

Myth: Some students are "right-brain" learners while other students are "left-brain" learners.

As you probably know, the brain is divided into two hemispheres: the left and the right. Some categorize people by their preferred or dominant mode of thinking. "Right-brain" thinkers are considered to be more intuitive, creative, and imaginative. "Left-brain" thinkers are more logical, verbal, and mathematical.

But another way to think about the brain is from the back to the front, where information goes from highly concrete to abstract. So, why don't we claim that some people are "back of the brain" thinkers who are highly concrete; whereas, others are "frontal thinkers" who are more abstract?

The brain is a highly interconnected organ. Each lobe hands off information to be processed by other lobes, and they are constantly talking to each other. So it's time to dispense with the distinction between right- and left-brain thinkers. We are all whole-brain thinkers!

#mathmythbusted

Talking Points

You can further support your student's learning by asking questions about the work they do in class or at home. Your student is continuing to reason about abstract geometric objects and constructions.

Questions to Ask

- Does your answer make sense? Why?
- Can you show me the strategy you used to solve this problem? Do you know another way to solve it?
- Is there anything you don't understand? How can you use today's lesson to help?

Key Terms

supplementary angles
Two angles are supplementary angles if the sum of their angle measures equals 180°.

complementary angles
Two angles are complementary angles if the sum of their angle measures equals 90°.

vertical angles
Vertical angles are two nonadjacent angles that are formed by two intersecting lines.

Triangle Inequality Theorem
The Triangle Inequality Theorem states that the sum of the lengths of any two sides of a triangle is greater than the length of the third side.

Here's Lookin' at Euclid

1

Geometric Constructions

WARM UP

1. How would you describe the difference between these two figures?

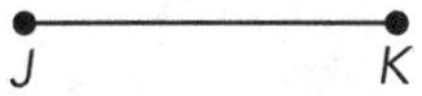

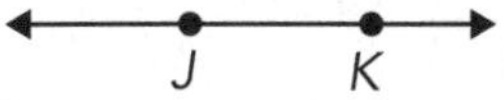

2. How many points are in this figure?

LEARNING GOALS

- Name geometric figures.
- Draw geometric shapes with given conditions.
- Use a compass to construct circles.
- Use a compass and straightedge to duplicate line segments and angles.

KEY TERMS

- constructions
- compass
- straightedge
- sketch
- draw
- point
- line
- plane
- line segment
- endpoints
- arc
- congruent
- angle
- ray
- sides of an angle
- vertex

You have used geometry to analyze plane figures such as triangles and squares. In this lesson, you will focus on the geometric building blocks of those figures—points and lines.

Getting Started

Euclid and Constructions

A **compass** is a tool used to create arcs and circles.

A **straightedge** is a ruler with no numbers.

A **sketch** is a freehand drawing of an object.

When you **draw** a geometric figure, the figure is created with the use of tools such as a ruler and protractor.

Euclid was a Greek mathematician who lived more than 2000 years ago. He put together a collection of ideas about geometry in a book called *The Elements*.

Euclid used special drawings, called *constructions*, to explain and prove geometric statements. **Constructions** are created using only a *compass* or a *straightedge* or both.

1. **Sketch a few circles.**

2. **Use a compass to construct a number of different circles.**

3. **Were the sketches or constructions more exact? Explain your thinking.**

ACTIVITY 1.1

The Building Blocks of Geometry

NOTES

Three essential building blocks of geometry are point, line, and plane.

A **point** is described as a location in space. A point has no size or shape, but it is often represented using a dot and is named with a capital letter.

As examples, points *A* and *B* are shown.

A **line** is a straight continuous arrangement of an infinite number of points. A line has an infinite length, but no width. Arrowheads are used to indicate that a line extends infinitely in opposite directions. The line symbol is $\leftrightarrow$.

Lines are named with either a lowercase single letter or by using two points through which the line passes with a line symbol above them. The names of the lines shown are line *m* and $\overleftrightarrow{CD}$ and are read as "line *m*" and "line *CD*."

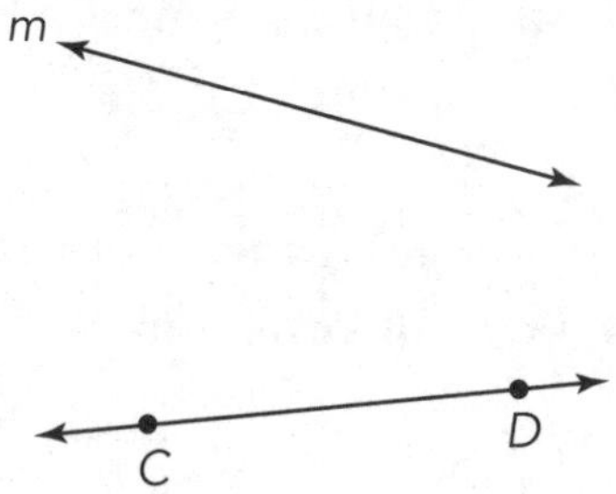

A **plane** is a flat surface. A plane has an infinite length and width, but no depth. A plane extends infinitely in all directions in two dimensions. Planes are determined by three points, but they are usually named using one uppercase letter. As an example, plane Q is shown.

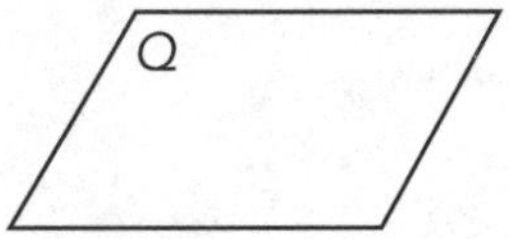

A **line segment** is a portion of a line that includes two points and all the points between those two points. The **endpoints** of a line segment are the points where the line segment ends. A line segment is named using the two capital letters that name its endpoints.

For example, the name of line segment *AB* can be written using symbols as $\overline{AB}$. This is read as "line segment *AB*." You should know that $\overline{AB}$ is the same as $\overline{BA}$. It does not matter which endpoint you use first to name a line segment.

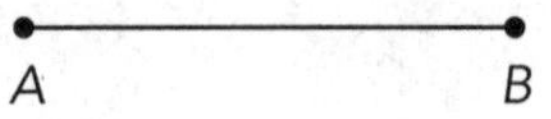

The radius of a circle is the distance from its center to any point on the circle. The plural of "radius" is "radii."

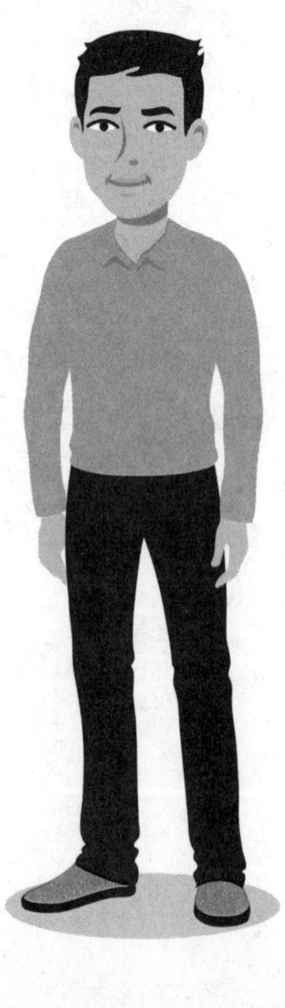

1. Construct a circle using line segment *CD* as the radius and *C* as the center.

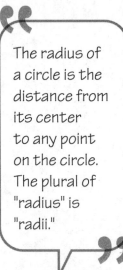

a. Draw and label points *A*, *B*, *E*, and *F* on the circle and then construct $\overline{AC}$, $\overline{BC}$, $\overline{EC}$, and $\overline{FC}$.

b. What conclusion can you make about all these line segments? Explain your reasoning.

c. Do you think the line segments you constructed are also radii of the circle? How do you know?

An *arc* is a part of a circle. You can also think of an **arc** as the curve between two points on the circle.

2. Construct an arc using $\overline{AC}$ as the radius and *C* as the center of the circle. Make your arc about one-half inch long, and make sure that it does not pass through *A*.

a. Draw and label two points *B* and *E* on the arc and then construct line segments *CE* and *CB*.

b. What conclusion(s) can you make about these line segments?

Line segments that have the same length are called *congruent* line segments. You can indicate that two line segments are congruent by using the congruence symbol, ≅, and writing the names of the line segments that are congruent on either side of it.

Congruent means to have the same size, shape, and measure.

For example, $\overline{CB} \cong \overline{CA}$ is read as "line segment *CB* is congruent to line segment *CA*."

3. How do you think you could construct congruent line segments? Use your compass and straightedge to try to construct a line segment congruent to line segment *XY* shown.

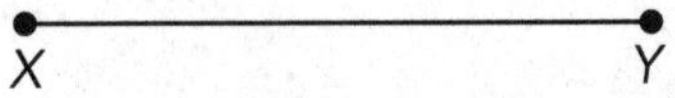

ACTIVITY 1.2 Duplicating Line Segments

In this activity, you will use construction tools to duplicate line segments.

Use only your construction tools. No measuring tools allowed.

WORKED EXAMPLE

You can duplicate a line segment by constructing an exact copy of the original line segment.

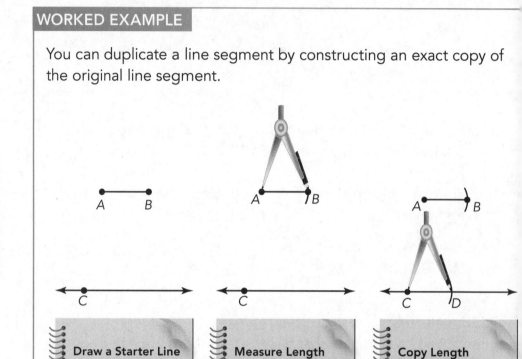

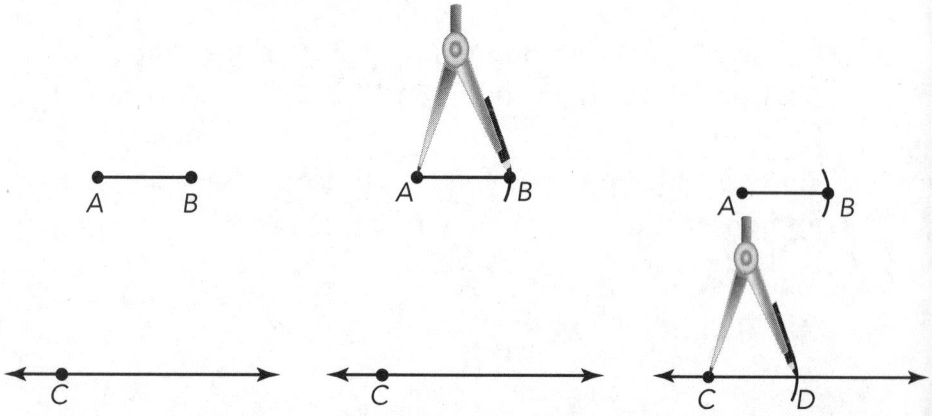

Draw a Starter Line

Use a straightedge to draw a starter line longer than segment *AB*. Label point *C* on the new segment.

Measure Length

Set your compass at the length *AB*.

Copy Length

Place the compass at *C*. Mark point *D* on the new segment.

1. Construct and label a line segment that is twice the length of line segment *AB*.

2. Duplicate each line segment using a compass and a straightedge.

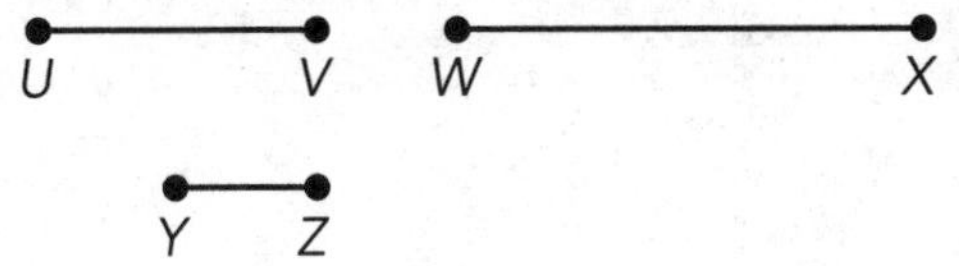

U
V
W
X
Y
Z

Be sure to label your new figures.

3. Use your constructions to answer each question.

   a. List the names of all the lines using symbols.

   b. List the names of all the labeled line segments using symbols.

ACTIVITY 1.3 Duplicating Angles

A **ray** is a part of a line that begins at a point and extends infinitely in one direction. Rays are named using two points. The first point represents the starting point, and the second point can be any other point on the ray. The name of ray AB can be written using symbols as $\overrightarrow{AB}$, which is read as "ray AB."

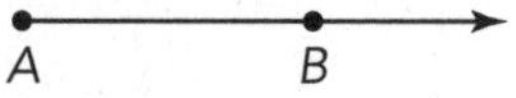

An **angle** is formed by two *rays* that share a common endpoint. The angle symbol is ∠. The **sides of an angle** are the two rays. The **vertex** of an angle is the common endpoint the two rays share.

WORKED EXAMPLE

You can duplicate an angle by constructing an exact copy of the original using your tools of geometry.

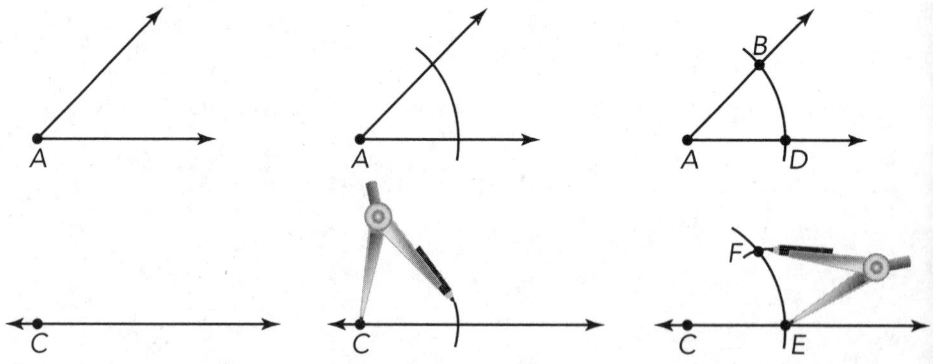

Draw a Starter Line
Use a straightedge to draw a starter line. Label point C on the new line.

Draw an Arc
Draw an arc with center A that intersects both sides of the angle. Using the same radius, draw an arc with center C.

Draw an Arc
Label points B, D, and E. Draw an arc with radius BD at center E. Label the intersection F.

Draw a Ray
Draw ray CF.
$\angle BAD \cong \angle FCE$.

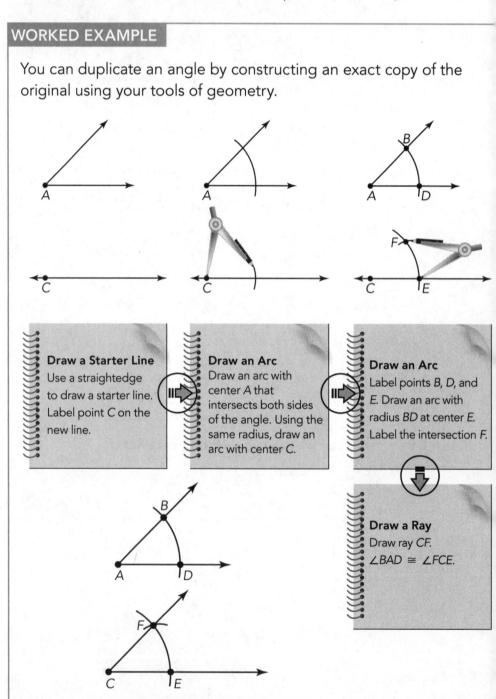

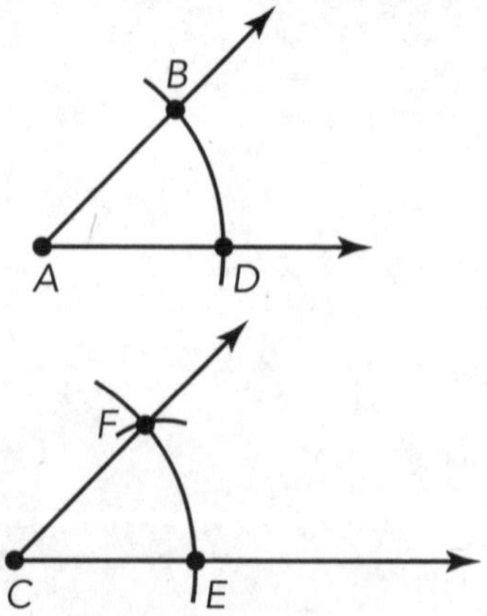

NOTES

1. Consider the worked example.

   a. How wide do you set your compass to start this type of construction? What is important about the first arc you draw?

   b. In the second step, what does "using the same radius" tell you about how to use your compass throughout the construction?

2. Construct and label an angle that is twice the measure of $\angle A$.

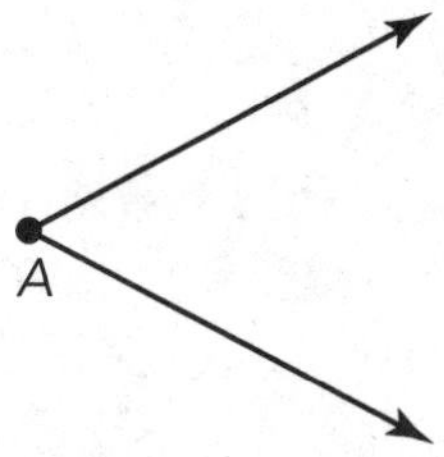

3. Use your construction to answer each question.

   a. List all the different angles using symbols.

   b. Identify the vertices of all the angles.

NOTES

TALK the TALK

Construct and Identify

Use the given sides and angles to complete each construction.

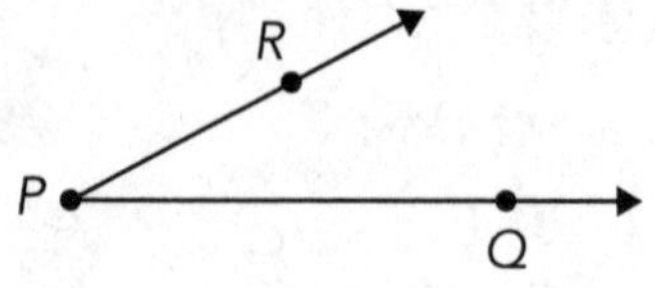

1. Construct and label a segment twice the length of segment *PQ*.

2. Construct and label an angle twice the measure of angle *P*.

3. Identify all the points, lines, line segments, rays, and angles that you can in the two figures in Questions 1 and 2.

Assignment

Write

Write the term that best completes the statement.

1. ______________ means to have the same size, shape, and measure.
2. A(n) ______________ is a ruler with no numbers.
3. ______________________ are line segments that have the same length.
4. A(n) ______________ is described as a straight continuous arrangement of an infinite number of points.
5. A(n) ______________ is part of a circle, or the curve between two points on a circle.
6. A(n) ______________ is a tool used to create arcs and circles.
7. When you ______________ a geometric figure, the figure is created without the use of tools.
8. A(n) ______________ is described as a location in space, and it has no size or shape.

Remember

Euclid was a Greek mathematician who lived more than 2000 years ago. He put together a collection of ideas about geometry in a book called *The Elements*.

Euclid used special drawings, called *constructions*, to explain and prove geometric statements. Constructions are created using only a *compass* or a *straightedge* or both.

Practice

Construct and label each circle with the given radius and center.

1. Construct a circle using $\overline{AB}$ as the radius and A as the center.

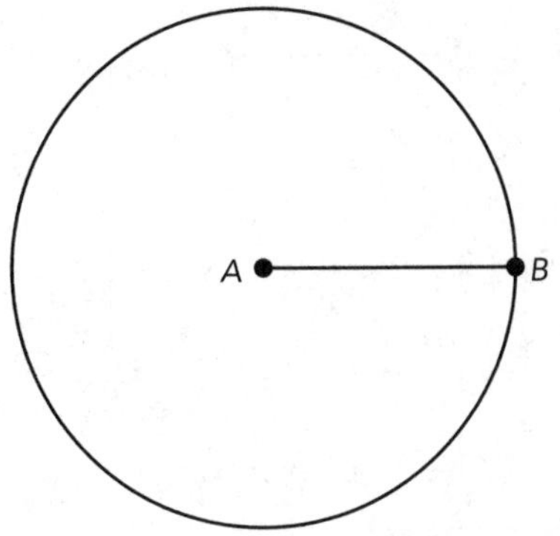

2. Construct a circle using $\overline{EF}$ as the radius and F as the center.

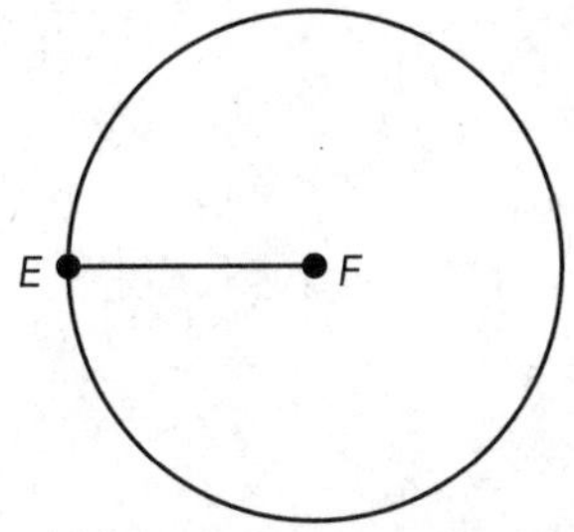

Construct and label each line segment using the given information.

3. Duplicate $\overline{AB}$.

4. Duplicate $\overline{CD}$.

Construct and label each angle using a compass and a straightedge.

5. Construct an angle that is congruent to $\angle A$.

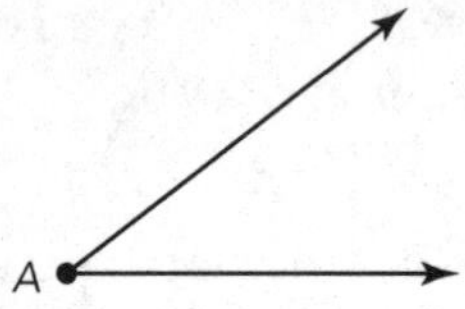

Construct an angle that is congruent to $\angle B$.

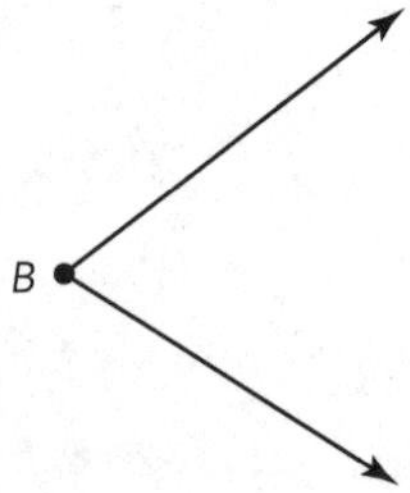

Stretch

In *The Elements*, Euclid demonstrates how to use only a compass and straightedge to construct an equilateral triangle from a given segment. Show how this can be done.

Review

1. A game requires spinning a spinner numbered 1 through 10 and rolling a 20-sided playing die.
   a. What is the probability of spinning a prime number and rolling an even number?
   b. What is the probability of spinning an odd number and rolling an odd number?
   c. What is the probability of spinning a number less than 6 or rolling a number less than 6?
   d. What is the probability of spinning a number less than 1 or rolling a number less than 10?
2. Solve each inequality and graph the solution.
   a. $-3x - 4 \leq 19$
   b. $\frac{x}{8} + \frac{3}{4} > 7$

Special Delivery

2

Special Angle Relationships

WARM UP

Solve each equation.

1. $90 = 5x + x$

2. $x + 3x = 180$

3. $(180 - x) + (90 - x) = 210$

4. $\frac{1}{2}x + x = 180 - x$

LEARNING GOALS

- Calculate the supplement of an angle.
- Calculate the complement of an angle.
- Classify adjacent angles, linear pairs, and vertical angles.
- Use facts about supplementary, complementary, vertical, and adjacent angles and linear pairs in multi-step problems to write and solve simple equations for unknown angles.

KEY TERMS

- straight angle
- supplementary angles
- complementary angles
- perpendicular
- collinear
- adjacent angles
- linear pair
- vertical angles

You know how to classify individual angles based on their measure. Now consider how angles are related to each other. What types of special relationships exist between pairs of angles?

Getting Started

Separated at Birth

A **straight angle** is formed when the sides of the angle point in exactly opposite directions. The two legs form a straight line through the vertex.

Let's use a straightedge and a protractor to investigate some special relationships between angles.

1. **Draw a *straight angle*, $\angle ABC$, and label each point.**

   a. **Draw a point D above line AC and use your straightedge to draw a ray, $\overrightarrow{BD}$. Next, use your protractor to measure the angles formed by $\overrightarrow{BD}$ and $\overleftrightarrow{AC}$.**

   b. **Draw a point E different from point D below line AC and use your straightedge to draw another ray, $\overrightarrow{BE}$. Next, use your protractor to measure the angles formed by $\overrightarrow{BE}$ and $\overleftrightarrow{AC}$.**

   c. **What do you notice about the measures of the angles formed by a single ray coming off of a line?**

2. Use the right angle shown to answer each question.

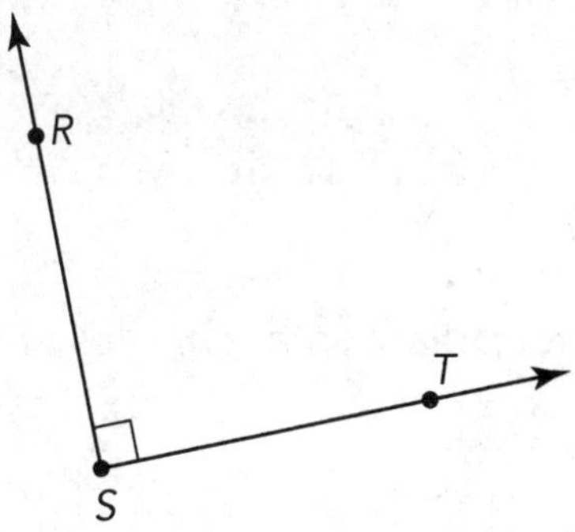

How do you know ∠RST is a right angle?

a. Draw a point V in the interior of $\angle RST$ and use your straightedge to draw a ray, $\overrightarrow{SV}$. Next, use your protractor to measure the angles formed by $\overrightarrow{SV}$ and $\angle RST$.

b. Draw a point Z in the interior of $\angle RST$ and use your straightedge to draw another ray, $\overrightarrow{SZ}$. Next, use your protractor to measure the angles formed by $\overrightarrow{SZ}$ and $\angle RST$.

c. What do you notice about the measures of the angles formed by a single ray that divides a right angle into two angles?

ACTIVITY 2.1 Supplements and Complements

Two angles are **supplementary angles** if the sum of their angle measures is equal to 180°.

Two angles are **complementary angles** if the sum of their angle measures is equal to 90°.

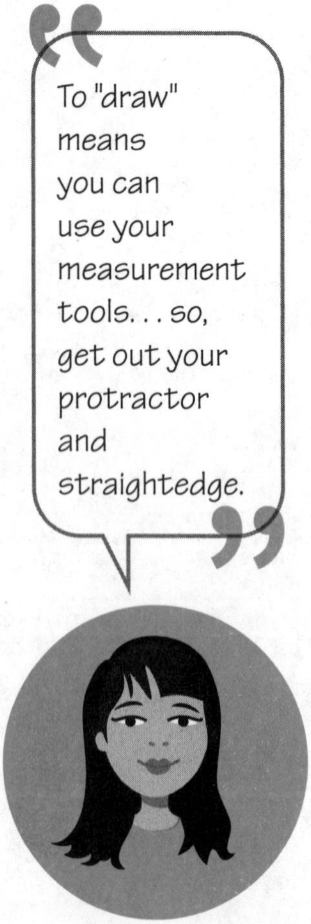

To "draw" means you can use your measurement tools. . . so, get out your protractor and straightedge.

In the previous activity, you created *supplementary angles* and *complementary angles.*

Let's create sets of supplementary angles.

1. **Use a protractor to draw a pair of supplementary angles that share a side. What is the measure of each angle?**

2. **Use a protractor to draw a pair of supplementary angles that do not share a side. What is the measure of each angle?**

3. **Calculate the measure of an angle that is supplementary to $\angle KJL$.**

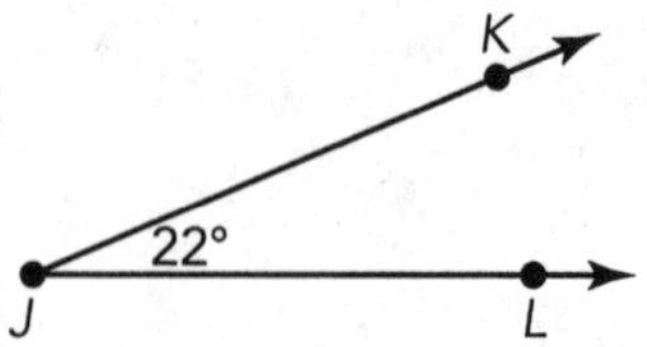

Now, let's create sets of complementary angles.

4. Use a protractor to draw a pair of complementary angles that share a side. What is the measure of each angle?

How can you check that your measurements are correct?

5. Use a protractor to draw a pair of complementary angles that do not share a side. What is the measure of each angle?

6. Calculate the measure of an angle that is complementary to $\angle J$.

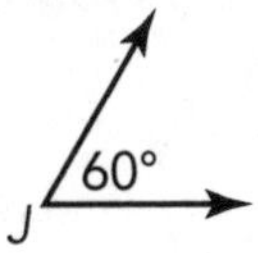

Congruent angles are angles that have the same measure.

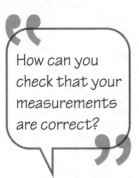

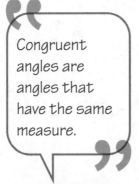

7. Given each statement, write and solve an equation to determine the measure of each angle in the angle pair.

a. Two angles are both congruent and supplementary.

b. Two angles are both congruent and complementary.

c. The supplement of an angle is half the measure of the angle itself.

d. The supplement of an angle is 20° more than the measure of the angle itself.

e. Angles 1 and 2 are complementary. The measure of angle 2 is 10° larger than the measure of angle 1.

f. Angles 1 and 2 are supplementary. The measure of angle 1 is three degrees less than twice the measure of angle 2.

8. Use the figure to determine the measure of $\angle ZXY$.

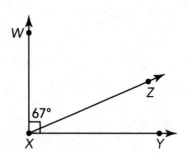

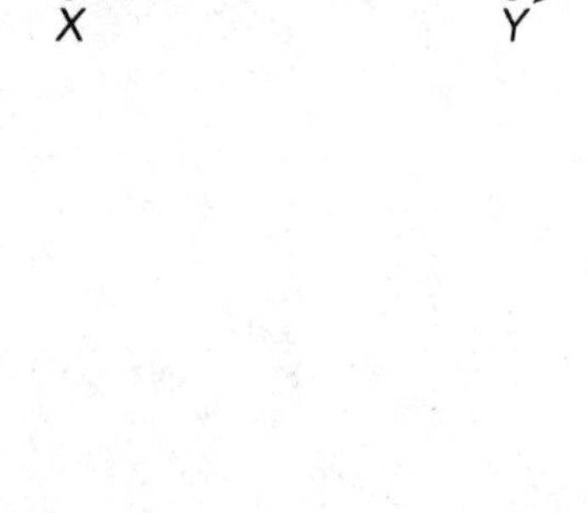

ACTIVITY
2.2 Perpendicular Lines

Let's explore angles formed by *perpendicular* lines.

Two lines, line segments, or rays are **perpendicular** if they intersect to form 90° angles. The symbol for perpendicular is ⊥.

1. Draw and label $\overleftrightarrow{AB} \perp \overleftrightarrow{CD}$ at point *E*. How many right angles are formed?

Compare your drawings with your partner's drawings. What do you notice?

2. Draw and label $\overleftrightarrow{BC} \perp \overleftrightarrow{AB}$ at point *B*. How many right angles are formed?

3. Name all angles that you know are right angles in the figure shown. Note: Points *A*, *D*, and *B* lie on the same line segment.

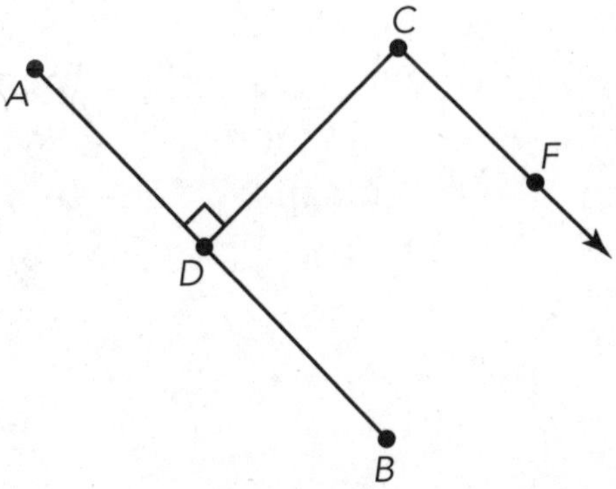

When points lie on the same line or line segment, they are said to be **collinear**.

Patty paper is traditionally a food service product, used to separate hamburger patties, meats, cheeses, and pastries.

You can use patty paper to create special angle pairs, just as you can use a protractor and straightedge.

4. **Draw a figure on a sheet of patty paper. What do you notice when you write on the paper? What about when you fold the paper?**

Read each question in its entirety before using your patty paper to illustrate the angles. You should use one sheet of patty paper for each question.

Store your patty paper notes in a safe place. You can use them to study.

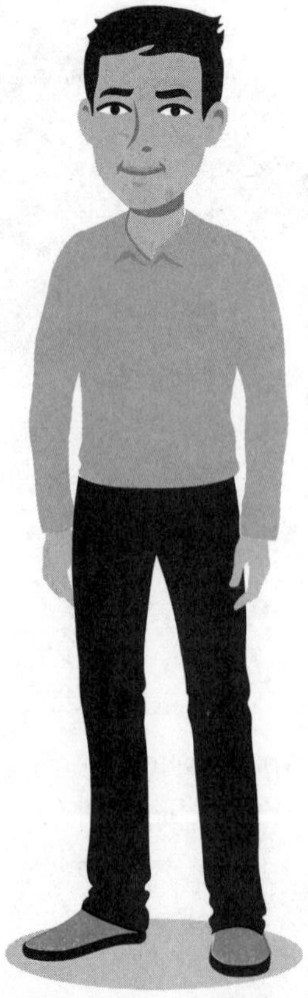

5. **Draw a straight angle on your patty paper. Then *fold* your patty paper to create a pair of supplementary angles that are not congruent. Label the patty paper "Supplementary Angles."**

6. **Draw a straight angle on your patty paper. Then *fold* your patty paper to create a pair of supplementary angles that are congruent. What do you know about the angles? What do you know about the straight angle and the line you created with your fold? Label the patty paper accordingly.**

7. **Draw a right angle on your patty paper. Then *fold* your patty paper to create a pair of complementary angles that are not congruent. Label the patty paper "Complementary Angles."**

ACTIVITY
2.3

Adjacent Angles

In each of the next three activities you will explore special angle pairs. Let's get started.

WORKED EXAMPLE

∠1 and ∠2 are adjacent angles.

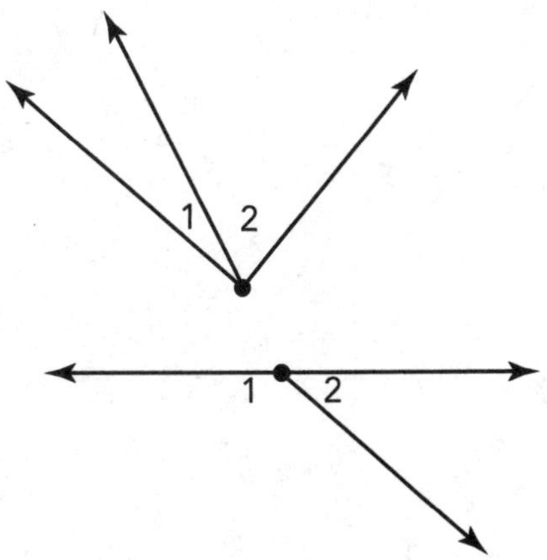

1
2
1
2

∠3 and ∠4 are *not* adjacent angles.

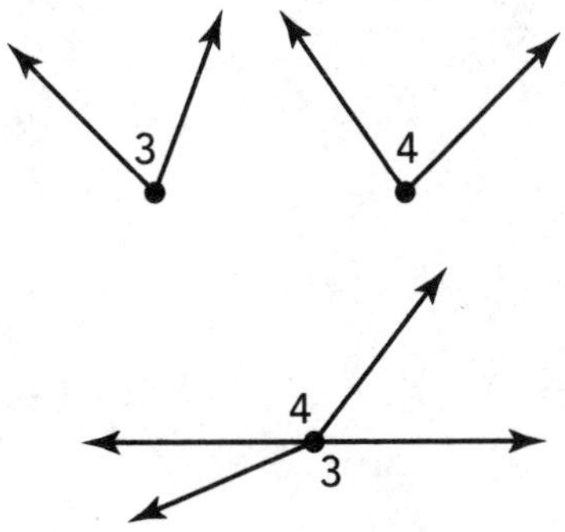

3
4
4
3

Can you think of other ways to draw ∠2 so that it is adjacent to ∠1?

1. Use the figures in the Worked Example to define *adjacent angles* in your own words.

2. Draw and label ∠2 so that it is adjacent to ∠1.

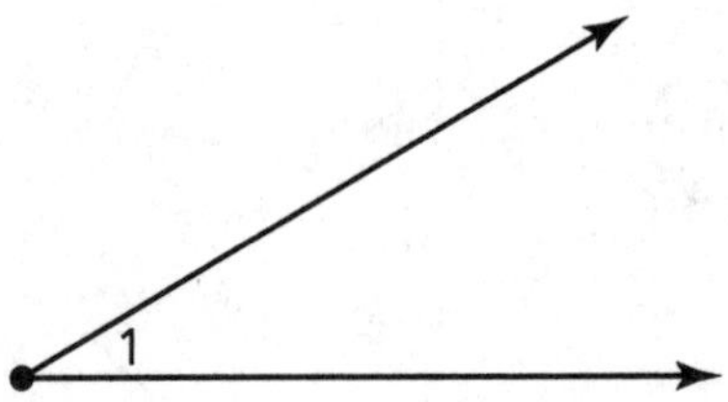

1

3. Is it possible to draw two angles that share a vertex, but do not share a common side? If so, draw an example. Would the angles be adjacent angles? If not, explain your reasoning.

Adjacent angles are two angles that share a common vertex and share a common side.

4. Is it possible to draw two angles that share a side, but do not share a vertex? If so, draw an example. If not, explain your reasoning.

5. Use one sheet of patty paper to create a set of *congruent* adjacent angles. Describe your process. Label the patty paper "Congruent Adjacent Angles."

How could you illustrate 2 non-adjacent angles on patty paper?

6. Use one sheet of patty paper to create a set of *non-congruent* adjacent angles. Describe your process. Label the patty paper "Adjacent Angles."

7. Are all adjacent angles supplementary?
Explain your reasoning.

8. **Are all supplementary angles adjacent? Explain your reasoning.**

NOTES

ACTIVITY 2.4 Linear Pairs

Let's explore a different angle relationship.

WORKED EXAMPLE

∠1 and ∠2 form a linear pair.

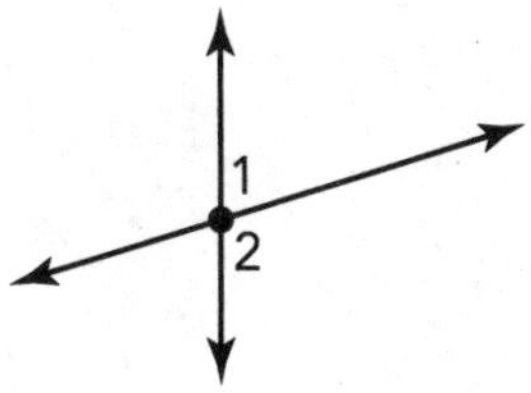

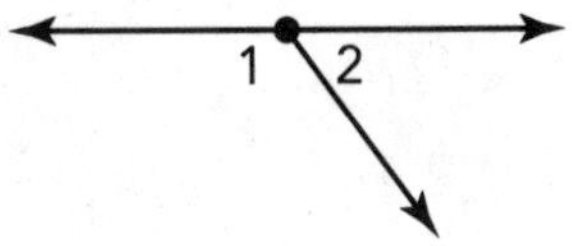

∠3 and ∠4 are do *not* form a linear pair.

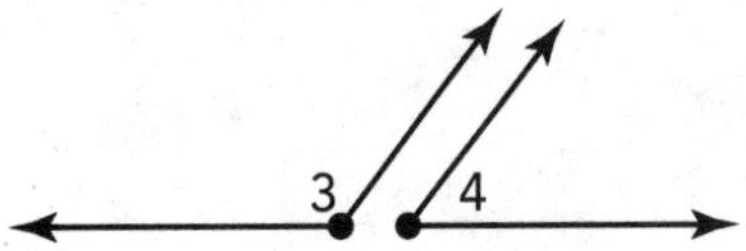

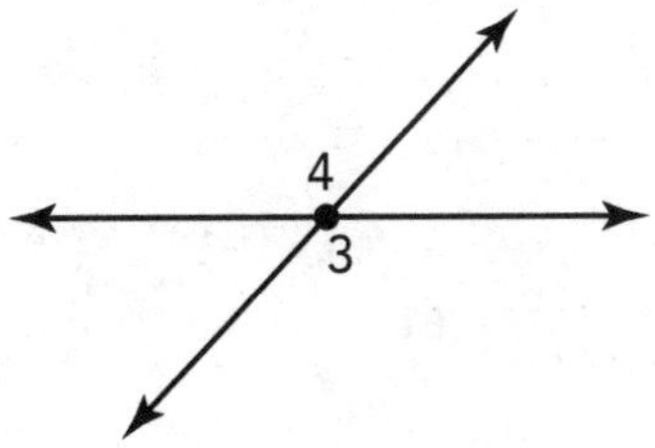

1. **Use the figures in the Worked Example to define a *linear pair of angles* in your own words.**

A **linear pair** of angles is formed by two adjacent angles that have noncommon sides that form a line.

2. Draw ∠2 so that it forms a linear pair with ∠1. Use one sheet of patty paper and record your response. Label your patty paper "Linear Pair."

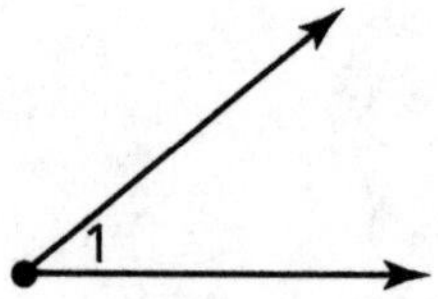

3. Name all linear pairs in the figure shown.

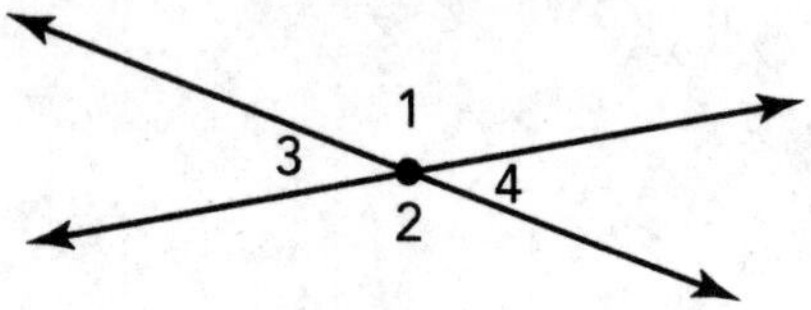

4. If the angles that form a linear pair are congruent, what can you conclude?

5. What is the difference between a linear pair of angles and supplementary angles that share a common side?

NOTES

6. **What is the difference between a linear pair of angles and supplementary angles that do not share a common side?**

7. **Angle *ABC* and angle *CBD* form a linear pair. Write and solve an equation to determine the measure of ∠*ABC*.**

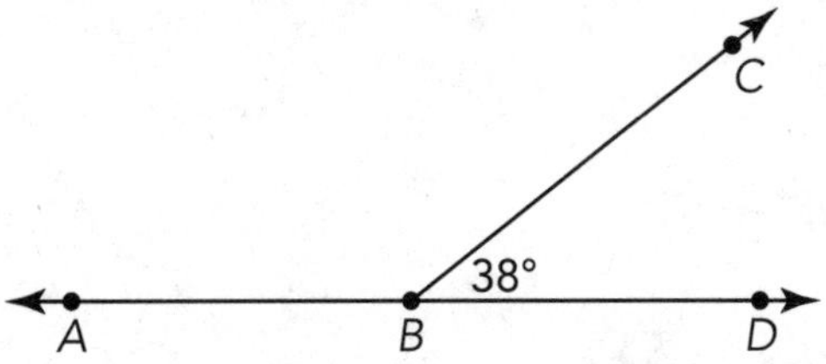

8. **The angles shown are a linear pair of angles. Solve for *x*.**

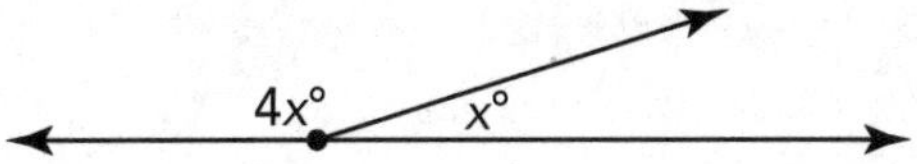

9. **Write and complete the sentence on your Linear Pairs patty paper.**

If two angles form a linear pair, then the sum of the measures of the linear pair of angles is ________________.

ACTIVITY 2.5 Vertical Angles

Let's explore one more special angle relationship.

WORKED EXAMPLE

$\angle 1$ and $\angle 2$ are vertical angles.

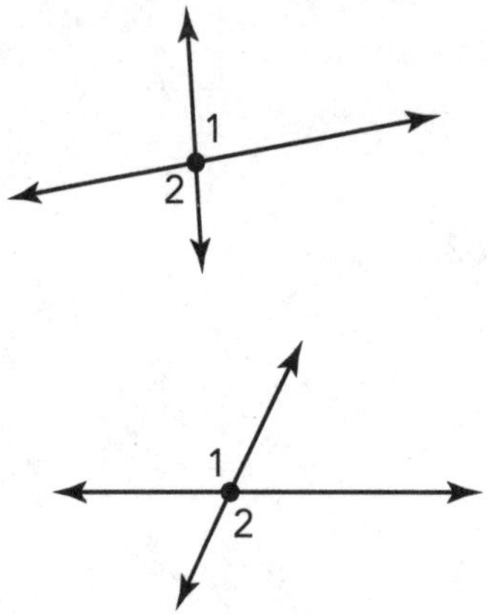

1
2
1
2

$\angle 3$ and $\angle 4$ are *not* vertical angles.

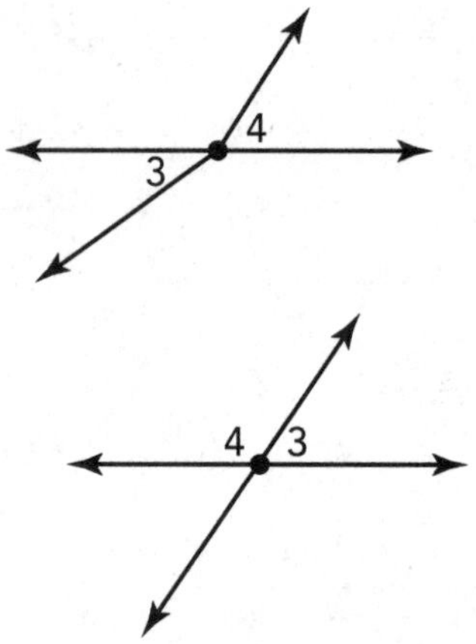

4
3
4
3

Is there another way you could draw ∠2 so that it forms a vertical angle pair with ∠1?

1. Use the figures in the Worked Example to define *vertical angles* in your own words.

2. Draw $\angle 2$ so that it forms a vertical angle pair with $\angle 1$.

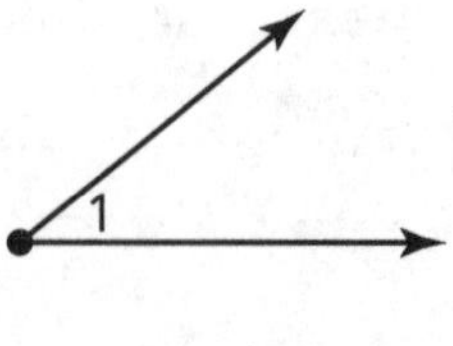

1

3. Name all vertical angle pairs in the diagram shown.

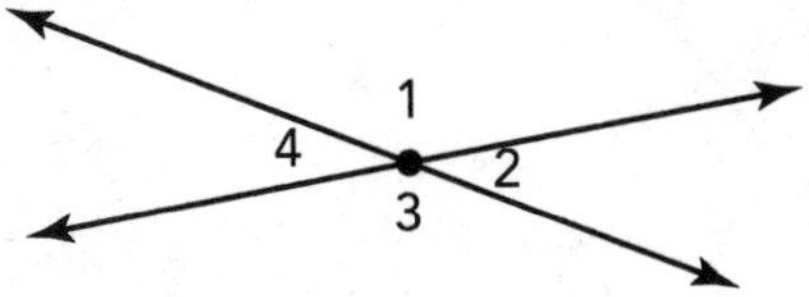

Vertical angles are two nonadjacent angles that are formed by two intersecting lines.

4. Trace the figure in Question 3 on two different sheets of patty paper. Be sure you number the angles. Use the patty paper to investigate the measures of vertical angles. What do you notice?

How can you rotate the patty paper to investigate vertical angles?

5. Use your protractor to measure each angle in Question 3. What do you notice?

6. Use what you know about supplementary angles and linear pairs to justify your investigations in Questions 4 and 5.

7. Label one sheet of your patty paper "Vertical Angles" and write and complete the sentence.

   When two lines intersect to form vertical angles, each pair of vertical angles _________________.

8. Write and solve an equation to determine the measures of all four angles in each diagram.

a.

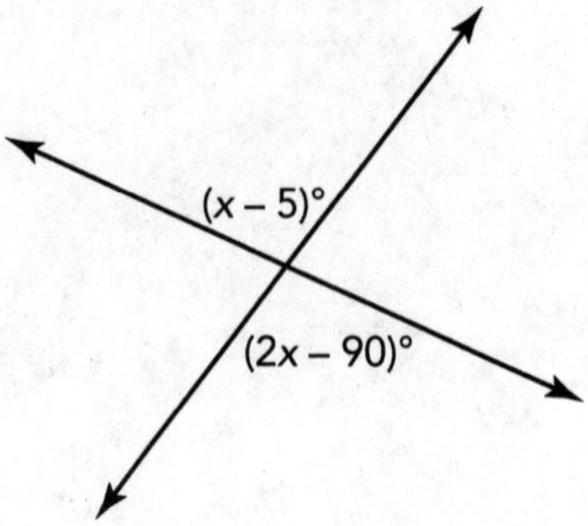

b.

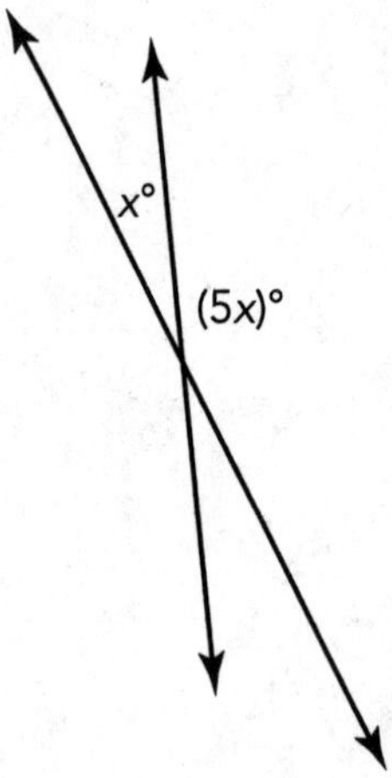

NOTES

TALK the TALK

Extra Special Delivery

Answer each question. Draw a figure to justify your response.

1. Two intersecting lines form how many
   a. pairs of supplementary angles?
   b. pairs of complementary angles?
   c. pairs of adjacent angles?
   d. linear pairs of angles?
   e. pairs of vertical angles?

2. Suppose two lines intersect. If you are given the measure of one angle, can you determine the measures of the remaining angles without using a protractor? Explain your reasoning.

NOTES

3. When two lines intersect, four different angles are formed as shown.

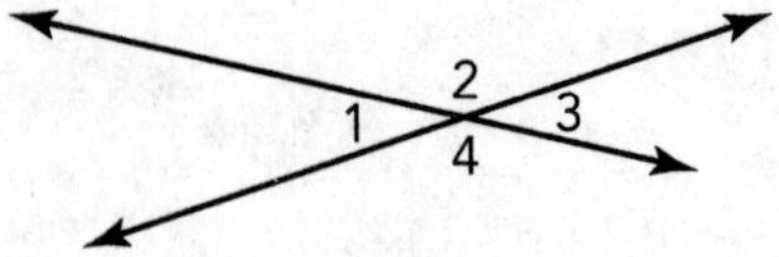

a. Describe the relationship between vertical angles.

b. Describe the relationship between adjacent angles.

4. Draw and label a diagram that includes at least one of each relationship. Then identify the angles that satisfy each description.

- complementary angles
- supplementary angles
- perpendicular lines
- adjacent angles
- linear pair
- vertical angles

Assignment

Write

Draw an example of each term. Provide an explanation when necessary.

1. supplementary angles
2. complementary angles
3. perpendicular lines
4. adjacent angles
5. linear pair
6. vertical angles

Remember

Many geometric figures contain a mixture of special angle pairs. Understanding the relationships between special angle pairs will help you understand more complex geometric diagrams.

Practice

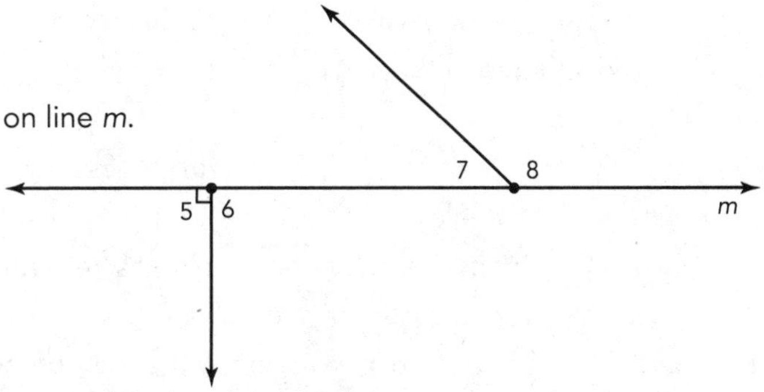

1. Use the diagram to identify the specified angles on line *m*.
   a. All adjacent angles
   b. All linear pairs
   c. All vertical angles
   d. All right angles
   e. All supplementary angles
2. Draw the supplementary angles described. Label each angle with its measure.
   a. Draw a pair of supplementary adjacent angles. One of the angles should have a measure of 85°.
   b. Draw a pair of supplementary angles that are not adjacent but share a common vertex. One of the angles should have a measure of 85°.
   c. Draw a pair of supplementary angles that are not adjacent and do not share a common vertex. One of the angles should have a measure of 85°.
3. Draw the complementary angles described. Label each angle with its measure.
   a. Draw a pair of complementary adjacent angles. One of the angles should have a measure of 62°.
   b. Draw a pair of complementary angles that are not adjacent but share a common vertex. One of the angles should have a measure of 62°.
   c. Draw a pair of complementary angles that are not adjacent and do not share a common vertex. One of the angles should have a measure of 62°.
4. Draw the angle pairs described and answer each question. Label each angle with its measure.
   a. Draw a linear pair of angles. One of the angles should have a measure of 123°.
   b. Draw two angles with the same measures as those in part (a), such that they are not a linear pair.
   c. Explain the differences and similarities between linear pairs and supplementary angles.

5. Suppose each street in the map shown represents a line. Provide an example of each angle relationship.
   a. vertical angles b. supplementary angles
   c. linear pair d. adjacent angles
   e. vertical angles f. congruent angles

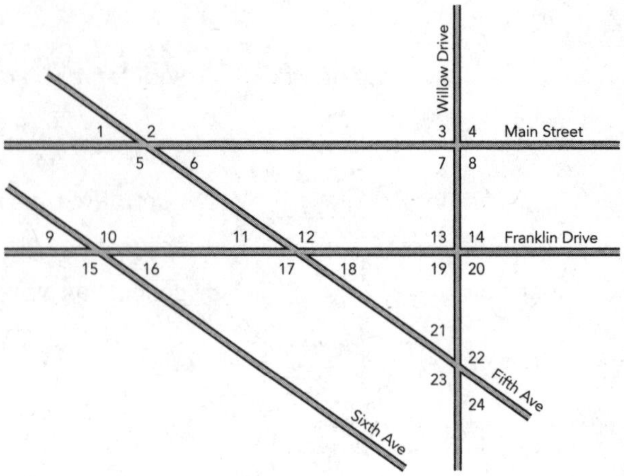

Calculate the measure of each unknown angle.

6. Angles C and D are complementary. The measure of angle D is 25 degrees greater than the measure of angle C. What is the measure of each angle?
7. If the supplement of an angle is 30 degrees more than the measure of the angle, what is the measure of the angle?
8. If the supplement of an angle is 12 degrees less than twice the measure of the angle, what is the measure of the angle?
9. If two angles form a linear pair and the measure of the first angle is one-fifth the measure of the second angle, what is the measure of each angle?
10. If two angles form a linear pair and the measure of the first angle is three times the measure of the second angle, what is the measure of each angle?

Stretch

If $\angle 1$ is the supplement of $\angle 2$, $\angle 3$ is the supplement of $\angle 4$, and $\angle 1$ is congruent to $\angle 3$, what can you conclude about the measures of $\angle 2$ and $\angle 4$? Write this conclusion in a general form.

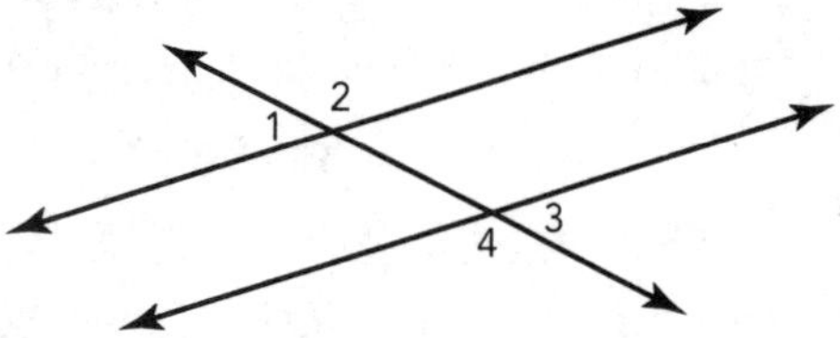

Review

1. Construct a line segment that is twice the length of $\overline{JK}$.

2. Construct an angle that is twice the measure of $\angle E$.

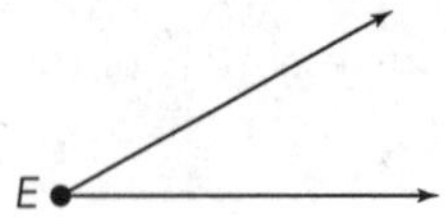

3. Consider the population of integers from −10 to 10.
   a. Select a sample of 6 numbers. Is this a random sample? Explain your reasoning.
   b. How can you assign random numbers to select a sample using a random number table?
   c. Use the random number table to choose 6 numbers from this population.
   d. Use a different line of the random number table to choose 6 numbers from this population.
   e. Compare the results from each sample. Do the results surprise you? Explain.
4. Estimate the likelihood of each event as 0, $\frac{1}{2}$, or 1.
   a. A dog greeting you with the words, "Good morning!"
   b. Rolling a prime number on a 6-sided number cube.

Consider Every Side

3

Constructing Triangles Given Sides

WARM UP

Use the coordinate plane to determine each distance. Show your work.

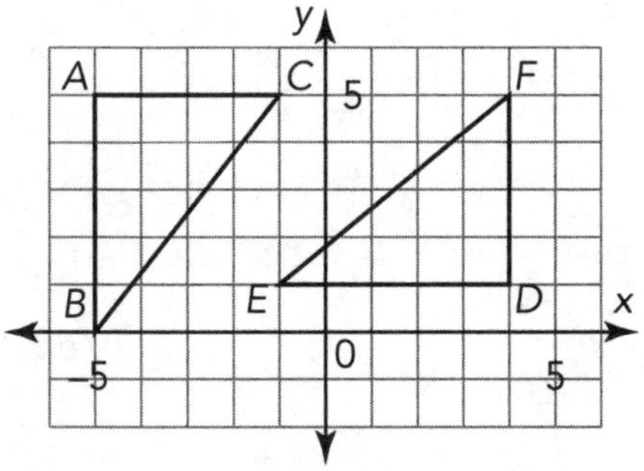

1. What is the distance from point *F* to point *D*?
2. What is the distance from point *A* to point *B*?
3. What is the distance from point *C* to point *A*?
4. What is the distance from point *E* to point *D*?

LEARNING GOALS

- Use patty paper to investigate triangles.
- Construct triangles from three angle measures or side lengths, identifying when the conditions determine a unique triangle, more than one triangle, or no triangle.

KEY TERM

- Triangle Inequality Theorem

You know how to draw a triangle. You know how to duplicate line segments and angles. Can you construct a specific triangle if you are given only two or three possible side lengths? Is there more than one possible triangle that you can construct?

Getting Started

Tri-, Tri-, and Tri- Again

Classify each statements as *always or sometimes* true about triangles.

- For each *always* true statement, explain your reasoning.
- For each *sometimes* true statement, provide an example and a counterexample.

1. The angles of a triangle have the same measure.

2. A triangle has three angles.

Think about special types of triangles.

3. Two sides of a triangle have the same measure.

4. One angle of a triangle measures 90 degrees.

ACTIVITY 3.1

A Triangle Given Two Line Segments

NOTES

If you know the lengths of two sides of a triangle, can you construct the triangle? Can you construct multiple triangles from this information?

Let's first investigate with patty paper.

1. **Trace the two line segments onto a sheet of patty paper to create an angle. Can you draw a new line segment to create a triangle?**

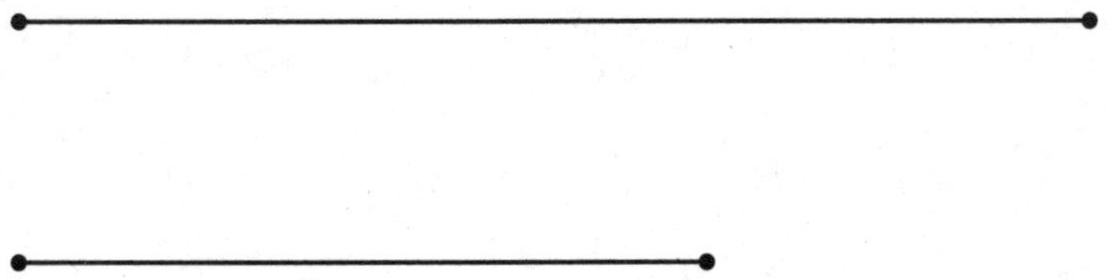

2. **Experiment with the two line segments and form different angles. Can you create different triangles? Use a different sheet of patty paper for each triangle attempt.**

3. **What do you notice? How many different triangles were you able to create?**

Label your sheets of patty paper "Given Two Segments" and store them in a safe place for use in the next lesson.

Now, let's use your construction tools: your compass and your straightedge.

4. **Construct a triangle using the two line segments shown. Write the steps.**

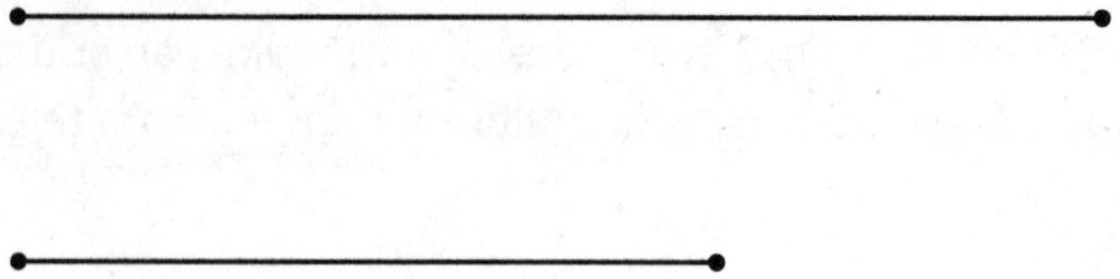

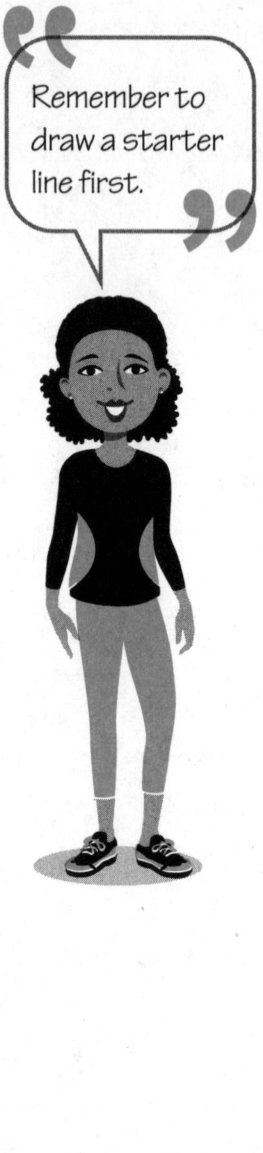
Remember to draw a starter line first.

5. **Use a protractor to measure each angle and a ruler to measure each side of your constructed triangle.**

6. **Classify your constructed triangle based on the measures of the angles and the lengths of the sides.**

7. **Compare the triangle that you constructed with the triangles that your classmates constructed. What do you observe? How does this compare to your patty paper triangles?**

ACTIVITY
3.2

Pasta Triangles

Let's investigate the conditions necessary for forming a triangle with different side lengths.

1. **Sarah claims that even though 2 segment lengths would form many different triangles, she could use any 3 segment lengths as the three sides of a triangle. Sam does not agree. He thinks some combinations will not work. Who is correct? Remember, you need one counterexample to disprove a statement.**

You only need one counterexample to disprove a statement.

Sam then claims that he can just look at the three lengths and know immediately if they will work. Sarah is unsure. She decides to explore this for herself.

Help Sarah by working through the following investigation.

To begin, you will need a piece of strand pasta. Break the pasta in two random points so the strand is divided into three pieces.

- Try to form a triangle from your three pieces of pasta.
- Measure each of your three pieces of pasta in centimeters.
- Repeat the experiment with a new piece of pasta.

2. **Record your measurements and the measurements of your group members in the table provided.**

3. Collect and record your classmates' measurements.

Piece 1 (cm)	Piece 2 (cm)	Piece 3 (cm)	Forms a Triangle? (yes or no)

4. What percent of the pasta pieces formed triangles when the pieces were connected end to end?

Is there a way you can always tell if three side lengths will form a triangle?

5. Examine the lengths of the pasta pieces that did form a triangle. Compare them with the lengths of the pasta pieces that did not form a triangle. Make a conjecture about the conditions under which it is possible to form a triangle.

ACTIVITY 3.3 A Triangle Given Three Segments

Let's continue to investigate Sarah's question and your conjecture with patty paper.

You and your partner should use different sets of segments for this investigation.

1. Trace each of the three segments onto its own sheet of patty paper.

   a. Overlay the sheets to determine if you can create a triangle. If you can, record the triangle on its own sheet of patty paper.

Set 1:

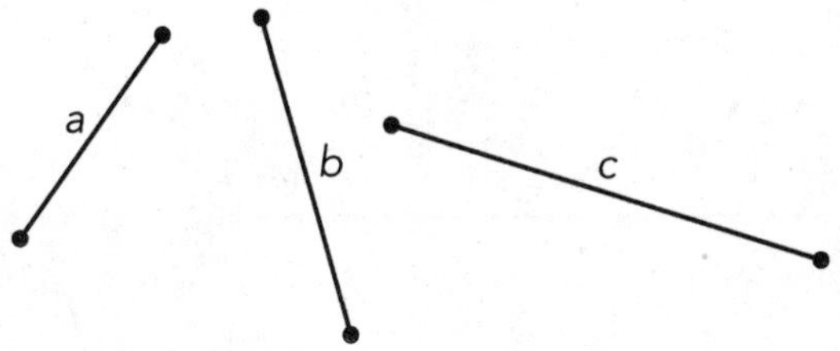

Set 2:

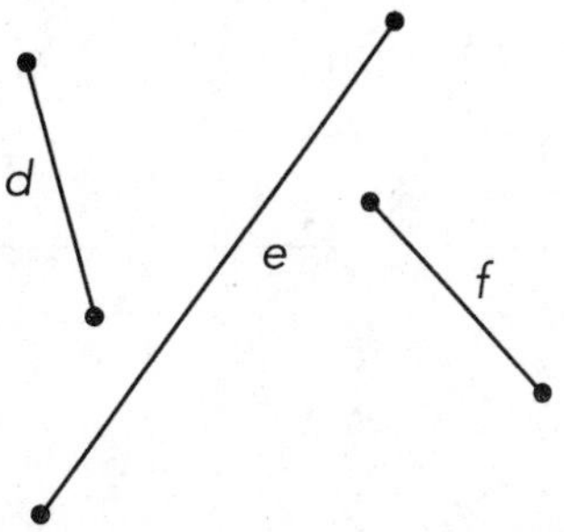

How can you determine the measures of the angles in your triangles?

b. Now create as many different triangles as you can, using the given segments as sides of a possible triangle. Use a different sheet of patty paper to record each unique triangle.

c. What do you notice? How many different triangles were you able to create?

2. Use the patty paper examples from Set 1 and Set 2 to make a conjecture about when three segments can be used to create a triangle. Test your conjecture by creating additional triangles.

Now, use your construction tools (your compass and your straightedge) to attempt to construct the triangles. Make sure at least one person in your group starts with each of the different segments.

3. Construct a triangle given the three segments from Set 1.

a. Use the starter line provided.

Triangles are *congruent* when all of their corresponding angle measures and corresponding side lengths are the same.

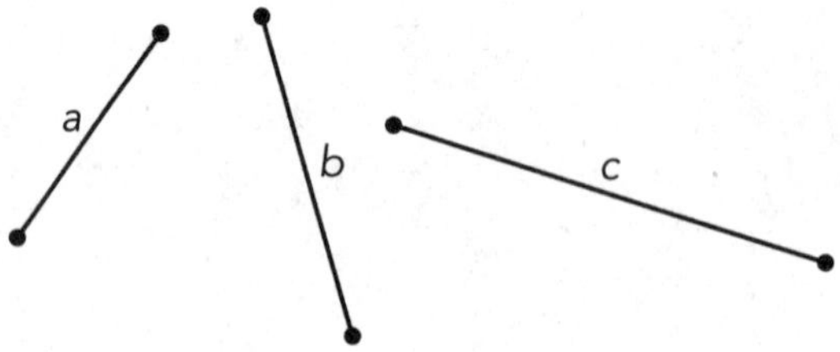

b. Compare the triangle you constructed with the triangles the other students in your group constructed. What do you notice?

4. Construct a triangle given the three segments from Set 2.

a. Use the starter line provided.

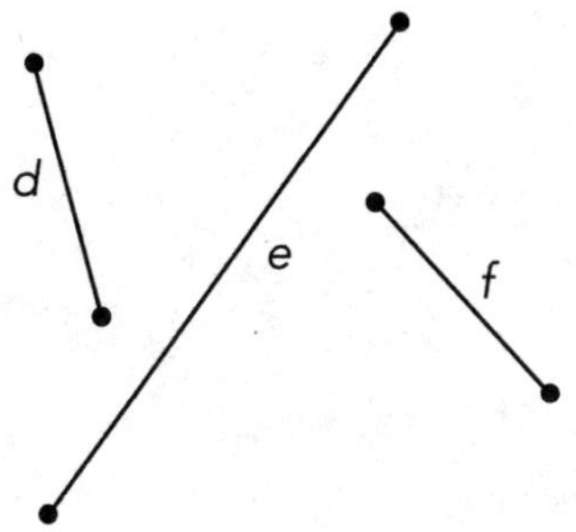

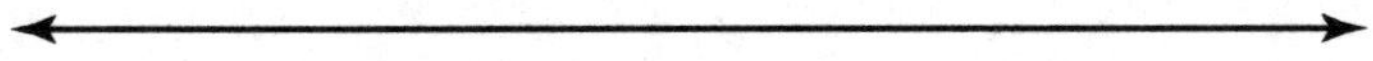

b. Compare the triangle you constructed with the triangles the other students in your group constructed. What do you notice?

When the given information can be used to construct congruent triangles, the information is said to define a unique triangle.

ACTIVITY
3.4 Triangle Inequality Theorem

The measure of $\overline{AB}$ can be expressed in two different ways. *AB* is read as "the distance from point *A* to point *B*." $m\overline{AB}$ is read as "the measure of line segment *AB*."

In Euclidean geometry—the geometry of straight lines on flat planes—the shortest distance between two points is a straight line.

That means that any distance *AC* + *CB* will be greater than the distance *AB*. It also means that any distance *BA* + *AC* will be greater than or equal to the distance *BC*.

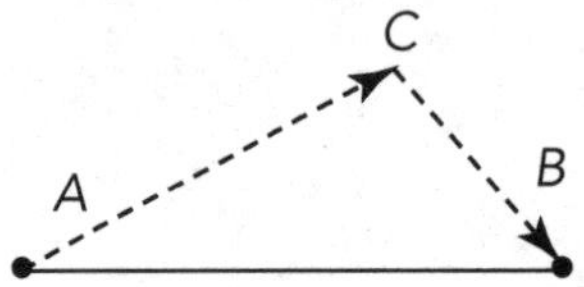

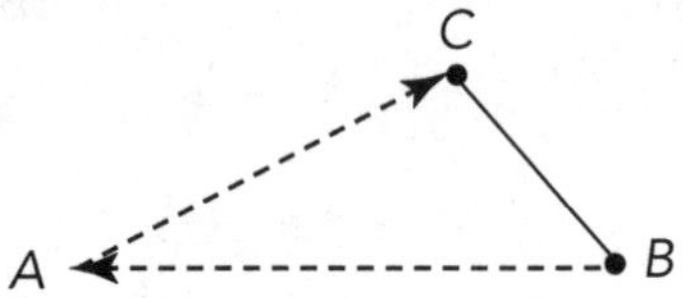

1. **How could you use this fact to test whether three line segments can form a triangle? Explain your reasoning.**

2. **Provide examples of line segments that cannot possibly form a triangle.**

3. What would it mean for the distance $AC + CB$ to be equal to the distance AB?

4. Based upon your observations, determine if it is possible to form a triangle using segments with the given measurements. Explain your reasoning.

a. 2 cm, 5.1 cm, 2.4 cm

b. 9.2 cm, 7 cm, 1.9 cm

The rule that you have been using is known as the *Triangle Inequality Theorem*. The **Triangle Inequality Theorem** states that the sum of the lengths of any two sides of a triangle is greater than the length of the third side.

A theorem is a mathematical rule that can be formally proven.

NOTES

TALK the TALK

None, One, or Many?

Determine if the given information could be used to form a unique triangle, many different triangles, or no triangles. Explain your reasoning.

1. **3 in., 2.9 in., 5 in.**

2. **112 mm, 300 mm**

3. **5 yd, 10 yd, 21 yd**

4. **8 ft, 9 ft, 11 ft**

5. **13.8 km, 6.3 km, 7.5 km**

Assignment

Write

Describe the Triangle Inequality Theorem in your own words.

Remember

When given two line segments, it is possible to construct an infinite number of triangles. When given three line segments, it is possible to construct 0 triangles, a unique triangle, or an infinite number of triangles.

Practice

1. Determine if the given side lengths could be used to form a unique triangle, many different triangles, or no triangles. Explain your reasoning.

    a. 300 mm, 190 mm

    b. 4 m, 5.1 m, 12.5 m

    c. 7.4 cm, 8.1 cm, 9.8 cm

    d. 12 ft, 7 ft, 14 ft

    e. 20.2 in., 11 in., 8.2 in.

2. Analyze the given line segments. If the given information would create a unique triangle, multiple triangles, or no triangles. Then use the information to construct a triangle, if possible.

    a.

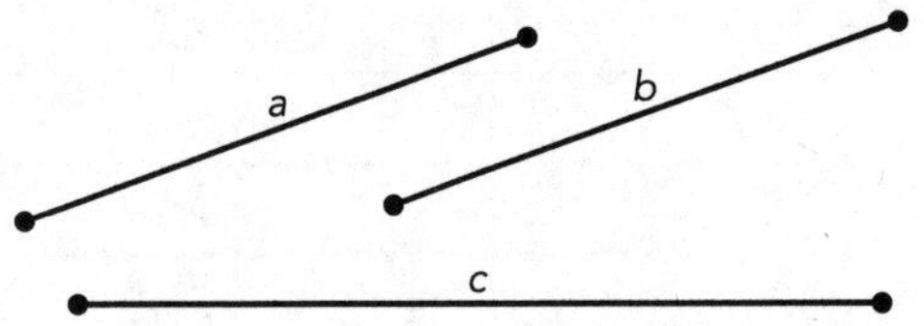

    b.

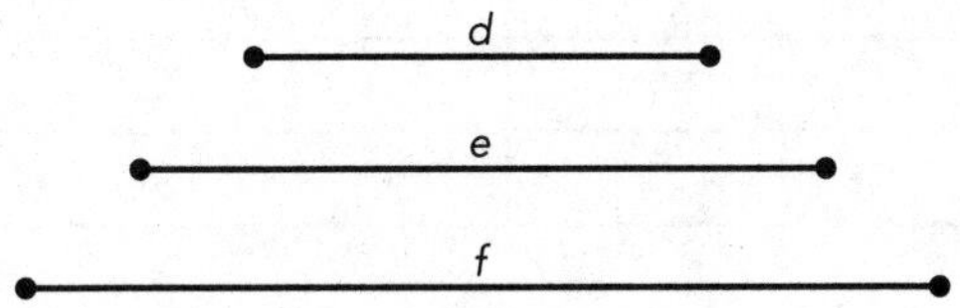

Stretch

Use your compass and straightedge to construct an equilateral triangle.

Review

1. Use the diagram to identify the specified angles given lines *a* and *b*.
   a. All adjacent angles
   b. All linear pairs
   c. All vertical angles
   d. All right angles
   e. All complementary angles

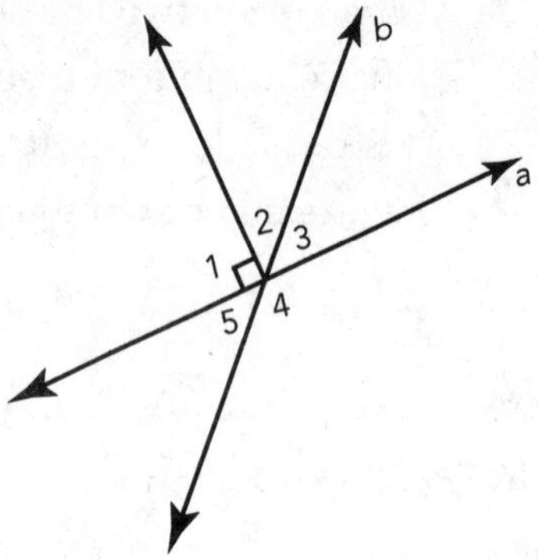

2. The average monthly rainfall in two Alaskan cities over a 30-year period is shown in the table. Use this data to answer the questions.
   a. Determine the five number summary describing the average monthly rainfall in each city.
   b. Construct a box-and-whisker plot to display the average monthly rainfall in each city.
   c. Describe the rainfall in each Alaskan city in terms of the median and IQR.

Month	Annette, Alaska Average Monthly Rainfall (inches)	Barrow, Alaska Average Monthly Rainfall (inches)
January	9.67	0.12
February	8.05	0.12
March	7.96	0.09
April	7.37	0.12
May	5.73	0.12
June	4.72	0.32
July	4.26	0.87
August	6.12	1.04
September	9.49	0.69
October	13.86	0.39
November	12.21	0.16
December	11.39	0.12

3. Number tiles containing the numbers 11–20 are in a bag. One tile is pulled from the bag. Determine each probability.
   a. *P*(prime) =
   b. *P*(multiple of 3) =

Unique or Not?

4

Constructing Triangles Given Angles

WARM UP

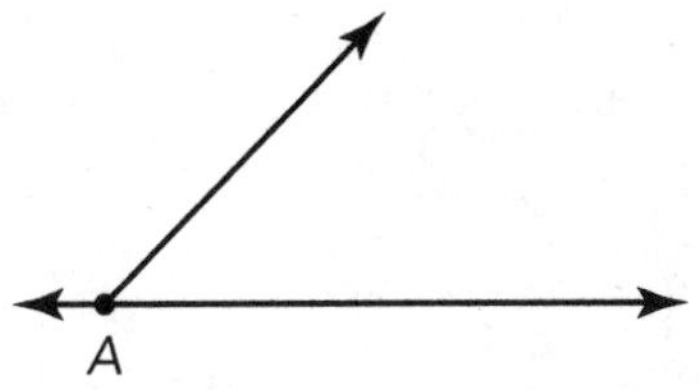

1. Use a compass and a straightedge to duplicate the angle.
2. Use a compass and a straightedge to construct an angle that is twice the measure of the given angle.

LEARNING GOALS

- Use patty paper to investigate triangles.
- Construct triangles when given at least one angle to determine whether a unique triangle, more than one triangle, or no triangle can be formed.

KEY TERMS

- included angle
- included side

You know how to duplicate line segments and angles. Can you construct a specific triangle if you are given at least one angle and two additional parts of the triangle? Is there more than one possible triangle that you can construct?

Getting Started

Copy Cat

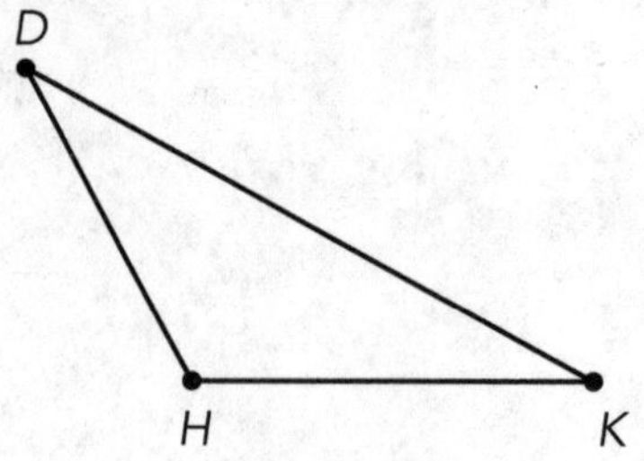

1. Duplicate $\overline{HK}$ on the given starter ray.

2. Duplicate $\angle H$ on the given starter ray.

3. Duplicate $\overline{HK}$ and $\angle H$ on the given starter ray.

Is this enough information to duplicate triangle *DHK*? Explain your reasoning.

ACTIVITY
4.1 A Triangle Given Three Angles

In this lesson, you will decide what specific information is needed in order to construct a triangle.

If you are given the three angles of a triangle, can you construct a triangle? Can you construct multiple triangles from this information?

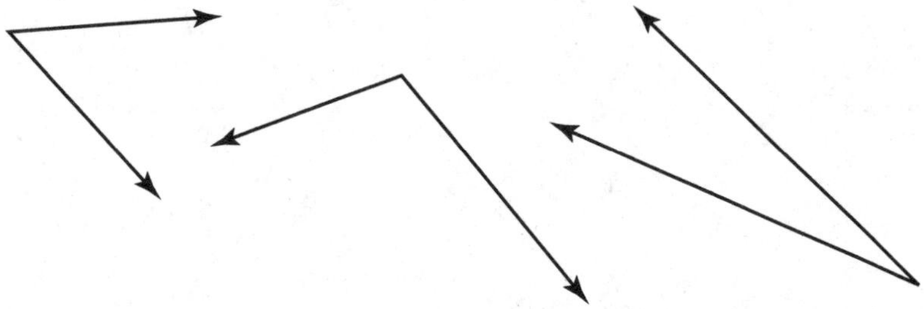

Rays go on forever in one direction. Therefore, you can extend the sides of the angles if you wish.

1. Let's first investigate with patty paper.

a. Trace each angle onto its own sheet of patty paper and overlay the patty papers to determine if you can create a triangle. Trace your triangle onto a piece of paper.

b. Experiment with the given angles and try to create as many different triangles as you can. Copy each triangle attempt onto a different sheet of patty paper.

c. What do you notice? How many different triangles were you able to create?

Now, let's use your construction tools: your compass and your straightedge.

2. Construct a triangle using the three angles shown.

a. Write the steps.

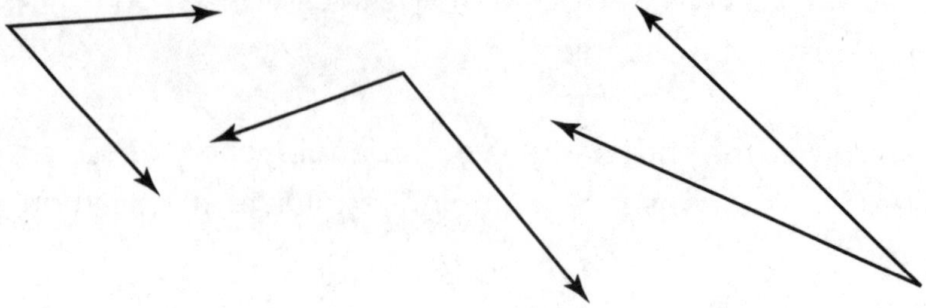

b. Use a protractor to measure each angle and a ruler to measure each side of your constructed triangle.

c. Classify your constructed triangle based on the measures of the angles and the lengths of the sides.

Label your sheets of patty paper with your triangle attempts "Given Three Angles" and store them in a safe place for use at the end of the lesson.

d. Compare the triangle that you constructed with the triangles that your classmates constructed. What do you observe? How does this compare to your patty paper triangles?

ACTIVITY
4.2 A Triangle Given Two Angles and One Line Segment

If you are given two angles and one side of a triangle, can you construct a triangle? Can you construct multiple triangles from this information?

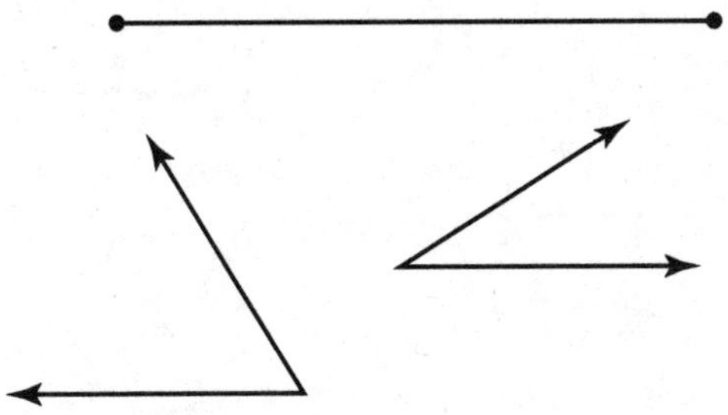

Let's first investigate with patty paper.

1. Trace each of the angles and the line segment onto its own sheet of patty paper.

   a. Overlay the pieces to determine if you can create a triangle. If you can, record the triangle on another piece of patty paper.

   b. Experiment with the given angles and line segment and try to create as many different triangles as you can. Use a different sheet of patty paper to record each unique triangle.

   c. What do you notice? How many different triangles were you able to create?

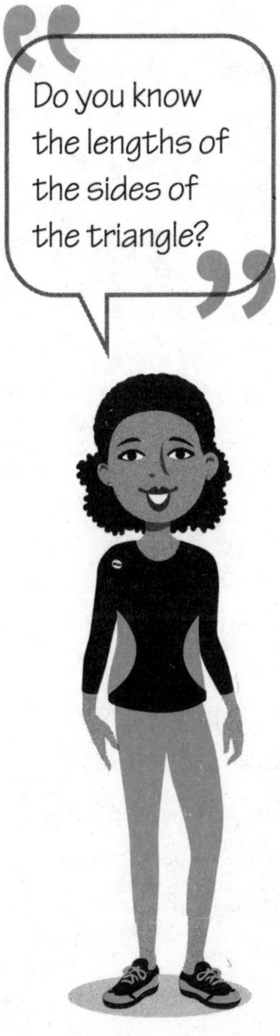

Do you know the lengths of the sides of the triangle?

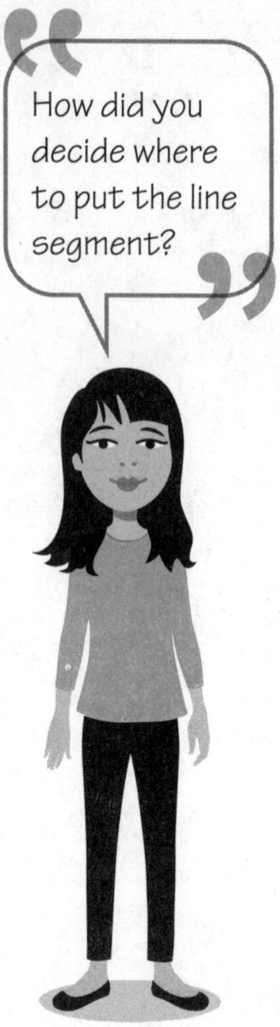

Now, let's use your construction tools: your compass and your straightedge.

2. **Construct a triangle using the one line segment and two angles shown.**

   a. **Write the steps.**

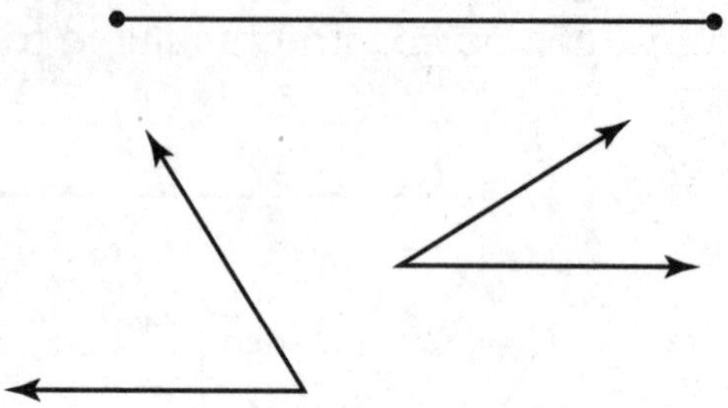

   b. **Use a protractor to measure each angle and a ruler to measure each side of your constructed triangle.**

   c. **Classify your constructed triangle based on the measures of the angles and the lengths of the sides.**

   d. **Compare the triangle that you constructed with the triangles that your classmates constructed. What do you observe? How does this compare to your patty paper triangles?**

Label the paper(s) with your triangle attempts "Given Two Angles and One Segment" and store them in a safe place for use at the end of the lesson.

ACTIVITY 4.3

A Triangle Given Included Angles or Included Sides

If you are given two sides and the angle between them, the *included angle*, of a triangle, can you construct a unique triangle? Can you construct multiple triangles from this information?

An **included angle** is the angle whose sides are made up of the given sides of the triangle.

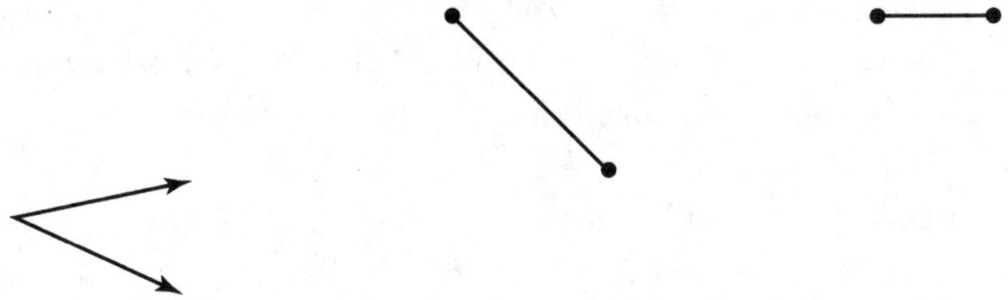

1. **Let's investigate with patty paper.**

    a. **Trace each of the 2 line segments and the angle on its own sheet of patty paper. If possible, arrange the three parts to form a triangle with the angle between the two given segments. Then, trace your triangle on another sheet of patty paper.**

Label your patty paper as "Two Sides and the Included Angle" and store it in a safe place for use at the end of the lesson.

    b. **What do you notice? How many different triangles were you and your classmates able to create?**

Now, use your construction tools to attempt to construct the triangle.

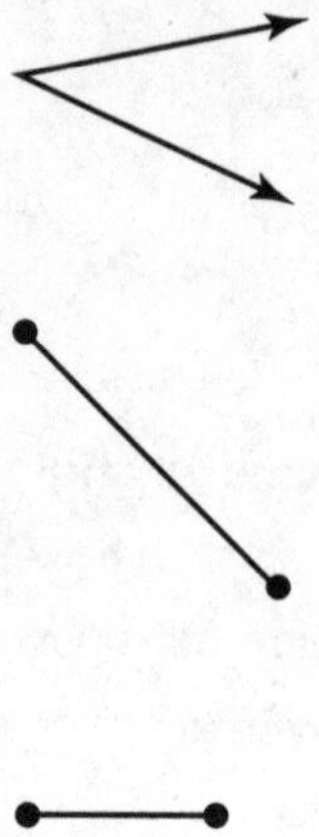

2. Construct a triangle given the two sides and the included angle.

    a. Use the starter line provided.

    b. Compare the triangle you constructed with the triangles your classmates constructed. What do you notice?

An **included side** is the side between the two given angles of the triangle.

If you are given two angles and the side between them, the *included side*, of a triangle, can you construct a unique triangle? Can you construct multiple triangles from this information?

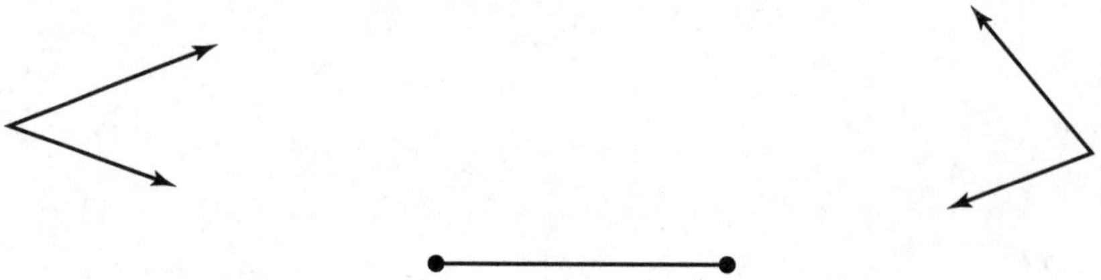

3. Let's investigate with patty paper.

Label your patty paper as "Two Angles and the Included Side" and store in a safe place for use in the Talk the Talk.

    a. Trace each angle and the line segment on its own sheet of patty paper. If possible, arrange the three parts to form a triangle with the segment between the two given angles. Then, trace your triangle on another sheet of patty paper.

b. What do you notice? How many different triangles were you and your classmates able to create?

Now, use your construction tools to attempt to construct the triangle.

4. Construct a triangle given the two angles and the included side.

   a. Use the starter line provided.

   b. Compare the triangle you constructed with the triangles your classmates constructed. What do you notice?

What do the labels of the given parts tell you about how they are related?

5. Use the given line segments and angle to answer each question.

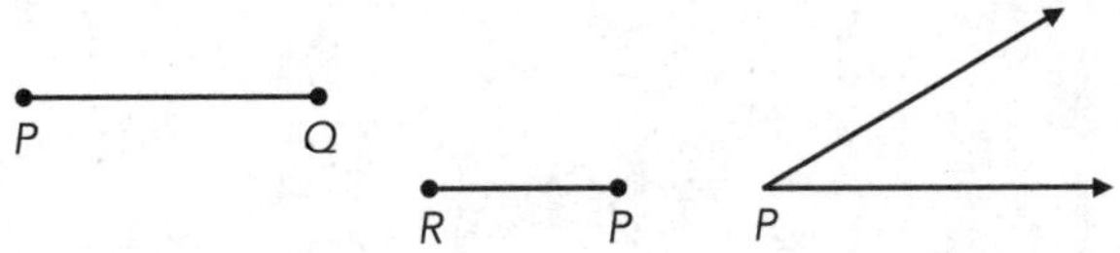

   a. Without constructing $\triangle PQR$, can you predict if the construction will result in a unique triangle or different triangles? Explain your reasoning.

   b. Construct $\triangle PQR$. Then compare your construction to those of your classmates. Was your prediction correct? Explain your reasoning.

6. A geometry teacher is hiding a picture of a triangle. She gives her students the following information:

   $m\angle S = 42°$

   $GS = 5$ cm

   $GE = 4$ cm

   She tells her students to work in pairs to draw a triangle exactly like her triangle. Jerry is trying to convince Alicia that if you are given the length of two sides and the measure of one angle in a triangle, you can draw the same triangle with no problem. Alicia wants to convince Jerry that he is incorrect. Who's correct? Explain your reasoning.

NOTES

TALK the TALK

Truly Unique

You have learned different ways to create triangles. Depending on what information you are provided about the triangle, you can create multiple triangles, a unique triangle, or no triangles.

1. **In the graphic organizer provided, list the three ways you can create multiple triangles and the three ways you can create a unique triangle, depending on what sides or angles you are given. Additionally, list at least one way that you cannot create a triangle given any combination of sides and angles.**

MULTIPLE TRIANGLES

A UNIQUE TRIANGLE

NO TRIANGLE

Assignment

Write

Draw a diagram to illustrate the terms *included angle* and *included side*. Provide an explanation of what each term means.

Remember

When you are given three of the six parts of a triangle, it may be possible to construct a unique triangle, more than one triangle, or no triangles from the information.

Practice

1. Analyze the given parts. State if the given information would create a unique triangle, multiple triangles, or no triangles. Then use the information to construct a triangle, if possible.

a. Use the two line segments and the included angle to construct $\triangle XYZ$.

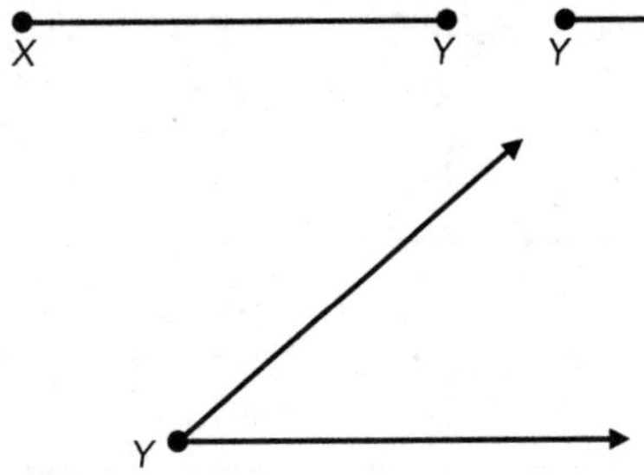

b. Use the three angles to construct $\triangle JKL$.

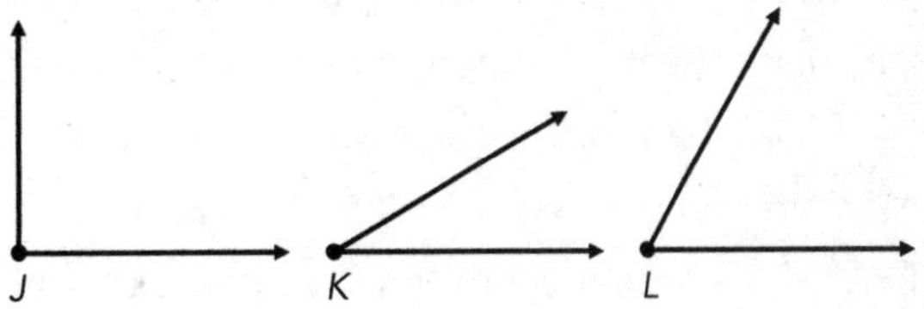

c. Use the two angles and the included side to construct $\triangle MNP$.

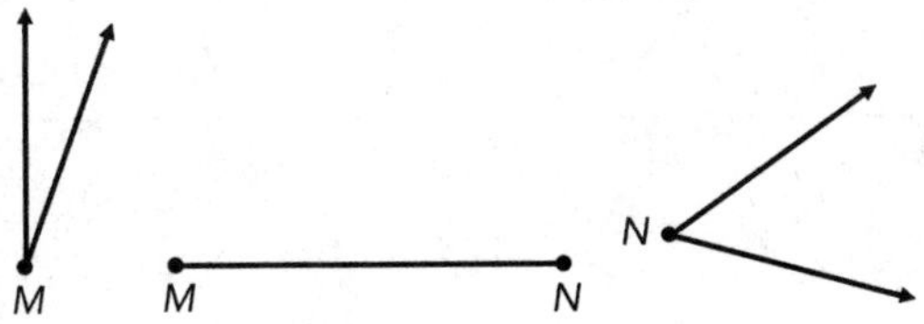

d. Use the three angles to construct $\triangle ABC$.

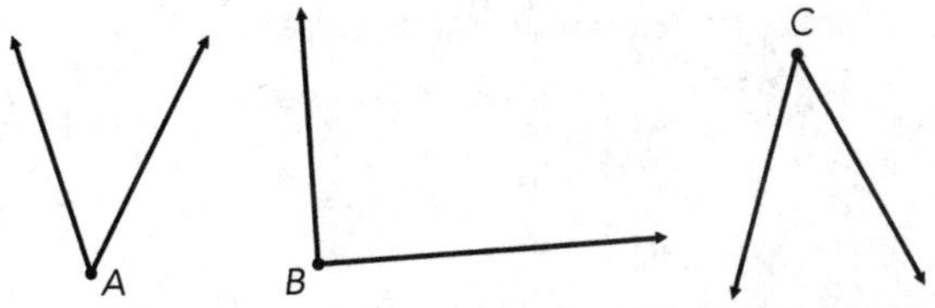

Stretch

Use patty paper to create an isosceles triangle. Then use your compass and straightedge to construct an isosceles triangle.

Review

1. Construct $\triangle UVW$ using the three line segments shown.

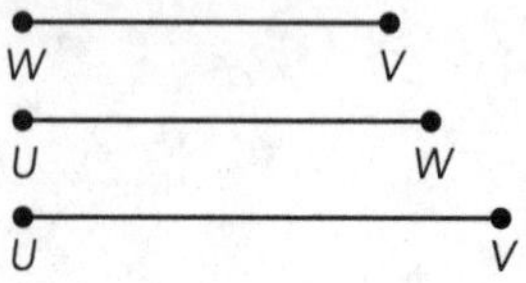

2. Construct $\triangle MNP$ using the three line segments shown.

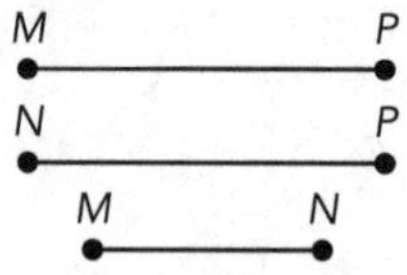

3. A consumer reporter was asked about the battery life of two different brands of batteries. He ran an experiment 10 times using identical lanterns to determine the battery life of each brand of battery. The results of his experiment are shown.
   a. Calculate the mean and median for the battery life for each brand of battery and convert the measurements to hours. What do you notice?
   b. Determine and interpret the five-number summary and IQR for each data set. Then, describe some observations from the data of each five-number summary.
   c. Construct box-and-whisker plots for each brand of battery using the same number line for both. In terms of the box-and-whisker plots, which brand of battery had more variation in the battery life? Explain your reasoning.
   d. If you were Fernando, which brand of battery would you use? Explain.

Brand A Battery Life (minutes)	Brand B Battery Life (minutes)
1029	970
1038	1264
1023	1088
1018	950
1050	893
1034	1000
1021	1028
1025	1064
1031	1007
1041	1046

4. Create a tree diagram to represent the sample space for each experiment.
   a. Rolling a 6-sided number cube and flipping a coin.
   b. Spinning a spinner with 4 equal sections numbered 1–4 twice and determining the product of the results.

Angles and Triangles Summary

KEY TERMS

- constructions
- compass
- straightedge
- sketch
- draw
- point
- line
- plane
- line segment
- endpoints
- arc
- congruent
- angle
- ray
- sides of an angle
- vertex
- straight angle
- supplementary angles
- complementary angles
- perpendicular
- collinear
- adjacent angles
- linear pair
- vertical angles
- Triangle Inequality Theorem
- included angle
- included side

LESSON 1

Here's Lookin' at Euclid

Constructions are drawings created using only a compass or straightedge or both. A **compass** is a tool used to create arcs and circles. A **straightedge** is a ruler with no numbers. A **sketch** is a freehand drawing of an object. When you **draw** a geometric figure, the figure is created with the use of tools such as a ruler and protractor.

Three essential building blocks of geometry are the point, line, and plane. A **point** is described as a location in space. It is often represented using a dot, and it is named with a capital letter. Points *C* and *D* lie on the line shown at right. A **line** is described as a straight continuous arrangement of an infinite number of points. The names of the lines shown are line *m* and $\overleftrightarrow{CD}$ and are read as "line *m*" and "line *CD*."

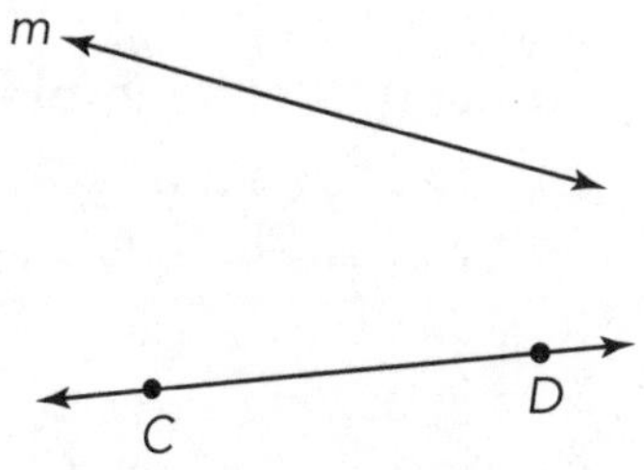

A **plane** is described as a flat surface. A plane extends infinitely in all directions. Planes are determined by three points, but they are usually named using one uppercase letter. Plane Q is shown at right.

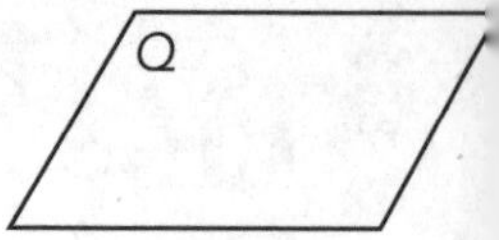

A **line segment** is a portion of a line that includes two points and all the points between those two points. The **endpoints** of a line segment are the points where the line segment ends. A line segment is named using the two capital letters that name its endpoints. The name of line segment *AB* can be written using symbols as $\overline{AB}$. This is read as "line segment *AB*."

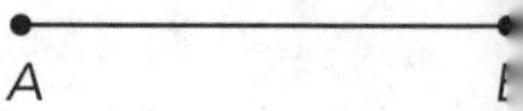

An **arc** is part of a circle. You can also think of an arc as the curve between two points on the circle.

Line segments that have the same length are called congruent line segments. **Congruent** means to have the same size, shape, and measure. You can indicate that two line segments are congruent by using the congruence symbol, $\cong$, between them.

An **angle** is formed by two rays that share a common endpoint. A **ray** is a part of a line that begins at a point and extend infinitely in one direction. The **sides of an angle** are the two rays. The **vertex** of an angle is the common endpoint that the two rays share.

LESSON 2

Special Delivery

A **straight angle** is formed when the sides of the angle point in exactly opposite directions. The two legs form a straight line through the vertex.

Two angles are **supplementary angles** if the sum of their angle measures is equal to 180 degrees. For example, angles *MJK* and *KJL* are supplementary angles.

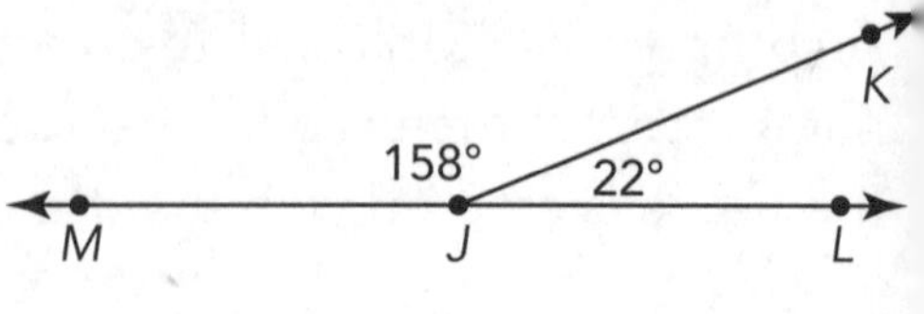

Two angles are **complementary angles** if the sum of their angle measures is equal to 90 degrees. For example, angles *WXZ* and *ZXY* are complementary angles.

Two lines, line segments, or rays are **perpendicular** if they intersect to form 90 degree angles. The symbol for perpendicular is $\perp$.

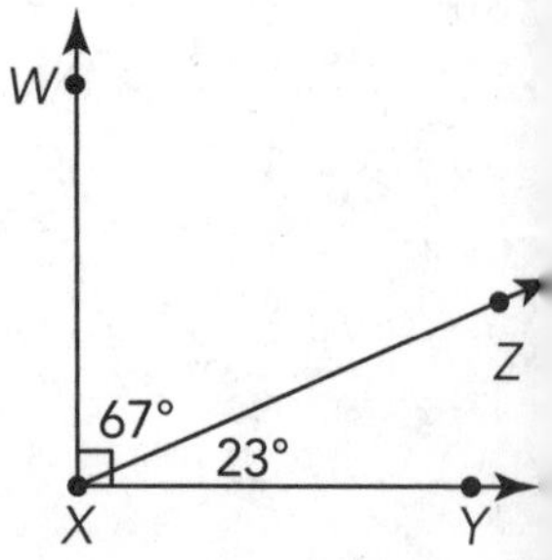

Adjacent angles are two angles that share a common vertex and share a common side.

∠1 and ∠2 are adjacent angles.

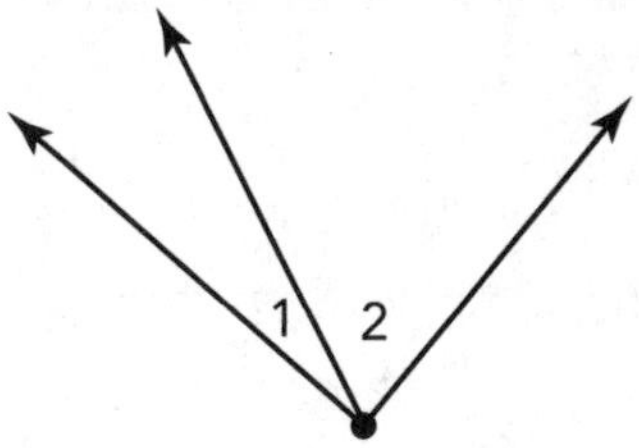

∠3 and ∠4 are *not* adjacent angles.

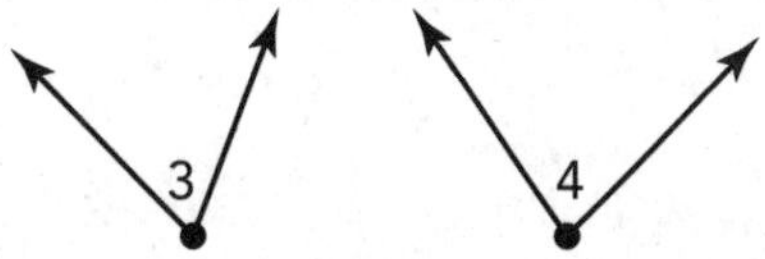

A **linear pair** of angles is formed by two adjacent angles that have noncommon sides that form a line. Linear pairs are supplementary.

∠1 and ∠2 form a linear pair.

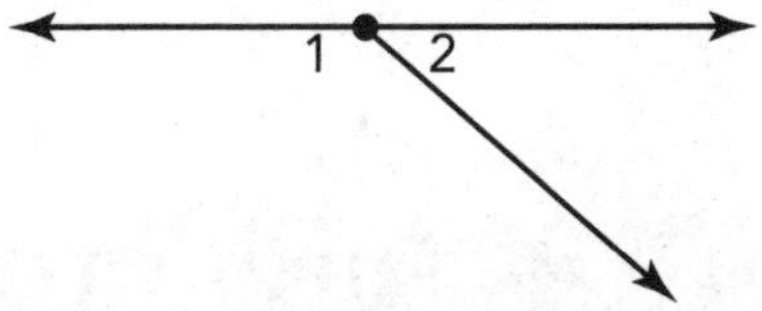

∠3 and ∠4 do *not* form a linear pair.

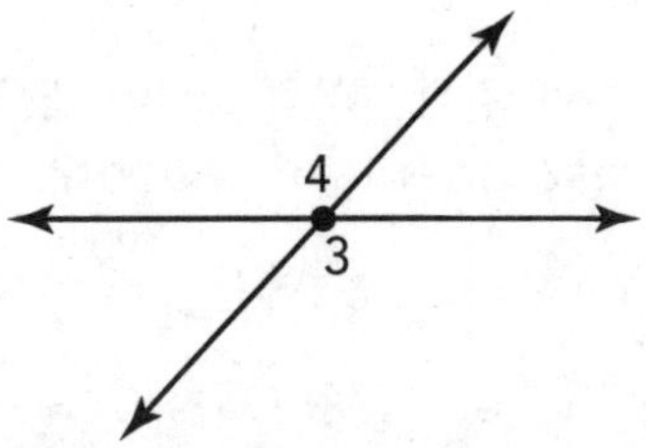

Vertical angles are two nonadjacent angles that are formed by two intersecting lines. Vertical angles are congruent.

∠1 and ∠2 are vertical angles.

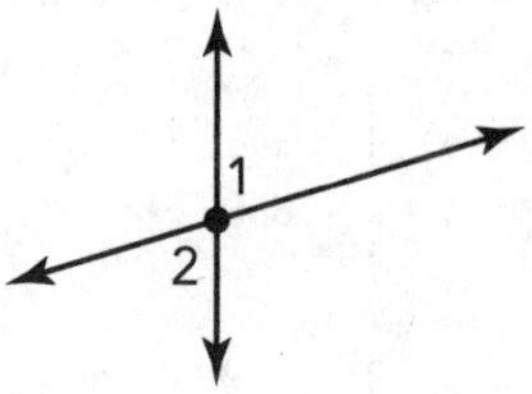

∠3 and ∠4 are *not* vertical angles.

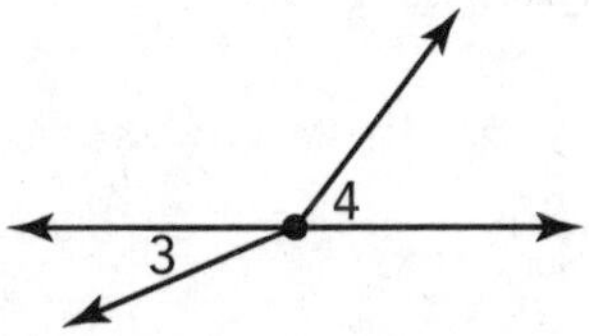

LESSON 3
Consider Every Side

Triangles are congruent when all of their corresponding angle measures and corresponding side lengths are the same. When given information can be used to construct congruent triangles, the information is said to define a unique triangle.

The **Triangle Inequality Theorem** states that the sum of the lengths of any two sides of a triangle is greater than the length of the third side.

$AC + CB > AB$

$BA + AC > BC$

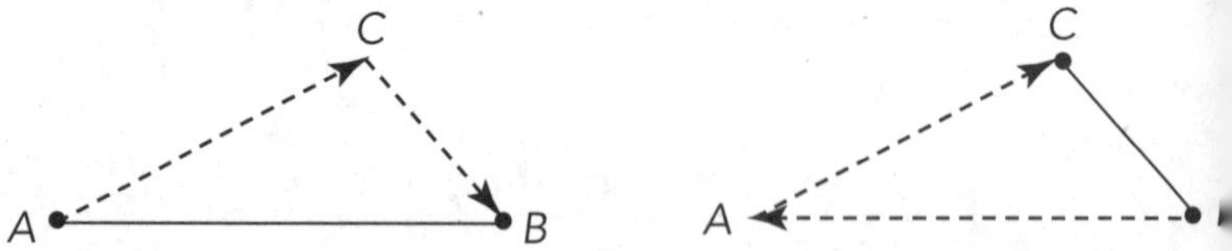

When given two line segments, it is possible to construct an infinite number of triangles. When given three line segments, it is possible to either construct a unique triangle, or no triangle.

LESSON 4
Unique or Not?

When you are given three of the six sides and angles of a triangle, it may be possible to construct a unique triangle, more than one triangle, or no triangles from the information.

An **included angle** is the angle whose sides are made up of the given sides of the triangle. If you are given two sides and the included angle, you can construct a unique triangle.

An **included side** is the side between the two given angles of the triangle. If you are given two angles and the included side, you can construct a unique triangle.

TOPIC 2

Three-Dimensional Figures

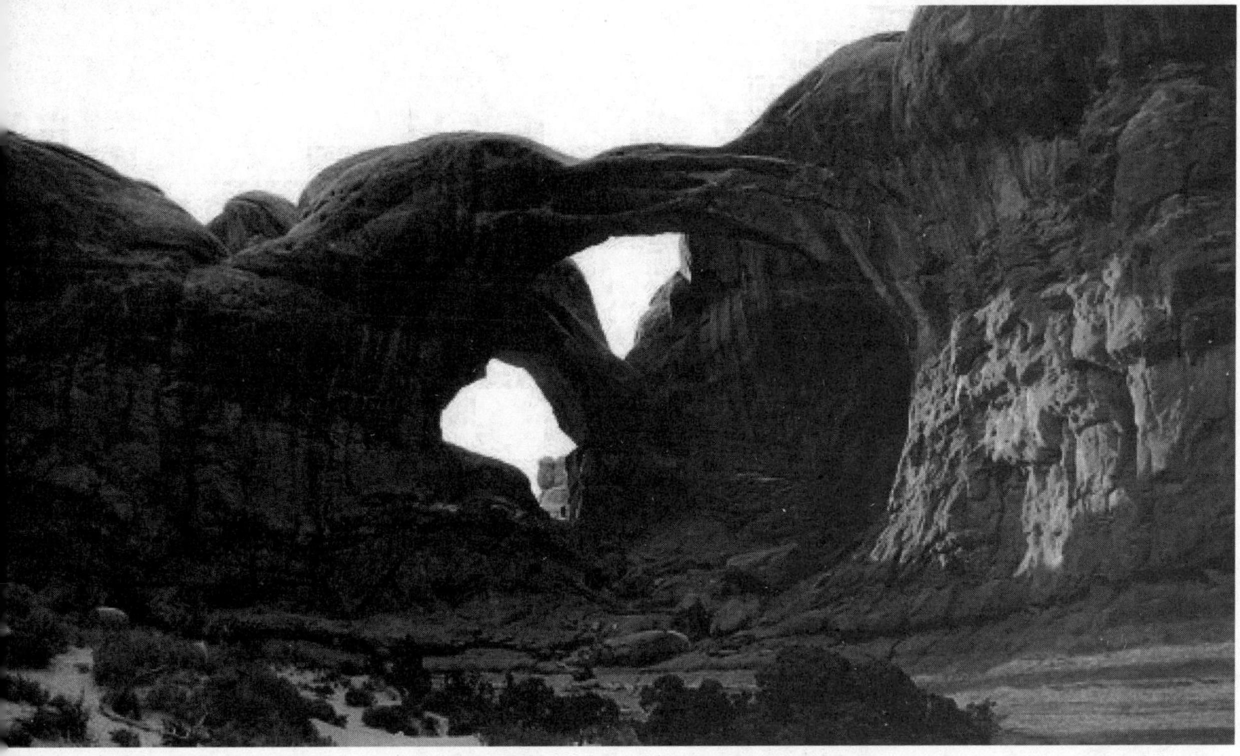

Arches National Park in eastern Utah has the highest density of natural arches in the world.

Module 5: Constructing and Measuring

TOPIC 2: THREE-DIMENSIONAL FIGURES

In this topic, students use nets of right rectangular prisms and pyramids, and discover that the volume of a pyramid is one-third the volume of the prism with the same base and height. Students practice using the volume formulas as they investigate the effect on the volume of doubling and tripling dimensions, and as they solve composite volume problems. Then students calculate the surface areas of familiar pyramids and prisms. Finally, students use strategies to calculate the volumes and surface areas of prisms and pyramids with non-rectangular bases.

Where have we been?

In grade 6, students learned to compose and decompose shapes in order to determine the area, volume, and surface area of a restricted set of geometric objects. They also learned the terminology associated with prisms and pyramids. Throughout this topic, students review the language of two- and three-dimensional geometry. As students move to measures of three-dimensional solids, they begin with the volume and surface area of prisms, which they computed in grade 6, and build up to additional solids.

Where are we going?

Generalizations of the formulas for the volume of prisms and pyramids will be used in grade 8 and in high school as students continue determining volumes of solids. They will also provide justifications for volume formulas in high school and use volume formulas to solve problems, building on the knowledge established in this topic.

Using Cross-Sections of Solids to Investigate Characteristics of 3D Figures

Students use clay and dental floss or wire to model cross-sections of three-dimensional figures. This image shows the intersection of a plane and a cube, which can form various cross-sections, including a pentagon, as shown.

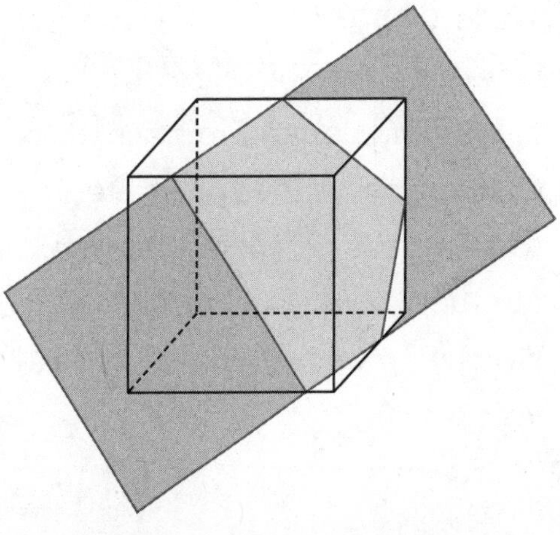

Myth: "Once I understand something, it has been learned."

Learning is tricky for three reasons. First, even when we learn something, we don't always recognize when that knowledge is useful. For example, you know there are four quarters in a dollar. But if someone asks you, "What is 75 times 2?" you might not immediately recognize that is the same thing as having six quarters.

Second, when you learn something new, it's not as if the old way of thinking goes away. For example, some children think of north as straight ahead. But have you ever been following directions on your phone and made a wrong turn, only to catch yourself and think, "I know better than that!"?

The final reason that learning is tricky is that it is balanced by a different mental process: forgetting. Even when we learn something (e.g., your phone number), when you stop using it (e.g., when you move), it becomes extremely hard to remember.

There should always be an asterisk next to the word when we say we learned* something.

#mathmythbusted

Talking Points

You can further support your student's learning by asking questions about the work they do in class or at home. Your student is continuing to reason about abstract geometric objects such as three-dimensional pyramids and prisms.

Questions to Ask

- How does this problem look like something you did in class?
- Can you show me the strategy you used to solve this problem? Do you know another way to solve it?
- Does your answer make sense? How do you know?

Key Terms

cross-section
A cross-section of a solid is the two-dimensional figure formed by the intersection of a plane and a solid when a plane passes through the solid.

regular polygon
A regular polygon is a polygon with all sides congruent and all angles congruent.

Slicing and Dicing

1

Cross-Sections of Rectangular Prisms

WARM UP

Define each term.

1. square

2. parallelogram

3. hexagon

4. pentagon

LEARNING GOALS

- Sketch, model, and describe two-dimensional cross-sections that result from slicing a cube.
- Sketch, model, and describe two-dimensional cross-sections that result from slicing a rectangular prism that is not a cube.

KEY TERM

- cross-section

You know that three-dimensional figures can be decomposed into two-dimensional figures using nets. How can you create two-dimensional figures by slicing right rectangular prisms?

Getting Started

Describing a Cube

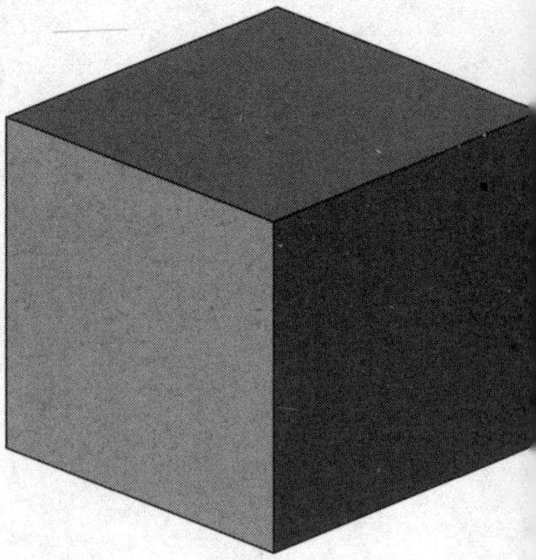

During this lesson, you will use clay to create and explore right rectangular prisms. In the first activities, you will explore slicing into a cube.

Use clay to make a model of a cube like the one shown.

1. **What do you know about the cube? How many edges, vertices, and faces does a cube have?**

2. **Explain the relationships between the faces of the cube. Are the faces of the cube parallel to each other? Are the faces of the cube perpendicular to each other?**

3. **Use dental floss or a piece of thin wire to slice off a corner of the cube.**

   a. **Describe the two-dimensional shaped formed by slicing off the corner.**

   b. **Compare your slice with your classmates' slices. What do you notice?**

ACTIVITY
1.1

Slicing a Cube

A **cross-section** of a solid is the two-dimensional figure formed by the intersection of a plane and a solid when a plane passes through the solid.

A plane can slice through a cube in a variety of ways. As a plane slices through a cube, a cross-section of the cube becomes viewable.

In the previous activity, you used dental floss or a piece of thin wire to simulate a plane and sliced through the clay cube so that a cross-section was viewable.

Recall that a plane is a flat surface with two dimensions, length and width, and it extends infinitely in all directions.

1. **How many edges of the cube did the plane, simulated by the floss or wire, intersect?**

2. **Slice through your cube such that the cross-section formed at the intersection of the plane and the cube is one of the six two-dimensional shapes listed.**
   - **Describe where or how you sliced your cube to create the cross-section.**
   - **Then compare your cross-section with your classmates' cross-sections.**

   a. triangle **b. square**

If you make a slice and realize it is not what you wanted, just put the clay cube back together and try again.

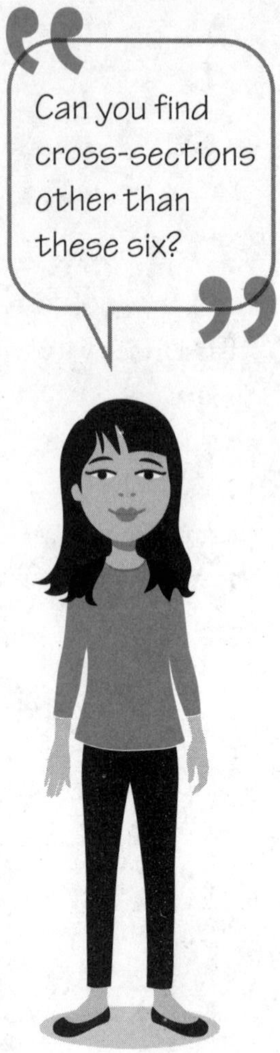

Can you find cross-sections other than these six?

c. rectangle that is not a square

d. parallelogram that is not a rectangle

e. hexagon

f. pentagon

3. What do you notice about all the cross-sections formed by the intersection of a plane that is either parallel or perpendicular to the base of a cube?

4. Consider the cross-sections that created the triangle and the hexagon.

   a. How can the cube be sliced to create an equilateral triangular cross-section?

   b. How can the cube be sliced to create a hexagonal cross-section with equal side lengths?

ACTIVITY
1.2

Cross-Sections of a Cube

In the previous activity, you were able to create some of the possible cross-sections of a cube. Let's now formally connect a name, diagram, and description for each cross-sectional shape of a cube.

1. **Cut out the diagrams and descriptions of cross-sectional shapes of cubes found at the end of the lesson. Match each cross-sectional name with its diagram and description. Then tape the diagrams and descriptions in the appropriate rows on the graphic organizers.**

   Each row of your graphic organizer will include:
   - **a name for the cross-sectional shape.**
   - **a diagram showing the cross-sectional shape.**
   - **a description that explains how to create the cross-sectional shape.**

Graphic organizers help me: Say It, See It, Talk about It.

I might say they help you: Name It, Visualize It, Describe It.

Cross-Sectional Shapes of a Cube

Name	Diagram	Explanation
A triangle		
A square		
A rectangle that is not a square		

Cross-Sectional Shapes of a Cube

Name	Diagram	Explanation
A parallelogram that is not a rectangle		
A hexagon		
A pentagon		

ACTIVITY
1.3

Slicing a Right Rectangular Prism

A right rectangular prism has rectangular bases and faces that are perpendicular to each other, forming right angles.

Use clay to make a model of a right rectangular prism that is not a cube, like the one shown. In this prism, the bases of the rectangular prism are squares, and the other faces are rectangles.

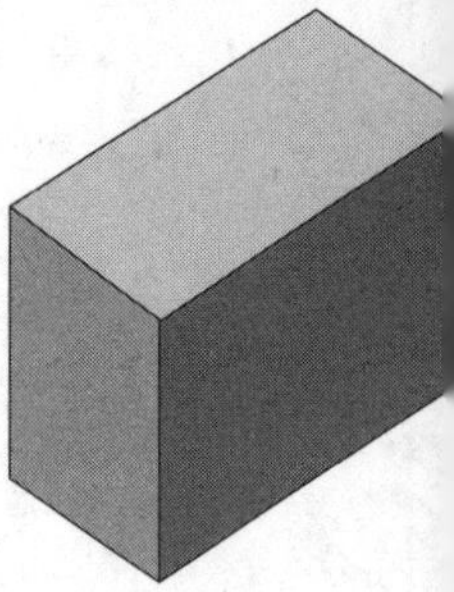

Just like with a cube, you can use a plane to slice through a right rectangular prism in a variety of ways.

1. **Slice through your right rectangular prism such that the cross-section formed at the intersection of the plane and the right rectangular prism is one of the six two-dimensional shapes listed.**

   - **Describe where or how you sliced to create the cross-section.**

   - **Then compare your cross-section with your classmates' cross-sections.**

   a. **triangle**

   b. **square**

   c. **rectangle that is not a square**

   d. **parallelogram that is not a rectangle**

   e. **hexagon**

   f. **pentagon**

2. What do you notice about all the cross-sections formed by the intersection of a plane that is either parallel or perpendicular to the base of a right rectangular prism?

NOTES

3. Consider the cross-sections that created the triangle. How can the prism be sliced to create an equilateral triangular cross-section?

ACTIVITY 1.4

Cross-Sections of a Right Rectangular Prism

In the previous activity, you were able to create some of the possible cross-sections of a right rectangular prism. Let's now formally connect a name, diagram, and description for each cross-sectional shape of a right rectangular prism with square bases.

1. Cut out the diagrams and descriptions of cross-sectional shapes of right rectangular prisms found at the end of the lesson. Match each cross-sectional name with its diagram and description. Then, tape the diagrams and descriptions in the appropriate rows on the graphic organizers.

   Each row of your graphic organizer will include:
   - a name for the cross-sectional shape.
   - a diagram that shows the cross-sectional shape.
   - a description that explains how to create the cross-sectional shape.

Cross-Sectional Shapes of a Right Rectangular Prism

Name	Diagram	Explanation
A triangle		
A square		
A rectangle that is not a square		

Cross-Sectional Shapes of a Right Rectangular Prism

Name	Diagram	Explanation
A parallelogram that is not a rectangle		
A hexagon		
A pentagon		

NOTES

TALK the TALK

They are All Right... Rectangular Prisms

1. How do the cross-sections of a cube compare to the cross-sections of a rectangular prism that is not a cube? Explain why this makes sense.

2. What happens when you slice any right rectangular prism

   a. parallel to the bases?

   b. perpendicular to the bases?

3. Explain why heptagons and octagons cannot be created from cross-sections of right rectangular prisms.

Diagrams of Cross-Sectional Shapes of Cubes

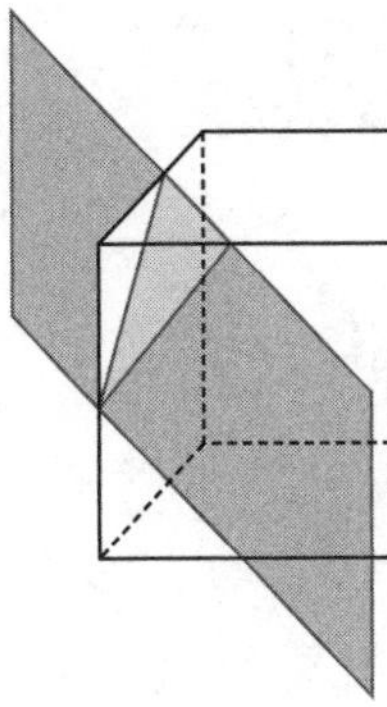

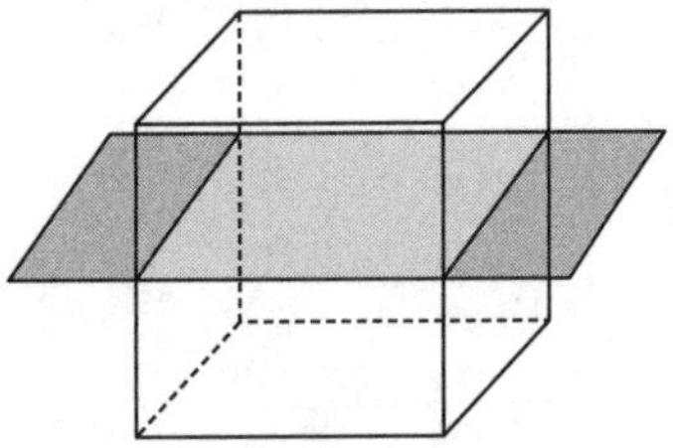

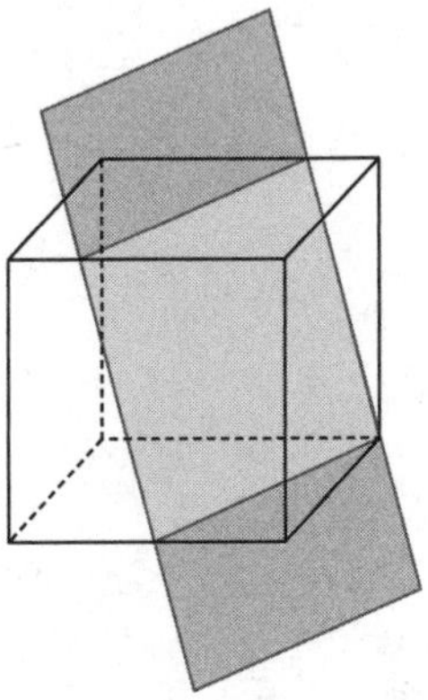

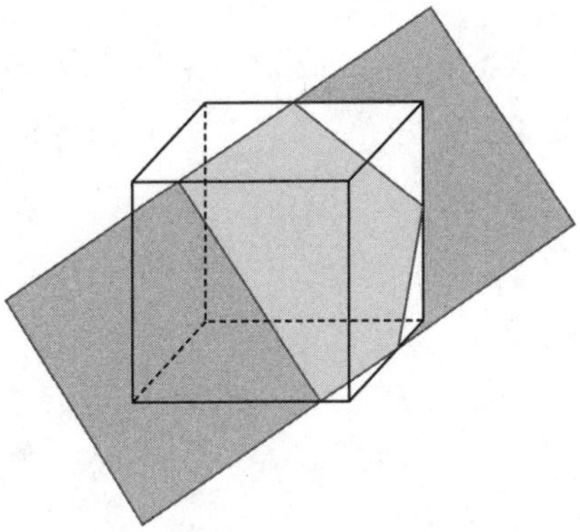

Think about
the models
you used.

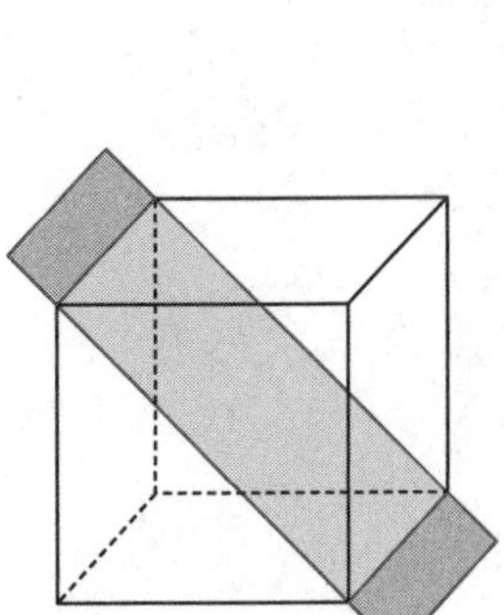

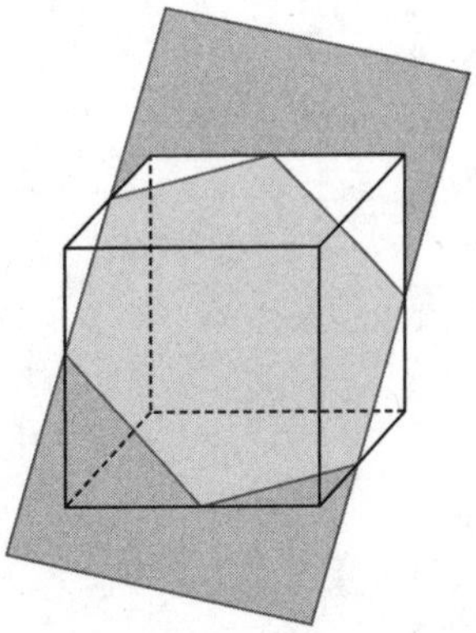

Descriptions of Cross-Sectional Shapes of Cubes

The cube is sliced in a way such that the plane passes through two parallel edges where one edge is in the upper-left portion of the cube and the other edge is in the lower-right portion of the cube.	The cube is sliced in a way such that the plane passes through three intersecting edges, cutting off a corner of the cube.
The cube is sliced in a way such that the plane passes through the middle of the parallel cube in a direction to the base.	The cube is sliced in a way such that the plane passes through five of the six faces of the cube.
The cube is sliced in a way such that the plane passes through the cube at an angle not perpendicular or parallel to the base.	The cube is sliced in a way such that the plane passes through all six faces of the cube.

Diagrams of Cross-Sectional Shapes of Right Rectangular Prisms

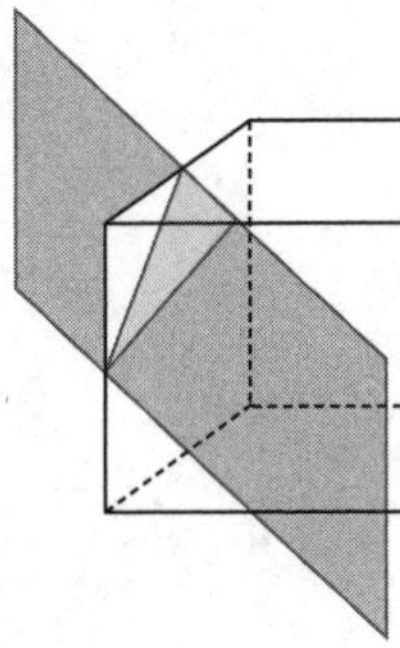

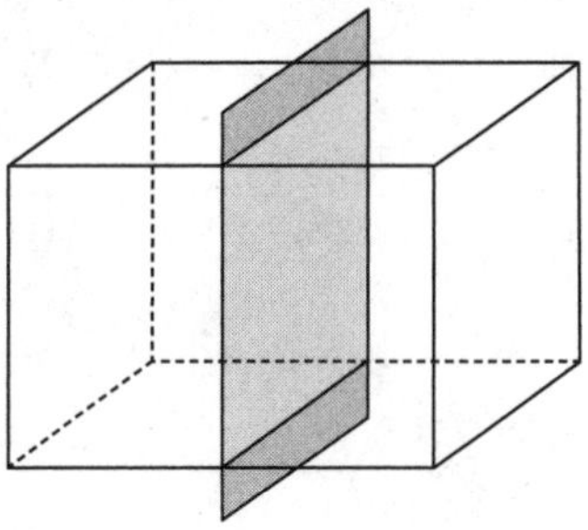

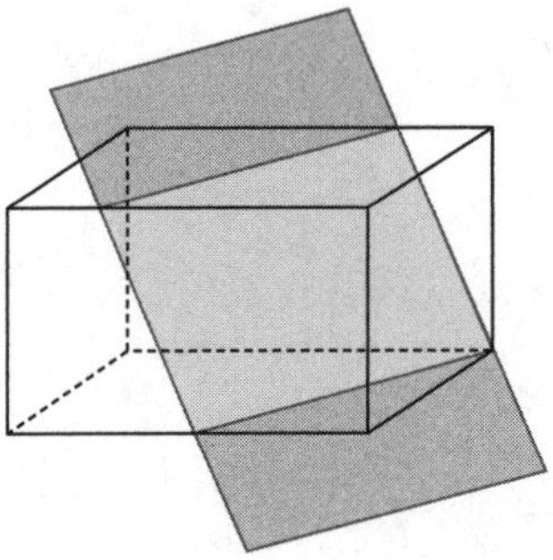

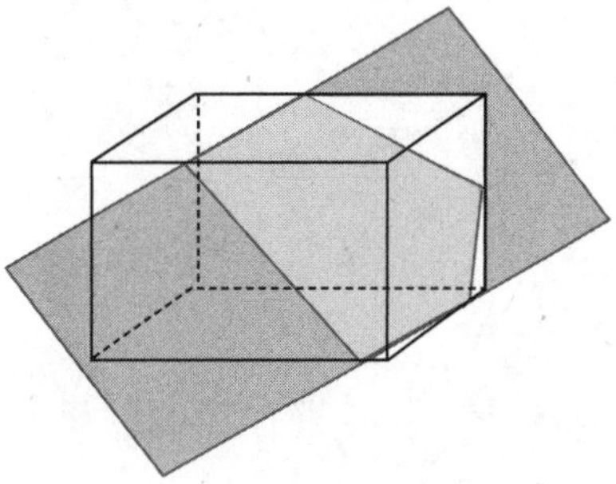

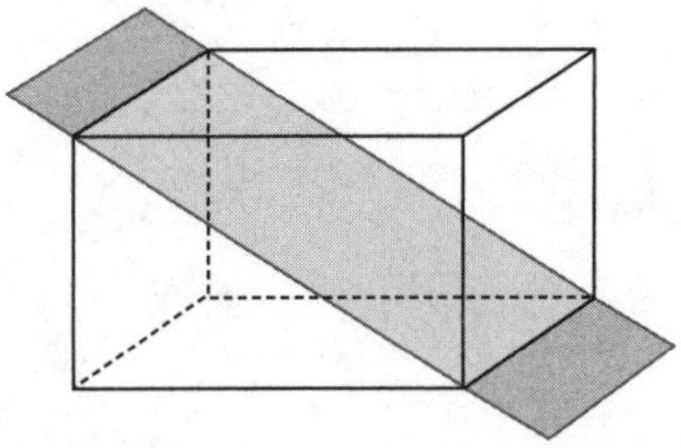

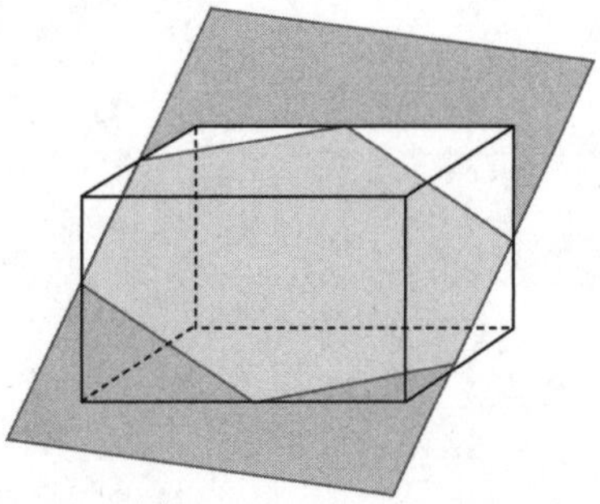

Descriptions of Cross-Sectional Shapes of Right Rectangular Prisms

The right rectangular prism is sliced in a way such that the plane passes through two parallel edges where one edge is in the upper-left portion of the prism and the other edge is in the lower-right portion of the prism.

The right rectangular prism is sliced in a way such that the plane passes through three intersecting edges, cutting off a corner of the prism.

The right rectangular prism is sliced in a way such that the plane passes through the middle of the prism in a direction parallel to the base.

The right rectangular prism is sliced in a way such that the plane passes through five of the six faces of the prism.

The right rectangular prism is sliced in a way such that the plane passes through the prism at an angle not perpendicular or parallel to the base.

The right rectangular prism is sliced in a way such that the plane passes through all six faces of the prism.

Assignment

Write

Define the term *cross-section* in your own words.

Remember

A prism is a geometric solid that has parallel and congruent polygonal bases and lateral sides that are parallelograms. The types of cross-sections of a cube are similar to the types of cross-sections of a rectangular prism (that is not a cube).

Practice

1. Dominique wants to paint a geometric border around her room. She has several sponges like the one shown. She decides to cut each of the sponges so that the cross-sections are different shapes. Then, she can dip the cut sponge in paint and stamp that shape on her wall.
   For each resulting sponge shown, describe how Dominque cut the sponge and what shape the sponge will make on the wall.

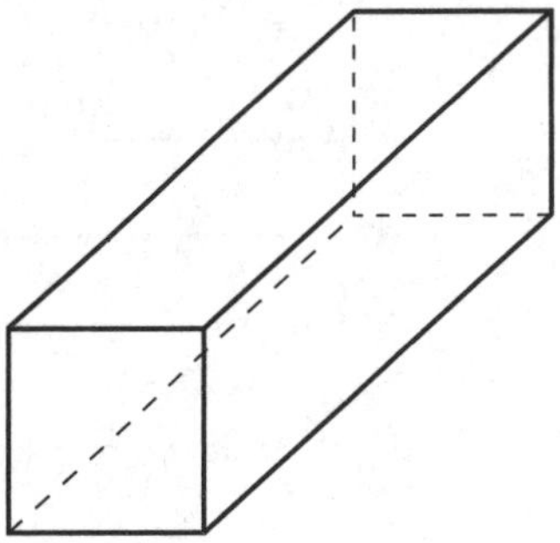

a.

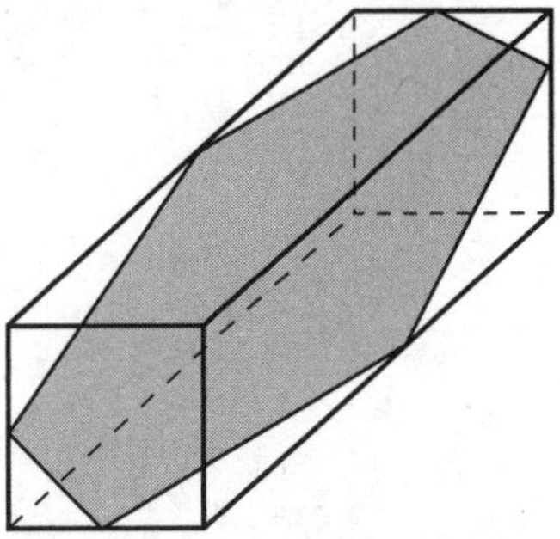

b.

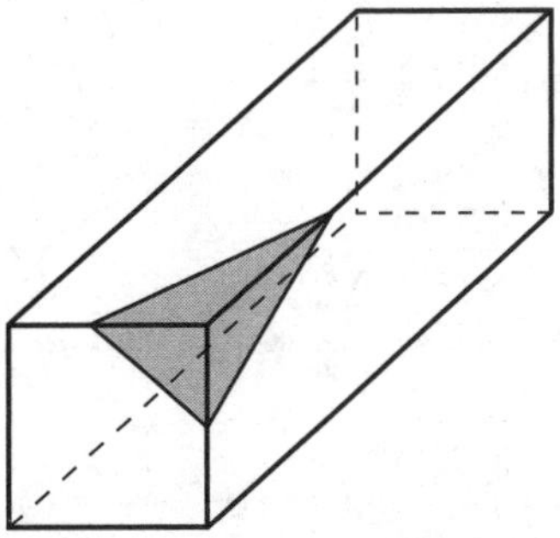

c.

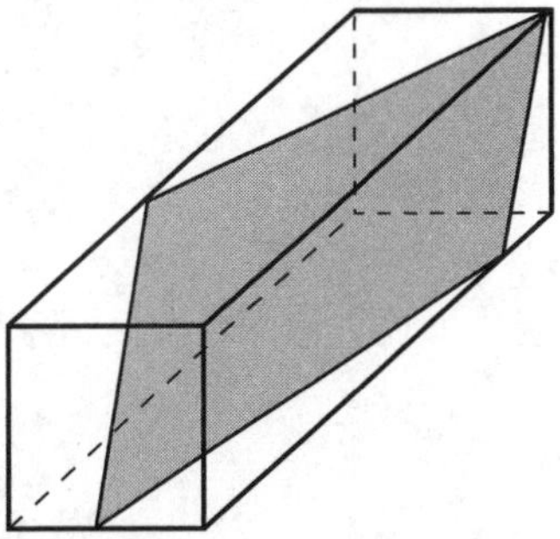

d.

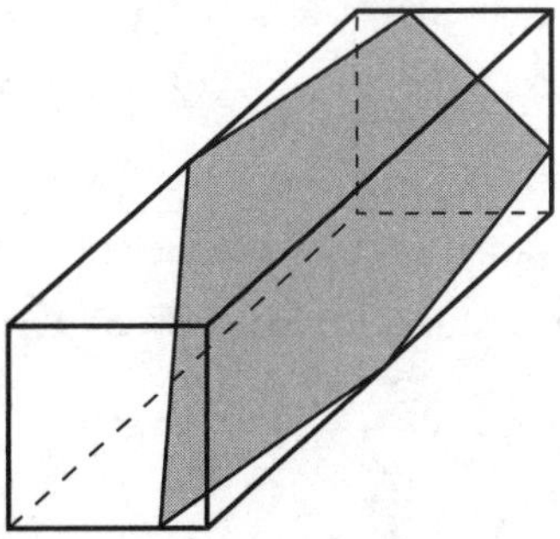

2. Describe the cross-section that results from the intersection of a plane and a right rectangular prism as described in each statement.
   a. A plane intersects exactly three vertices of a cube.
   b. A plane intersects two opposite vertices of the base of a cube, but is not perpendicular to the base. The plane intersects two edges of the other base of the cube.
   c. A plane intersects a right rectangular prism parallel to its rectangular base.
   d. A plane intersects two opposite vertices of the base, but is not parallel to the base. The plane does not intersect the other base.

Stretch

Describe all of the possible shapes that can be created by taking cross-sections of a cylinder. Use clay to demonstrate each cross-section.

Review

1. Construct ΔDEF using the two line segments and included angle shown.

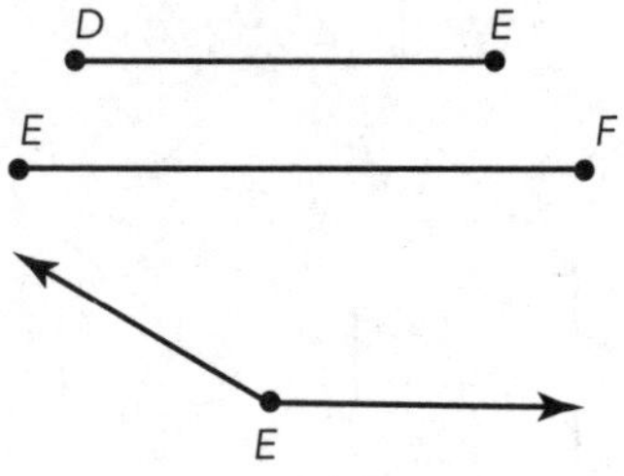

2. Construct a triangle using the given sides.

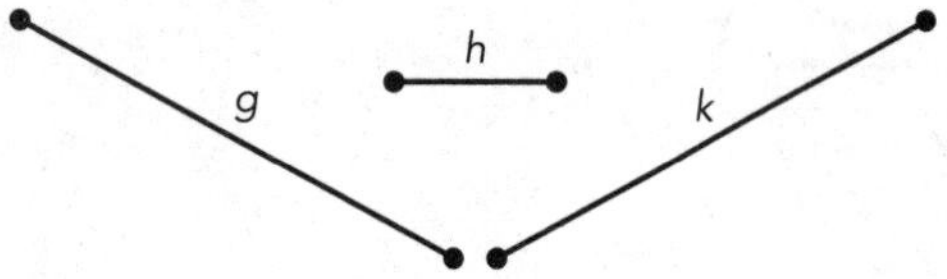

3. Use the diagram of three intersecting line segments to identify the specified angle pairs.
   a. supplementary angles
   b. vertical angles

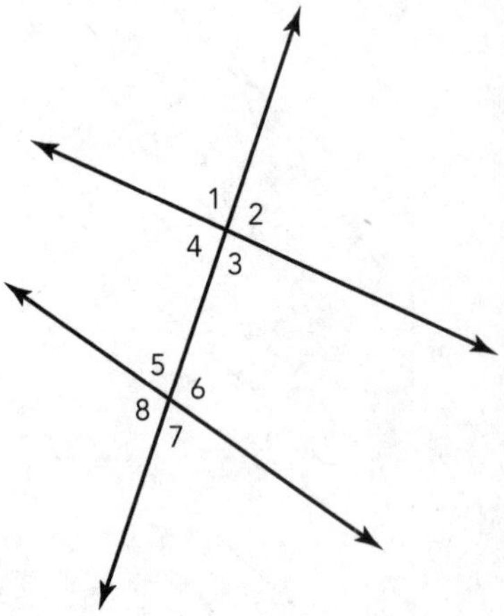

4. Determine the area and circumference of each circle with the given dimension. Use 3.14 for π and round to the nearest hundredth, if necessary.
   a. $d = 5.2$ ft
   b. $r = 14.9$ cm

Dissecting a Pyramid

2

Cross-Sections of Rectangular Pyramids

WARM UP

Define each term.

1. trapezoid
2. equilateral triangle
3. prism
4. pyramid

LEARNING GOAL

- Sketch, model, and describe the two-dimensional cross-sections that result from slicing right rectangular pyramids.
- Compare the two-dimensional cross-sections of right rectangular pyramids and right rectangular prisms.

You have explored cross-sections of right rectangular prisms. What shapes result from cross-sections of right rectangular pyramids?

Getting Started

Describing a Pyramid

During this lesson, you will create and explore right rectangular pyramids. Use clay to make a model of a right rectangular pyramid like the one shown.

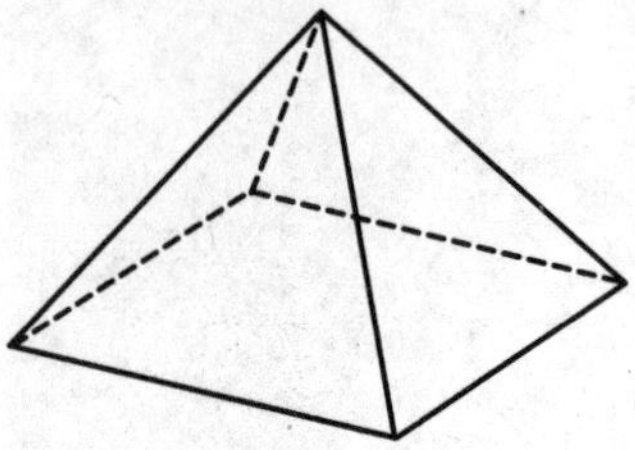

Like prisms, pyramids are classified by the shape of the base and the relationships between the parts of the pyramid.

1. **What do you know about a right rectangular pyramid? How many edges, vertices, and faces are on a right rectangular pyramid?**

2. **Explain the relationships between the faces of the right rectangular pyramid.**

   - **What does the word *right* in the name indicate?**

   - **What does the word *rectangular* in the name indicate?**

   - **Are the faces the same size?**

3. **Explain the relationships between the heights of the right rectangular pyramid. Are the heights of the triangular faces the same as the height of the pyramid?**

ACTIVITY
2.1

Slicing a Right Rectangular Pyramid

Just as you did with right rectangular prisms in the previous lesson, you can create cross-sections of right rectangular pyramids.

Use the clay pyramid you created in the previous activity for this activity.

1. **Slice through your right rectangular pyramid such that the cross-section formed at the intersection of the plane and the right rectangular pyramid is one of the three two-dimensional shapes listed.**

   - **Describe where or how you sliced to create the cross-section.**
   - **Then compare your cross-section with your classmates' cross-sections.**

   a. **triangle**

   b. **rectangle**

   c. **trapezoid**

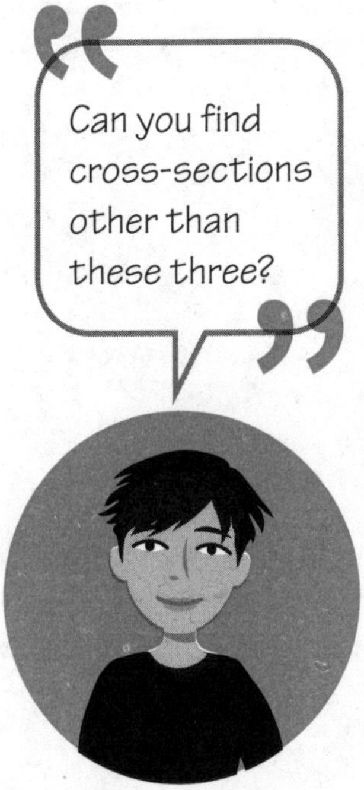

Can you find cross-sections other than these three?

NOTES

2. Is it possible to create a square cross-section from a right rectangular pyramid? Explain your reasoning.

3. Is it possible to create an equilateral triangular cross-section from a right rectangular pyramid? Explain your reasoning.

ACTIVITY 2.2

Cross-Sections of a Right Rectangular Pyramid

In this lesson, you created possible cross-sections of a right rectangular pyramid. Let's now formally connect a name, diagram, and description for each cross-sectional shape of a right rectangular pyramid.

1. Cut out the diagrams and descriptions at the end of the lesson. Match each cross-sectional name with its diagram and description. Then tape the diagrams and descriptions in the appropriate rows on the graphic organizer.

   Each row of your graphic organizer will include:

   - a name for the cross-sectional shape.
   - a diagram that shows the cross-sectional shape.
   - a description that explains how to create the cross-sectional shape.

Cross-Sectional Shapes of a Right Rectangular Pyramid

Name	Diagram	Explanation
A triangle		
A rectangle		
A trapezoid		

NOTES

TALK the TALK

Comparing Cross-Sections

One of your classmates missed this lesson, but was in class for the lesson on cross-sections of prisms. Help them to catch up by writing them an overview of this lesson. Be sure to answer these questions.

1. **How would the cross-sections of a square pyramid compare to the cross-sections of a right rectangular pyramid that does not have a square base?**

2. **How do the cross-sections of right rectangular pyramids compare to the cross-sections of right rectangular prisms?**

Diagrams of Cross-Sectional Shapes

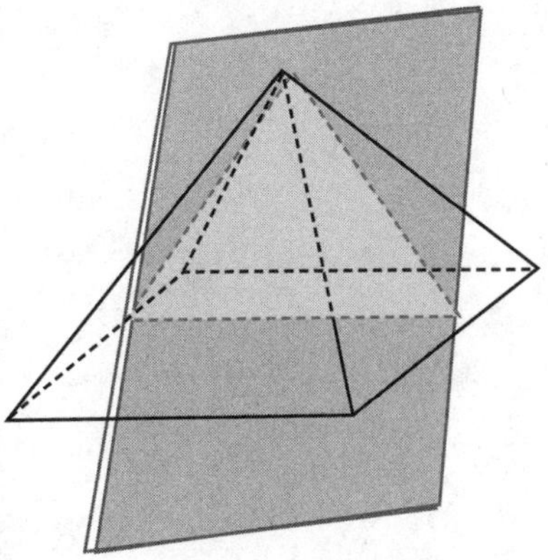

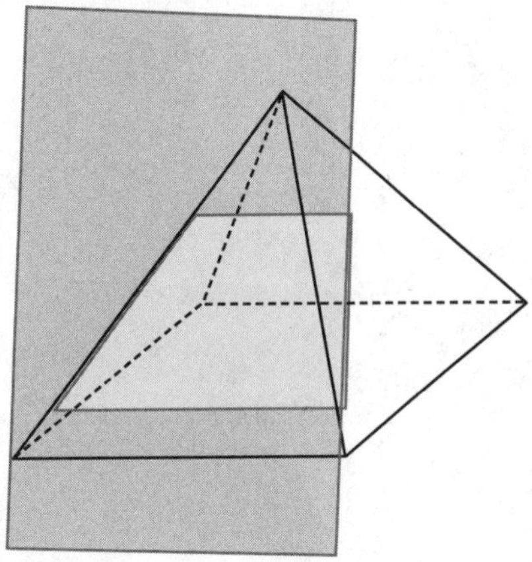

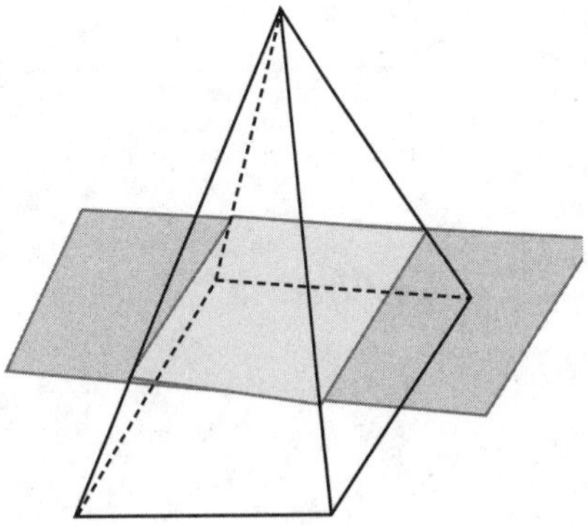

Descriptions of Cross-Sectional Shapes

The pyramid is sliced in a way such that the plane passes through the middle of the clay pyramid in a direction perpendicular to the base.	The pyramid is sliced in a way such that the plane passes through the middle of the clay pyramid in a direction parallel to the base.	The pyramid is sliced in a way such that the direction of the slice is neither parallel nor perpendicular to the base.

Assignment

Write

Explain why the greatest number of sides of a cross-section of a right rectangular pyramid is four.

Remember

A pyramid is a polyhedron formed by connecting one polygonal face to several triangular faces. Similar to prisms, pyramids are classified by their bases. The triangular faces of a pyramid intersect at the vertex of a pyramid.

Practice

1. Mr. Anthony's class is studying the Great Pyramid of Giza, so he gives his students the assignment of creating a model of a pyramid. Cleopatra decides to build a right rectangular pyramid.
   a. Draw a sketch of a right rectangular pyramid.
   b. Cleopatra wants to have 2 floors in her model. She will have to add an interior floor to the model to divide the pyramid into 2 floors. Sketch the shape of this floor and explain how you determined your answer.
   c. Will the interior floor be the same size as the bottom floor of the pyramid? Explain your reasoning.
   d. Add the interior floor to your sketch in part (a).
   e. Cleopatra wants to have 3 rooms on the first floor of her model. She will have to add 2 interior walls to create the 3 rooms. Sketch the shape of these walls and explain how you determined your answer.
   f. Add the first floor interior walls to your sketch in part (a).
   g. Cleopatra wants to have 2 rooms of the same size on the second floor of her model. She will have to add 1 interior wall to create the 2 rooms. Sketch the shape of this wall and explain how you determined your answer.
   h. Add the second floor interior wall to your sketch in part (a).

Stretch

Describe all of the possible shapes that can be created by taking cross-sections of a cone.

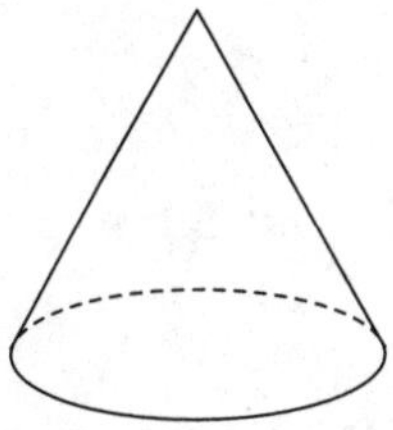

Review

1. Describe the cross-section that results from the intersection of a plane and a right rectangular prism as described in each problem.
   a. A plane intersects a right rectangular prism perpendicular to its base.
   b. A plane intersects a right rectangular prism parallel to its square base.
2. For each diagram, write and solve an equation to determine angle measures.

a.

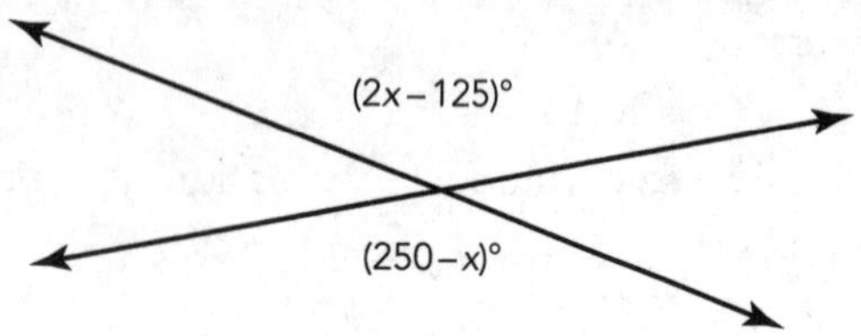

b.

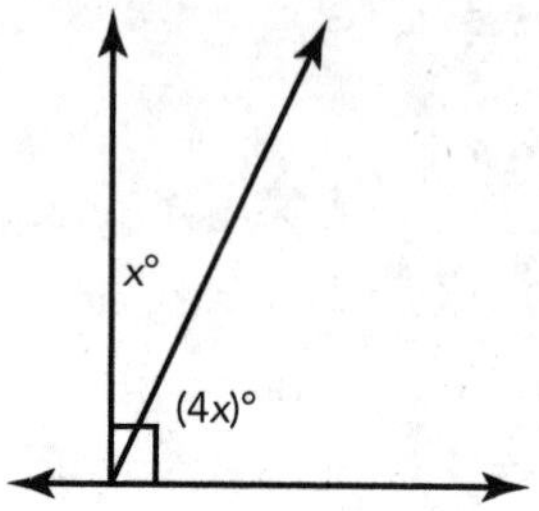

3. A magician is holding 4 playing cards – a jack, a queen, a king, and an ace. A spectator is asked to select a card, look at it, replace it, and then select a card again. Determine each probability.
   a. $P(\text{ace and ace}) =$
   b. $P(\text{king or queen}) =$

Hey, Mister, Got Some Bird Seed?

3

Volume of Pyramids

WARM UP

Calculate the volume of each cube.

1.

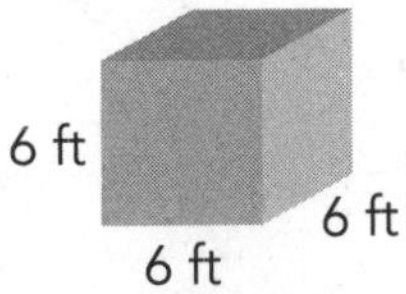

2.

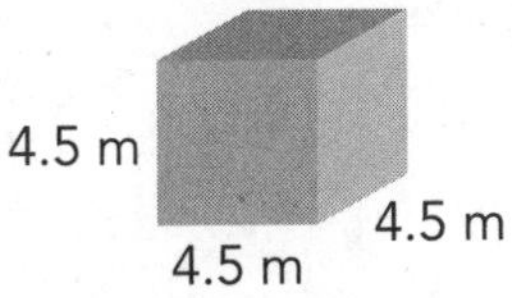

3. A cube that has a side length of 150 millimeters

LEARNING GOALS

- Determine the volume of pyramids.
- Determine how volume is affected when dimensions are doubled or tripled.
- Solve mathematical and real-world problems involving volumes of pyramids and objects composed of solid figures.

You have learned about the volume of rectangular prisms. How does the volume of pyramids compare? How are these measures affected by doubling and tripling dimensions?

Getting Started

You're a Real Cut-Up

Cut out Figures A and B at the end of the lesson and fold along the dashed lines to form solid figures. Tape the sides together so that the sides do not overlap.

1. **Name each solid figure.**

2. **Compare the bases of the figures. What do you notice?**

3. **Compare the heights of the figures? What do you notice?**

4. **Which figure appears to have a greater volume? Explain your reasoning.**

ACTIVITY 3.1

Rectangular Prism Volume vs. Rectangular Pyramid Volume

NOTES

Use the pyramid you built in the previous activity. Fill the pyramid with birdseed. Then, dump the birdseed from the pyramid into the prism. Repeat this process until the prism is full.

1. **How many times did you fill the pyramid?**

2. **Compare the volume of a rectangular pyramid to the volume of a rectangular prism when the bases are congruent polygons and the heights are of equal measure.**

3. **Write an equation that shows the relationship between the volume of a rectangular prism and the volume of a rectangular pyramid that have congruent bases and heights of equal measure. Let V_{prism} represent the volume of the prism and let $V_{pyramid}$ represent the volume of the pyramid.**

4. **Use a separate piece of paper to create your own nets for a rectangular prism and a rectangular pyramid that have congruent bases and heights of equal measure. What do you notice about their volumes?**

5. **Write formulas for both the volume of a rectangular prism and the volume of a rectangular pyramid. Use *V* for the volume, *B* for the area of the base, and *h* for the height.**

$V_{prism} =$ ____________________

$V_{pyramid} =$ ____________________

ACTIVITY 3.2 Triangular Prism Volume vs. Triangular Pyramid Volume

Cut out Figures C and D at the end of the lesson and fold along the dashed lines to form a triangular prism and a triangular pyramid. Tape the sides together so that the sides do not overlap.

1. **Fill the pyramid with birdseed. Then, dump the birdseed from the pyramid into the prism. Repeat this process until the prism is full. How many times did you fill the pyramid?**

2. **Compare the volume of a triangular pyramid to the volume of a triangular prism when the bases are congruent polygons and the heights are of equal measure.**

NOTES

3. Write an equation that shows the relationship between the volume of a triangular prism and the volume of a triangular pyramid that have congruent bases and heights of equal measure. Let V_{prism} represent the volume of the prism and let $V_{pyramid}$ represent the volume of the pyramid.

4. Use a separate piece of paper to create your own nets for a triangular prism and triangular pyramid that have congruent bases and heights of equal measure. What do you notice about their volumes?

5. Write formulas for both the volume of a triangular prism and the volume of a triangular pyramid. Use *V* for the volume, *B* for the area of the base, and *h* for the height.

V_{prism} = ____________________

$V_{pyramid}$ = ____________________

6. Compare your formulas for the volume of a triangular prism and the volume of a triangular pyramid to the formulas for the volume of a rectangular prism and the volume of a rectangular pyramid. What do you notice?

ACTIVITY 3.3 Applying the Volume of Pyramids

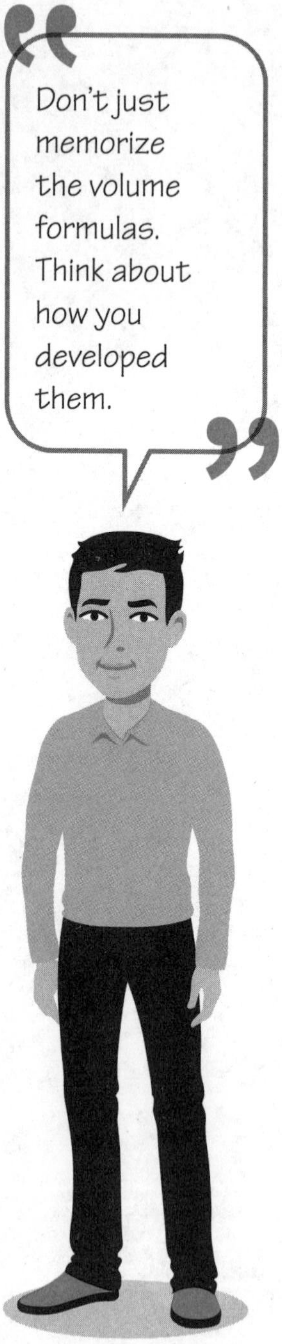

Don't just memorize the volume formulas. Think about how you developed them.

Now, apply what you know about pyramid volume to solve mathematical and real-world problems.

1. **Models of the Walter Pyramid and the Pyramid Arena are shown. Calculate the volume of each pyramid. Which is larger?**

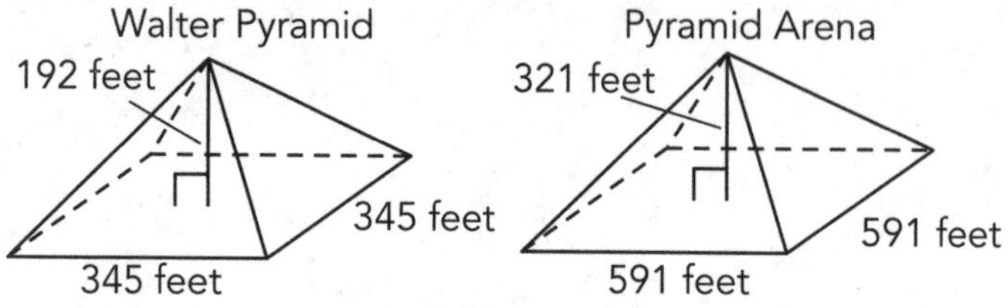

2. **A pyramid designed by I.M. Pei, a well-known Chinese-American architect, sits in front of the Louvre art museum in Paris. This square pyramid has a base that has a side length of 115 feet and a height of about 70 feet. Calculate the volume of this pyramid.**

Calculate the volume of each pyramid.

a.

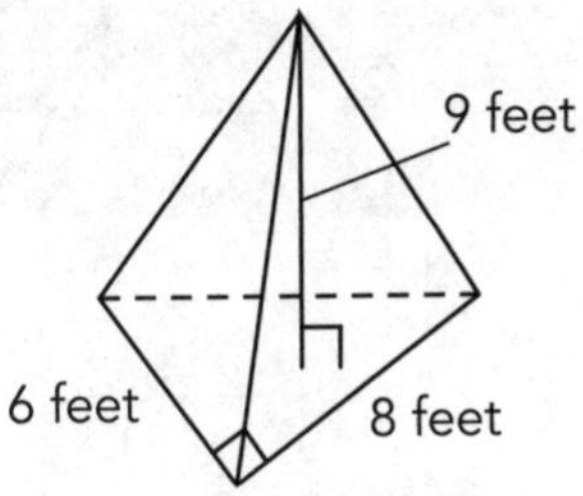

b.

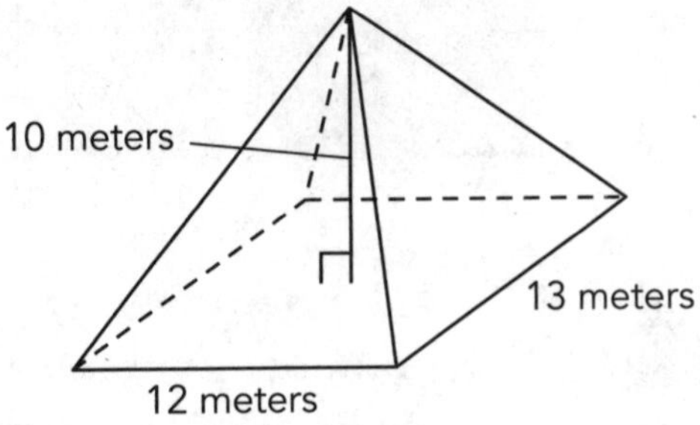

c.

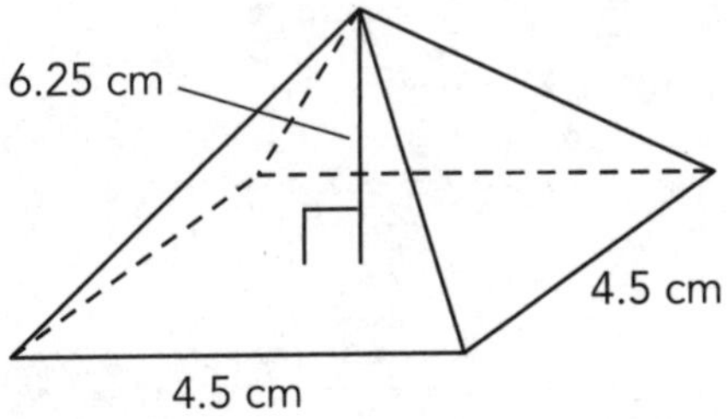

d.

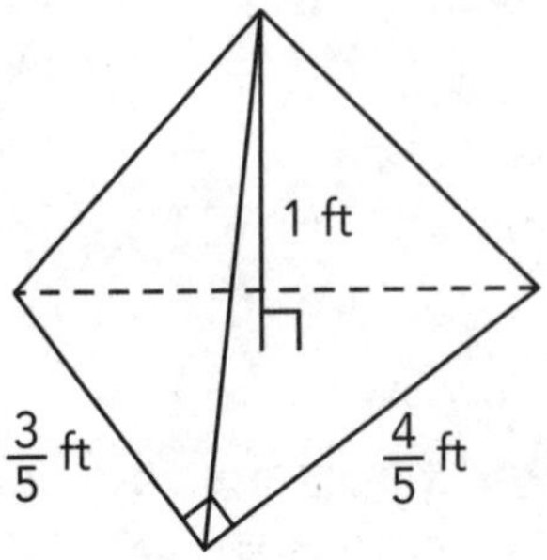

ACTIVITY
3.4

The Effects of Doubling and Tripling on Volume

1. Damian says that when the height of a rectangular prism is doubled, its volume also doubles. Cherise says that when the height of a rectangular prism is doubled, its volume quadruples. Who is correct? Explain your reasoning.

2. What happens to the volume of a rectangular prism when its height is tripled?

3. What happens to the volume of a triangular pyramid when its height is tripled?

4. What happens to the volume of a triangular prism when the area of its base is doubled?

. What happens to the volume of a rectangular pyramid when the width of the rectangular base is doubled?

. Jax and Miguel each describe the effects of doubling the side length of a square pyramid on the volume of the pyramid.

Jax

If I double the side length of a square pyramid, it has the same effect on the volume that doubling the height does. That is, the volume of the square pyramid also doubles.

Miguel

The volume of a square pyramid quadruples if I double the side length of the square base.

Explain why Miguel is correct and Jax is incorrect.

7. What happens to the volume of a square pyramid when the side length of the square base is tripled?

8. Suppose that Jerome wants to create two solids—a rectangular prism and a rectangular pyramid. He wants to create the solids such that their bases have the same size and shape. He also wants their volumes to be equal. How do their heights compare?

9. Suppose that Luisa wants to create two solids—a triangular prism and a triangular pyramid. She wants to create the solids such that their heights and volumes are both equal. How do their bases compare?

ACTIVITY
3.5 Composite Figures

1. An artist carved the sculpture shown using wood in the shape of a rectangular prism. She hollowed out the top in the shape of a pyramid. The artist used red oak, which weighs about 45 pounds per cubic foot. What is the weight of the artist's wood sculpture?

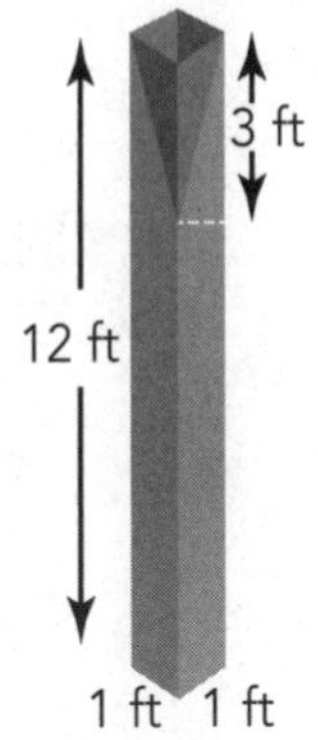

2. What is the volume of the house model shown? Show your work.

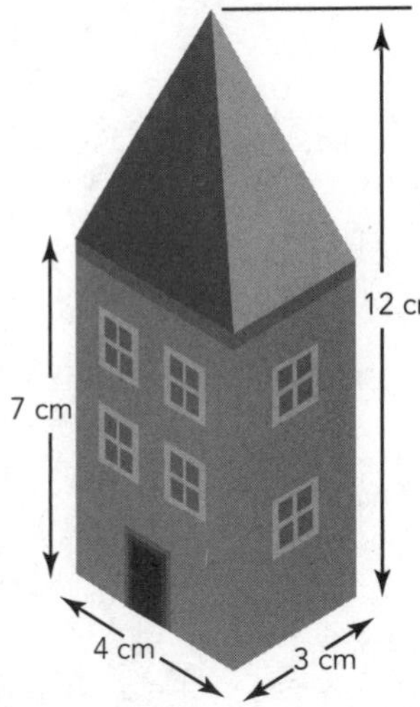

3. An octahedron is a solid that is composed of two congruent pyramids. Each pyramid has a square base.

What formula could you write to represent the volume of an octahedron?

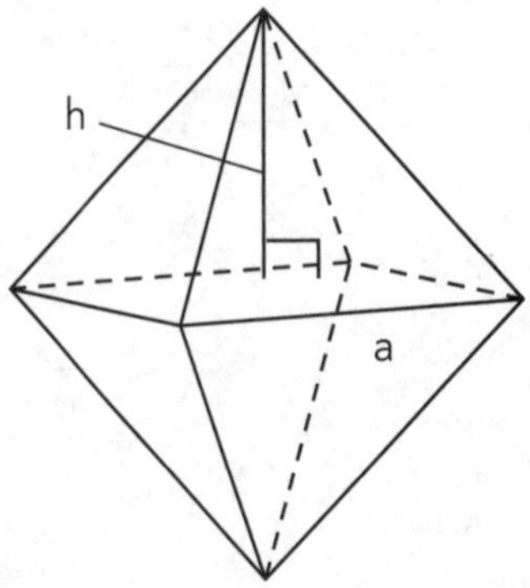

NOTES

TALK the TALK

The Sun and the Moon

Most people know about Egypt's Great Pyramids at Giza. However, there are a number of pyramids located in the Americas. The Mayan, Aztec, and Inca civilizations all built pyramids to bury their kings. Two of these pyramids are the Pyramid of the Sun and the Pyramid of the Moon located in Teotihuacán, Mexico.

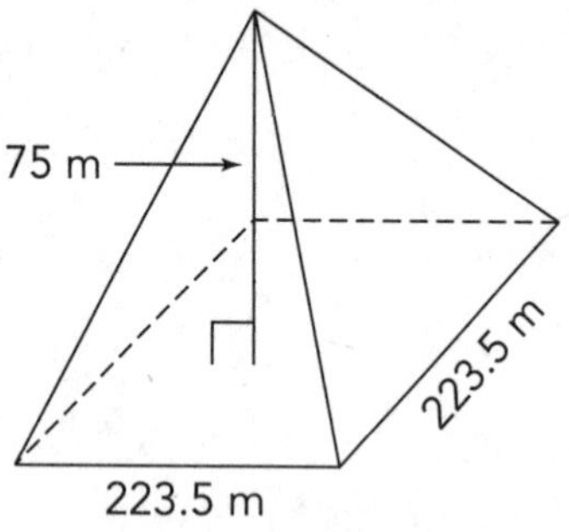

Pyramid of the Sun

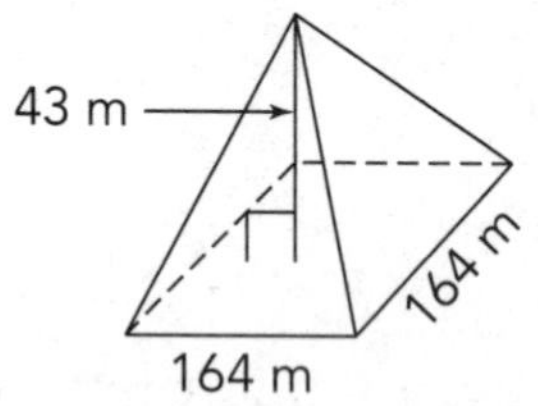

Pyramid of the Moon

1. Determine the volume of each pyramid. Show your work.

Figure A

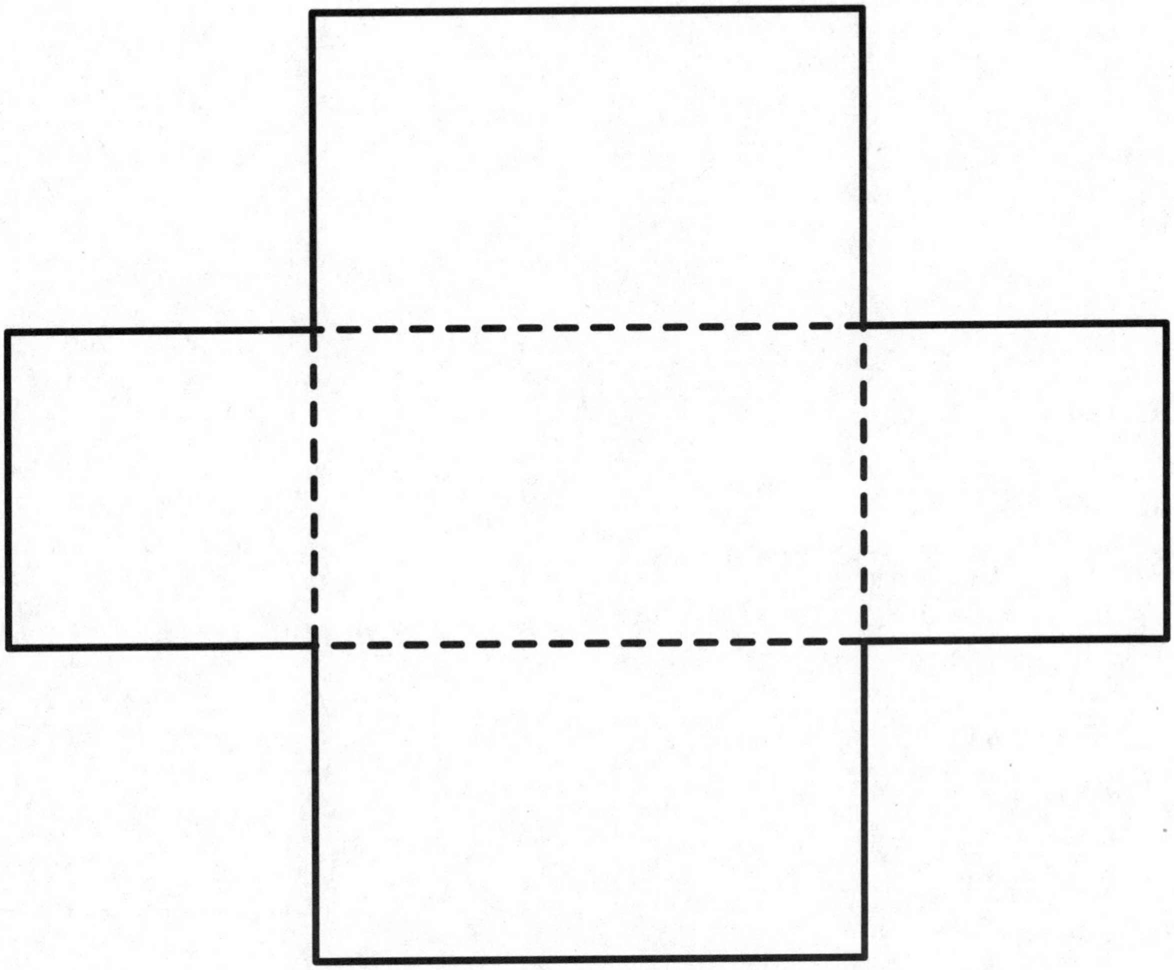

Figure B

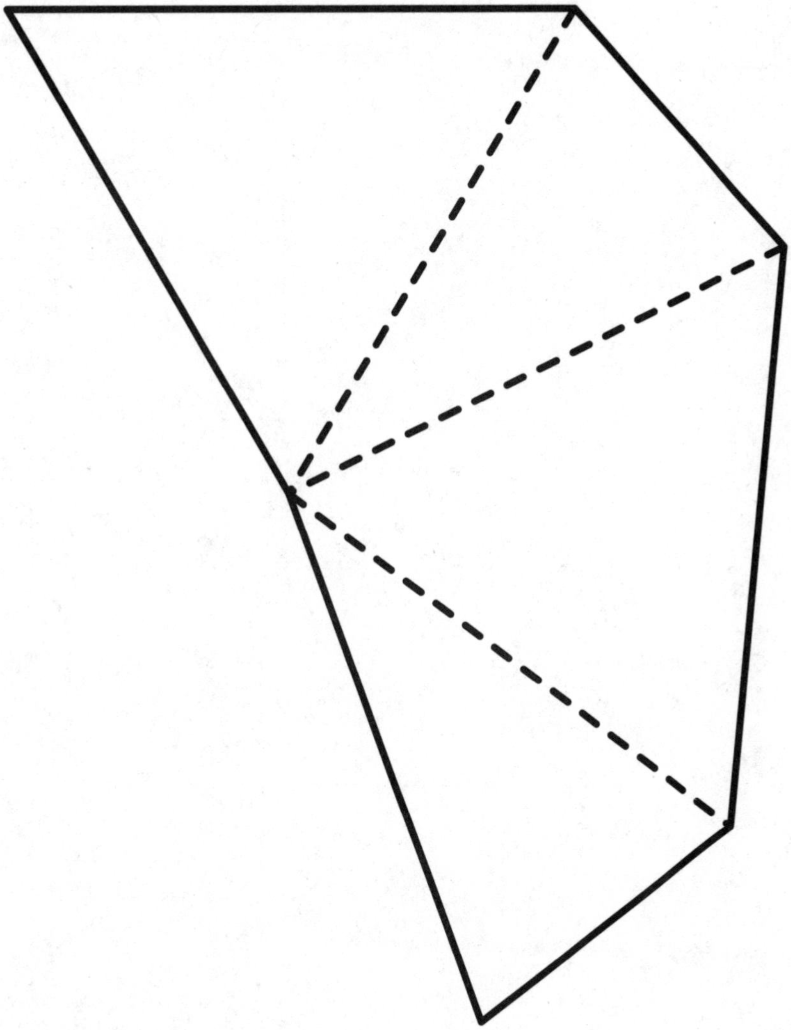

Figure C

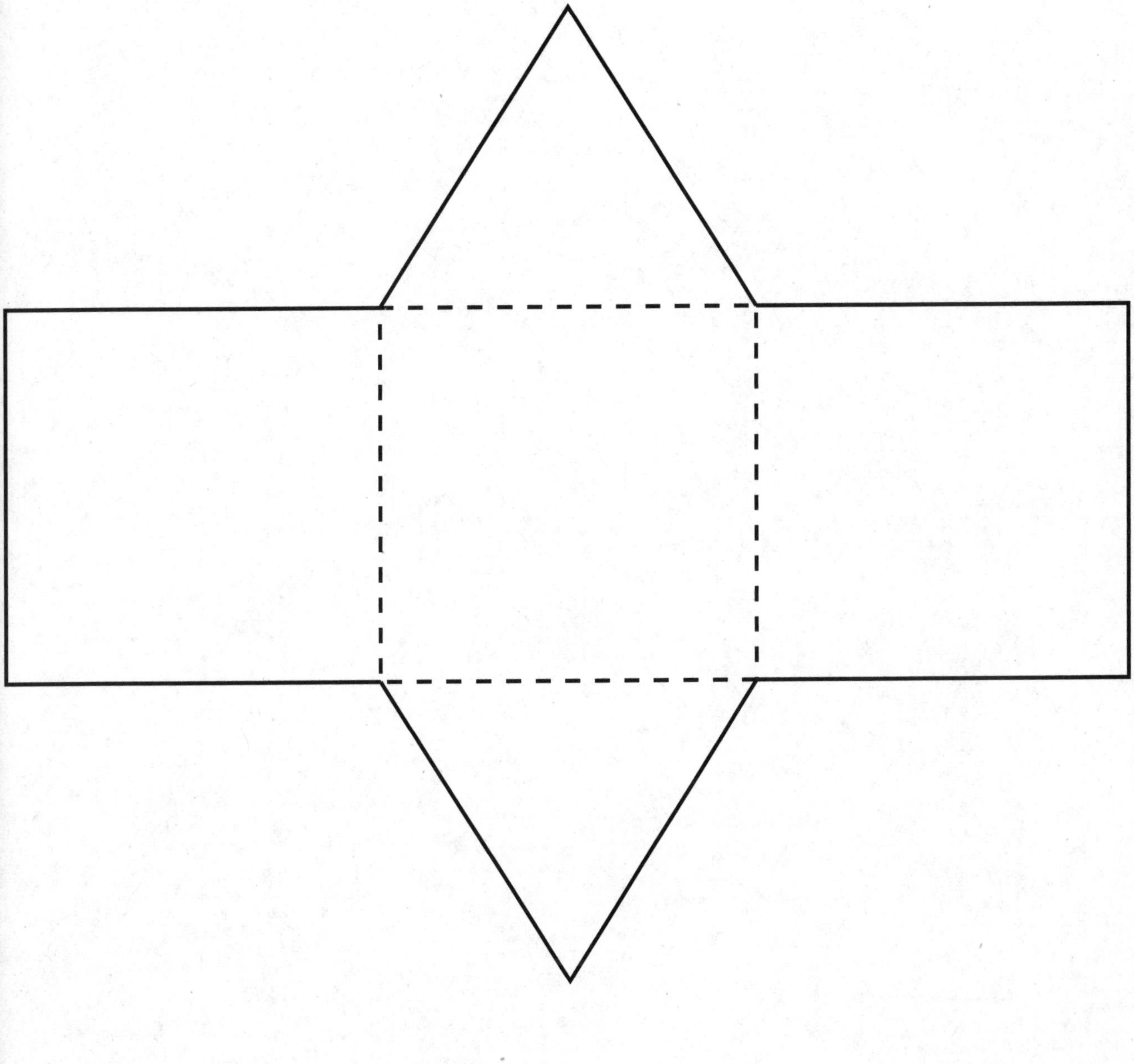

Figure D

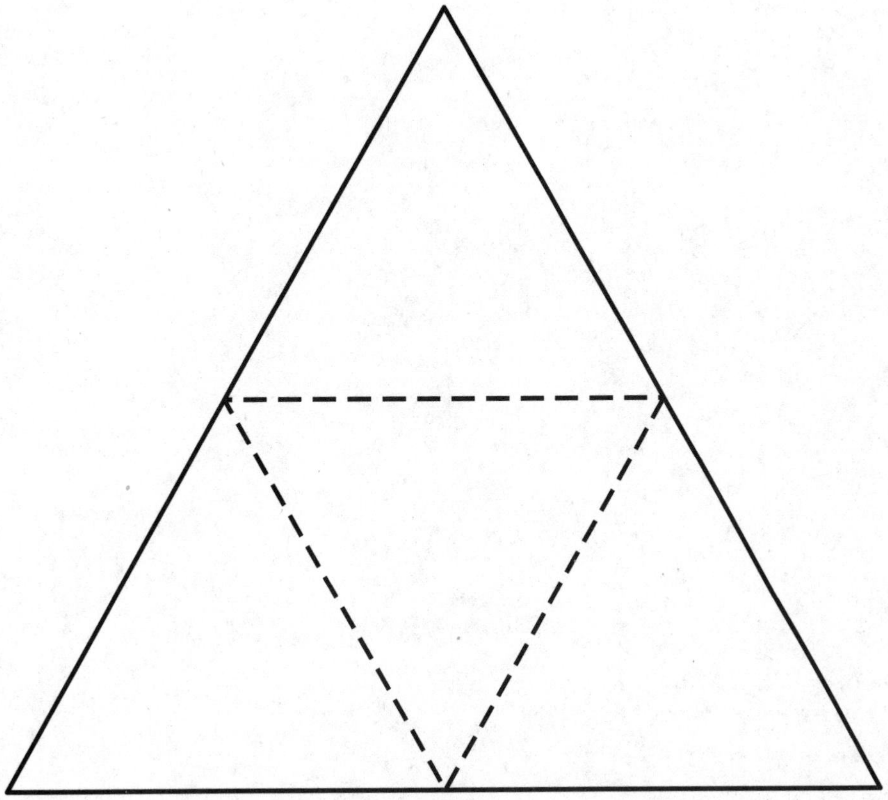

Assignment

Write

Describe the differences between pyramids and prisms. Use examples to help illustrate your description.

Remember

The volume of a pyramid is one third the volume of a prism with the same base and height.

$$V = \frac{1}{3}Bh$$

Practice

Pyramid tents were popular for a time during the 19th century. Although their popularity declined during the 20th century, they have recently begun to regain popularity. The design is ideal for shaping canvas, and it only requires one pole and some stakes to secure it. Joe wants to make a right square pyramid tent and is considering two different sizes. He will either make one with a base that is 10 feet by 10 feet and has a height of 12 feet, or he will make one with a base that is 12 feet by 12 feet and has a height of 8 feet.

1. Sketch the two pyramid designs Joe is considering and label them with the given measurements.
2. How can you determine which pyramid tent will have the most interior space?
3. Calculate the volume of each proposed pyramid tent. Show your work.
4. Which tent would you recommend Joe make? Explain your reasoning.

Stretch

A rectangular pyramid has one half the volume of a rectangular prism with the same base area. What do you know about the height of the pyramid compared with the height of the prism?

Review

Describe the cross section that you would obtain if you sliced through a cube in the way described.

1. The cube is sliced in a way such that the plane passes through five of the six faces of the cube.
2. The cube is sliced in a way such that the plane passes through three intersecting edges, cutting off a corner of the cube.

Tell whether a triangle could be formed from the three side lengths. Explain your answer.

3. 4 cm, 5 cm, 6 cm
4. 12 ft, 8 ft, 2 ft

Solve each inequality.

5. $7 > -0.8y + 27$
6. $-2\frac{1}{2} \leq -\frac{1}{4}g + 3$

The Sound of Surface Area

4

Surface Area of Pyramids

WARM UP

A rectangular prism has a height of 6 feet, a length of 7.5 feet, and a width of 5 feet.

1. Calculate the surface area of the prism.

2. Calculate the volume of the prism.

LEARNING GOALS

- Compare and contrast the surface areas of geometric solids.
- Apply volume and surface area concepts to solve real-world and mathematical problems involving surface area of pyramids and composite solids.

You have used the volume of pyramids to solve problems. How can you use the surface area of pyramids to solve problems?

Getting Started

Noise-Canceling Geometry

In small recording studios and large auditoriums, acoustical foam is placed on walls and ceilings to control sound and correct sound problems. The size and shape of the foam that is used depends on the sound problem. Two different acoustical foam shapes are shown.

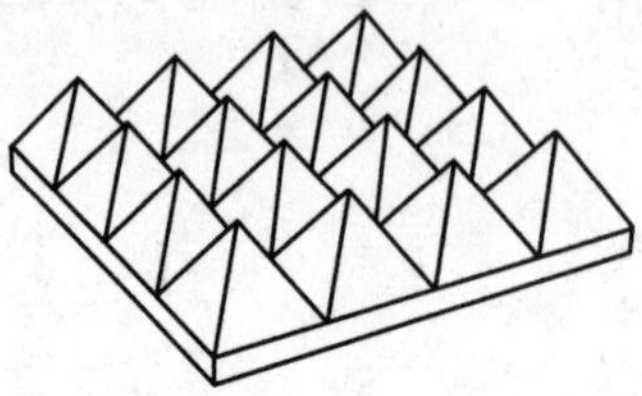

Pyramidal foam

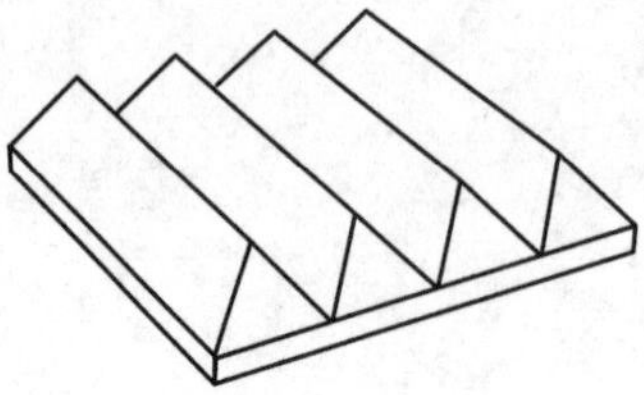

Wedge foam

1. **Describe the polyhedrons used in each type of acoustical foam board.**

2. **Compare the top surface areas of each piece of foam board.**

ACTIVITY 4.1

Surface Area of a Pyramid

One square pyramid from the pyramidal foam board in the previous activity is shown. A net of the square pyramid is also shown.

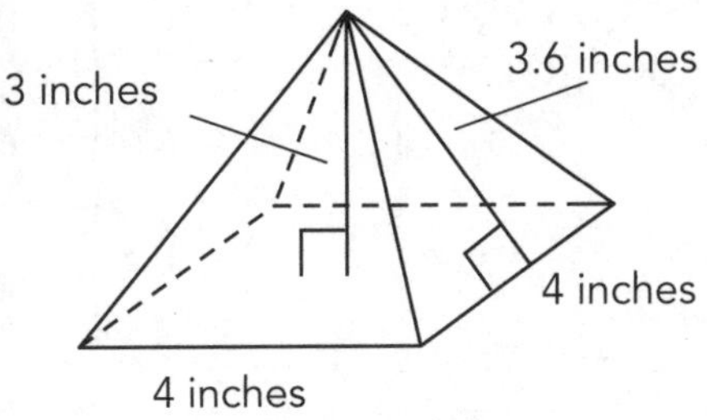

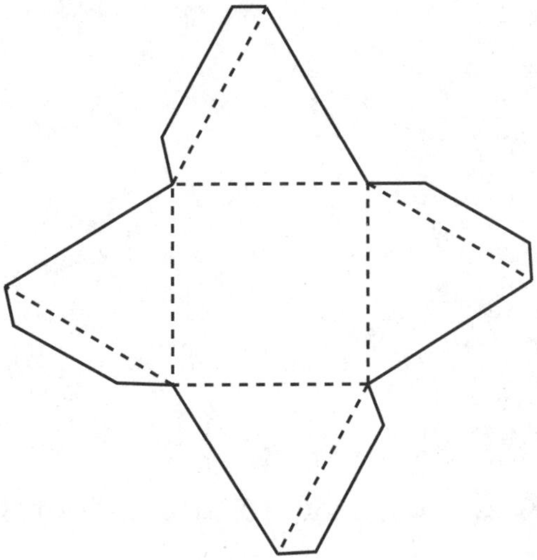

All pyramids have a height and a slant height. The slant height is not the actual height of the pyramid. Rather, it is the height of an individual triangle that is a face of the pyramid.

1. Label all known dimensions on the net shown.

2. Calculate the surface area of the pyramid.

3. Consider the original piece of pyramidal foam board. Calculate the amount of foam that covers the top surface area of the entire piece of pyramidal foam board.

One triangular prism from the wedge foam board is shown. A net of the triangular prism and its dimensions are also shown.

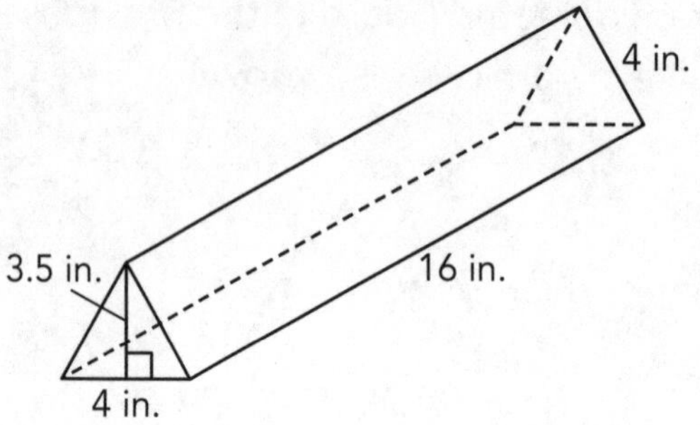

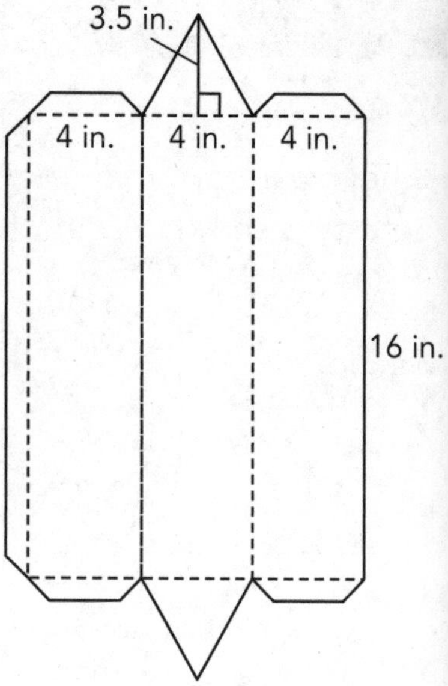

4. Calculate the surface area of the prism.

5. Consider the original piece of wedge foam board. Calculate the amount of foam that covers the top surface area of the entire piece of wedge foam board.

6. What is the difference between the total amount of foam that covers the top surface area of the piece of pyramidal foam and the top surface area of the piece of wedge foam?

NOTES

ACTIVITY
4.2 Surface Area Problems

When solving a problem, it may not be obvious whether you should use the formula for the volume or surface area of a solid. So, it is important to think about the context of the problem situation, and then make a decision about which formula to use.

1. Consider the square pyramid shown.

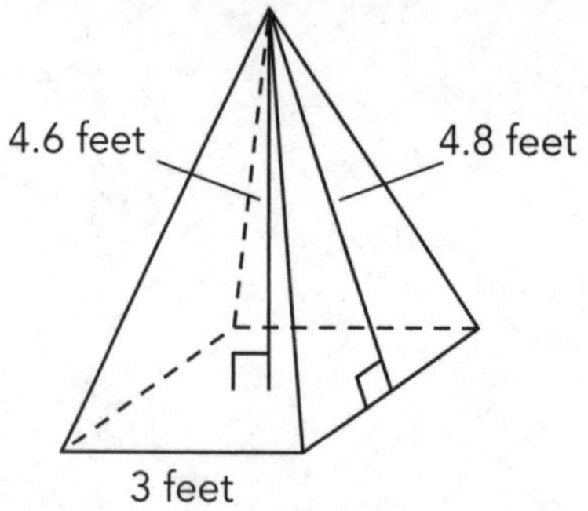

a. Draw a net to represent the square pyramid. Label the dimensions.

b. Suppose that the base of the pyramid is made of wood, and the triangular faces are made of plastic covered in blue felt. How much blue felt do you need?

c. Suppose that the pyramid is filled with rice. How much rice is needed?

Consider the triangular pyramid shown. The base is an equilateral triangle. The area of the base is 15.59 square centimeters.

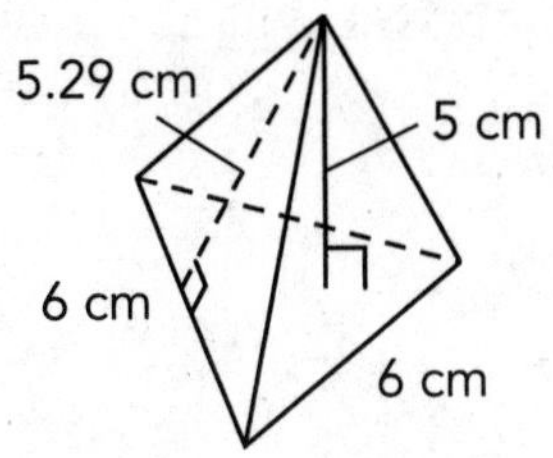

a. Draw a net to represent the triangular pyramid. Label the dimensions.

b. If Kira fills the triangular pyramid with sand, how much sand will she need?

c. If Destiny covers the triangular pyramid with foil, how muc foil will she need?

d. If Destiny covers the entire pyramid except for the base with foil, how much foil will she need?

3. Micah has a picnic table that has two wooden seats. Each seat is a rectangular prism that is 72 inches long, 18 inches wide, and 1 inch thick.

   a. Draw a net that represents one seat from the picnic table. Label the dimensions.

b. Micah wants to cover the seats with a weather-proofing stain. How much stain will he need?

c. Suppose that Micah decides he is not going to stain the sides that are 18 inches by 1 inch. How much stain will he need?

4. Gustavo is creating an ornament by gluing the bases of two square pyramid blocks together, as shown.

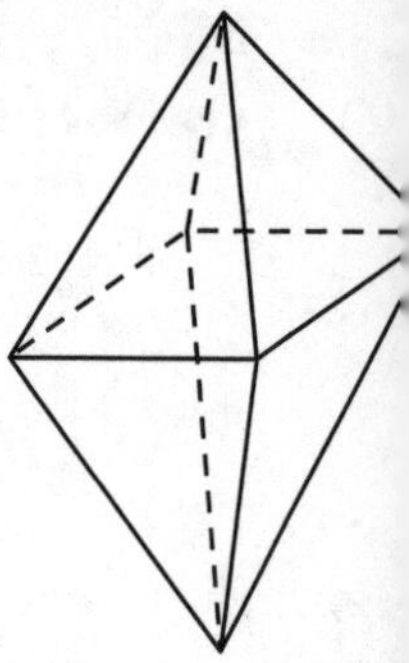

The square base of each pyramid has a side length of 1 inch, the height of each pyramid is 1.5 inches, and the slant height of each pyramid is 1.6 inches.

a. Draw a net to represent one of the square pyramids. Label the dimensions.

b. After gluing the pyramids together, Gustavo decides to cover the ornament with metallic paint. How much of the ornament will be covered in paint?

ACTIVITY 4.3

Building a Surface Area Formula

NOTES

The five faces of a square pyramid are shown.

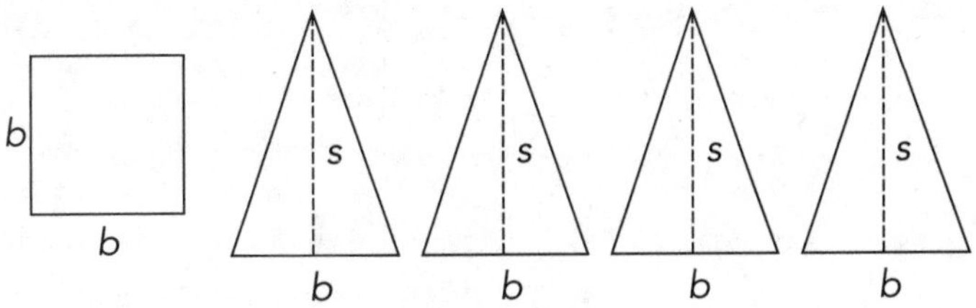

The variable *s* represents the height of each triangular face of the pyramid.

1. **Write an equation to represent the surface area of a square pyramid. Explain how the equation describes the surface area.**

2. **Use your formula to calculate each surface area.**

a.

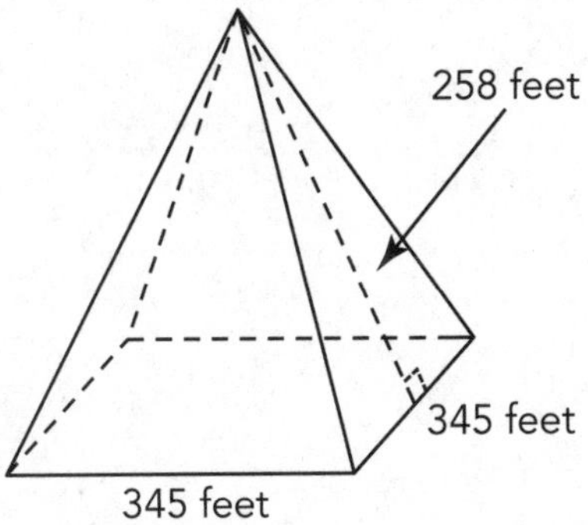

b.

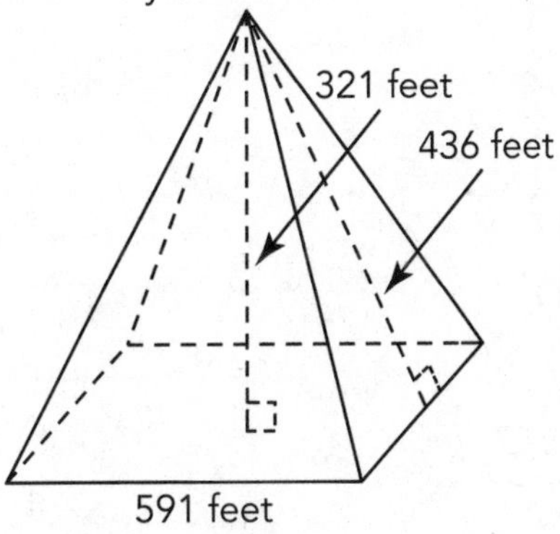

NOTES

TALK the TALK

The Information You Need

1. What information do you need to determine the volume of a pyramid? Provide an example to explain your reasoning.

2. What information do you need to determine the surface area of a pyramid? Provide an example to explain your reasoning.

Assignment

Write

In your own words, explain how to determine the surface area of any square pyramid. Use an example to illustrate your explanation.

Remember

The surface area of a pyramid is the sum of the areas of all of its faces. The lateral area of a pyramid is the total surface are of the pyramid excluding the base.

Practice

Calculate the volume, surface area, and lateral area of each solid described.

1. The base of a pyramid is an equilateral triangle with a side length of 12 inches. The height of the base is 10.4 inches. The height of the pyramid is 10 inches, and its slant height is 10.6 inches.
   a. Volume:
   b. Surface area:
   c. Lateral area:
2. A square pyramid has a base length of 1.5 meters, a height of 2.3 meters, and a slant height of 2.4 meters.
   a. Volume:
   b. Surface area:
   c. Lateral area:

Stretch

You have learned about the diameter, radius, and circumference of circles. How could you determine the surface area of a cylinder, like the one shown?

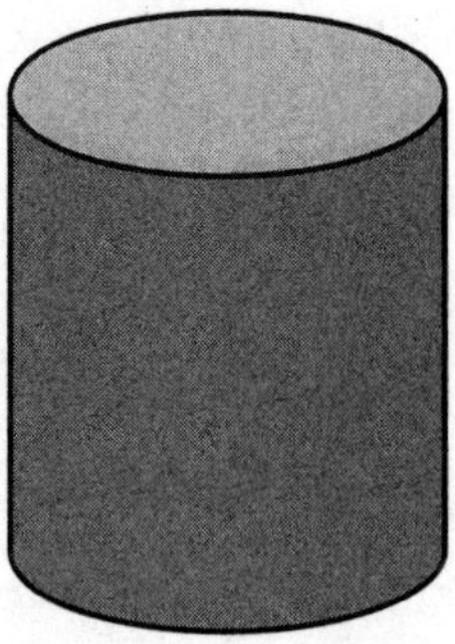

Review

Calculate the volume of each pyramid.

1.

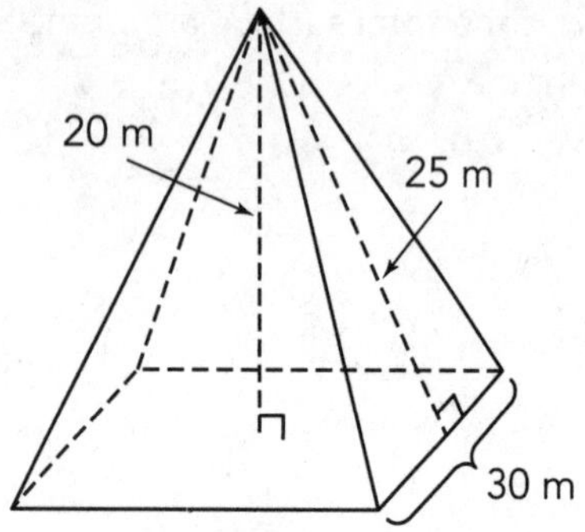

2.

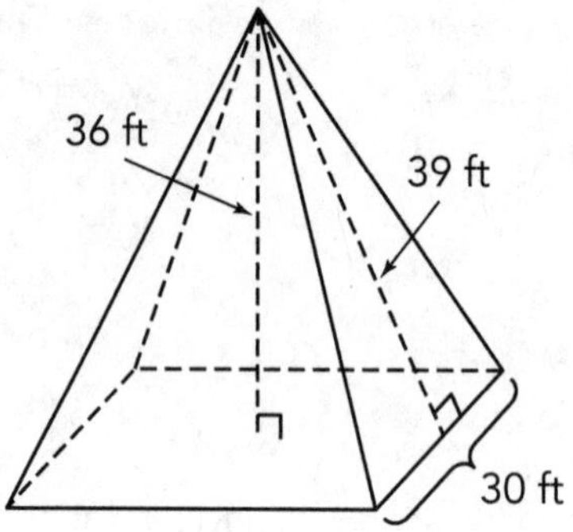

Draw each pair of special angles.

3. Draw a pair of supplementary angles. Explain why the angles are supplementary.
4. Draw a pair of complementary angles. Explain why the angles are complementary.

Write an equation and solve for the unknown angle measures in each figure.

5.

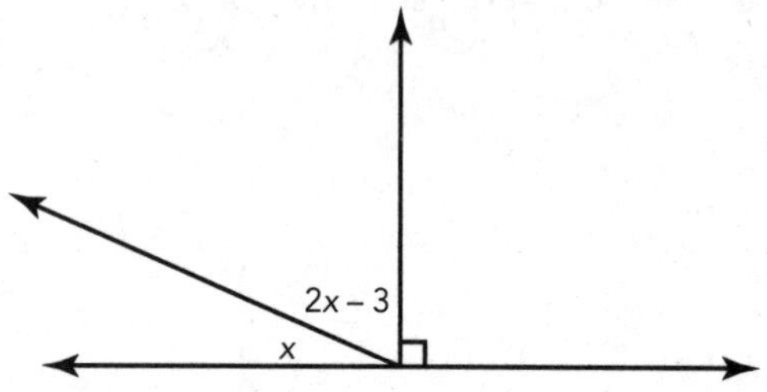

6.

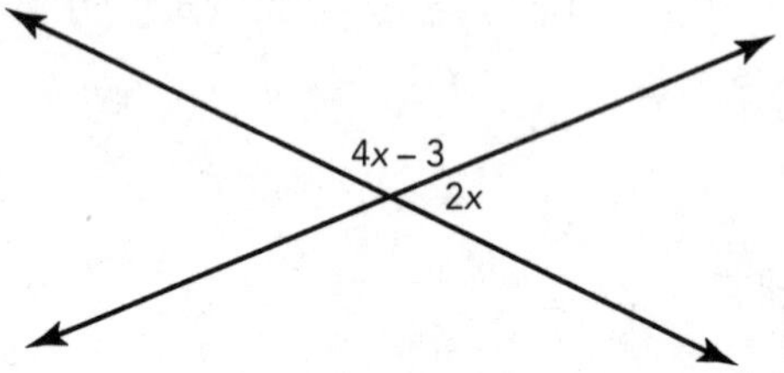

More Than Four Sides of the Story

5

Volume and Surface Area of Prisms and Pyramids

WARM UP

Calculate the volume of each right rectangular prism or pyramid.

1. Prism: length = $\frac{4}{3}$ ft, width = 1.8 ft, height = 3 ft
2. Prism: area of the base = 26 cm^2 and the height = 5 cm
3. Pyramid: length = $\frac{4}{3}$ ft, width = 1.8 ft, height = 3 ft
4. Pyramid: area of the base = 26 cm^2 and the height = 5 cm

LEARNING GOALS

- Calculate the volumes of prisms and pyramids with regular polygon bases.
- Calculate the surface areas of prisms and pyramids with regular polygon bases.
- Develop a strategy to calculate the areas of regular polygons.
- Calculate the areas of regular polygons.
- Calculate the surface areas and volumes of composite solids.
- Solve real-world and mathematical problems involving volume and surface area of two- and three-dimensional objects.

KEY TERM

- regular polygon

You know how to calculate the volume and surface area of right rectangular prisms and pyramids. How do you calculate the volume and surface area of solids with non-rectangular bases?

Getting Started

Other Prisms and Pyramids

Previously, you learned how to name pyramids and prisms by their bases and their faces. Identify the geometric solid that would be formed by each net.

1.

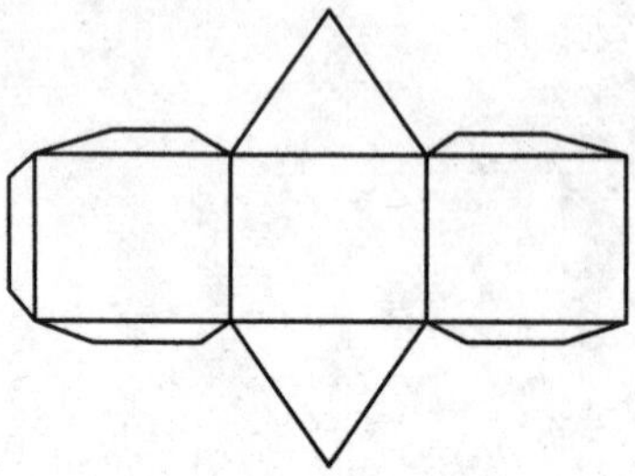

2.

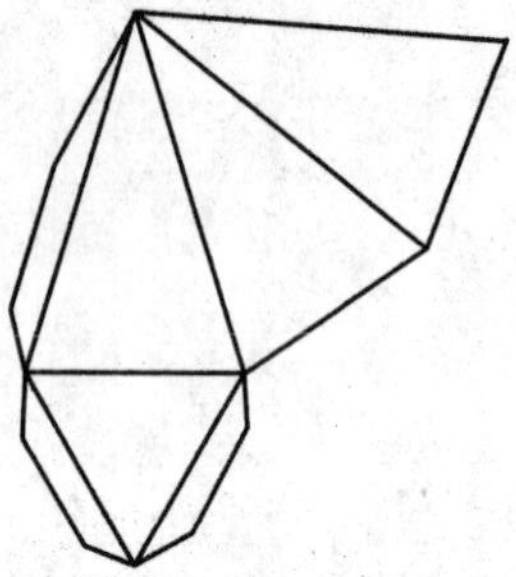

3.

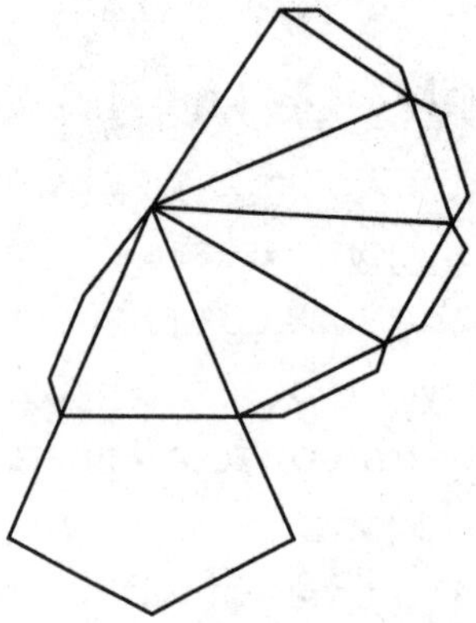

4.

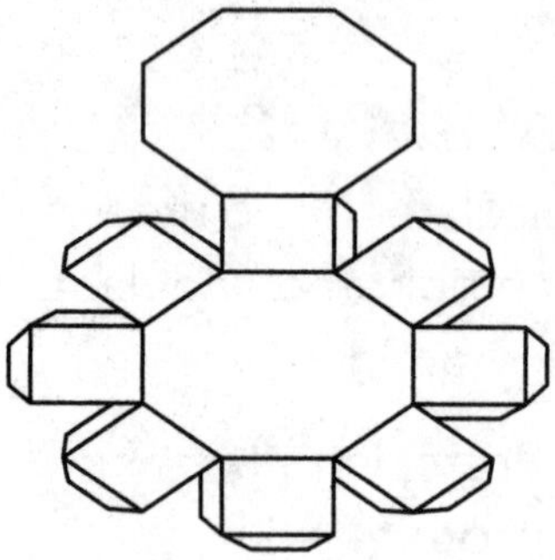

5.

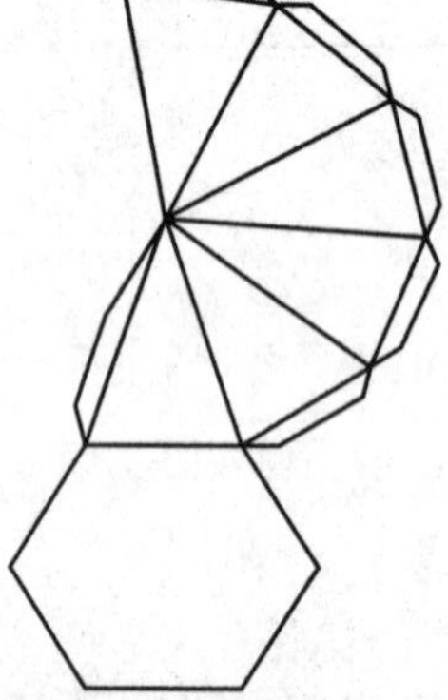

6.

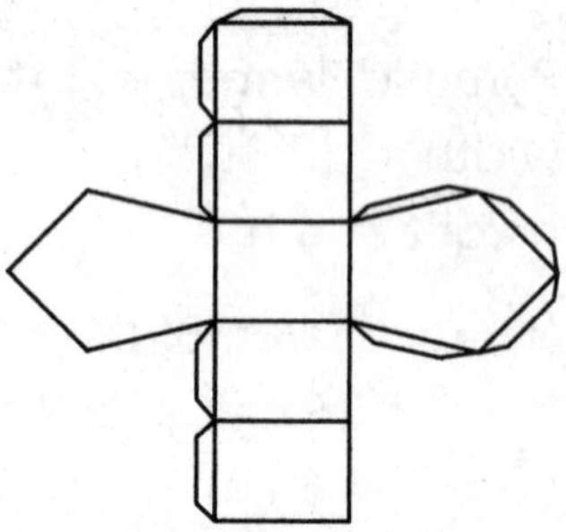

ACTIVITY 5.1

Measures of All Right Prisms and Right Pyramids

The strategies you used to calculate the volumes and surface areas of right rectangular prisms and pyramids can be used to calculate the volumes and surface areas of any prisms and pyramids.

The adjective *right* indicates that the faces and bases of a prism are perpendicular.

1. **Explain how to calculate the volume of a right rectangular prism.**

   How could you apply this strategy to calculate the volume of the prisms in the previous activity? What information do you need?

2. **Explain how to calculate the volume of a right rectangular pyramid.**

   How could you apply this strategy to calculate the volume of the pyramids in the previous activity? What information do you need?

3. **Explain how to calculate the surface area of a right rectangular prism or pyramid.**

   How could you apply this strategy to calculate the surface area of the prisms and pyramids in the previous activity? What information do you need?

Remember to use the appropriate units in your answers.

4. Calculate the volume and surface area of each prism or pyramid.

   a. The height of the triangular prism is 7 in.

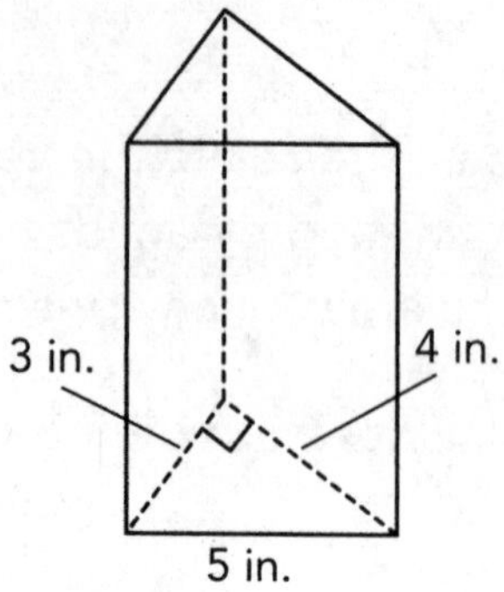

   b. The height of the square pyramid is 5.3 cm.

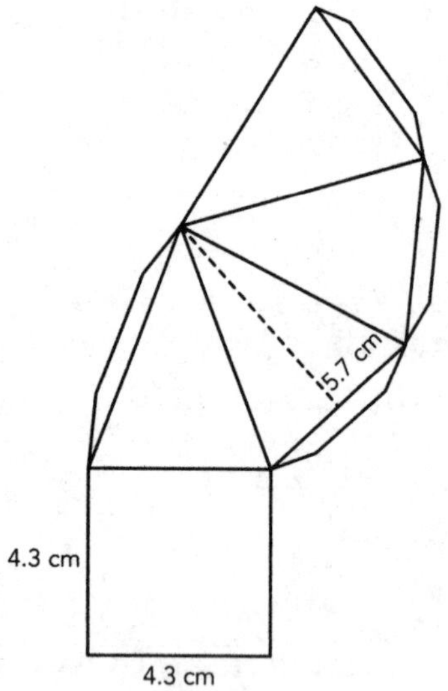

   c. The area of the hexagon is 37.62 cm^2, and the height of the hexagonal pyramid is 4.15 cm.

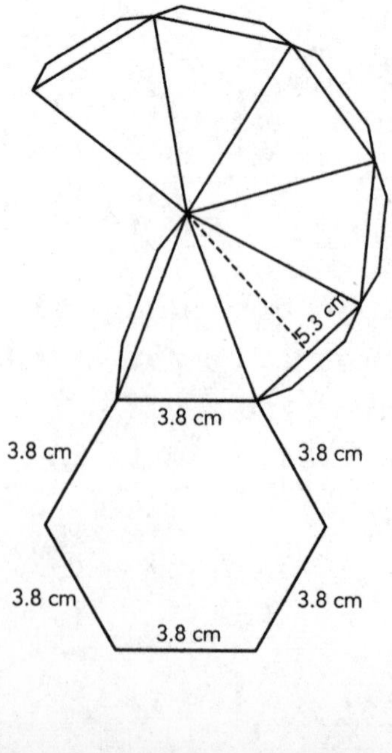

. How was the information provided in part (c) different from the information provided in parts (a) and (b)? Could you have calculated the volume and surface area in part (c) without this different information?

ACTIVITY
5.2

Areas of Regular Polygons

To calculate the surface areas and volumes of prisms and pyramids, you either need the area or need to be able to calculate the area of the base polygon. You know how to calculate the areas of triangles, parallelograms, and composite shapes.

You know how to determine the areas of the non-base faces of prisms and pyramids.

All of the polygonal bases in this lesson have bases that are *regular polygons*. A **regular polygon** is a polygon with all sides congruent and all angles congruent. The area of a regular polygon can be thought of as the area of a composite shape.

1. A regular pentagon is shown.

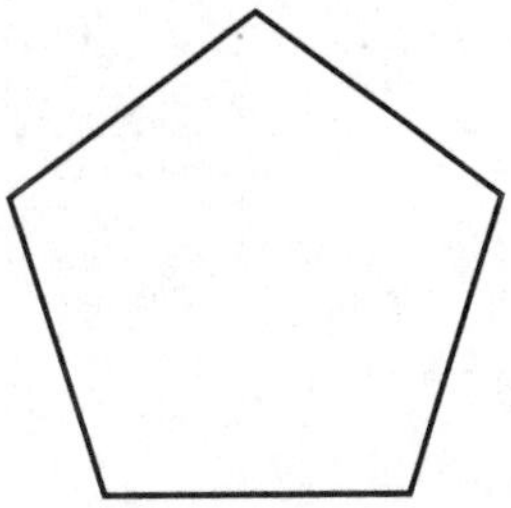

a. Locate and place a point at the center of the regular pentagon. From the center point, draw line segments to connect the point with each vertex of the pentagon.

b. Describe the new polygons formed by adding these line segments.

c. What information do you need to calculate the area of each new polygon?

d. What formula is used to calculate the area of each new polygon?

e. Describe a strategy to determine the area of the entire pentagonal base.

One base of a regular hexagonal prism is shown.

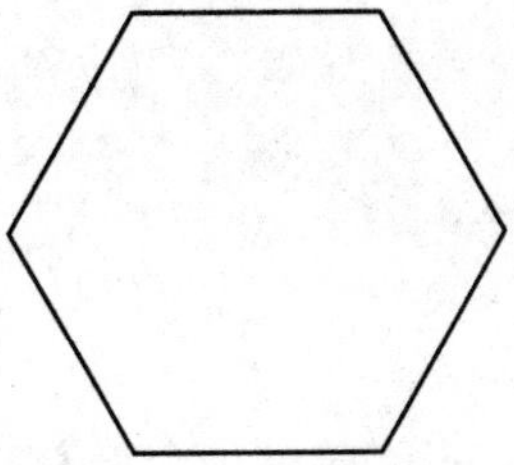

NOTES

2. Use the same strategy you used in Question 1 to divide the hexagon into new polygons.

   a. Describe the new polygons formed by adding these line segments.

   b. What information do you need to calculate the area of each new polygon?

   c. What formula is used to calculate the area of each new polygon?

   d. Describe a strategy to determine the area of the entire hexagonal base.

3. Do you think this strategy works for any regular polygonal base of a prism or pyramid? Explain your reasoning.

ACTIVITY 5.3

Calculating Areas of Regular Polygons

For each regular polygon, draw in the congruent triangles and then calculate the area.

1. 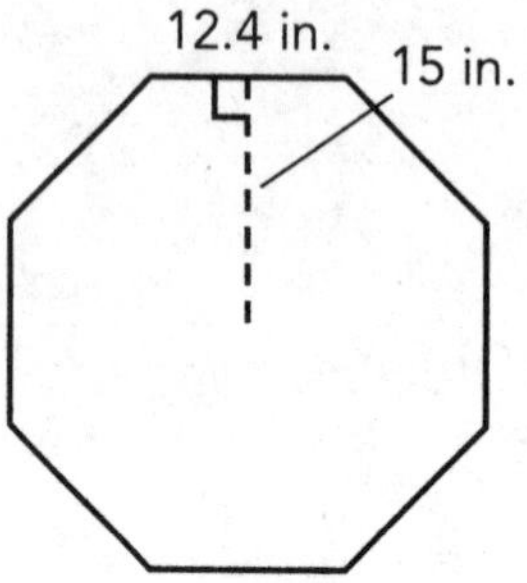

2. 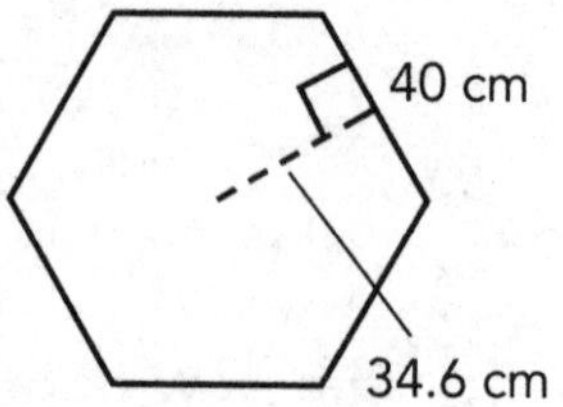

3. 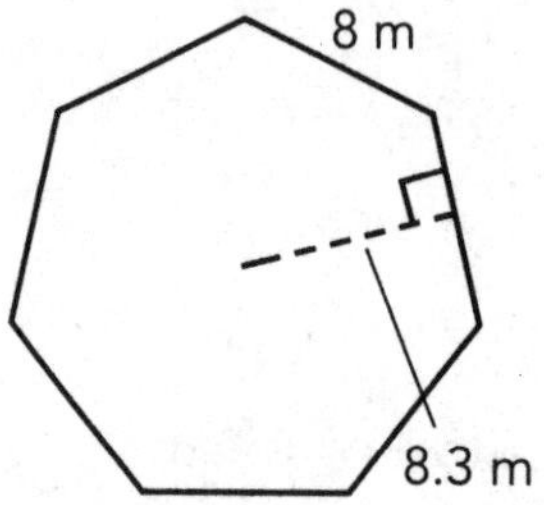

4. 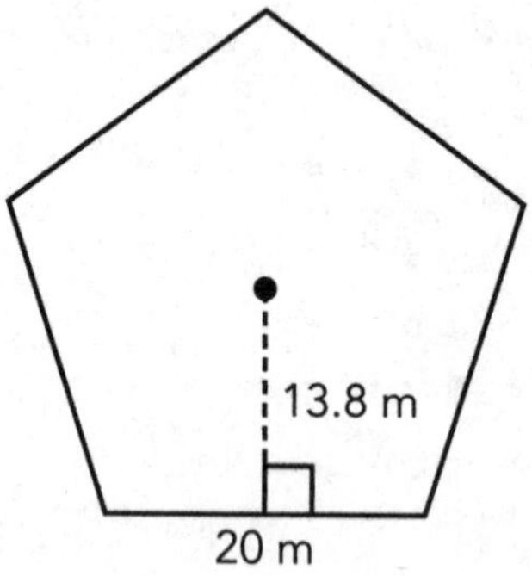

Solve each problem involving regular polygons.

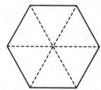

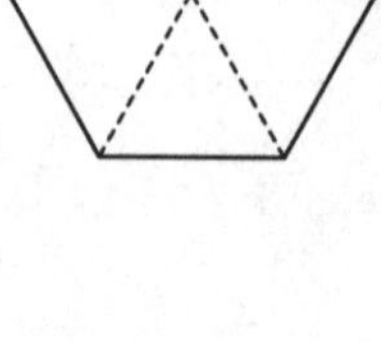

5. **A regular hexagon has an area of 540 cm^2, and its side lengths are each 15 cm. Calculate the height of the congruent triangles in the hexagon.**

. A regular octagon has an octagonal hole as shown. Calculate the area of the shaded region.

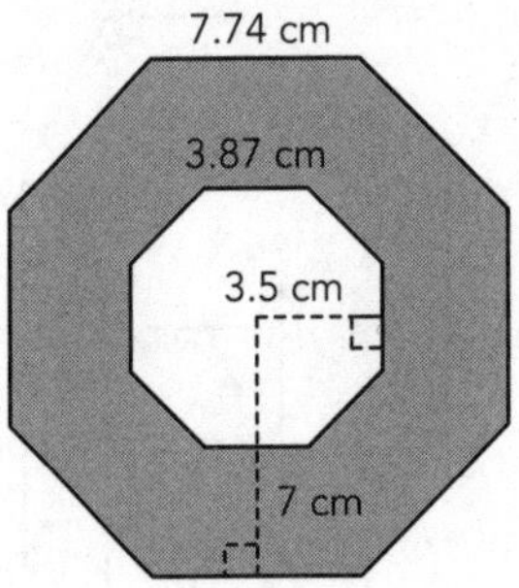

. Calculate the area of the figure composed of a regular pentagon and 2 congruent trapezoids.

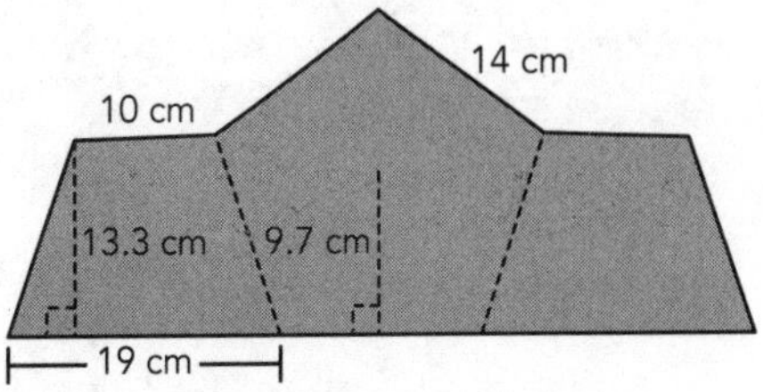

ACTIVITY 5.4 Solids with Regular Bases

1. Analyze the prism shown.

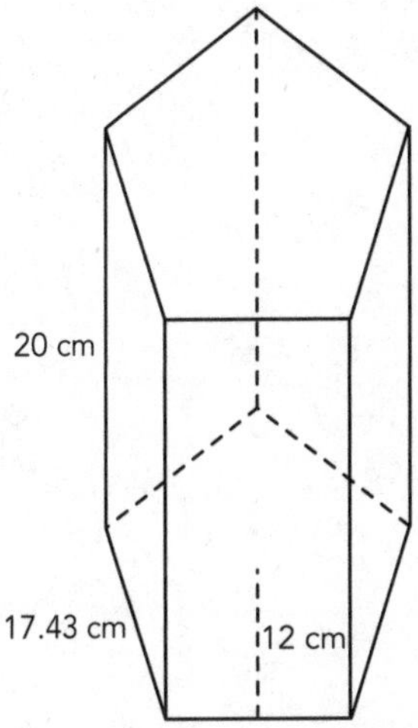

   a. Name the regular polygon that is the base of this prism.

   b. How many faces of the prism are lateral faces?

   c. Identify the number of vertices, edges, and faces.

   d. Determine the volume and surface area of the prism.

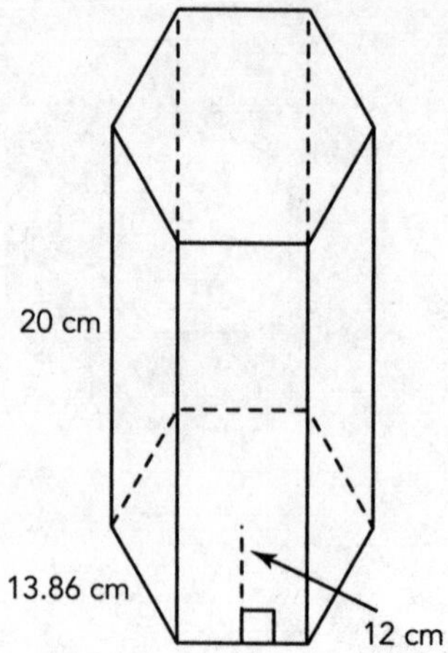

2. Analyze the prism shown.

a. Name the regular polygon that is the base of this prism.

b. How many faces of the prism are lateral faces?

c. Identify the number of vertices, edges, and faces.

d. Determine the volume and surface area of the prism.

. A $1 coin in Canada is sometimes called a loonie, because it features images of birds called common loons. It is made of steel and has an eleven-sided base, which is almost, but not quite, a regular polygon.

Suppose the coin has a regular 11-gon, or hendecagon, base. The perimeter of the coin is 81.125 millimeters, and the perpendicular distance from the center to a side is 12.713 millimeters. The coin is 1.95 millimeters thick. About how much steel would the coin contain?

NOTES

TALK the TALK

General Eyes

1. Explain how you could determine the volume of any right prism. Use examples to explain your reasoning.

2. Explain how you could determine the volume of any right pyramid. Use examples to explain your reasoning.

Assignment

Write

Explain how to determine the surface area and volume of any right prism or right pyramid.

Remember

To calculate the area of a regular polygon, decompose the polygon into congruent triangles, calculate the area of one triangle, and multiply the area of the triangle by the number of congruent triangles that comprise the polygon.

Practice

1. Use the area of the bases and the height to calculate the volume of each solid.

   a. Area of the base = 40 in.^2
   The height of the prism = 8 in.

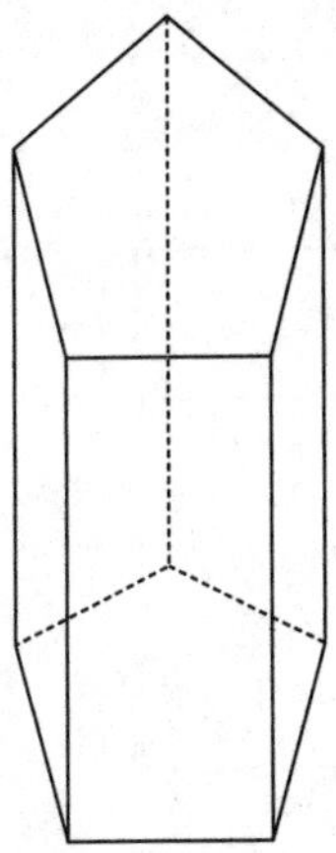

   b. Area of the base = 696 cm^2
   The height of the pyramid = 20 cm

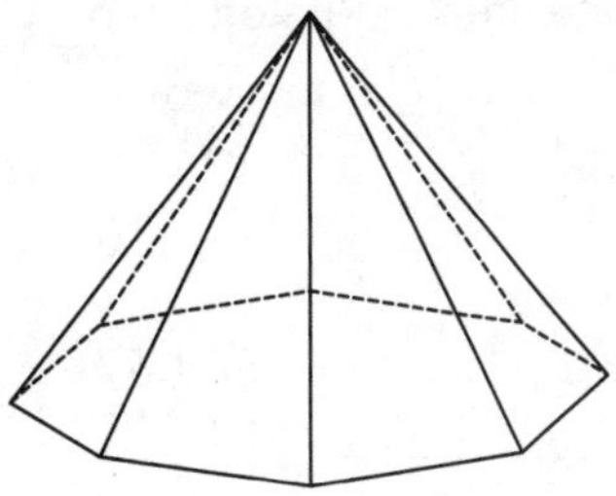

2. Calculate the area of each shaded region.

   a.

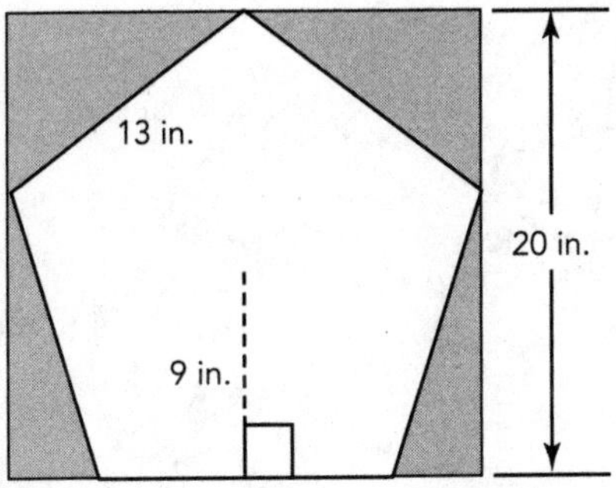

   b.

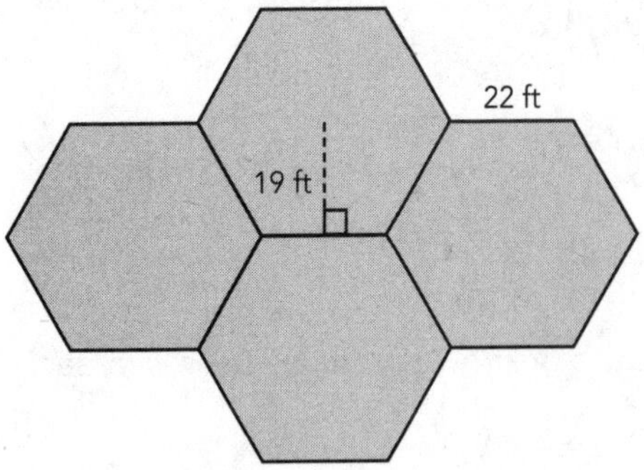

3. Calculate the volume and surface area of each solid.

   a.

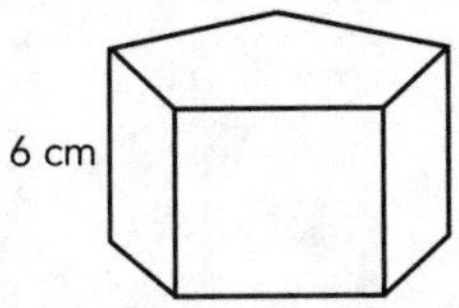

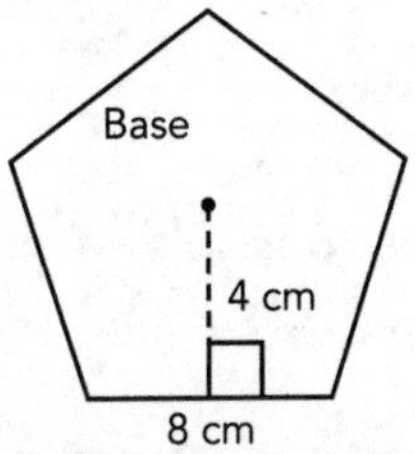

   b.

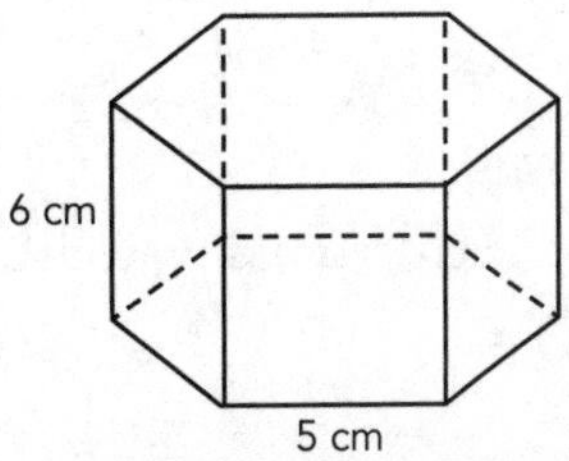

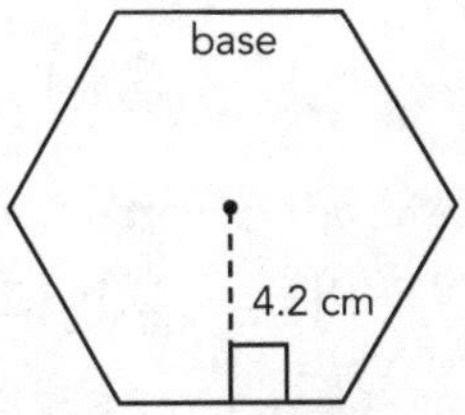

c.

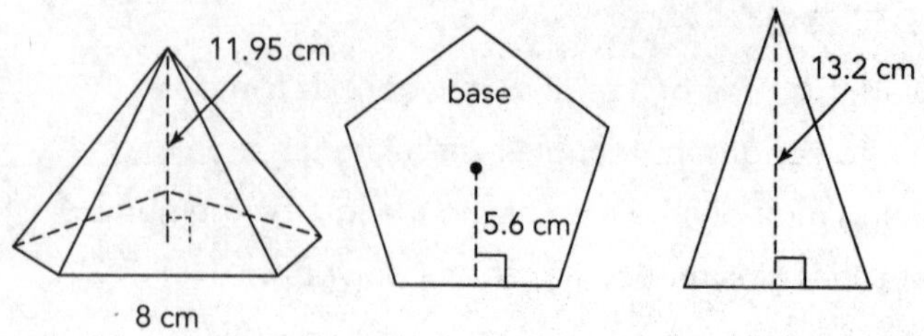

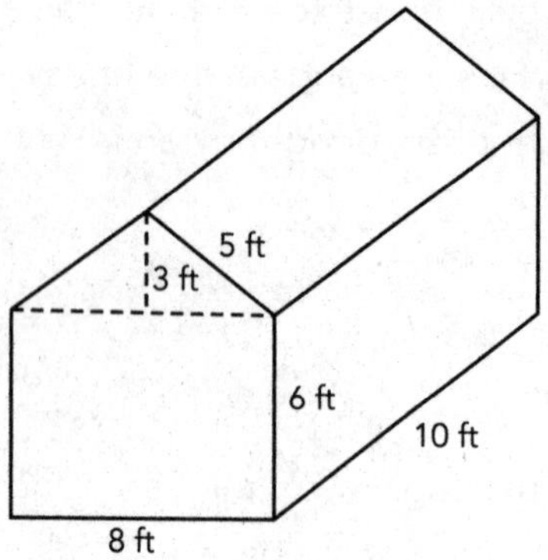

4. Khaled works for the Happy Camper tent-making company.
   He is working on a design for a new tent.
   A sketch of his design is shown. The tent is a right prism.

Use the sketch of Khaled's tent to answer each question. Decompose the solid as necessary.

a. Calculate the surface area of Khaled's tent.

b. Calculate the volume of Khaled's tent.

Stretch

Calculate the volume and surface area of the cylinder.

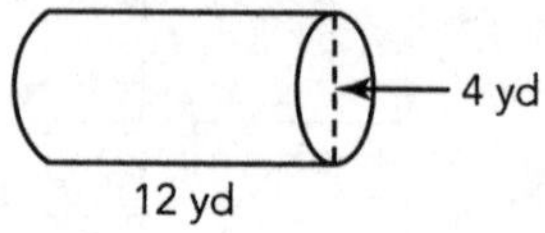

Review

1. Calculate the surface area of each right rectangular pyramid.

a.

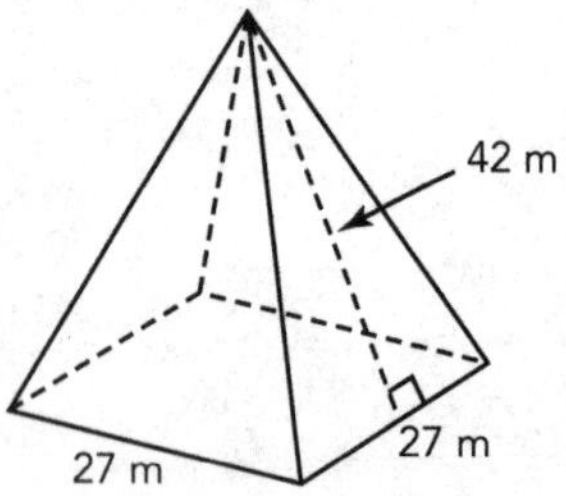

b.

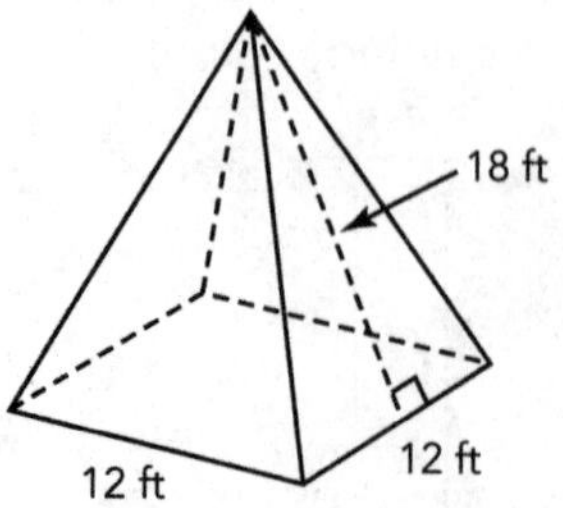

2. Calculate the unknown angle measures in each.

a.

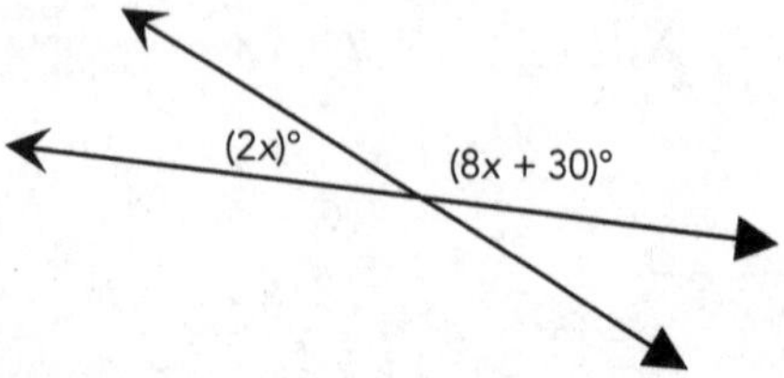

b.

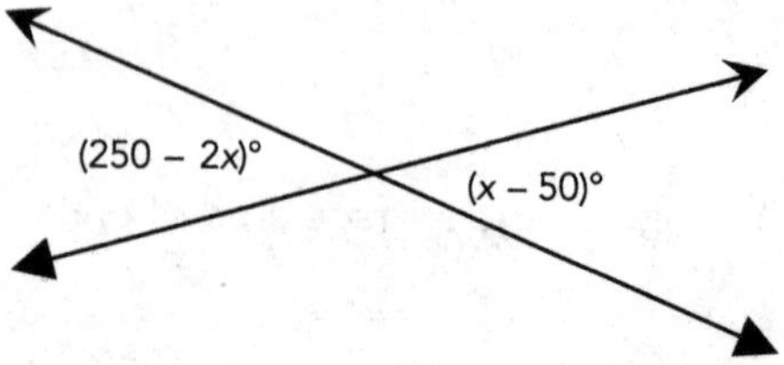

3. Use properties to rewrite each expression with as few terms as possible.

a. $7 + 9\left(\frac{1}{2}x - 12\right) - 2\frac{1}{2}$

b. $\frac{1}{4}\left(\frac{24 + 21x}{3} - 15x\right)$

Three-Dimensional Figures Summary

KEY TERMS

- cross-section
- regular polygon

LESSON 1

Slicing and Dicing

A **cross-section** of a solid is the two-dimensional figure formed by the intersection of a plane and a solid when a plane passes through the solid.

A prism is a geometric solid that has parallel and congruent polygonal bases and lateral sides that are parallelograms. The types of cross-sections of a cube are similar to the types of cross-sections of a rectangular prism (that is not a cube).

Some of the shapes of the cross-sections of a cube include a triangle, a square, a rectangle that is not a square, a parallelogram that is not a rectangle, a pentagon, and a hexagon.

For example, the cross-section shown is a square.

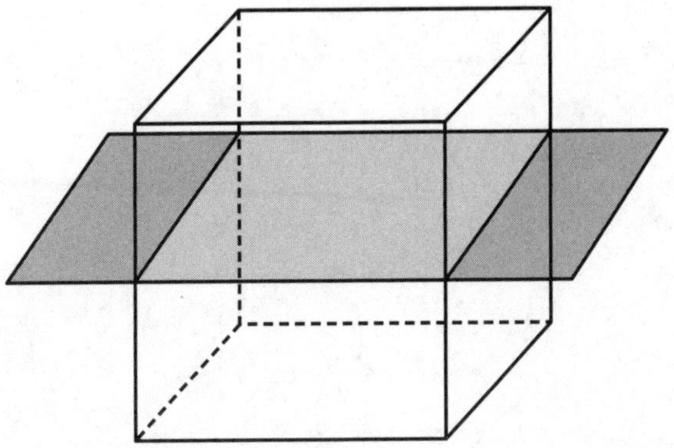

LESSON 2

Dissecting a Pyramid

A pyramid is a polyhedron formed by connecting one polygonal face to several triangular faces. Similar to prisms, pyramids are classified by their bases. The triangular faces of a pyramid intersect at the vertex of a pyramid.

For example, the cross-section of the right rectangular prism shown is a trapezoid. Other possible shapes of the cross-section of a pyramid are a triangle and a rectangle.

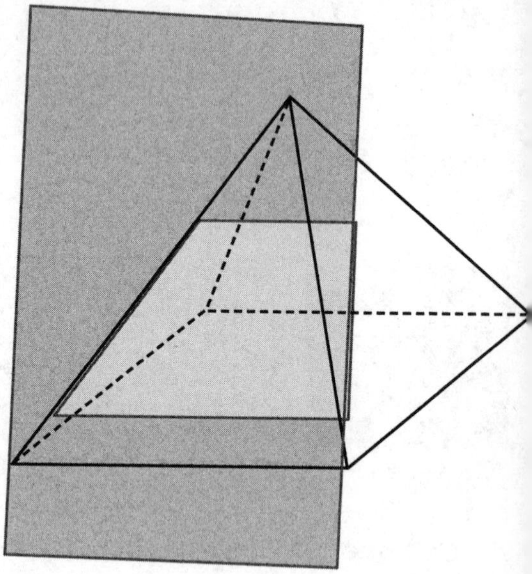

LESSON 3

Hey, Mister, Got Some Bird Seed?

The volume of a pyramid is one-third the volume of a prism with the same base and height, so $V = \frac{1}{3}Bh$.

For example, calculate the volume of the pyramid shown.

$$B = 750 \cdot 600$$
$$B = 450{,}000$$
$$V = \frac{1}{3}Bh$$
$$V = \frac{1}{3}Bh\ (450{,}000)\ (500)$$
$$V = 75{,}000{,}000$$

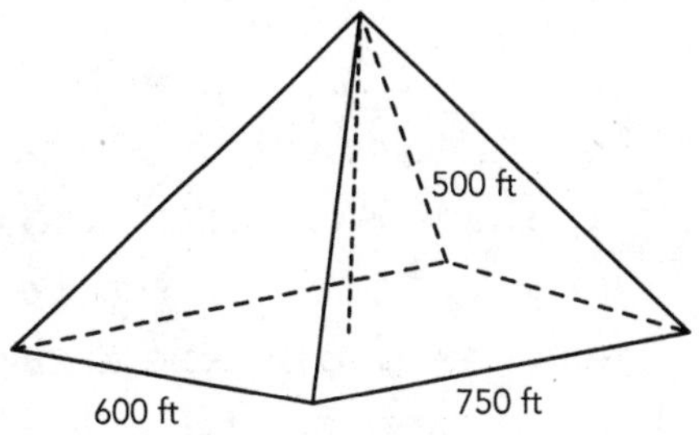

The volume of the pyramid is 75,000,000 cubic feet.

Doubling one dimension of a pyramid doubles the volume, while doubling more than one dimension quadruples the volume.

LESSON 4

The Sound of Surface Area

The surface area of a pyramid is the sum of the areas of all of its faces. The lateral area of a pyramid is the total surface area of the pyramid excluding the base. The dimensions of a polyhedron are used to calculate lateral surface area in a real-world problem situation.

The formula for the surface area of a square pyramid is $SA = 2bs + b^2$, where b is the length of the square base and s is the slant height of each triangle.

For example, calculate the surface area of the pyramid shown.

$$SA = 2bs + b^2$$
$$SA = 2\ (9)\ (12) + (9)^2$$
$$SA = 216 + 81$$
$$SA = 297$$

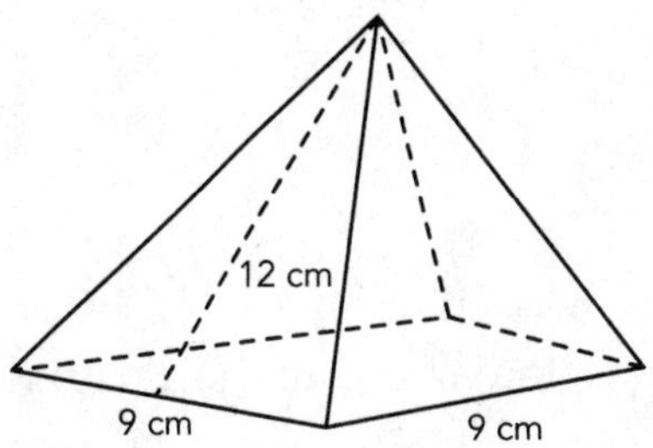

The surface area of the pyramid is 297 cubic centimeters.

When solving a problem, it may not be obvious whether you should use the formula for the volume or surface area of a solid. Therefore, it is important to think about the context of the problem situation, and then make a decision about which formula to use.

LESSON 5

More Than Four Sides of the Story

The strategies you used to calculate the volumes and surface areas of right rectangular prisms and pyramids can be used to calculate the volumes and surface areas of any prisms and pyramids. To calculate the surface areas and volumes of prisms and pyramids, you either need the area or need to be able to calculate the area of the base polygon.

A **regular polygon** is a polygon with all sides congruent and all angles congruent. The area of a regular polygon can be thought of as the area of a composite shape. To calculate the area of a regular polygon, decompose the polygon into congruent triangles, calculate the area of one triangle, and multiply the area of the triangle by the number of congruent triangles that comprise the polygon.

The area of a regular hexagon can be determined if you know the side length of the hexagon and the height of one of the six congruent triangles you decompose the shape into.

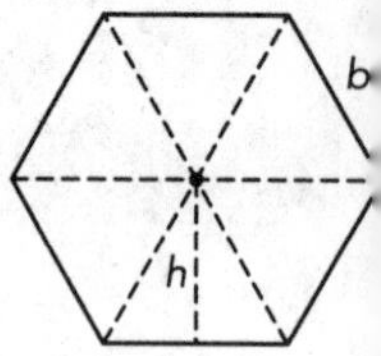

$$A = \frac{1}{2}bh\,(6) = 3bh$$

For example, calculate the volume of the right hexagonal prism shown. You know that the volume of a right prism can be calculated by multiplying the area of the base by the height.

$$B = 3bh$$
$$B = 3(20.8)(18)$$
$$B = 1123.2$$
$$V = Bh$$
$$V = (1123.2)(30)$$
$$V = 33{,}696$$

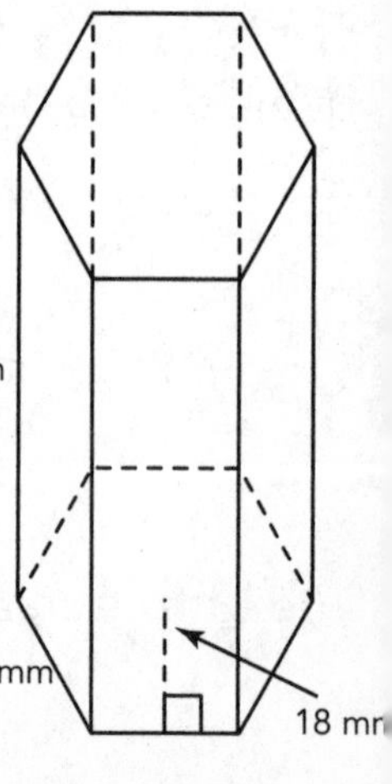

The volume of the prism is 33,696 square millimeters.

Glossary

A

absolute value

The absolute value, or magnitude, of a number is its distance from zero on a number line.

Example

The absolute value of −3 is the same as the absolute value of 3 because they are both a distance of 3 from zero on a number line.

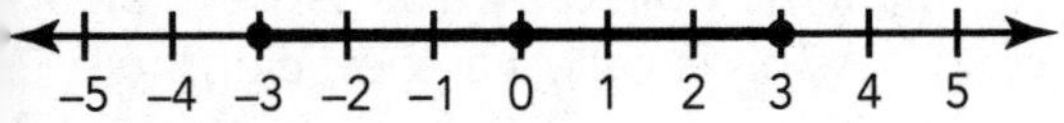

$|-3| = |3|$

additive inverses

Two numbers with the sum of zero are called additive inverses.

Examples

$-19 + 19 = 0$ $a + -a = 0$

adjacent angles

Adjacent angles are two angles that share a common vertex and share a common side.

Examples

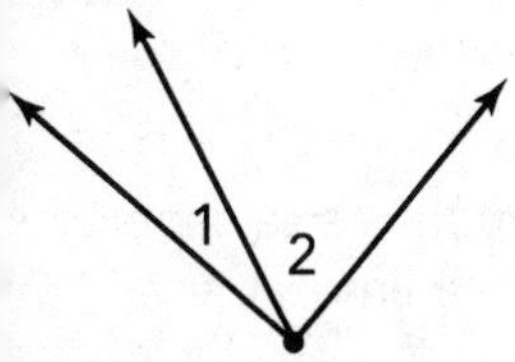

Angles 1 and 2 are adjacent angles.

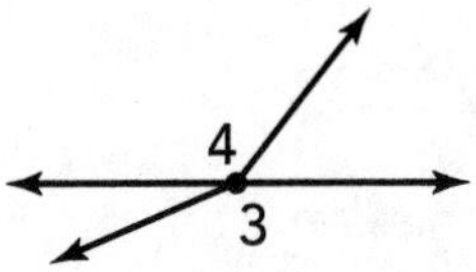

Angles 3 and 4 are NOT adjacent angles.

algebraic expression

An algebraic expression is a mathematical phrase that has at least one variable, and it can contain numbers and operation symbols.

Examples

a $2a + b$ xy $\frac{4}{p}$ z^2

angle

An angle is formed by two rays that share a common endpoint.

Example

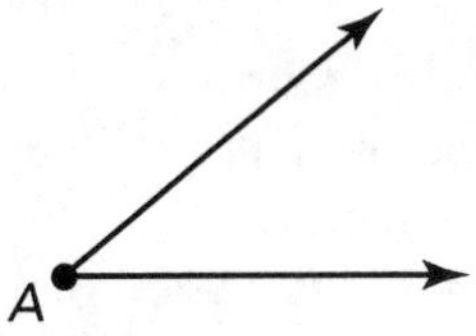

appreciation

Appreciation is an increase in price or value.

arc

An arc is the curve between two points on a circle.

Example

Arc *AB* is shown.

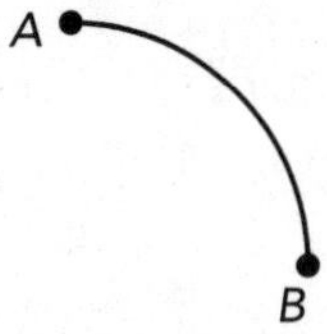

B

bar notation

Bar notation is used to indicate the digits that repeat in a repeating decimal.

Example

In the quotient of 3 and 7, the sequence 428571 repeats. The numbers that lie underneath the bar are the numbers that repeat.

$\frac{3}{7} = 0.4285714285714... = 0.\overline{428571}$

C

census

A census is the data collected from every member of a population.

Example

The U.S. Census is taken every 10 years. The U.S. government counts every member of the population every 10 years.

circle

A circle is a collection of points on the same plane equidistant from the same point. The center of a circle is the point from which all points on the circle are equidistant. Circles are named by their center point.

Example

The circle shown is Circle O.

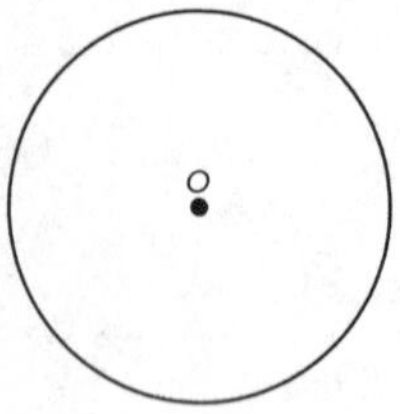

circumference

The distance around a circle is called the circumference of the circle. The circumference is calculated by the formula: $C = \pi(d)$.

Example

The diameter of Circle O is 12 centimeters. The circumference of Circle O is 12π.

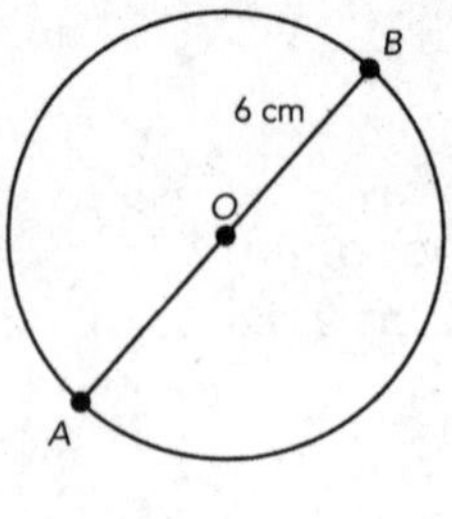

coefficient

A number that is multiplied by a variable in an algebraic expression is called a coefficient.

Examples

$14x$ $\quad \frac{1}{3}(g)$ $\quad \pi d$ $\quad w + 2.5$

coefficient

The coefficient is 1 even though it is not shown.

collinear

When points lie on the same line or line segment, they are said to be collinear.

Example

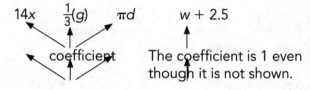

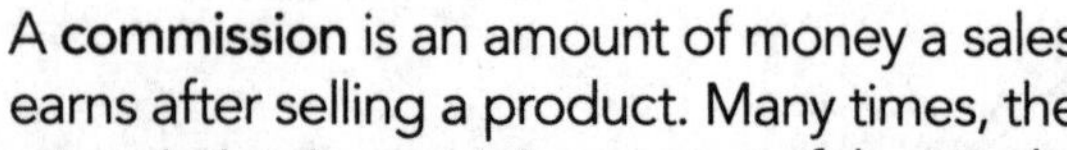

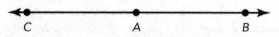

Points C, A, and B are collinear.

commission

A **commission** is an amount of money a salesperson earns after selling a product. Many times, the commission is a certain percent of the product.

Example

5% commission on $350

$0.05 \times 350 = \$17.50 \leftarrow$ commission

ommon factor

common factor is a number that is a factor of wo or more numbers.

xample

actors of 60: **1**, **2**, **3**, **4**, 5, **6**, 10, **12**, 15, 20, 30, 60

actors of 24: **1**, **2**, **3**, **4**, **6**, 8, **12**, 24

ommon factors of 60 and 24: 1, 2, 3, 4, 6, and 12

ompass

compass is a tool used to create arcs and circles.

omplementary angles

wo angles are complementary angles if the sum f their angle measures is equal to 90°.

xample

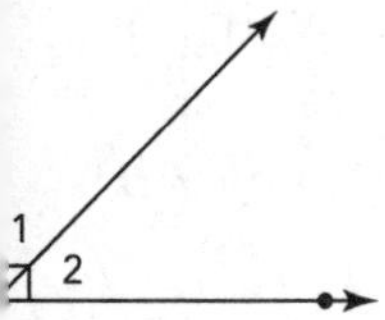

ngles 1 and 2 are complementary angles.

omplementary events

omplementary events are events that together ontain all of the outcomes in the sample space.

xample

Vhen rolling a six-sided number cube with the umbers 1 through 6 on each face, the event of olling an even number and the event of rolling an dd number (not even) are complementary events.

omplex ratio

ratio in which one or both of the quantities eing compared are written as fractions is a omplex ratio.

xample

raveling $\frac{1}{3}$ mile in $\frac{1}{2}$ hour represents a ratio of ractions, or a complex ratio.

compound event

A compound event combines two or more events, using the word "and" or the word "or."

congruent

Congruent means to have the same size, shape, and measure.

Example

Square *ABCD* is congruent to Square *QRST*.

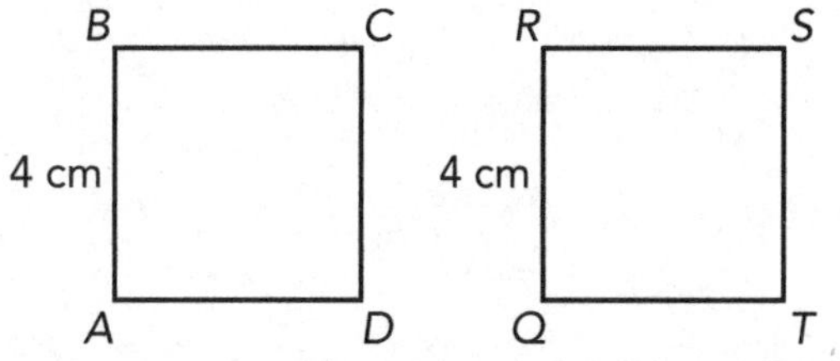

constant of proportionality

In a proportional relationship, the ratio of all *y*-values to their corresponding *x*-values is constant. This specific ratio, $\frac{y}{x}$, is called the constant of proportionality. Generally, the variable *k* is used to represent the constant of proportionality.

constraint

A constraint is a condition that a solution or problem must satisfy. A constraint can be a restriction set in advance of solving a problem or a limit placed on a solution or graph so the answer makes sense in terms of a real-world scenario.

Example

The expressions 0, x, $2x$, $-x$, and $-2x$ are graphed on a number line using the constraint $x < 0$.

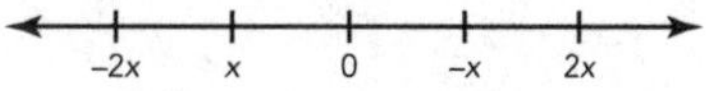

constructions

Constructions are created using only a compass or a straightedge or both.

corresponding

Corresponding means to have the same relative position in geometric figures, usually referring to sides and angles.

Example

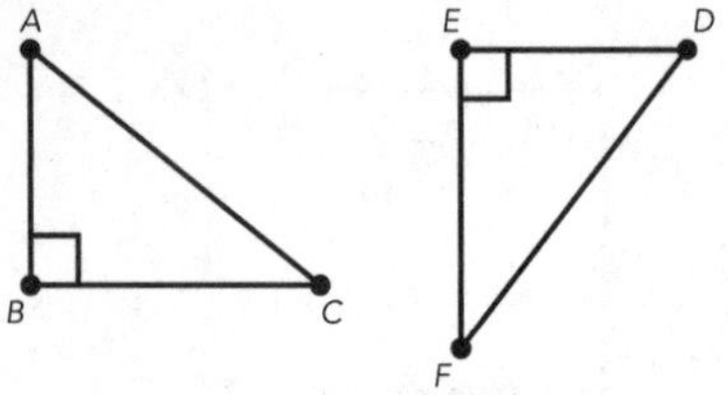

Sides *AB* and *DE* are corresponding sides.

Angle *B* and Angle *E* are corresponding angles.

cross-section

A cross-section of a solid is the two-dimensional figure formed by the intersection of a plane and a solid when a plane passes through the solid.

Example

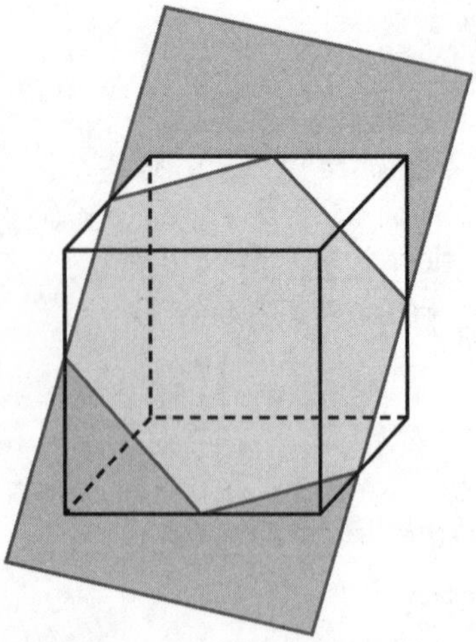

When a plane intersects a cube through all six faces, the cross-section is a hexagon.

D

data

Data are categories, numbers, or observations gathered in response to a statistical question.

Examples

favorite foods of sixth graders,
heights of different animals at the zoo

depreciation

Depreciation is a decrease in price or value

diameter

The diameter of a circle is a line segment formed by connecting two points on the circle such that the line segment passes through the center point.

Example

In Circle *O*, segment *AB* is a diameter. The length of diameter *AB* is two times the length of radius *OA*. The length of radius *OA* is 6 centimeters, so the length of diameter *AB* is 12 centimeters.

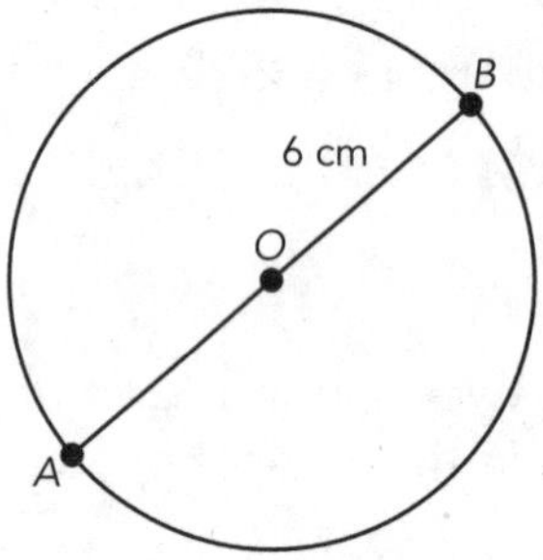

direct variation

A situation represents a direct variation if the ratio between the *y*-value and its corresponding *x*-value is constant for every point. The quantities are said to vary directly.

Example

If Melissa earns $8.25 per hour, then the amount she earns is in direct variation with the number of hours she works. The amount $8.25 is the constant of proportionality.

draw

When you draw a geometric figure, the figure is created with the use of tools such as a straightedge and protractor.

E

endpoints

The endpoints of a line segment are the points where the line segment ends. A line segment is named using the two capital letters that name its endpoints.

Example

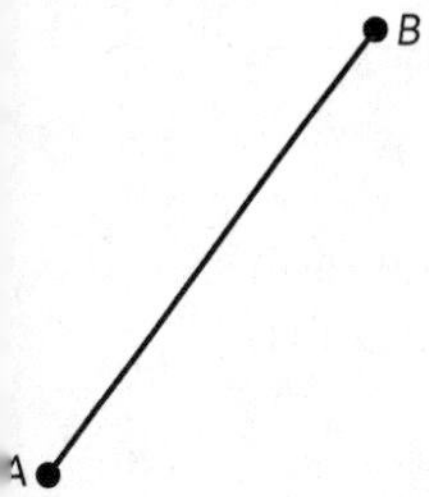

The endpoints A and B name line segment AB.

equally likely

When the probabilities of all the outcomes of an experiment are equal, then the outcomes are called equally likely.

Example

When rolling a six-sided number cube with the numbers 1 through 6 on each face, the probability of rolling each number from 1 through 6 is equally likely.

equation

An equation is a mathematical sentence that uses an equals sign to show that two quantities are the same as one another.

Examples

$$y = 2x + 4$$

$$6 = 3 + 3$$

$$2(8) = 26 - 10$$

$$\frac{1}{4} \cdot 4 = \frac{8}{4} - \frac{4}{4}$$

evaluate an algebraic expression

To evaluate an algebraic expression means to determine the value of the expression for a given value of each variable.

Example

Evaluate the expression $\frac{4x + (2^3 - y)}{p}$ for $x = 2.5$, $y = 8$, and $p = 2$.

- First replace the variables with numbers: $\frac{4(2.5) + (2^3 - 8)}{2}$.
- Then calculate the value of the expression: $\frac{10 + 0}{2} = \frac{10}{2} = 5$.

event

An event is one possible outcome or a group of possible outcomes for a given situation.

Example

When rolling a six-sided number cube with the numbers 1 through 6 on each face, an event could be rolling an even number.

experiment

An experiment is a situation involving chance that leads to results, or outcomes.

Example

Rolling a six-sided number cube is an experiment.

experimental probability

Experimental probability is the ratio of the number of times an event occurs to the total number of trials performed.

Example

Suppose there is one red, one blue, one green, and one yellow marble in a jar. You draw the blue marble 20 times out of 50 trials. The experimental probability, P_E(blue), is $\frac{20}{25}$ or $\frac{2}{5}$.

extremes

In a proportion that is written $a : b = c : d$, the two values on the outside, a and d, are the extremes.

Example

7 books : 14 days = 3 books : 6 days

extremes

F

factor

To factor an expression means to rewrite the expression as a product of factors.

Example

$5(12) + 5(9) = 5(12 + 9)$

G

greatest common factor (GCF)

The greatest common factor, or GCF, is the largest factor two or more numbers have in common.

Example

factors of 16: **1**, **2**, **4**, 8, 16

factors of 12: **1**, **2**, 3, **4**, 6, 12

common factors: 1, 2, 4

greatest common factor: 4

I

included angle

An included angle is the angle whose sides are made up of the given sides of the triangle.

Example

In Triangle *ABC*, $\angle A$ is the included angle formed by consecutive sides *AB* and *AC*.

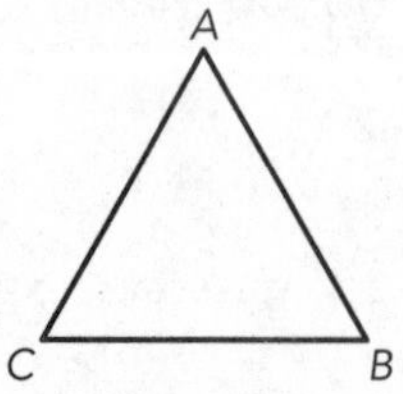

included side

An included side is the side between the two given angles of the triangle.

Example

In Triangle *ABC*, side *AB* is the included side formed by consecutive angles *A* and *B*.

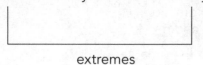

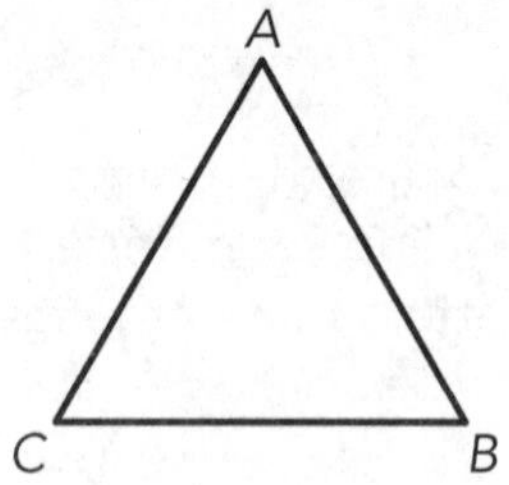

income tax

Income tax is a percentage of a person's or company's earnings that is collected by the government.

Example

If a person earns \$90,000 in one year and has to pay an income tax rate of 28%, then that person owes $90{,}000 \times 0.28$ or \$25,200 in income tax to the government.

inequality

An inequality is any mathematical sentence that has an inequality symbol.

Examples

$8 > 2$ $\quad a \leq b$ $\quad 6.051 > 6.009$ $\quad 2x + 4 \geq 16$

inverse operations

Inverse operations are pairs of operations that reverse the effects of each other.

Examples

Addition and subtraction are inverse operations: $351 + 25 - 25 = 351$.

Multiplication and division are inverse operations: $351 \times 25 \div 25 = 351$.

isolate the variable

When you isolate the variable in an equation, you perform an operation, or operations, to get the variable by itself on one side of the equals sign.

Example

In the equation $\frac{a}{b} = \frac{c}{d}$, you can multiply both sides by b to isolate the variable a.

$b \cdot \frac{a}{b} = b \cdot \frac{c}{d} \longrightarrow a = \frac{bc}{d}$

L

like terms

In an algebraic expression, like terms are two or more terms that have the same variable raised to the same power.

Examples

like terms

$4x + 3p + x + 2 = 5x + 3p + 2$

like terms

$24a^2 + 2a - 9a^2 = 13a^2 + 2a$

no like terms

$m + m^2 - x = x^3$

line

A line is a straight continuous arrangement of an infinite number of points. A line has an infinite length, but no width. Arrowheads are used to indicate that a line extends infinitely in opposite directions.

Example

Line AB is shown.

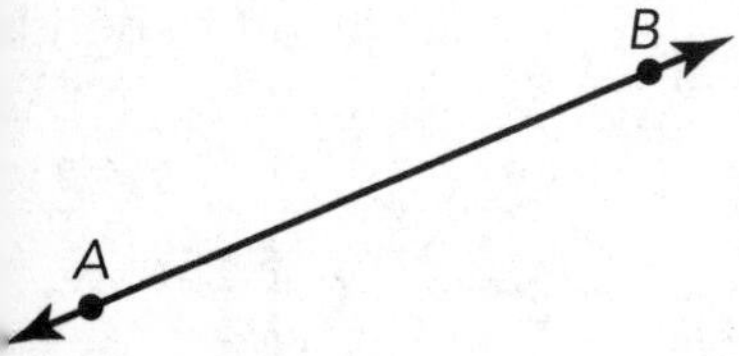

line segment

A line segment is a portion of a line that includes two points and all the points between those two points.

Example

Line segment AB is shown.

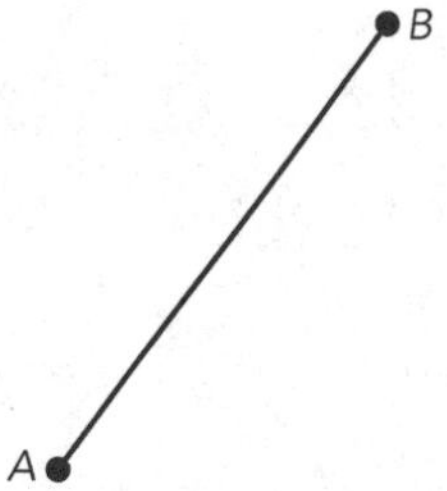

linear expression

A linear expression is any expression in which each term is either a constant or the product of a constant and a single variable raised to the first power.

Examples

$\frac{1}{2}x + 2$, $-3 + 12.5x$, $-1 + 3x + \frac{5}{2}x - \frac{4}{3}$

linear pair

A linear pair of angles is formed by two adjacent angles that have noncommon sides that form a line.

Examples

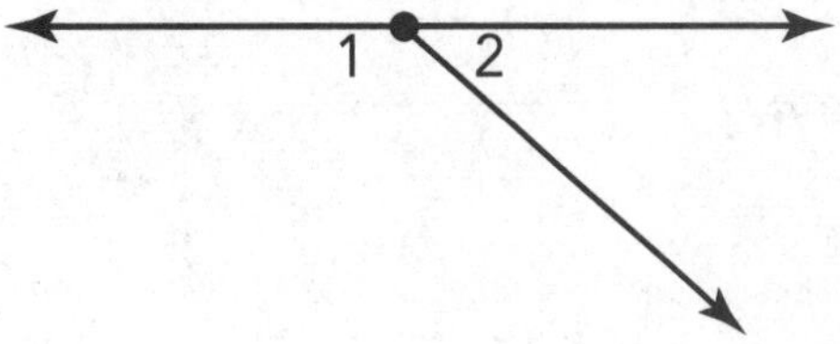

Angles 1 and 2 form a linear pair.

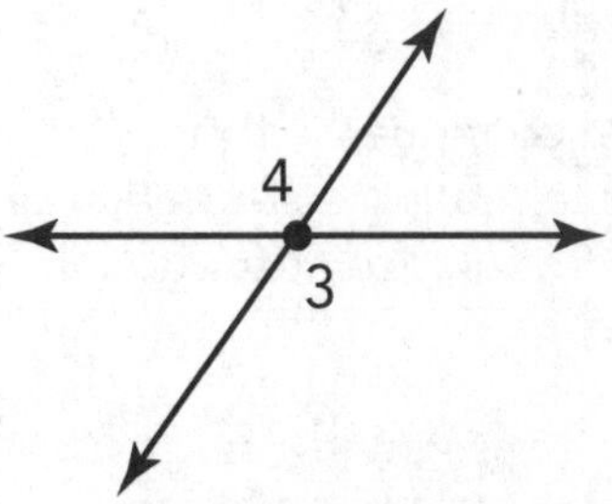

Angles 3 and 4 do NOT form a linear pair.

literal equation

A literal equation is an equation in which the variables represent specific measures.

Examples

$A = lw$ $\quad A = \frac{1}{2}bh$ $\quad d = rt$

M

markdown

When businesses sell an item at a lower price than the original price, it is called a markdown.

markup

To make money, businesses often buy products from a wholesaler or distributor for one amount and add to that amount to determine the price they use to sell the product to their customers. This is called a markup.

means

In a proportion that is written $a : b = c : d$, the two values in the middle, b and c, are the means.

Example

7 books : 14 days = 3 books : 6 days

means

N

non-repeating decimals

A non-repeating decimal continues without terminating and without repeating a sequence of digits. Non-repeating decimals are not rational numbers.

Examples

$\sqrt{3} = 1.73205080757\ldots$ $\quad \pi = 3.14159265359\ldots$

non-terminating decimal

A non-terminating decimal is a decimal that continues on infinitely without ending in a sequence of zeros.

Examples

0.333… 1.7272… 3.14159...

non-uniform probability model

A non-uniform probability model occurs when all the probabilities in a probability model are not equal to each other.

Example

Outcome	Red	Green	Blue
Probability	$\frac{1}{8}$	$\frac{1}{2}$	$\frac{3}{8}$

O

Order of Operations

The Order of Operations is a set of rules that ensures the same result every time an expression is evaluated.

Example

$44 + (6 - 5) - 2 \times 75 \div 5^1$ Parentheses

↓

$44 + 1 - 2 \times 75 \div 5^1$ Exponents

↓

$44 + 1 - 2 \times 75 \div 5$ Multiplication and Division (from left to right)

↓

$44 + 1 - 150 \div 5$

↓

$44 + 1 - 30$ addition and subtraction (from left to right)

↓

$45 - 30$

↓

15